£4.90

E3

R. REUBEN.

ELEMENTS OF
X-RAY DIFFRACTION

ELEMENTS OF
X-RAY DIFFRACTION

by

B. D. CULLITY

*Department of Metallurgical Engineering
and Materials Science
University of Notre Dame*

ADDISON-WESLEY PUBLISHING COMPANY, INC.

READING, MASSACHUSETTS · PALO ALTO · LONDON · DON MILLS, ONTARIO

PREFACE

X-ray diffraction is a tool for the investigation of the fine structure of matter. This technique had its beginnings in von Laue's discovery in 1912 that crystals diffract x-rays, the manner of the diffraction revealing the structure of the crystal. At first, x-ray diffraction was used only for the determination of crystal structure. Later on, however, other uses were developed, and today the method is applied, not only to structure determination, but to such diverse problems as chemical analysis and stress measurement, to the study of phase equilibria and the measurement of particle size, to the determination of the orientation of one crystal or the ensemble of orientations in a polycrystalline aggregate.

The purpose of this book is to acquaint the reader who has no previous knowledge of the subject with the theory of x-ray diffraction, the experimental methods involved, and the main applications. Because the author is a metallurgist, the majority of these applications are described in terms of metals and alloys. However, little or no modification of experimental method is required for the examination of nonmetallic materials, inasmuch as the physical principles involved do not depend on the material investigated. This book should therefore be useful to metallurgists, chemists, physicists, ceramists, mineralogists, etc., namely, to all who use x-ray diffraction purely as a laboratory tool for the sort of problems already mentioned.

Members of this group, unlike x-ray crystallographers, are not normally concerned with the determination of complex crystal structures. For this reason the rotating-crystal method and space-group theory, the two chief tools in the solution of such structures, are described only briefly.

This is a book of principles and methods intended for the student, and not a reference book for the advanced research worker. Thus no metallurgical data are given beyond those necessary to illustrate the diffraction methods involved. For example, the theory and practice of determining preferred orientation are treated in detail, but the reasons for preferred orientation, the conditions affecting its development, and actual orientations found in specific metals and alloys are not described, because these topics are adequately covered in existing books. In short, x-ray diffraction is stressed rather than metallurgy.

The book is divided into three main parts: fundamentals, experimental methods, and applications. The subject of crystal structure is approached through, and based on, the concept of the point lattice (Bravais lattice), because the point lattice of a substance is so closely related to its diffrac-

v

tion pattern.   The entire book is written in terms of the Bragg law and can be read without any knowledge of the reciprocal lattice. (However, a brief treatment of reciprocal-lattice theory is given in an appendix for those who wish to pursue the subject further.)   The methods of calculating the intensities of diffracted beams are introduced early in the book and used throughout.   Since a rigorous derivation of many of the equations for diffracted intensity is too lengthy and complex a matter for a book of this kind, I have preferred a semiquantitative approach which, although it does not furnish a rigorous proof of the final result, at least makes it physically reasonable.   This preference is based on my conviction that it is better for a student to grasp the physical reality behind a mathematical equation than to be able to glibly reproduce an involved mathematical derivation of whose physical meaning he is only dimly aware.

Chapters on chemical analysis by diffraction and fluorescence have been included because of the present industrial importance of these analytical methods.   In Chapter 7 the diffractometer, the newest instrument for diffraction experiments, is described in some detail; here the material on the various kinds of counters and their associated circuits should be useful, not only to those engaged in diffraction work, but also to those working with radioactive tracers or similar substances who wish to know how their measuring instruments operate.

Each chapter includes a set of problems.   Many of these have been chosen to amplify and extend particular topics discussed in the text, and as such they form an integral part of the book.

Chapter 18 contains an annotated list of books suitable for further study. The reader should become familiar with at least a few of these, as he progresses through this book, in order that he may know where to turn for additional information.

Like any author of a technical book, I am greatly indebted to previous writers on this and allied subjects.   I must also acknowledge my gratitude to two of my former teachers at the Massachusetts Institute of Technology, Professor B. E. Warren and Professor John T. Norton: they will find many an echo of their own lectures in these pages.   Professor Warren has kindly allowed me to use many problems of his devising, and the advice and encouragement of Professor Norton has been invaluable.   My colleague at Notre Dame, Professor G. C. Kuczynski, has read the entire book as it was written, and his constructive criticisms have been most helpful.   I would also like to thank the following, each of whom has read one or more chapters and offered valuable suggestions: Paul A. Beck, Herbert Friedman, S. S. Hsu, Lawrence Lee, Walter C. Miller, William Parrish, Howard Pickett, and Bernard Waldman.   I am also indebted to C. G. Dunn for the loan of illustrative material and to many graduate students, August

Freda in particular, who have helped with the preparation of diffraction patterns. Finally but not perfunctorily, I wish to thank Miss Rose Kunkle for her patience and diligence in preparing the typed manuscript.

B. D. CULLITY

Notre Dame, Indiana
March, 1956

CONTENTS

EXPERIMENTAL METHODS

APPLICATIONS

APPENDIXES

CHAPTER 1

PROPERTIES OF X-RAYS

1-1 Introduction. X-rays were discovered in 1895 by the German physicist Roentgen and were so named because their nature was unknown at the time. Unlike ordinary light, these rays were invisible, but they traveled in straight lines and affected photographic film in the same way as light. On the other hand, they were much more penetrating than light and could easily pass through the human body, wood, quite thick pieces of metal, and other "opaque" objects.

It is not always necessary to understand a thing in order to use it, and x-rays were almost immediately put to use by physicians and, somewhat later, by engineers, who wished to study the internal structure of opaque objects. By placing a source of x-rays on one side of the object and photographic film on the other, a shadow picture, or *radiograph*, could be made, the less dense portions of the object allowing a greater proportion of the x-radiation to pass through than the more dense. In this way the point of fracture in a broken bone or the position of a crack in a metal casting could be located.

Radiography was thus initiated without any precise understanding of the radiation used, because it was not until 1912 that the exact nature of x-rays was established. In that year the phenomenon of x-ray *diffraction* by crystals was discovered, and this discovery simultaneously proved the wave nature of x-rays and provided a new method for investigating the fine structure of matter. Although radiography is a very important tool in itself and has a wide field of applicability, it is ordinarily limited in the internal detail it can resolve, or disclose, to sizes of the order of 10^{-1} cm. Diffraction, on the other hand, can indirectly reveal details of internal structure of the order of 10^{-8} cm in size, and it is with this phenomenon, and its applications to metallurgical problems, that this book is concerned. The properties of x-rays and the internal structure of crystals are here described in the first two chapters as necessary preliminaries to the discussion of the diffraction of x-rays by crystals which follows.

1-2 Electromagnetic radiation. We know today that x-rays are electromagnetic radiation of exactly the same nature as light but of very much shorter wavelength. The unit of measurement in the x-ray region is the angstrom (A), equal to 10^{-8} cm, and x-rays used in diffraction have wavelengths lying approximately in the range 0.5–2.5A, whereas the wavelength of visible light is of the order of 6000A. X-rays therefore occupy the

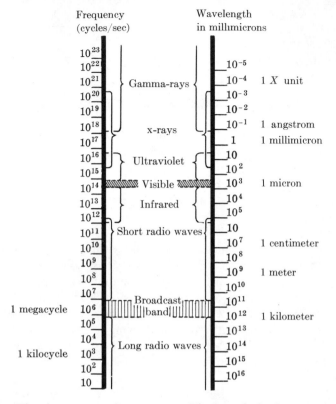

FIG. 1–1. The electromagnetic spectrum. The boundaries between regions are arbitrary, since no sharp upper or lower limits can be assigned. (F. W. Sears, *Optics*, 3rd ed., Addison-Wesley Publishing Company, Inc., Cambridge, Mass., 1949.)

region between gamma and ultraviolet rays in the complete electromagnetic spectrum (Fig. 1–1). Other units sometimes used to measure x-ray wavelength are the kX unit (XU) and the kilo X unit (kX $=$ 1000 XU).* The X unit is only slightly larger than the angstrom, the exact relation being

$$1 \text{ kX} = 1.00202\text{A}.$$

It is worth while to review briefly some properties of electromagnetic waves. Suppose a monochromatic beam of x-rays, i.e., x-rays of a single wavelength, is traveling in the x direction (Fig. 1–2). Then it has associated with it an electric field $\mathbf{E}$ in, say, the y direction and, at right angles to this, a magnetic field $\mathbf{H}$ in the z direction. If the electric field is confined to the xy-plane as the wave travels along, the wave is said to be plane-polarized. (In a completely unpolarized wave, the electric field vector $\mathbf{E}$ and hence the magnetic field vector $\mathbf{H}$ can assume all directions in the

* For the origin of these units, see Sec. 3–4.

yz-plane.) The magnetic field is of no concern to us here and we need not consider it further.

In the plane-polarized wave considered, **E** is not constant with time but varies from a maximum in the $+y$ direction through zero to a maximum in the $-y$ direction and back again, at any particular point in space, say $x = 0$. At any instant of time, say $t = 0$, **E** varies in the same fashion with distance along the *x*-axis.

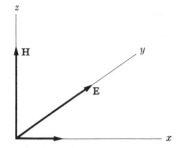

FIG. 1–2.   Electric and magnetic fields associated with a wave moving in the *x*-direction.

If both variations are assumed to be sinusoidal, they may be expressed in the one equation

$$\mathbf{E} = A \sin 2\pi \left(\frac{x}{\lambda} - \nu t \right), \tag{1–1}$$

where A = amplitude of the wave, λ = wavelength, and ν = frequency. The variation of **E** is not necessarily sinusoidal, but the exact form of the wave matters little; the important feature is its periodicity. Figure 1–3 shows the variation of **E** graphically. The wavelength and frequency are connected by the relation

$$\lambda = \frac{c}{\nu}, \tag{1–2}$$

where c = velocity of light = 3.00×10^{10} cm/sec.

Electromagnetic radiation, such as a beam of x-rays, carries energy, and the rate of flow of this energy through unit area perpendicular to the direction of motion of the wave is called the *intensity I*. The average value of the intensity is proportional to the square of the amplitude of the wave, i.e., proportional to A^2. In absolute units, intensity is measured in ergs/cm^2/sec, but this measurement is a difficult one and is seldom carried out; most x-ray intensity measurements are made on a relative basis in

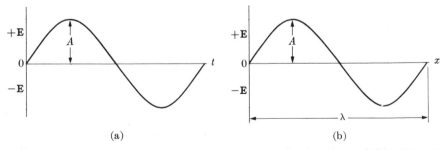

FIG. 1–3.   The variation of E, (a) with t at a fixed value of x and (b) with x at a fixed value of t.

arbitrary units, such as the degree of blackening of a photographic film exposed to the x-ray beam.

An accelerated electric charge radiates energy. The acceleration may, of course, be either positive or negative, and thus a charge continuously oscillating about some mean position acts as an excellent source of electromagnetic radiation. Radio waves, for example, are produced by the oscillation of charge back and forth in the broadcasting antenna, and visible light by oscillating electrons in the atoms of the substance emitting the light. In each case, the frequency of the radiation is the same as the frequency of the oscillator which produces it.

Up to now we have been considering electromagnetic radiation as *wave* motion in accordance with classical theory. According to the quantum theory, however, electromagnetic radiation can also be considered as a stream of *particles* called quanta or photons. Each photon has associated with it an amount of energy $h\nu$, where h is Planck's constant (6.62×10^{-27} erg·sec). A link is thus provided between the two viewpoints, because we can use the frequency of the wave motion to calculate the energy of the photon. Radiation thus has a dual wave-particle character, and we will use sometimes one concept, sometimes the other, to explain various phenomena, giving preference in general to the classical wave theory whenever it is applicable.

1–3 The continuous spectrum. X-rays are produced when any electrically charged particle of sufficient kinetic energy is rapidly decelerated. Electrons are usually used for this purpose, the radiation being produced in an *x-ray tube* which contains a source of electrons and two metal electrodes. The high voltage maintained across these electrodes, some tens of thousands of volts, rapidly draws the electrons to the anode, or target, which they strike with very high velocity. X-rays are produced at the point of impact and radiate in all directions. If e is the charge on the electron (4.80×10^{-10} esu) and $\mathrm{\mathcal{U}}$ the voltage (in esu)* across the electrodes, then the kinetic energy (in ergs) of the electrons on impact is given by the equation

$$\mathrm{KE} = e\mathrm{\mathcal{U}} = \tfrac{1}{2}mv^2, \qquad (1\text{–}3)$$

where m is the mass of the electron (9.11×10^{-28} gm) and v its velocity just before impact. At a tube voltage of 30,000 volts (practical units), this velocity is about one-third that of light. Most of the kinetic energy of the electrons striking the target is converted into heat, less than 1 percent being transformed into x-rays.

When the rays coming from the target are analyzed, they are found to consist of a mixture of different wavelengths, and the variation of intensity

---

* 1 volt (practical units) = $\frac{1}{300}$ volt (esu).

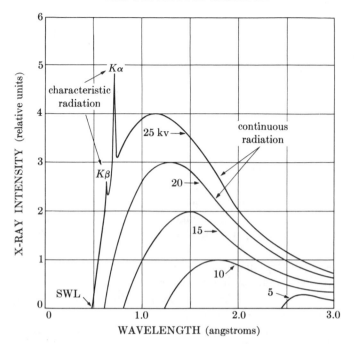

FIG. 1–4.   X-ray spectrum of molybdenum as a function of applied voltage (schematic).   Line widths not to scale.

with wavelength is found to depend on the tube voltage.   Figure 1–4 shows the kind of curves obtained.   The intensity is zero up to a certain wavelength, called the *short-wavelength limit* (λ_{SWL}), increases rapidly to a maximum and then decreases, with no sharp limit on the long wavelength side.   When the tube voltage is raised, the intensity of all wavelengths increases, and both the short-wavelength limit and the position of the maximum shift to shorter wavelengths.   We are concerned now with the smooth curves in Fig. 1–4, those corresponding to applied voltages of 20 kv or less in the case of a molybdenum target.   The radiation represented by such curves is called *heterochromatic, continuous,* or *white* radiation, since it is made up, like white light, of rays of many wavelengths.

   The continuous spectrum is due to the rapid deceleration of the electrons hitting the target since, as mentioned above, any decelerated charge emits energy.   Not every electron is decelerated in the same way, however; some are stopped in one impact and give up all their energy at once, while others are deviated this way and that by the atoms of the target, successively losing fractions of their total kinetic energy until it is all spent.   Those electrons which are stopped in one impact will give rise to photons of maximum energy, i.e., to x-rays of minimum wavelength.   Such electrons transfer all their energy $e\mathcal{V}$ into photon energy and we may write

$$e\mathcal{V} = h\nu_{max},$$

$$\lambda_{\text{SWL}} = \frac{c}{\nu_{\max}} = \frac{hc}{eʊ},$$

$$\boxed{\lambda_{\text{SWL}} = \frac{12,400}{V}}. \tag{1--4}$$

This equation gives the short-wavelength limit (in angstroms) as a function of the applied voltage V (in practical units). If an electron is not completely stopped in one encounter but undergoes a glancing impact which only partially decreases its velocity, then only a fraction of its energy $eʊ$ is emitted as radiation and the photon produced has energy less than $h\nu_{\max}$. In terms of wave motion, the corresponding x-ray has a frequency lower than $\nu_{\max}$ and a wavelength longer than λ_{SWL}. The totality of these wavelengths, ranging upward from λ_{SWL}, constitutes the continuous spectrum.

We now see why the curves of Fig. 1–4 become higher and shift to the left as the applied voltage is increased, since the number of photons produced per second and the average energy per photon are both increasing. The total x-ray energy emitted per second, which is proportional to the area under one of the curves of Fig. 1–4, also depends on the atomic number Z of the target and on the tube current i, the latter being a measure of the number of electrons per second striking the target. This total x-ray intensity is given by

$$I_{\text{cont. spectrum}} = AiZV^m, \tag{1--5}$$

where A is a proportionality constant and m is a constant with a value of about 2. Where large amounts of white radiation are desired, it is therefore necessary to use a heavy metal like tungsten ($Z = 74$) as a target and as high a voltage as possible. Note that the material of the target affects the intensity but not the wavelength distribution of the continuous spectrum.

1–4 The characteristic spectrum. When the voltage on an x-ray tube is raised above a certain critical value, characteristic of the target metal, sharp intensity maxima appear at certain wavelengths, superimposed on the continuous spectrum. Since they are so narrow and since their wavelengths are characteristic of the target metal used, they are called *characteristic lines*. These lines fall into several sets, referred to as K, L, M, etc., in the order of increasing wavelength, all the lines together forming the *characteristic spectrum* of the metal used as the target. For a molybdenum target the K lines have wavelengths of about 0.7A, the L lines about 5A, and the M lines still higher wavelengths. Ordinarily only the K lines are useful in x-ray diffraction, the longer-wavelength lines being too easily absorbed. There are several lines in the K set, but only the three strongest are observed in normal diffraction work.   These are the $K\alpha_1$, $K\alpha_2$, and $K\beta_1$, and for molybdenum their wavelengths are:

$$K\alpha_1: \qquad 0.70926\text{A},$$
$$K\alpha_2: \qquad 0.71354\text{A},$$
$$K\beta_1: \qquad 0.63225\text{A}.$$

The α_1 and α_2 components have wavelengths so close together that they are not always resolved as separate lines; if resolved, they are called the *Kα doublet* and, if not resolved, simply the *Kα line.* Similarly, $K\beta_1$ is usually referred to as the *Kβ line*, with the subscript dropped. $K\alpha_1$ is always about twice as strong as $K\alpha_2$, while the intensity ratio of $K\alpha_1$ to $K\beta_1$ depends on atomic number but averages about 5/1.

These characteristic lines may be seen in the uppermost curve of Fig. 1–4.   Since the critical *K excitation voltage*, i.e., the voltage necessary to excite K characteristic radiation, is 20.01 kv for molybdenum, the K lines do not appear in the lower curves of Fig. 1–4.   An increase in voltage above the critical voltage increases the intensities of the characteristic lines relative to the continuous spectrum but *does not change their wavelengths*.   Figure 1–5 shows the spectrum of molybdenum at 35 kv on a compressed vertical scale relative to that of Fig. 1–4; the increased voltage has shifted the continuous spectrum to still shorter wavelengths and increased the intensities of the K lines relative to the continuous spectrum but has not changed their wavelengths.

The intensity of any characteristic line, measured above the continuous spectrum, depends both on the tube current i and the amount by which the applied voltage V exceeds the critical excitation voltage for that line. For a K line, the intensity is given by

$$I_{K\text{ line}} = Bi(V - V_K)^n, \tag{1–6}$$

where B is a proportionality constant, V_K the K excitation voltage, and n a constant with a value of about 1.5.   The intensity of a characteristic line can be quite large: for example, in the radiation from a copper target operated at 30 kv, the $K\alpha$ line has an intensity about 90 times that of the wavelengths immediately adjacent to it in the continuous spectrum.   Besides being very intense, characteristic lines are also very narrow, most of them less than 0.001A wide measured at half their maximum intensity, as shown in Fig. 1–5.   The existence of this strong sharp $K\alpha$ line is what makes a great deal of x-ray diffraction possible, since many diffraction experiments require the use of monochromatic or approximately monochromatic radiation.

* The wavelength of an unresolved $K\alpha$ doublet is usually taken as the weighted average of the wavelengths of its components, $K\alpha_1$ being given twice the weight of $K\alpha_2$, since it is twice as strong.   Thus the wavelength of the unresolved Mo $K\alpha$ line is $\frac{1}{3}(2 \times 0.70926 + 0.71354) = 0.71069\text{A}$.

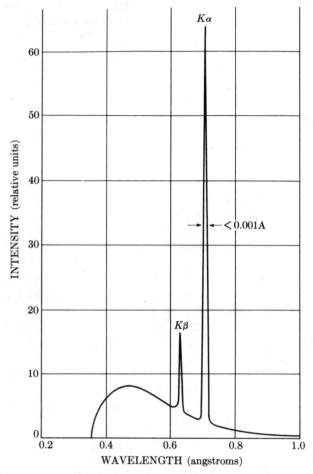

Fɪɢ. 1–5.   Spectrum of Mo at 35 kv (schematic).   Line widths not to scale.

The characteristic x-ray lines were discovered by W. H. Bragg and systematized by H. G. Moseley. The latter found that the wavelength of any particular line decreased as the atomic number of the emitter increased. In particular, he found a linear relation (Moseley's law) between the square root of the line frequency ν and the atomic number Z:

$$\sqrt{\nu} = C(Z - \sigma), \tag{1–7}$$

where C and σ are constants. This relation is plotted in Fig. 1–6 for the $K\alpha_1$ and $L\alpha_1$ lines, the latter being the strongest line in the L series. These curves show, incidentally, that L lines are not always of long wavelength: the $L\alpha_1$ line of a heavy metal like tungsten, for example, has about the same wavelength as the $K\alpha_1$ line of copper, namely about 1.5A. The

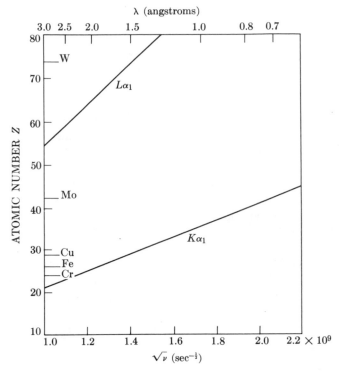

FIG. 1–6. Moseley's relation between $\sqrt{\nu}$ and Z for two characteristic lines.

wavelengths of the characteristic x-ray lines of almost all the known elements have been precisely measured, mainly by M. Siegbahn and his
associates, and a tabulation of these wavelengths for the strongest lines
of the K and L series will be found
in Appendix 3.

While the continuous spectrum is
caused by the rapid deceleration of
electrons by the target, the origin of
the characteristic spectrum lies in the
atoms of the target material itself.
To understand this phenomenon, it
is enough to consider an atom as consisting of a central nucleus surrounded
by electrons lying in various shells
(Fig. 1–7). If one of the electrons
bombarding the target has sufficient
kinetic energy, it can knock an electron out of the K shell, leaving the
atom in an excited, high-energy state.

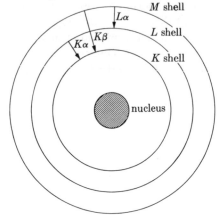

FIG. 1–7. Electronic transitions in
an atom (schematic). Emission processes indicated by arrows.

One of the outer electrons immediately falls into the vacancy in the K shell, emitting energy in the process, and the atom is once again in its normal energy state. The energy emitted is in the form of radiation of a definite wavelength and is, in fact, characteristic K radiation.

The K-shell vacancy may be filled by an electron from any one of the outer shells, thus giving rise to a series of K lines; $K\alpha$ and $K\beta$ lines, for example, result from the filling of a K-shell vacancy by an electron from the L or M shells, respectively. It is *possible* to fill a K-shell vacancy either from the L or M shell, so that one atom of the target may be emitting $K\alpha$ radiation while its neighbor is emitting $K\beta$; however, it is more *probable* that a K-shell vacancy will be filled by an L electron than by an M electron, and the result is that the $K\alpha$ line is stronger than the $K\beta$ line. It also follows that it is impossible to excite one K line without exciting all the others. L characteristic lines originate in a similar way: an electron is knocked out of the L shell and the vacancy is filled by an electron from some outer shell.

We now see why there should be a critical excitation voltage for characteristic radiation. K radiation, for example, cannot be excited unless the tube voltage is such that the bombarding electrons have enough energy to knock an electron out of the K shell of a target atom. If W_K is the work required to remove a K electron, then the necessary kinetic energy of the electrons is given by

$$\tfrac{1}{2}mv^2 = W_K. \tag{1-8}$$

It requires less energy to remove an L electron than a K electron, since the former is farther from the nucleus; it therefore follows that the L excitation voltage is less than the K and that K characteristic radiation cannot be produced without L, M, etc., radiation accompanying it.

1–5 Absorption. Further understanding of the electronic transitions which can occur in atoms can be gained by considering not only the interaction of electrons and atoms, but also the interaction of x-rays and atoms. When x-rays encounter any form of matter, they are partly transmitted and partly absorbed. Experiment shows that the fractional decrease in the intensity I of an x-ray beam as it passes through any homogeneous substance is proportional to the distance traversed, x. In differential form,

$$-\frac{dI}{I} = \mu \, dx, \tag{1-9}$$

where the proportionality constant μ is called the *linear absorption coefficient* and is dependent on the substance considered, its density, and the wavelength of the x-rays. Integration of Eq. (1–9) gives

$$I_x = I_0 e^{-\mu x}, \tag{1-10}$$

where I_0 = intensity of incident x-ray beam and I_x = intensity of transmitted beam after passing through a thickness x.

The linear absorption coefficient μ is proportional to the density ρ, which means that the quantity μ/ρ is a constant of the material and independent of its physical state (solid, liquid, or gas). This latter quantity, called the *mass absorption coefficient*, is the one usually tabulated. Equation (1–10) may then be rewritten in a more usable form:

$$I_x = I_0 e^{-(\mu/\rho)\rho x}.$$ (1–11)

Values of the mass absorption coefficient μ/ρ are given in Appendix 4 for various characteristic wavelengths used in diffraction.

It is occasionally necessary to know the mass absorption coefficient of a substance containing more than one element. Whether the substance is a mechanical mixture, a solution, or a chemical compound, and whether it is in the solid, liquid, or gaseous state, its mass absorption coefficient is simply the weighted average of the mass absorption coefficients of its constituent elements. If w_1, w_2, etc., are the weight fractions of elements 1, 2, etc., in the substance and $(\mu/\rho)_1$, $(\mu/\rho)_2$, etc., their mass absorption coefficients, then the mass absorption coefficient of the substance is given by

$$\frac{\mu}{\rho} = w_1 \left(\frac{\mu}{\rho}\right)_1 + w_2 \left(\frac{\mu}{\rho}\right)_2 + \cdots.$$ (1–12)

The way in which the absorption coefficient varies with wavelength gives the clue to the interaction of x-rays and atoms. The lower curve of Fig. 1–8 shows this variation for a nickel absorber; it is typical of all materials. The curve consists of two similar branches separated by a sharp discontinuity called an absorption edge. Along each branch the absorption coefficient varies with wavelength approximately according to a relation of the form

$$\frac{\mu}{\rho} = k\lambda^3 Z^3,$$ (1–13)

where k = a constant, with a different value for each branch of the curve, and Z = atomic number of absorber. Short-wavelength x-rays are therefore highly penetrating and are

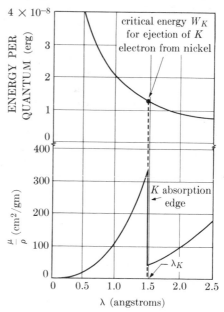

Fig. 1–8. Variation with wavelength of the energy per x-ray quantum and of the mass absorption coefficient of nickel.

termed *hard*, while long-wavelength x-rays are easily absorbed and are said to be *soft*.

Matter absorbs x-rays in two distinct ways, by scattering and by true absorption, and these two processes together make up the total absorption measured by the quantity μ/ρ. The *scattering* of x-rays by atoms is similar in many ways to the scattering of visible light by dust particles in the air. It takes place in all directions, and since the energy in the scattered beams does not appear in the transmitted beam, it is, so far as the transmitted beam is concerned, said to be absorbed. The phenomenon of scattering will be discussed in greater detail in Chap. 4; it is enough to note here that, except for the very light elements, it is responsible for only a small fraction of the total absorption. *True absorption* is caused by electronic transitions within the atom and is best considered from the viewpoint of the quantum theory of radiation. Just as an electron of sufficient energy can knock a K electron, for example, out of an atom and thus cause the emission of K characteristic radiation, so also can an incident quantum of x-rays, provided it has the same minimum amount of energy W_K. In the latter case, the ejected electron is called a *photoelectron* and the emitted characteristic radiation is called *fluorescent radiation*. It radiates in all directions and has exactly the same wavelength as the characteristic radiation caused by electron bombardment of a metal target. (In effect, an atom with a K-shell vacancy always emits K radiation no matter how the vacancy was originally created.) This phenomenon is the x-ray counterpart of the photoelectric effect in the ultraviolet region of the spectrum; there, photoelectrons can be ejected from the outer shells of a metal atom by the action of ultraviolet radiation, provided the latter has a wavelength less than a certain critical value.

To say that the energy of the incoming quanta must exceed a certain value W_K is equivalent to saying that the wavelength must be less than a certain value λ_K, since the energy per quantum is $h\nu$ and wavelength is inversely proportional to frequency. These relations may be written

$$W_K = h\nu_K = \frac{hc}{\lambda_K}, \qquad (1\text{--}14)$$

where ν_K and λ_K are the frequency and wavelength, respectively, of the K absorption edge. Now consider the absorption curve of Fig. 1–8 in light of the above. Suppose that x-rays of wavelength 2.5A are incident on a sheet of nickel and that this wavelength is continuously decreased. At first the absorption coefficient is about 180 cm^2/gm, but as the wavelength decreases, the frequency increases and so does the energy per quantum, as shown by the upper curve, thus causing the absorption coefficient to decrease, since the greater the energy of a quantum the more easily it passes through an absorber. When the wavelength is reduced just below the critical value λ_K, which is 1.488A for nickel, the absorption coefficient suddenly increases about eightfold in value. True absorption is now occurring and a large fraction of the incident quanta simply disappear, their energy being converted into fluorescent radiation and the kinetic energy of ejected photoelectrons. Since energy must be conserved in the process, it follows that the energy per quantum of the fluorescent radiation must be less than that of the incident radiation, or that the wavelength λ_K of the K absorption edge must be shorter than that of any K characteristic line.

As the wavelength of the incident beam is decreased below λ_K, the absorption coefficient begins to decrease again, even though the production of K fluorescent radiation and photoelectrons is still occurring. At a wavelength of 1.0A, for example, the incident quanta have more than enough energy to remove an electron from the K shell of nickel. But the more energetic the quanta become, the greater is their probability of passing right through the absorber, with the result that less and less of them take part in the ejection of photoelectrons.

If the absorption curve of nickel is plotted for longer wavelengths than 2.5A, i.e., beyond the limit of Fig. 1–8, other sharp discontinuities will be found. These are the L, M, N, etc., absorption edges; in fact, there are three closely spaced L edges (L_I, L_{II}, and L_{III}), five M edges, etc. Each of these discontinuities marks the wavelength of the incident beam whose quanta have just sufficient energy to eject an L, M, N, etc., electron from the atom. The right-hand branch of the curve of Fig. 1–8, for example, lies between the K and L absorption edges; in this wavelength region incident x-rays have enough energy to remove L, M, etc., electrons from nickel but not enough to remove K electrons. Absorption-edge wavelengths vary with the atomic number of the absorber in the same way, but not quite as exactly, as characteristic emission wavelengths, that is, according to Moseley's law. Values of the K and L absorption-edge wavelengths are given in Appendix 3.

The measured values of the absorption edges can be used to construct an energy-level diagram for the atom, which in turn can be used in the calculation of characteristic-line wavelengths. For example, if we take the energy of the neutral atom as zero, then the energy of an ionized atom (an atom in an excited state) will be some positive quantity, since work must be done to pull an electron away from the positively charged nucleus. If a K electron is removed, work equal to W_K must be done and the atom is said to be in the K energy state. The energy W_K may be calculated from the wavelength of the K absorption edge by the use of Eq. (1–14). Similarly, the energies of the L, M, etc., states can be calculated from the wavelengths of the L, M, etc., absorption edges and the results plotted in the form of an energy-level diagram for the atom (Fig. 1–9).

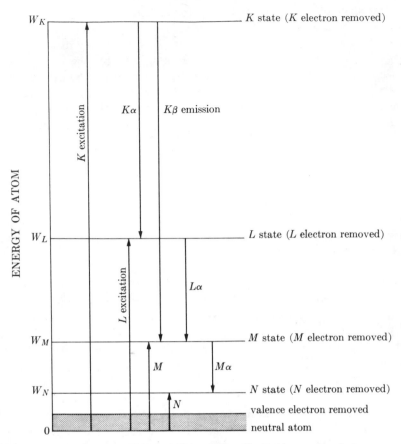

Fig. 1-9. Atomic energy levels (schematic). Excitation and emission processes indicated by arrows. (From *Structure of Metals*, by C. S. Barrett, McGraw-Hill Book Company, Inc., 1952.)

Although this diagram is simplified, in that the substructure of the L, M, etc., levels is not shown, it illustrates the main principles. The arrows show the transitions of the *atom*, and their directions are therefore just the opposite of the arrows in Fig. 1-7, which shows the transitions of the *electron*. Thus, if a K electron is removed from an atom (whether by an incident electron or x-ray), the atom is raised to the K state. If an electron then moves from the L to the K level to fill the vacancy, the atom undergoes a transition from the K to the L state. This transition is accompanied by the emission of $K\alpha$ characteristic radiation and the arrow indicating $K\alpha$ emission is accordingly drawn *from* the K state *to* the L state.

Figure 1-9 shows clearly how the wavelengths of characteristic emission lines can be calculated, since the difference in energy between two states will equal $h\nu$, where ν is the frequency of the radiation emitted when the atom goes from one state to the other. Consider the $K\alpha_1$ characteristic line, for example. The "L level" of an atom is actually a group of three closely spaced levels (L_I, L_{II}, and L_{III}), and the emission of the $K\alpha_1$ line is due to a $K \rightarrow L_{III}$ transition. The frequency $\nu_{K\alpha_1}$ of this line is therefore given by the equations

$$h\nu_{K\alpha_1} = W_K - W_{L_{III}},$$

$$h\nu_{K\alpha_1} = h\nu_K - h\nu_{L_{III}},$$

$$\frac{1}{\lambda_{K\alpha_1}} = \frac{1}{\lambda_K} - \frac{1}{\lambda_{L_{III}}}, \tag{1-15}$$

where the subscripts K and L_{III} refer to absorption edges and the subscript $K\alpha_1$ to the emission line.

Excitation voltages can be calculated by a relation similar to Eq. (1–4). To excite K radiation, for example, in the target of an x-ray tube, the bombarding electrons must have energy equal to W_K. Therefore

$$e\mathcal{V}_K = W_K = h\nu_K = \frac{hc}{\lambda_K},$$

$$\mathcal{V}_K = \frac{hc}{e\lambda_K},$$

$$V_K = \frac{12{,}400}{\lambda_K}, \tag{1-16}$$

where V_K is the K excitation voltage (in practical units) and λ_K is the K absorption edge wavelength (in angstroms).

Figure 1–10 summarizes some of the relations developed above. This curve gives the short-wavelength limit of the continuous spectrum as a function of applied voltage. Because of the similarity between Eqs. (1–4) and (1–16), the same curve also enables us to determine the critical excitation voltage from the wavelength of an absorption edge.

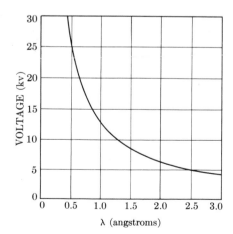

Fig. 1–10. Relation between the voltage applied to an x-ray tube and the short-wavelength limit of the continuous spectrum, and between the critical excitation voltage of any metal and the wavelength of its absorption edge.

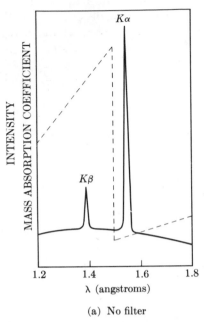
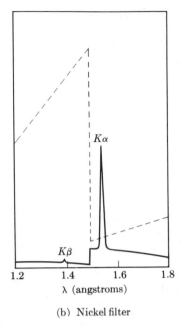

(a) No filter

(b) Nickel filter

FIG. 1–11. Comparison of the spectra of copper radiation (a) before and (b) after passage through a nickel filter (schematic). The dashed line is the mass absorption coefficient of nickel.

1–6 Filters. Many x-ray diffraction experiments require radiation which is as closely monochromatic as possible. However, the beam from an x-ray tube operated at a voltage above V_K contains not only the strong $K\alpha$ line but also the weaker $K\beta$ line and the continuous spectrum. The intensity of these undesirable components can be decreased relative to the intensity of the $K\alpha$ line by passing the beam through a *filter* made of a material whose K absorption edge lies between the $K\alpha$ and $K\beta$ wavelengths of the target metal. Such a material will have an atomic number 1 or 2 less than that of the target metal.

A filter so chosen will absorb the $K\beta$ component much more strongly than the $K\alpha$ component, because of the abrupt change in its absorption coefficient between these two wavelengths. The effect of filtration is shown in Fig. 1–11, in which the partial spectra of the unfiltered and filtered beams from a copper target ($Z = 29$) are shown superimposed on a plot of the mass absorption coefficient of the nickel filter ($Z = 28$).

The thicker the filter the lower the ratio of intensity of $K\beta$ to $K\alpha$ in the transmitted beam. But filtration is never perfect, of course, no matter how thick the filter, and one must compromise between reasonable suppression of the $K\beta$ component and the inevitable weakening of the $K\alpha$ component which accompanies it. In practice it is found that a reduction

TABLE 1–1

FILTERS FOR SUPPRESSION OF $K\beta$ RADIATION

Target	Filter	Incident beam $\dfrac{I(K\alpha)}{I(K\beta)}$	Filter thickness for $\dfrac{I(K\alpha)}{I(K\beta)} = \dfrac{500}{1}$ in trans. beam		$\dfrac{I(K\alpha) \text{ trans.}}{I(K\alpha) \text{ incident}}$
			mg/cm^2	in.	
Mo	Zr	5.4	70	0.0043	0.30
Cu	Ni	7.5	18	0.0008	0.42
Co	Fe	9.4	13	0.0006	0.47
Fe	Mn	9.0	12	0.0006	0.47
Cr	V	8.5	9	0.0006	0.48

in the intensity of the $K\alpha$ line to about half its original value will decrease the ratio of intensity of $K\beta$ to $K\alpha$ from about $\frac{1}{9}$ in the incident beam to about $\frac{1}{500}$ in the transmitted beam; this level is sufficiently low for most purposes. Table 1–1 shows the filters used in conjunction with the common target metals, the thicknesses required, and the transmission factors for the $K\alpha$ line. Filter materials are usually used in the form of thin foils. If it is not possible to obtain a given metal in the form of a stable foil, the oxide of the metal may be used. The powdered oxide is mixed with a suitable binder and spread on a paper backing, the required mass of metal per unit area being given in Table 1–1.

1–7 Production of x-rays. We have seen that x-rays are produced whenever high-speed electrons collide with a metal target. Any x-ray tube must therefore contain (a) a source of electrons, (b) a high accelerating voltage, and (c) a metal target. Furthermore, since most of the kinetic energy of the electrons is converted into heat in the target, the latter must be water-cooled to prevent its melting.

All x-ray tubes contain two electrodes, an anode (the metal target) maintained, with few exceptions, at ground potential, and a cathode, maintained at a high negative potential, normally of the order of 30,000 to 50,000 volts for diffraction work. X-ray tubes may be divided into two basic types, according to the way in which electrons are provided: filament tubes, in which the source of electrons is a hot filament, and gas tubes, in which electrons are produced by the ionization of a small quantity of gas in the tube.

Filament tubes, invented by Coolidge in 1913, are by far the more widely used. They consist of an evacuated glass envelope which insulates the anode at one end from the cathode at the other, the cathode being a tungsten filament and the anode a water-cooled block of copper containing the desired target metal as a small insert at one end. Figure 1–12

FIG. 1–12. Sealed-off nonshockproof filament x-ray tube. (Courtesy of Machlett Laboratories, Inc.)

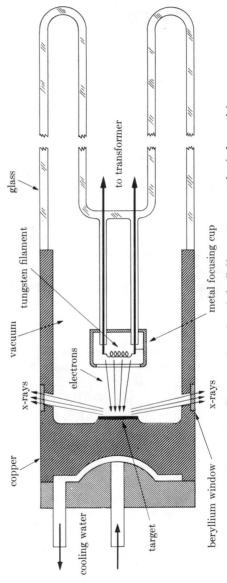

FIG. 1–13. Cross section of sealed-off filament x-ray tube (schematic).

is a photograph of such a tube, and Fig. 1–13 shows its internal construction. One lead of the high-voltage transformer is connected to the filament and the other to ground, the target being grounded by its own cooling-water connection. The filament is heated by a *filament current* of about 3 amp and emits electrons which are rapidly drawn to the target by the high voltage across the tube. Surrounding the filament is a small metal cup maintained at the same high (negative) voltage as the filament: it therefore repels the electrons and tends to focus them into a narrow region of the target, called the focal spot. X-rays are emitted from the focal spot in all directions and escape from the tube through two or more windows in the tube housing. Since these windows must be vacuum tight and yet highly transparent to x-rays, they are usually made of beryllium, aluminum, or mica.

Although one might think that an x-ray tube would operate only from a DC source, since the electron flow must occur only in one direction, it is actually possible to operate a tube from an AC source such as a transformer because of the rectifying properties of the tube itself. Current exists during the half-cycle in which the filament is negative with respect to the target; during the reverse half-cycle the filament is positive, but no electrons can flow since only the filament is hot enough to emit electrons. Thus a simple circuit such as shown in Fig. 1–14 suffices for many installations, although more elaborate circuits, containing rectifying tubes, smoothing capacitors, and voltage stabilizers, are often used, particularly when the x-ray intensity must be kept constant within narrow limits. In Fig. 1–14, the voltage applied to the tube is controlled by the autotransformer which controls the voltage applied to the primary of the high-voltage transformer. The voltmeter shown measures the input voltage but may be calibrated, if desired, to read the output voltage applied to the tube.

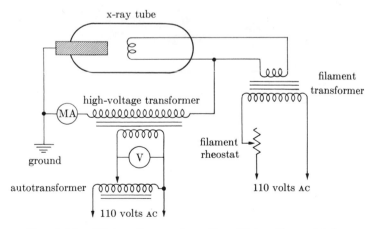

FIG. 1–14.   Wiring diagram for self-rectifying filament tube.

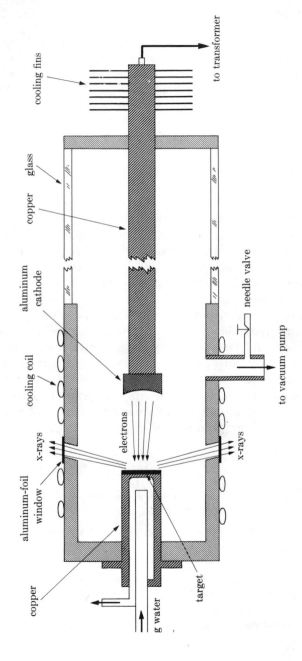

FIG. 1-15.   Cross section of gas x-ray tube (schematic).

The milliammeter measures the *tube current*, i.e., the flow of electrons from filament to target. This current is normally of the order of 15 to 25 ma and is controlled by the filament rheostat. This rheostat controls the output voltage of the filament transformer; this voltage determines the filament current and, in turn, the temperature of the filament and the number of electrons it can emit per second. Although the filament transformer is a low-voltage step-down transformer, since it need apply only about 5 volts to the filament, it is itself at a high negative voltage relative to ground and must be well insulated.

X-ray tubes of the filament type can be obtained in two forms, sealed-off or demountable, the former being more popular in the United States, the latter in Europe. A sealed-off tube is evacuated and sealed off at the factory. It is by far the easiest kind to operate, since no high-vacuum pumping equipment is needed; however, it is expensive (one needs as many tubes as there are target metals required), and the life of the tube is determined by the life of the filament. In demountable tubes both the filament and the target are accessible for replacement; burned-out filaments can be replaced and targets can be interchanged at will. However, the demountable tube must be pumped out continuously during operation, and both a diffusion and a mechanical pump are necessary to obtain the high vacuum required.

The **gas tube** (Fig. 1–15) was the original x-ray tube, but it is now almost obsolete, although there are a number of old ones performing faithfully in laboratories here and abroad. It contains an aluminum cathode, with a concave face to focus the electrons, and operates at an air pressure of about 0.01 mm Hg. This pressure can be easily obtained by continuous pumping with a mechanical vacuum pump against a controlled leak through a needle valve. Although the actual processes which go on in the tube are not well understood, they appear to be as follows. A few electrons and positive nitrogen and oxygen ions are always present in the air, and when a voltage is applied to the tube, these particles are attracted to the anode and cathode respectively. The positive ions hitting the cathode eject electrons from it. These electrons proceed at high speed toward the anode, and some of them collide with air molecules and produce further ionization. The rate of electron and ion production thus rapidly builds up to a constant value. The anode is cooled in the usual way, and the heat produced in the cathode by ion bombardment is dissipated by cooling fins.

It is clear that the air pressure within the tube is critical: too little air and there is no source of electrons, too much air and so much ionization occurs that tube currents are quite high and very little voltage can be built up between the electrodes. However, the operation of a tube is judged, not by the gas pressure (very few tubes are equipped with pressure gauges), but by the electrical characteristics, i.e., by the tube current and voltage. These latter quantities, each of which one would like to control independently, are unfortunately dependent in a complicated way on one another and on the gas pressure. In practice, the tube current is regulated mainly by the needle valve, since an increased air leak causes an increased current, and also by the applied voltage, since an increase in voltage also causes an increase in current. Some tubes are quite temperamental and require considerable juggling of voltage and gas pressure in order to obtain the desired voltage and tube current and to keep them constant with time.

On the credit side, however, gas tubes are the cheapest kind available, require only a simple mechanical pump, and need no filament transformer. They are demountable, which means that one tube and a set of targets of various metals will produce any desired kind of radiation. Furthermore, they produce the purest radiation available, since the target never becomes contaminated with a foreign metal. In filament tubes, on the other hand, some tungsten occasionally evaporates from the filament and deposits on the target, and the tungsten then emits characteristic L radiation (the L excitation voltage of tungsten is only 10,200 volts), as well as the radiation characteristic of the target metal itself.

The size and shape of the **focal spot** of an x-ray tube of any type is one of its most important characteristics. Within limits, it should be as small as possible in order to concentrate the electron energy into a small area of the target and so produce an x-ray source of high intensity. In some filament tubes, the focal spot is made unusually small by maintaining the focusing cup at a potential a few hundred volts more negative than the filament, thus concentrating the electrons into a narrower beam.

Filament tubes usually have the filament wound in a helix in order to produce a so-called "line focus" which is actually a narrow rectangle (Fig. 1–16). The total electron energy is thus spread over a rather large focal spot A, which helps to dissipate the heat formed; yet the cross section B of the beam issuing at a small target-to-beam angle α is that of a small square, and this beam is of greater intensity than one leaving the focal spot at some larger angle α. The best value of α is about 6°, and a good tube will have a projected focal-spot size at this angle of less than 1 mm square. If the tube has a window so arranged that a beam can issue from the focal spot A almost normal to the plane of the drawing and at a small angle α, then the cross section of the beam will be an extremely narrow line; such a beam is quite useful in some diffraction experiments.

All x-ray tubes have a maximum **power** rating which cannot be exceeded without injury to the tube. This limit is fixed by the amount of heat that can be dissipated by the target and is usually stated by the manufacturer in terms of the maximum allowable tube current (in ma) for a given tube voltage (in kv).

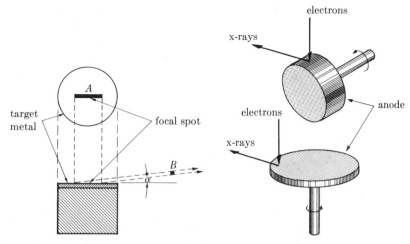

Fig. 1–16. Reduction in apparent size of focal spot.

Fig. 1–17. Schematic drawings of two types of rotating anode for high-power x-ray tubes.

Since an x-ray tube is less than 1 percent efficient in producing x-rays and since the diffraction of x-rays by crystals is far less efficient than this, it follows that the intensities of diffracted x-ray beams are extremely low. In fact, it may require as much as several hours exposure to a photographic film in order to detect them at all. Constant efforts are therefore being made to increase the intensity of the x-ray source. One solution to this problem is the *rotating-anode tube*, in which rotation of the anode continuously brings fresh target metal into the focal-spot area and so allows a greater power input without excessive heating of the anode. Figure 1–17 shows two designs that have been used successfully; the shafts rotate through vacuum-tight seals in the tube housing. Such tubes can operate at a power level 5 to 10 times higher than that of a fixed-focus tube, with corresponding reductions in exposure time.

1–8 Detection of x-rays. The principal means used to detect x-ray beams are fluorescent screens, photographic film, and ionization devices.

Fluorescent screens are made of a thin layer of zinc sulfide, containing a trace of nickel, mounted on a cardboard backing. Under the action of x-rays, this compound fluoresces in the visible region, i.e., emits visible light, in this case yellow light. Although most diffracted beams are too weak to be detected by this method, fluorescent screens are widely used in diffraction work to locate the position of the primary beam when adjusting apparatus. A fluorescing crystal may also be used in conjunction with a phototube; the combination, called a *scintillation counter*, is a very sensitive detector of x-rays.

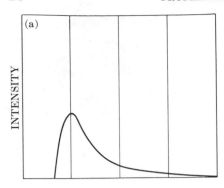

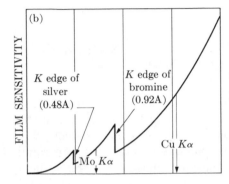

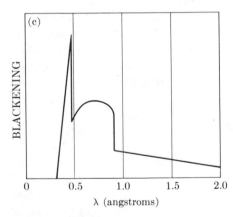

Fig. 1–18. Relation between film sensitivity and effective shape of continuous spectrum (schematic): (a) continuous spectrum from a tungsten target at 40 kv; (b) film sensitivity; (c) blackening curve for spectrum shown in (a).

Photographic film is affected by x-rays in much the same way as by visible light, and film is the most widely used means of recording diffracted x-ray beams. However, the emulsion on ordinary film is too thin to absorb much of the incident x-radiation, and only absorbed x-rays can be effective in blackening the film. For this reason, x-ray films are made with rather thick layers of emulsion on both sides in order to increase the total absorption. The grain size is also made large for the same purpose: this has the unfortunate consequence that x-ray films are grainy, do not resolve fine detail, and cannot stand much enlargement.

Because the mass absorption coefficient of any substance varies with wavelength, it follows that film sensitivity, i.e., the amount of blackening caused by x-ray beams of the same intensity, depends on their wavelength. This should be borne in mind whenever white radiation is recorded photographically; for one thing, this sensitivity variation alters the effective shape of the continuous spectrum. Figure 1–18(a) shows the intensity of the continuous spectrum as a function of wavelength and (b) the variation of film sensitivity. This latter curve is merely a plot of the mass absorption coefficient of silver bromide, the active ingredient of the emulsion, and is marked by discontinuities at the K absorption edges of silver and bromine. (Note, incidentally, how much more sensitive the film is to the K radiation from copper than to the K radiation from molybdenum, other things being equal.) Curve (c) of Fig. 1–18 shows the net result, namely the amount of film blackening caused by the various wavelength components of the continuous spectrum, or what might be called the "effective photographic intensity" of the continuous spectrum.   These curves are only approximate, however, and in practice it is almost impossible to measure photographically the relative intensities of two beams of different wavelength.   On the other hand, the relative intensities of beams of the *same* wavelength can be accurately measured by photographic means, and such measurements are described in Chap. 6.

Ionization devices measure the intensity of x-ray beams by the amount of ionization they produce in a gas.   X-ray quanta can cause ionization just as high-speed electrons can, namely, by knocking an electron out of a gas molecule and leaving behind a positive ion.   This phenomenon can be made the basis of intensity measurements by passing the x-ray beam through a chamber containing a suitable gas and two electrodes having a constant potential difference between them.   The electrons are attracted to the anode and the positive ions to the cathode and a current is thus produced in an external circuit.   In the *ionization chamber*, this current is constant for a constant x-ray intensity, and the magnitude of the current is a measure of the x-ray intensity.   In the *Geiger counter* and *proportional counter*, this current pulsates, and the number of pulses per unit of time is proportional to the x-ray intensity.   These devices are discussed more fully in Chap. 7.

In general, fluorescent screens are used today only for the detection of x-ray beams, while photographic film and the various forms of counters permit both detection and measurement of intensity.   Photographic film is the most widely used method of observing diffraction effects, because it can record a number of diffracted beams at one time and their relative positions in space and the film can be used as a basis for intensity measurements if desired.   Intensities can be measured much more rapidly with counters, and these instruments are becoming more and more popular for quantitative work.   However, they record only one diffracted beam at a time.

1–9 Safety precautions.   The operator of x-ray apparatus is exposed to two obvious dangers, electric shock and radiation injury, but both of these hazards can be reduced to negligible proportions by proper design of equipment and reasonable care on the part of the user.   Nevertheless, it is only prudent for the x-ray worker to be continually aware of these hazards.

The danger of **electric shock** is always present around high-voltage apparatus.   The anode end of most x-ray tubes is usually grounded and therefore safe, but the cathode end is a source of danger.   Gas tubes and filament tubes of the nonshockproof variety (such as the one shown in Fig. 1–12) must be so mounted that their cathode end is absolutely inaccessible to the user during operation; this may be accomplished by placing the cathode end below a table top, in a box, behind a screen, etc. The installation should be so contrived that it is impossible for the operator to touch the high-voltage parts without automatically disconnecting the high voltage. Shockproof sealed-off tubes are also available: these are encased in a grounded metal covering, and an insulated, shockproof cable connects the cathode end to the transformer. Being shockproof, such a tube has the advantage that it need not be permanently fixed in position but may be set up in various positions as required for particular experiments.

The **radiation hazard** is due to the fact that x-rays can kill human tissue; in fact, it is precisely this property which is utilized in x-ray therapy for the killing of cancer cells. The biological effects of x-rays include burns (due to localized high-intensity beams), radiation sickness (due to radiation received generally by the whole body), and, at á lower level of radiation intensity, genetic mutations. The burns are painful and may be difficult, if not impossible, to heal. Slight exposures to x-rays are not cumulative, but above a certain level called the "tolerance dose," they do have a cumulative effect and can produce permanent injury. The x-rays used in diffraction are particularly harmful because they have relatively long wavelengths and are therefore easily absorbed by the body.

There is no excuse today for receiving serious injuries as early x-ray workers did through ignorance. There would probably be no accidents if x-rays were visible and produced an immediate burning sensation, but they are invisible and burns may not be immediately felt. If the body has received general radiation above the tolerance dose, the first noticeable effect will be a lowering of the white-blood-cell count, so periodic blood counts are advisable if there is any doubt about the general level of intensity in the laboratory.

The safest procedure for the experimenter to follow is: first, to locate the *primary* beam from the tube with a small fluorescent screen fixed to the end of a rod and thereafter avoid it; and second, to make sure that he is well shielded by lead or lead-glass screens from the radiation *scattered* by the camera or other apparatus which may be in the path of the primary beam. Strict and constant attention to these precautions will ensure safety.

PROBLEMS

1–1. What is the frequency (per second) and energy per quantum (in ergs) of x-ray beams of wavelength 0.71A (Mo *Kα*) and 1.54A (Cu *Kα*)?

1–2. Calculate the velocity and kinetic energy with which the electrons strike the target of an x-ray tube operated at 50,000 volts. What is the short-wavelength limit of the continuous spectrum emitted and the maximum energy per quantum of radiation?

1–3. Graphically verify Moseley's law for the $K\beta_1$ lines of Cu, Mo, and W.

1–4. Plot the ratio of transmitted to incident intensity *vs.* thickness of lead sheet for Mo $K\alpha$ radiation and a thickness range of 0.00 to 0.02 mm.

1–5. Graphically verify Eq. (1–13) for a lead absorber and Mo $K\alpha$, Rh $K\alpha$, and Ag $K\alpha$ radiation. (The mass absorption coefficients of lead for these radiations are 141, 95.8, and 74.4, respectively.) From the curve, determine the mass absorption coefficient of lead for the shortest wavelength radiation from a tube operated at 60,000 volts.

1–6. Lead screens for the protection of personnel in x-ray diffraction laboratories are usually at least 1 mm thick. Calculate the "transmission factor" ($I_{\text{trans.}}/I_{\text{incident}}$) of such a screen for Cu $K\alpha$, Mo $K\alpha$, and the shortest wavelength radiation from a tube operated at 60,000 volts.

1–7. (a) Calculate the mass and linear absorption coefficients of air for Cr $K\alpha$ radiation. Assume that air contains 80 percent nitrogen and 20 percent oxygen by weight. (b) Plot the transmission factor of air for Cr $K\alpha$ radiation and a path length of 0 to 20 cm.

1–8. A sheet of aluminum 1 mm thick reduces the intensity of a monochromatic x-ray beam to 23.9 percent of its original value. What is the wavelength of the x-rays?

1–9. Calculate the K excitation voltage of copper.

1–10. Calculate the wavelength of the L_{III} absorption edge of molybdenum.

1–11. Calculate the wavelength of the Cu $K\alpha_1$ line.

1–12. Plot the curve shown in Fig. 1–10 and save it for future reference.

1–13. What voltage must be applied to a molybdenum-target tube in order that the emitted x-rays excite K fluorescent radiation from a piece of copper placed in the x-ray beam? What is the wavelength of the fluorescent radiation?

In Problems 14 and 15 take the intensity ratios of $K\alpha$ to $K\beta$ in unfiltered radiation from Table 1–1.

1–14. Suppose that a nickel filter is required to produce an intensity ratio of Cu $K\alpha$ to Cu $K\beta$ of 100/1 in the filtered beam. Calculate the thickness of the filter and the transmission factor for the Cu $K\alpha$ line. (μ/ρ of nickel for Cu $K\beta$ radiation = 286 cm²/gm.)

1–15. Filters for Co K radiation are usually made of iron oxide (Fe_2O_3) powder rather than iron foil. If a filter contains 5 mg Fe_2O_3/cm², what is the transmission factor for the Co $K\alpha$ line? What is the intensity ratio of Co $K\alpha$ to Co $K\beta$ in the filtered beam? (Density of Fe_2O_3 = 5.24 gm/cm³, μ/ρ of iron for Co $K\alpha$ radiation = 59.5 cm²/gm, μ/ρ of oxygen for Co $K\alpha$ radiation = 20.2, μ/ρ of iron for Co $K\beta$ radiation = 371, μ/ρ of oxygen for Co $K\beta$ radiation = 15.0.)

1–16. What is the power input to an x-ray tube operating at 40,000 volts and a tube current of 25 ma? If the power cannot exceed this level, what is the maximum allowable tube current at 50,000 volts?

1–17. A copper-target x-ray tube is operated at 40,000 volts and 25 ma. The efficiency of an x-ray tube is so low that, for all practical purposes, one may assume that all the input energy goes into heating the target. If there were no dissipation of heat by water-cooling, conduction, radiation, etc., how long would it take a 100-gm copper target to melt? (Melting point of copper = 1083°C, mean specific heat = 6.65 cal/mole/°C, latent heat of fusion = 3,220 cal/mole.)

1–18. Assume that the sensitivity of x-ray film is proportional to the mass absorption coefficient of the silver bromide in the emulsion for the particular wavelength involved. What, then, is the ratio of film sensitivities to Cu $K\alpha$ and Mo $K\alpha$ radiation?

CHAPTER 2

THE GEOMETRY OF CRYSTALS

2–1 Introduction. Turning from the properties of x-rays, we must now consider the geometry and structure of crystals in order to discover what there is about crystals in general that enables them to diffract x-rays. We must also consider particular crystals of various kinds and how the very large number of crystals found in nature are classified into a relatively small number of groups. Finally, we will examine the ways in which the orientation of lines and planes in crystals can be represented in terms of symbols or in graphical form.

A crystal may be defined as *a solid composed of atoms arranged in a pattern periodic in three dimensions.* As such, crystals differ in a fundamental way from gases and liquids because the atomic arrangements in the latter do not possess the essential requirement of periodicity. Not all solids are crystalline, however; some are *amorphous*, like glass, and do not have any regular interior arrangement of atoms. There is, in fact, no essential difference between an amorphous solid and a liquid, and the former is often referred to as an "undercooled liquid."

2–2 Lattices. In thinking about crystals, it is often convenient to ignore the actual atoms composing the crystal and their periodic arrangement in space, and to think instead of a set of imaginary points which has a fixed relation in space to the atoms of the crystal and may be regarded as a sort of framework or skeleton on which the actual crystal is built up.

This set of points can be formed as follows. Imagine space to be divided by three sets of planes, the planes in each set being parallel and equally spaced. This division of space will produce a set of cells each identical in size, shape, and orientation to its neighbors. Each cell is a parallelepiped, since its opposite faces are parallel and each face is a parallelogram. The space-dividing planes will intersect each other in a set of lines (Fig. 2–1), and these lines in turn intersect in the set of points referred to above. A set of points so formed has an important property: it constitutes a *point lattice*, which is defined as *an array of points in space so arranged that each point has identical surroundings.* By "identical surroundings" we mean that the lattice of points, when viewed in a particular direction from one lattice point, would have exactly the same appearance when viewed in the same direction from any other lattice point.

Since all the cells of the lattice shown in Fig. 2–1 are identical, we may choose any one, for example the heavily outlined one, as a *unit cell.* The

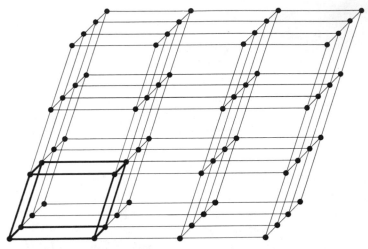

FIG. 2–1. A point lattice.

size and shape of the unit cell can in turn be described by the three vectors* **a**, **b**, and **c** drawn from one corner of the cell taken as origin (Fig. 2–2). These vectors define the cell and are called the *crystallographic axes* of the cell. They may also be described in terms of their lengths (a, b, c) and the angles between them (α, β, γ). These lengths and angles are the *lattice constants* or *lattice parameters* of the unit cell.

Note that the vectors **a**, **b**, **c** define, not only the unit cell, but also the whole point lattice through the translations provided by these vectors. In other words, the whole set of points in the lattice can be produced by repeated action of the vectors **a**, **b**, **c** on one lattice point located at the origin, or, stated alternatively, the vector coordinates of any point in the lattice are *P***a**, *Q***b**, and *R***c**, where P, Q, and R are whole numbers. It follows that the arrangement of points in a point lattice is absolutely periodic in three dimensions, points being repeated at regular intervals along any line one chooses to draw through the lattice.

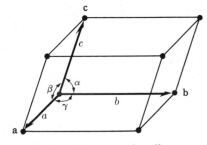

FIG. 2–2. A unit cell.

2–3 Crystal systems. In dividing space by three sets of planes, we can of course produce unit cells of various shapes, depending on how we arrange the planes. For example, if the planes in the three sets are all equally

---

* Vectors are here represented by boldface symbols. The same symbol in italics stands for the absolute value of the vector.

TABLE 2-1

CRYSTAL SYSTEMS AND BRAVAIS LATTICES

(The symbol $\neq$ implies nonequality by reason of symmetry. Accidental equality may occur, as shown by an example in Sec. 2–4.)

System	Axials lengths and angles	Bravais lattice	Lattice symbol
Cubic	Three equal axes at right angles $a = b = c, \ \alpha = \beta = \gamma = 90°$	Simple Body-centered Face-centered	P I F
Tetragonal	Three axes at right angles, two equal $a = b \neq c, \ \alpha = \beta = \gamma = 90°$	Simple Body-centered	P I
Orthorhombic	Three unequal axes at right angles $a \neq b \neq c, \ \alpha = \beta = \gamma = 90°$	Simple Body-centered Base-centered Face-centered	P I C F
Rhombohedral*	Three equal axes, equally inclined $a = b = c, \ \alpha = \beta = \gamma \neq 90°$	Simple	R
Hexagonal	Two equal coplanar axes at 120°, third axis at right angles $a = b \neq c, \ \alpha = \beta = 90°, \ \gamma = 120°$	Simple	P
Monoclinic	Three unequal axes, one pair not at right angles $a \neq b \neq c, \ \alpha = \gamma = 90° \neq \beta$	Simple Base-centered	P C
Triclinic	Three unequal axes, unequally inclined and none at right angles $a \neq b \neq c, \ \alpha \neq \beta \neq \gamma \neq 90°$	Simple	P

* Also called trigonal.

spaced and mutually perpendicular, the unit cell is cubic. In this case the vectors **a**, **b**, **c** are all equal and at right angles to one another, or $a = b = c$ and $\alpha = \beta = \gamma = 90°$. By thus giving special values to the axial lengths and angles, we can produce unit cells of various shapes and therefore various kinds of point lattices, since the points of the lattice are located at the cell corners. It turns out that only seven different kinds of cells are necessary to include all the possible point lattices. These correspond to the seven *crystal systems* into which all crystals can be classified. These systems are listed in Table 2–1.

Seven different point lattices can be obtained simply by putting points at the corners of the unit cells of the seven crystal systems. However, there are other arrangements of points which fulfill the requirements of a point lattice, namely, that each point have identical surroundings. The French crystallographer Bravais worked on this problem and in 1848 demonstrated that there are fourteen possible point lattices and no more; this important result is commemorated by our use of the terms *Bravais*

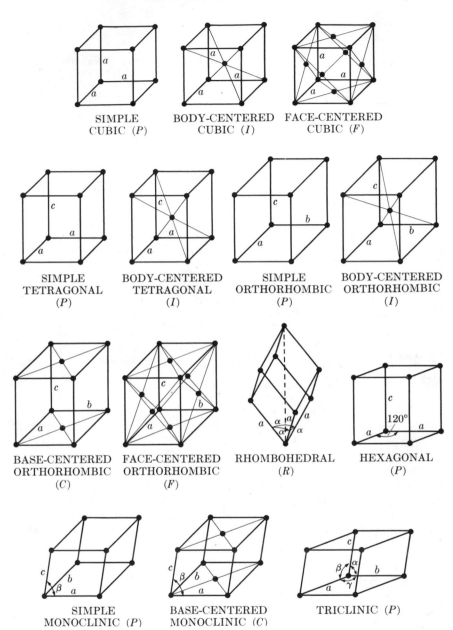

FIG. 2–3.   The fourteen Bravais lattices.

lattice and *point lattice* as synonymous.   For example, if a point is placed at the center of each cell of a cubic point lattice, the new array of points also forms a point lattice.   Similarly, another point lattice can be based on a cubic unit cell having lattice points at each corner and in the center of each face.

The fourteen Bravais lattices are described in Table 2–1 and illustrated in Fig. 2–3, where the symbols P, F, I, etc., have the following meanings. We must first distinguish between *simple*, or *primitive*, cells (symbol P or R) and *nonprimitive* cells (any other symbol): primitive cells have only one lattice point per cell while nonprimitive have more than one. A lattice point in the interior of a cell "belongs" to that cell, while one in a cell face is shared by two cells and one at a corner is shared by eight. The number of lattice points per cell is therefore given by

$$N = N_i + \frac{N_f}{2} + \frac{N_c}{8}, \qquad (2\text{–}1)$$

where N_i = number of interior points, N_f = number of points on faces, and N_c = number of points on corners. Any cell containing lattice points on the corners only is therefore primitive, while one containing additional points in the interior or on faces is nonprimitive. The symbols F and I refer to face-centered and body-centered cells, respectively, while A, B, and C refer to base-centered cells, centered on one pair of opposite faces A, B, or C. (The A face is the face defined by the b and c axes, etc.) The symbol R is used especially for the rhombohedral system. In Fig. 2–3, axes of equal length in a particular system are given the same symbol to indicate their equality, e.g., the cubic axes are all marked a, the two equal tetragonal axes are marked a and the third one c, etc.

At first glance, the list of Bravais lattices in Table 2–1 appears incomplete. Why not, for example, a base-centered tetragonal lattice? The full lines in Fig. 2–4 delineate such a cell, centered on the C face, but we see that the same array of lattice points can be referred to the simple tetragonal cell shown by dashed lines, so that the base-centered arrangement of points is not a new lattice.

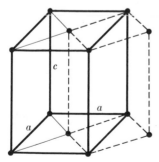

FIG. 2–4. Relation of tetragonal C lattice (full lines) to tetragonal P lattice (dashed lines).

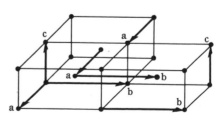

FIG. 2–5. Extension of lattice points through space by the unit cell vectors **a, b, c.**

The lattice points in a nonprimitive unit cell can be extended through space by repeated applications of the unit-cell vectors **a**, **b**, **c** just like those of a primitive cell. We may regard the lattice points associated with a unit cell as being translated one by one or as a group. In either case, equivalent lattice points in adjacent unit cells are separated by one of the vectors **a**, **b**, **c**, wherever these points happen to be located in the cell (Fig. 2–5).

2–4 Symmetry. Both Bravais lattices and the real crystals which are built up on them exhibit various kinds of symmetry. A body or structure is said to be symmetrical when its component parts are arranged in such balance, so to speak, that certain operations can be performed on the body which will bring it into coincidence with itself. These are termed *symmetry operations*. For example, if a body is symmetrical with respect to a plane passing through it, then reflection of either half of the body in the plane as in a mirror will produce a body coinciding with the other half. Thus a cube has several planes of symmetry, one of which is shown in Fig. 2–6(a).

There are in all four macroscopic* symmetry operations or elements: *reflection, rotation, inversion, and rotation-inversion.* A body has n-fold rotational symmetry about an axis if a rotation of $360°/n$ brings it into self-coincidence. Thus a cube has a 4-fold rotation axis normal to each face, a 3-fold axis along each body diagonal, and 2-fold axes joining the centers of opposite edges. Some of these are shown in Fig. 2–6(b) where the small plane figures (square, triangle, and ellipse) designate the various

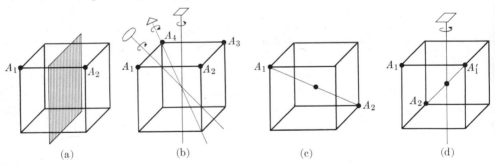

FIG. 2–6. Some symmetry elements of a cube. (a) Reflection plane. A_1 becomes A_2. (b) Rotation axes. 4-fold axis: A_1 becomes A_2; 3-fold axis: A_1 becomes A_3; 2-fold axis: A_1 becomes A_4. (c) Inversion center. A_1 becomes A_2. (d) Rotation-inversion axis. 4-fold axis: A_1 becomes A_1'; inversion center: A_1' becomes A_2.

---

* So called to distinguish them from certain microscopic symmetry operations with which we are not concerned here. The macroscopic elements can be deduced from the angles between the faces of a well-developed crystal, without any knowledge of the atom arrangement inside the crystal. The microscopic symmetry elements, on the other hand, depend entirely on atom arrangement, and their presence cannot be inferred from the external development of the crystal.

kinds of axes. In general, rotation axes may be 1-, 2-, 3-, 4-, or 6-fold. A 1-fold axis indicates no symmetry at all, while a 5-fold axis or one of higher degree than 6 is impossible, in the sense that unit cells having such symmetry cannot be made to fill up space without leaving gaps.

A body has an inversion center if corresponding points of the body are located at equal distances from the center on a line drawn through the center. A body having an inversion center will come into coincidence with itself if every point in the body is inverted, or "reflected," in the inversion center. A cube has such a center at the intersection of its body diagonals [Fig. 2–6(c)]. Finally, a body may have a rotation-inversion axis, either 1-, 2-, 3-, 4-, or 6-fold. If it has an n-fold rotation-inversion axis, it can be brought into coincidence with itself by a rotation of $360°/n$ about the axis followed by inversion in a center lying on the axis. Figure 2–6(d) illustrates the operation of a 4-fold rotation-inversion axis on a cube.

Now, the possession of a certain minimum set of symmetry elements is a fundamental property of each crystal system, and one system is distinguished from another just as much by its symmetry elements as by the values of its axial lengths and angles. In fact, these are interdependent. The minimum number of symmetry elements possessed by each crystal system is listed in Table 2–2. Some crystals may possess more than the minimum symmetry elements required by the system to which they belong, but none may have less.

Symmetry operations apply not only to the unit cells shown in Fig. 2–3, considered merely as geometric shapes, but also to the point lattices associated with them. The latter condition rules out the possibility that the cubic system, for example, could include a base-centered point lattice, since such an array of points would not have the minimum set of symmetry elements required by the cubic system, namely four 3-fold rotation axes. Such a lattice would be classified in the tetragonal system, which has no 3-fold axes and in which accidental equality of the a and c axes is

TABLE 2–2

SYMMETRY ELEMENTS

System	Minimum symmetry elements
Cubic	Four 3-fold rotation axes
Tetragonal	One 4-fold rotation (or rotation-inversion) axis
Orthorhombic	Three perpendicular 2-fold rotation (or rotation-inversion) axes
Rhombohedral	One 3-fold rotation (or rotation-inversion) axis
Hexagonal	One 6-fold rotation (or rotation-inversion) axis
Monoclinic	One 2-fold rotation (or rotation-inversion) axis
Triclinic	None

allowed; as mentioned before, however, this lattice is simple, not base-centered, tetragonal.

Crystals in the rhombohedral (trigonal) system can be referred to either a rhombohedral or a hexagonal lattice. Appendix 2 gives the relation between these two lattices and the transformation equations which allow the Miller indices of a plane (see Sec. 2–6) to be expressed in terms of either set of axes.

2–5 Primitive and nonprimitive cells. In any point lattice a unit cell may be chosen in an infinite number of ways and may contain one or more lattice points per cell. It is important to note that unit cells do not "exist" as such in a lattice: they are a mental construct and can accordingly be chosen at our convenience. The conventional cells shown in Fig. 2–3 are chosen simply for convenience and to conform to the symmetry elements of the lattice.

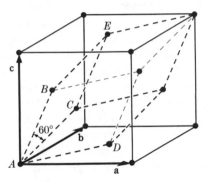

Any of the fourteen Bravais lattices may be referred to a primitive unit cell. For example, the face-centered cubic lattice shown in Fig. 2–7 may be referred to the primitive cell indicated by dashed lines. The latter cell is rhombohedral, its axial angle α is 60°, and each of its axes is $1/\sqrt{2}$ times the length of the axes of the cubic cell. Each cubic cell has four lattice points associated with it, each rhombohedral cell has one, and the

Fig. 2–7. Face-centered cubic point lattice referred to cubic and rhombohedral cells.

former has, correspondingly, four times the volume of the latter. Nevertheless, it is usually more convenient to use the cubic cell rather than the rhombohedral one because the former immediately suggests the cubic symmetry which the lattice actually possesses. Similarly, the other centered nonprimitive cells listed in Table 2–1 are preferred to the primitive cells possible in their respective lattices.

If nonprimitive lattice cells are used, the vector from the origin to any point in the lattice will now have components which are nonintegral multiples of the unit-cell vectors **a**, **b**, **c**. The position of any lattice point in a cell may be given in terms of its *coordinates*; if the vector from the origin of the unit cell to the given point has components $x\mathbf{a}$, $y\mathbf{b}$, $z\mathbf{c}$, where x, y, and z are fractions, then the coordinates of the point are $x\ y\ z$. Thus, point A in Fig. 2–7, taken as the origin, has coordinates 0 0 0 while points B, C, and D, when referred to cubic axes, have coordinates $0\ \frac{1}{2}\ \frac{1}{2}$, $\frac{1}{2}\ 0\ \frac{1}{2}$, and $\frac{1}{2}\ \frac{1}{2}\ 0$, respectively. Point E has coordinates $\frac{1}{2}\ \frac{1}{2}\ 1$ and is equivalent to point D, being separated from it by the vector **c**. The coordinates of equivalent points in different unit cells can always be made identical by the addition or subtraction of a set of integral coordinates; in this case, subtraction of 0 0 1 from $\frac{1}{2}$ $\frac{1}{2}$ 1 (the coordinates of E) gives $\frac{1}{2}$ $\frac{1}{2}$ 0 (the coordinates of D).

Note that the coordinates of a body-centered point, for example, are always $\frac{1}{2}$ $\frac{1}{2}$ $\frac{1}{2}$ no matter whether the unit cell is cubic, tetragonal, or ortho-rhombic, and whatever its size. The coordinates of a point position, such as $\frac{1}{2}$ $\frac{1}{2}$ $\frac{1}{2}$, may also be regarded as an operator which, when "applied" to a point at the origin, will move or translate it to the position $\frac{1}{2}$ $\frac{1}{2}$ $\frac{1}{2}$, the final position being obtained by simple addition of the operator $\frac{1}{2}$ $\frac{1}{2}$ $\frac{1}{2}$ and the original position 0 0 0. In this sense, the positions 0 0 0, $\frac{1}{2}$ $\frac{1}{2}$ $\frac{1}{2}$ are called the "body-centering translations," since they will produce the two point positions characteristic of a body-centered cell when applied to a point at the origin. Similarly, the four point positions characteristic of a face-centered cell, namely 0 0 0, 0 $\frac{1}{2}$ $\frac{1}{2}$, $\frac{1}{2}$ 0 $\frac{1}{2}$, and $\frac{1}{2}$ $\frac{1}{2}$ 0, are called the face-centering translations. The base-centering translations depend on which pair of opposite faces are centered; if centered on the C face, for example, they are 0 0 0, $\frac{1}{2}$ $\frac{1}{2}$ 0.

2–6 Lattice directions and planes. The direction of any line in a lattice may be described by first drawing a line through the origin parallel to the given line and then giving the coordinates of any point on the line through the origin. Let the line pass through the origin of the unit cell and any point having coordinates $u\,v\,w$, where these numbers are not necessarily integral. (This line will also pass through the points $2u\,2v\,2w$, $3u\,3v\,3w$, etc.) Then [uvw], written in square brackets, are the *indices* of the direction of the line. They are also the indices of any line parallel to the given line, since the lattice is infinite and the origin may be taken at any point. Whatever the values of u, v, w, they are always converted to a set of smallest integers by multi-plication or division throughout: thus, [$\frac{1}{2}$ $\frac{1}{2}$ 1], [112], and [224] all represent the same direction, but [112] is the preferred form. Negative indices are written with a bar over the number, e.g., [$\bar{u}vw$]. Direction indices are illustrated in Fig. 2–8.

Directions related by symmetry are called *directions of a form*, and a set of these are represented by the indices of one of them enclosed in angular brackets; for example, the four body

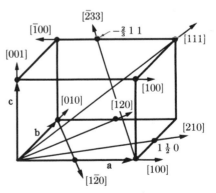

FIG. 2–8.　Indices of directions.

diagonals of a cube, [111], [1$\bar{1}$1], [$\bar{1}\bar{1}$1], and [$\bar{1}$11], may all be represented by the symbol ⟨111⟩.

The orientation of planes in a lattice may also be represented symbolically, according to a system popularized by the English crystallographer Miller. In the general case, the given plane will be tilted with respect to the crystallographic axes, and, since these axes form a convenient frame of reference, we might describe the orientation of the plane by giving the actual distances, measured from the origin, at which it intercepts the three axes. Better still, by expressing these distances as fractions of the axial lengths, we can obtain numbers which are independent of the particular axial lengths involved in the given lattice. But a difficulty then arises when the given plane is parallel to a certain crystallographic axis, because such a plane does not intercept that axis, i.e., its "intercept" can only be described as "infinity." To avoid the introduction of infinity into the description of plane orientation, we can use the reciprocal of the fractional intercept, this reciprocal being zero when the plane and axis are parallel. We thus arrive at a workable symbolism for the orientation of a plane in a lattice, the *Miller indices*, which are defined as *the reciprocals of the fractional intercepts which the plane makes with the crystallographic axes.* For example, if the Miller indices of a plane are (hkl), written in parentheses, then the plane makes fractional intercepts of $1/h$, $1/k$, $1/l$ with the axes, and, if the axial lengths are a, b, c, the plane makes actual intercepts of a/h, b/k, c/l, as shown in Fig. 2–9(a). Parallel to any plane in any lattice, there is a whole set of parallel equidistant planes, one of which passes through the origin; the Miller indices (hkl) usually refer to that plane in the set which is nearest the origin, although they may be taken as referring to any other plane in the set or to the whole set taken together.

We may determine the Miller indices of the plane shown in Fig. 2–9(b) as follows:

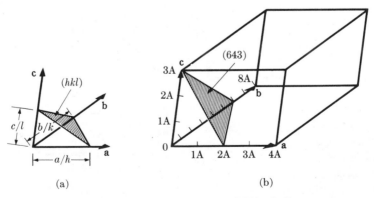

Fig. 2–9. Plane designation by Miller indices.

Axial lengths	4A	8A	3A
Intercept lengths	2A	6A	3A
Fractional intercepts	$\frac{1}{2}$	$\frac{3}{4}$	1
Miller indices	$\begin{cases} 2 \\ 6 \end{cases}$	$\frac{4}{3}$ / 4	1 / 3

Miller indices are always cleared of fractions, as shown above. As stated earlier, if a plane is parallel to a given axis, its fractional intercept on that axis is taken as infinity and the corresponding Miller index is zero. If a plane cuts a negative axis, the corresponding index is negative and is written with a bar over it. Planes whose indices are the negatives of one another are parallel and lie on opposite sides of the origin, e.g., $(\bar{2}10)$ and $(2\bar{1}0)$. The planes $(nh\ nk\ nl)$ are parallel to the planes (hkl) and have $1/n$ the spacing. The same plane may belong to two different sets, the Miller indices of one set being multiples of those of the other; thus the same plane belongs to the (210) set and the (420) set, and, in fact, the planes of the (210) set form every second plane in the (420) set. In the cubic system, it is convenient to remember that a direction $[hkl]$ is always perpendicular to a plane (hkl) of the same indices, but this is not generally true in other systems. Further familiarity with Miller indices can be gained from a study of Fig. 2–10.

A slightly different system of plane indexing is used in the hexagonal system. The unit cell of a hexagonal lattice is defined by two equal and coplanar vectors $\mathbf{a}_1$ and $\mathbf{a}_2$, at 120° to one another, and a third axis $\mathbf{c}$ at right angles [Fig. 2–11(a)]. The complete lattice is built up, as usual, by

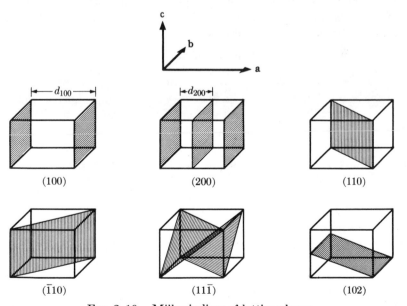

FIG. 2–10. Miller indices of lattice planes.

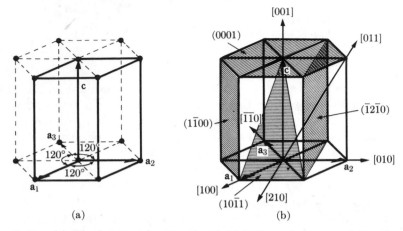

FIG. 2–11.   (a) The hexagonal unit cell and (b) indices of planes and directions.

repeated translations of the points at the unit cell corners by the vectors a_1, a_2, c. Some of the points so generated are shown in the figure, at the ends of dashed lines, in order to exhibit the hexagonal symmetry of the lattice, which has a 6-fold rotation axis parallel to c. The third axis a_3, lying in the basal plane of the hexagonal prism, is so symmetrically related to a_1 and a_2 that it is often used in conjunction with the other two. Thus the indices of a plane in the hexagonal system, called Miller-Bravais indices, refer to *four* axes and are written $(hkil)$. The index i is the reciprocal of the fractional intercept on the a_3 axis. Since the intercepts of a plane on a_1 and a_2 determine its intercept on a_3, the value of i depends on the values of h and k. The relation is

$$h + k = -i. \tag{2–2}$$

Since i is determined by h and k, it is sometimes replaced by a dot and the plane symbol written $(hk \cdot l)$. However, this usage defeats the purpose for which Miller-Bravais indices were devised, namely, to give similar indices to similar planes. For example, the side planes of the hexagonal prism in Fig. 2–11(b) are all similar and symmetrically located, and their relationship is clearly shown in their full Miller-Bravais symbols: $(10\bar{1}0)$, $(01\bar{1}0)$, $(\bar{1}100)$, $(\bar{1}010)$, $(0\bar{1}10)$, $(1\bar{1}00)$. On the other hand, the abbreviated symbols of these planes, $(10 \cdot 0)$, $(01 \cdot 0)$, $(\bar{1}1 \cdot 0)$, $(\bar{1}0 \cdot 0)$, $(0\bar{1} \cdot 0)$, $(1\bar{1} \cdot 0)$ do not immediately suggest this relationship.

Directions in a hexagonal lattice are best expressed in terms of the *three* basic vectors a_1, a_2, and c. Figure 2–11(b) shows several examples of both plane and direction indices. (Another system, involving four indices, is sometimes used to designate directions. The required direction is broken up into four component vectors, parallel to a_1, a_2, a_3, and c and so chosen that the third index is the negative of the sum of the first two. Thus

[100], for example, becomes [$2\bar{1}\bar{1}0$], [210] becomes [$10\bar{1}0$], [010] becomes [$\bar{1}2\bar{1}0$], etc.)

In any crystal system there are sets of equivalent lattice planes related by symmetry. These are called *planes of a form*, and the indices of any one plane, enclosed in braces {hkl}, stand for the whole set. In general, planes of a form have the same spacing but different Miller indices. For example, the faces of a cube, (100), (010), ($\bar{1}$00), (0$\bar{1}$0), (001), and (00$\bar{1}$), are planes of the form {100}, since all of them may be generated from any one by operation of the 4-fold rotation axes perpendicular to the cube faces. In the tetragonal system, however, only the planes (100), (010), ($\bar{1}$00), and (0$\bar{1}$0) belong to the form {100}; the other two planes, (001) and (00$\bar{1}$), belong to the different form {001}; the first four planes mentioned are related by a 4-fold axis and the last two by a 2-fold axis.*

Planes of a zone are planes which are all parallel to one line, called the *zone axis*, and the zone, i.e., the set of planes, is specified by giving the indices of the zone axis. Such planes may have quite different indices and spacings, the only requirement being their parallelism to a line. Figure 2–12 shows some examples. If the axis of a zone has indices [uvw], then any plane belongs to that zone whose indices (hkl) satisfy the relation

$$hu + kv + lw = 0. \quad (2\text{–}3)$$

(A proof of this relation is given in Section 3 of Appendix 15.) Any two nonparallel planes are planes of a zone since they are both parallel to their line of intersection. If their indices are ($h_1k_1l_1$) and ($h_2k_2l_2$), then the indices of their zone axis [uvw] are given by the relations

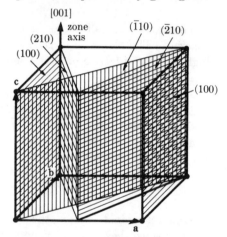

FIG. 2–12. All shaded planes in the cubic lattice shown are planes of the zone [001].

$$u = k_1l_2 - k_2l_1,$$

$$v = l_1h_2 - l_2h_1, \quad (2\text{–}4)$$

$$w = h_1k_2 - h_2k_1.$$

---

* Certain important crystal planes are often referred to by name without any mention of their Miller indices. Thus, planes of the form {111} in the cubic system are often called octahedral planes, since these are the bounding planes of an octahedron. In the hexagonal system, the (0001) plane is called the basal plane, planes of the form {$10\bar{1}0$} are called prismatic planes, and planes of the form {$10\bar{1}1$} are called pyramidal planes.

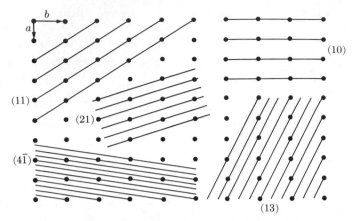

FIG. 2–13.   Two-dimensional lattice, showing that lines of lowest indices have the greatest spacing and the greatest density of lattice points.

The various sets of planes in a lattice have various values of interplanar spacing.   The planes of large spacing have low indices and pass through a high density of lattice points, whereas the reverse is true of planes of small spacing.   Figure 2–13 illustrates this for a two-dimensional lattice, and it is equally true in three dimensions.   The interplanar spacing d_{hkl}, measured at right angles to the planes, is a function both of the plane indices (hkl) and the lattice constants $(a, b, c, \alpha, \beta, \gamma)$.   The exact relation depends on the crystal system involved and for the cubic system takes on the relatively simple form

$$\text{(Cubic)} \quad d_{hkl} = \frac{a}{\sqrt{h^2 + k^2 + l^2}}. \tag{2–5}$$

In the tetragonal system the spacing equation naturally involves both a and c since these are not generally equal:

$$\text{(Tetragonal)} \quad d_{hkl} = \frac{a}{\sqrt{h^2 + k^2 + l^2 \, (a^2/c^2)}}. \tag{2–6}$$

Interplanar spacing equations for all systems are given in Appendix 1.

2–7 Crystal structure.   So far we have discussed topics from the field of *mathematical (geometrical) crystallography* and have said practically nothing about actual crystals and the atoms of which they are composed. In fact, all of the above was well known long before the discovery of x-ray diffraction, i.e., long before there was any certain knowledge of the interior arrangements of atoms in crystals.

It is now time to describe the structure of some actual crystals and to relate this structure to the point lattices, crystal systems, and symmetry

elements discussed above. The cardi-
nal principle of crystal structure is
that *the atoms of a crystal are set in
space either on the points of a Bravais
lattice or in some fixed relation to those
points.* It follows from this that the
atoms of a crystal will be arranged
periodically in three dimensions and
that this arrangement of atoms will
exhibit many of the properties of a
Bravais lattice, in particular many of
its symmetry elements.

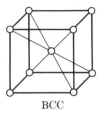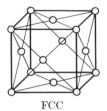

BCC   FCC

FIG. 2–14.   Structures of some common metals. Body-centered cubic: α-
Fe, Cr, Mo, V, etc.; face-centered
cubic: γ-Fe, Cu, Pb, Ni, etc.

The simplest crystals one can imagine are those formed by placing atoms
of the same kind *on* the points of a Bravais lattice. Not all such crystals
exist but, fortunately for metallurgists, many metals crystallize in this
simple fashion, and Fig. 2–14 shows two common structures based on the
body-centered cubic (BCC) and face-centered cubic (FCC) lattices. The
former has two atoms per unit cell and the latter four, as we can find by
rewriting Eq. (2–1) in terms of the number of atoms, rather than lattice
points, per cell and applying it to the unit cells shown.

The next degree of complexity is encountered when two or more atoms
of the same kind are "associated with" each point of a Bravais lattice, as
exemplified by the hexagonal close-packed (HCP) structure common to
many metals. This structure is simple hexagonal and is illustrated in
Fig. 2–15. There are two atoms per unit cell, as shown in (a), one at 0 0 0
and the other at $\frac{2}{3}\frac{1}{3}\frac{1}{2}$ (or at $\frac{1}{3}\frac{2}{3}\frac{1}{2}$, which is an equivalent position).
Figure 2–15(b) shows the same structure with the origin of the unit cell
shifted so that the point 1 0 0 in the new cell is midway between the atoms
at 1 0 0 and $\frac{2}{3}\frac{1}{3}\frac{1}{2}$ in (a), the nine atoms shown in (a) corresponding to the
nine atoms marked with an X in (b). The "association" of pairs of atoms
with the points of a simple hexagonal Bravais lattice is suggested by the
dashed lines in (b). Note, however, that the atoms of a close-packed
hexagonal structure do not themselves form a point lattice, the surround-
ings of an atom at 0 0 0 being different from those of an atom at $\frac{2}{3}\frac{1}{3}\frac{1}{2}$.
Figure 2–15(c) shows still another representation of the HCP structure:
the three atoms in the interior of the hexagonal prism are directly above
the centers of alternate triangles in the base and, if repeated through space
by the vectors $\mathbf{a}_1$ and $\mathbf{a}_2$, would also form a hexagonal array just like
the atoms in the layers above and below.

The HCP structure is so called because it is one of the two ways in
which spheres can be packed together in space with the greatest possible
density and still have a periodic arrangement. Such an arrangement of
spheres in contact is shown in Fig. 2–15(d). If these spheres are regarded

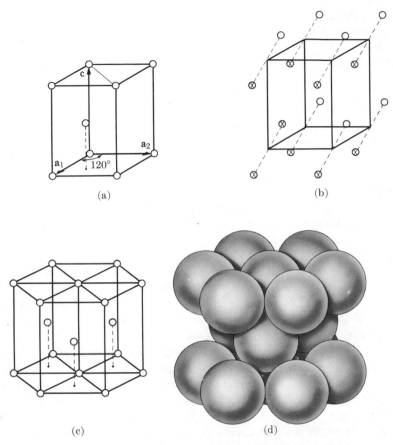

Fig. 2–15.   The hexagonal close-packed structure, shared by Zn, Mg, Be, α-Ti, etc.

as atoms, then the resulting picture of an HCP metal is much closer to physical reality than is the relatively open structure suggested by the drawing of Fig. 2–15(c), and this is true, generally, of all crystals. On the other hand, it may be shown that the ratio of c to a in an HCP structure formed of spheres in contact is 1.633 whereas the c/a ratio of metals having this structure varies from about 1.58 (Be) to 1.89 (Cd). As there is no reason to suppose that the atoms in these crystals are not in contact, it follows that they must be ellipsoidal in shape rather than spherical.

The FCC structure is an equally close-packed arrangement. Its relation to the HCP structure is not immediately obvious, but Fig. 2–16 shows that the atoms on the (111) planes of the FCC structure are arranged in a hexagonal pattern just like the atoms on the (0002) planes of the HCP structure. The only difference between the two structures is the way in which these hexagonal sheets of atoms are arranged above one another. In an HCP metal, the atoms in the second layer are above the hollows in

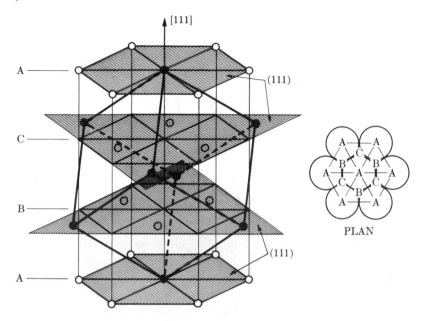

FACE-CENTERED CUBIC

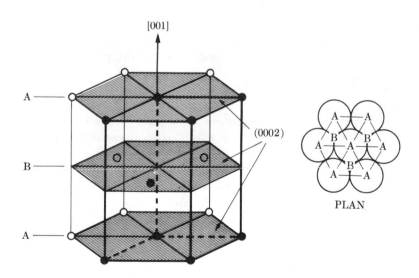

HEXAGONAL CLOSE-PACKED

FIG. 2–16.   Comparison of FCC and HCP structures.

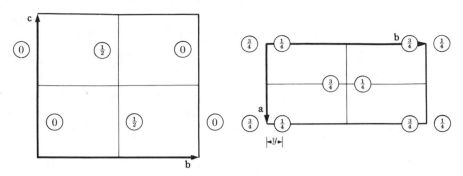

FIG. 2–17.   The structure of α-uranium.   (C. W. Jacob and B. E. Warren, *J.A.C.S.* **59**, 2588, 1937.)

the first layer and the atoms in the third layer are above the atoms in the first layer, so that the layer stacking sequence can be summarized as $A\,B\,A\,B\,A\,B\,\ldots$. The first two atom layers of an FCC metal are put down in the same way, but the atoms of the third layer are placed in the hollows of the second layer and not until the fourth layer does a position repeat. FCC stacking therefore has the sequence $A\,B\,C\,A\,B\,C\,\ldots$. These stacking schemes are indicated in the plan views shown in Fig. 2–16.

Another example of the "association" of more than one atom with each point of a Bravais lattice is given by uranium. The structure of the form stable at room temperature, α-uranium, is illustrated in Fig. 2–17 by plan and elevation drawings. In such drawings, the height of an atom (expressed as a fraction of the axial length) above the plane of the drawing (which includes the origin of the unit cell and two of the cell axes) is given by the numbers marked on each atom. The Bravais lattice is base-centered orthorhombic, centered on the C face, and Fig. 2–17 shows how the atoms occur in pairs through the structure, each pair associated with a lattice point. There are four atoms per unit cell, located at $0\,y\,\frac{1}{4}$, $0\,\bar{y}\,\frac{3}{4}$, $\frac{1}{2}\,(\frac{1}{2}+y)\,\frac{1}{4}$, and $\frac{1}{2}\,(\frac{1}{2}-y)\,\frac{3}{4}$. Here we have an example of a variable parameter y in the atomic coordinates. Crystals often contain such variable parameters, which may have any fractional value without destroying any of the symmetry elements of the structure. A quite different substance might have exactly the same structure as uranium except for slightly different values of a, b, c, and y. For uranium y is 0.105 ± 0.005.

Turning to the crystal structure of *compounds* of unlike atoms, we find that the structure is built up on the skeleton of a Bravais lattice but that certain other rules must be obeyed, precisely because there are unlike atoms present. Consider, for example, a crystal of A_xB_y which might be an ordinary chemical compound, an intermediate phase of relatively fixed composition in some alloy system, or an ordered solid solution. Then the arrangement of atoms in A_xB_y must satisfy the following conditions:

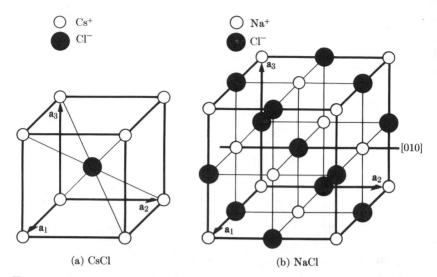

(a) CsCl   (b) NaCl

FIG. 2–18. The structures of (a) CsCl (common to CsBr, NiAl, ordered β-brass, ordered CuPd, etc.) and (b) NaCl (common to KCl, CaSe, PbTe, etc.).

(1) Body-, face-, or base-centering translations, if present, must begin and end on atoms of the same kind. For example, if the structure is based on a body-centered Bravais lattice, then it must be possible to go from an A atom, say, to *another* A atom by the translation $\frac{1}{2} \frac{1}{2} \frac{1}{2}$.

(2) The set of A atoms in the crystal and the set of B atoms must separately possess the same symmetry elements as the crystal as a whole, since in fact they make up the crystal. In particular, the operation of any symmetry element present must bring a given atom, A for example, into coincidence with another atom of the same kind, namely A.

Suppose we consider the structures of a few common crystals in light of the above requirements. Figure 2–18 illustrates the unit cells of two ionic compounds, CsCl and NaCl. These structures, both cubic, are common to many other crystals and, wherever they occur, are referred to as the "CsCl structure" and the "NaCl structure." In considering a crystal structure, one of the most important things to determine is its Bravais lattice, since that is the basic framework on which the crystal is built and because, as we shall see later, it has a profound effect on the x-ray diffraction pattern of that crystal.

What is the Bravais lattice of CsCl? Figure 2–18(a) shows that the unit cell contains two atoms, ions really, since this compound is completely ionized even in the solid state: a caesium ion at 0 0 0 and a chlorine ion at $\frac{1}{2} \frac{1}{2} \frac{1}{2}$. The Bravais lattice is obviously not face-centered, but we note that the body-centering translation $\frac{1}{2} \frac{1}{2} \frac{1}{2}$ connects two atoms. However, these are unlike atoms and the lattice is therefore *not* body-centered. It is, by elimination, simple cubic. If one wishes, one may think of both ions, the caesium at 0 0 0 and the chlorine at $\frac{1}{2}$ $\frac{1}{2}$ $\frac{1}{2}$, as being associated with the lattice point at 0 0 0. It is not possible, however, to associate any one caesium ion with any particular chlorine ion and refer to them as a CsCl molecule; the term "molecule" therefore has no real physical significance in such a crystal, and the same is true of most inorganic compounds and alloys.

Close inspection of Fig. 2–18(b) will show that the unit cell of NaCl contains 8 ions, located as follows:

$$4 \text{ Na}^+ \text{ at } 0\,0\,0,\; \tfrac{1}{2}\,\tfrac{1}{2}\,0,\; \tfrac{1}{2}\,0\,\tfrac{1}{2},\; \text{and } 0\,\tfrac{1}{2}\,\tfrac{1}{2}$$

$$4 \text{ Cl}^- \text{ at } \tfrac{1}{2}\,\tfrac{1}{2}\,\tfrac{1}{2},\; 0\,0\,\tfrac{1}{2},\; 0\,\tfrac{1}{2}\,0,\; \text{and } \tfrac{1}{2}\,0\,0.$$

The sodium ions are clearly face-centered, and we note that the face-centering translations (0 0 0, $\tfrac{1}{2}\,\tfrac{1}{2}\,0$, $\tfrac{1}{2}\,0\,\tfrac{1}{2}$, $0\,\tfrac{1}{2}\,\tfrac{1}{2}$), when applied to the chlorine ion at $\tfrac{1}{2}\,\tfrac{1}{2}\,\tfrac{1}{2}$, will reproduce all the chlorine-ion positions. The Bravais lattice of NaCl is therefore face-centered cubic. The ion positions, incidentally, may be written in summary form as:

$$4 \text{ Na}^+ \text{ at } 0\,0\,0 + \text{face-centering translations}$$

$$4 \text{ Cl}^- \text{ at } \tfrac{1}{2}\,\tfrac{1}{2}\,\tfrac{1}{2} + \text{face-centering translations.}$$

Note also that in these, as in all other structures, the operation of any symmetry element possessed by the lattice must bring similar atoms or ions into coincidence. For example, in Fig. 2–18(b), 90° rotation about the 4-fold [010] rotation axis shown brings the chlorine ion at $0\,1\,\tfrac{1}{2}$ into coincidence with the chlorine ion at $\tfrac{1}{2}\,1\,1$, the sodium ion at 0 1 1 with the sodium ion at 1 1 1, etc.

Elements and compounds often have closely similar structures. Figure 2–19 shows the unit cells of diamond and the zinc-blende form of ZnS. Both are face-centered cubic. Diamond has 8 atoms per unit cell, located at

$$0\,0\,0 + \text{face-centering translations}$$

$$\tfrac{1}{4}\,\tfrac{1}{4}\,\tfrac{1}{4} + \text{face-centering translations.}$$

The atom positions in zinc blende are identical with these, but the first set of positions is now occupied by one kind of atom (S) and the other by a different kind (Zn).

Note that diamond and a metal like copper have quite dissimilar structures, although both are based on a face-centered cubic Bravais lattice. To distinguish between these two, the terms "diamond cubic" and "face-centered cubic" are usually used.

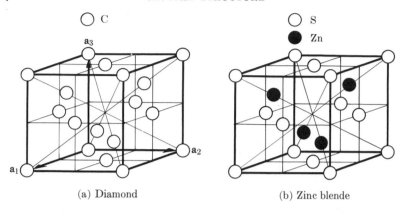

(a) Diamond   (b) Zinc blende

FIG. 2–19.   The structures of (a) diamond (common to Si, Ge, and gray Sn) and (b) the zinc-blende form of ZnS (common to HgS, CuI, AlSb, BeSe, etc.).

The number of atoms per unit cell in any crystal is partially dependent on its Bravais lattice. For example, the number of atoms per unit cell in a crystal based on a body-centered lattice must be a multiple of 2, since there must be, for any atom in the cell, a corresponding atom of the same kind at a translation of $\frac{1}{2}\,\frac{1}{2}\,\frac{1}{2}$ from the first. The number of atoms per cell in a base-centered lattice must also be a multiple of 2, as a result of the base-centering translations. Similarly, the number of atoms per cell in a face-centered lattice must be a multiple of 4.

The reverse of these propositions is not true. It would be a mistake to assume, for example, that if the number of atoms per cell is a multiple of 4, then the lattice is necessarily face-centered. The unit cell of the intermediate phase AuBe, for example (Fig. 2–20), contains 8 atoms and yet it is based on a simple cubic Bravais lattice. The atoms are located as follows:

4 Au at $u\,u\,u$, $(\frac{1}{2} + u)\,(\frac{1}{2} - u)\,\bar{u}$, $\bar{u}\,(\frac{1}{2} + u)\,(\frac{1}{2} - u)$, $(\frac{1}{2} - u)\,\bar{u}\,(\frac{1}{2} + u)$,

4 Be at

$w\,w\,w$, $(\frac{1}{2} + w)\,(\frac{1}{2} - w)\,\bar{w}$, $\bar{w}\,(\frac{1}{2} + w)\,(\frac{1}{2} - w)$, $(\frac{1}{2} - w)\,\bar{w}\,(\frac{1}{2} + w)$,

where $u = 0.100$ and $w = 0.406$, each ± 0.005. If the parameter u is put equal to zero, the atomic coordinates of the gold atoms become those of a face-centered cubic cell. The structure of AuBe may therefore be regarded as distorted face-centered cubic, in which the presence of the beryllium atoms has forced the gold atoms out of their original positions by a distance $\pm u$, $\pm u$, $\pm u$. These translations are all in directions of the form $\langle 111 \rangle$, i.e., parallel to body diagonals of the cube, and are shown as dotted lines in Fig. 2–20.

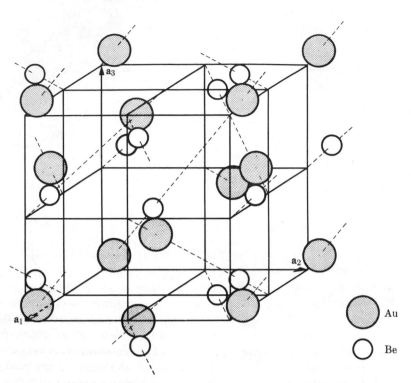

Fig. 2–20. The structure of AuBe, shared by FeSi, NiSi, CoSi, MnSi, etc. It is known as the FeSi structure. [B. D. Cullity, *Trans. A.I.M.E.* **171**, 396 (1947).]

It should now be apparent that the term "simple," when applied to a Bravais lattice, is used in a very special, technical sense and that some very complex structures can be built up on a "simple" lattice. In fact, they may contain more than a hundred atoms per unit cell. The only workable definition of a simple lattice is a negative one: a given lattice is simple if it is neither body-, base-, nor face-centered; these latter possibilities can be ruled out by showing that the set of atomic positions does not contain the body-, base-, or face-centering translations. There is no rule governing the allowable number of atoms per cell in a simple lattice: this number may take on any one of the values 1, 2, 3, 4, 5, etc., although not in every crystal system and not every higher integer is permitted. Incidentally, not every theoretical possibility known to mathematical crystallography is realized in nature; for example, no known element crystallizes with a simple cubic lattice containing one atom per unit cell.

There is one other way of arranging unlike atoms on a point lattice besides those considered so far and that is exemplified by the structure of *solid solutions*. These solutions are of two types, substitutional and interstitial; in the former, solute atoms substitute for, or replace, solvent atoms

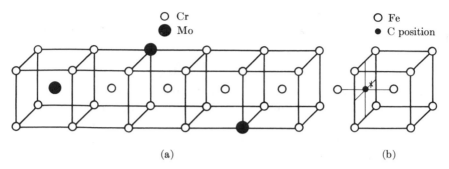

Fig. 2–21. Structure of solid solutions: (a) Mo in Cr (substitutional); (b) C in α-Fe (interstitial).

on the lattice of the solvent, while in the latter, solute atoms fit into the interstices of the solvent lattice. The interesting feature of these structures is that the solute atoms are distributed more or less at random. For example, consider a 10 atomic percent solution of molybdenum in chromium, which has a BCC structure. The molybdenum atoms can occupy either the corner or body-centered positions of the cube in a random, irregular manner, and a small portion of the crystal might have the appearance of Fig. 2–21(a). Five adjoining unit cells are shown there, containing a total of 29 atoms, 3 of which are molybdenum. This section of the crystal therefore contains somewhat more than 10 atomic percent molybdenum, but the next five cells would probably contain somewhat less. Such a structure does not obey the ordinary rules of crystallography: for example, the right-hand cell of the group shown does not have cubic symmetry, and one finds throughout the structure that the translation given by one of the unit cell vectors may begin on an atom of one kind and end on an atom of another kind. All that can be said of this structure is that it is BCC *on the average,* and experimentally we find that it displays the x-ray diffraction effects proper to a BCC lattice. This is not surprising since the x-ray beam used to examine the crystal is so large compared to the size of a unit cell that it observes, so to speak, millions of unit cells at the same time and so obtains only an average "picture" of the structure.

The above remarks apply equally well to interstitial solid solutions. These form whenever the solute atom is small enough to fit into the solvent lattice without causing too much distortion. Ferrite, the solid solution of carbon in α-iron, is a good example. In the unit cell shown in Fig. 2–21(b), there are two kinds of "holes" in the lattice: one at $\frac{1}{2} 0 \frac{1}{2}$ (marked •) and equivalent positions in the centers of the cube faces and edges, and one at $\frac{1}{4} 0 \frac{1}{2}$ (marked ×) and equivalent positions. All the evidence at hand points to the fact that the carbon atoms in ferrite are located in the holes at $\frac{1}{2} 0 \frac{1}{2}$ and equivalent positions. On the average, however, no more than about 1 of these positions in 500 unit cells is occupied, since the maximum solubility of carbon in ferrite is only about 0.1 atomic percent.

Still another type of structure worth noting is that of *ordered solid solutions*. As described above, a typical substitutional solid solution has solute atoms distributed more or less at random on the lattice points of the solvent.* On the other hand, there are solutions in which this is true only at elevated temperatures; when cooled to lower temperatures, the solute atoms take up an orderly, periodic arrangement while still remaining on the lattice points of the solvent. The solid solution is then said to be *ordered* and to possess a *superlattice*. The alloy AuCu$_3$ is a classic example: at high temperatures the copper and gold atoms are located more or less at random on face-centered cubic lattice sites, while at low temperature the gold atoms occupy only the cube corner positions and the copper atoms only the face-centered positions. In its temperature range of stability then, an ordered solid solution resembles a chemical compound, with atoms of one kind on one set of lattice sites and atoms of a different kind on another set. Crystallographically, the structures of the disordered and ordered solutions are quite different; in the example cited, the structure of the former is, on the average, face-centered cubic while that of the latter is simple cubic. Such structures will be discussed more fully in Chap. 13.

2–8 Atom sizes and coordination. When two or more unlike atoms unite to form a chemical compound, intermediate phase, or solid solution, the kind of structure formed is dependent, in part, on the relative sizes of the atoms involved. But what is meant by the size of an atom? To regard an atom as something like a billiard ball with a sharply defined bounding surface is surely an oversimplification, since we know that the electron density decreases gradually at the "surface" of the atom and that there is a small but finite probability of finding an electron at quite large distances from the nucleus. And yet the only practical way we have of defining atomic size lies in considering a crystal as a collection of rigid spheres in contact. The size of an atom, then, is given by the distance of closest approach of atom centers in a crystal of the element, and this distance can be calculated from the lattice parameters.

For example, the lattice parameter a of α-iron is 2.87A, and in a BCC lattice the atoms are in contact only along the diagonals of the unit cube. The diameter of an iron atom is therefore equal to one-half the length of the cube diagonal, or $(\sqrt{3}/2)a = 2.48$A. The following formulas give

---

* Of course, when the solution becomes concentrated, there is no real distinction between "solvent" and "solute." There is only one lattice, with two or more kinds of atoms distributed on it.

the distance of closest approach in the three common metal structures:

$$\text{BCC} = \frac{\sqrt{3}}{2}\,a,$$

$$\text{FCC} = \frac{\sqrt{2}}{2}\,a,$$ \hfill (2-7)

$$\text{HCP} = a \qquad \text{(between atoms in basal plane)},$$

$$= \sqrt{\frac{a^2}{3} + \frac{c^2}{4}} \quad \begin{array}{l}\text{(between atom in basal plane} \\ \text{and neighbors above or below).}\end{array}$$

Values of the distance of closest approach, together with the crystal structures and lattice parameters of the elements, are tabulated in Appendix 13.

To a first approximation, the size of an atom is a constant. In other words, an iron atom has the same size whether it occurs in pure iron, an intermediate phase, or a solid solution. This is a very useful fact to remember when investigating unknown crystal structures, for it enables us to predict roughly how large a hole is necessary in a proposed structure to accommodate a given atom. More precisely, it is known that the size of an atom has a slight dependence on its *coordination number*, which is the number of nearest neighbors of the given atom and which depends on crystal structure. The coordination number of an atom in the FCC or HCP structures is 12, in BCC 8, and in diamond cubic 4. The smaller the coordination number, the smaller the volume occupied by a given atom, and the amount of contraction to be expected with decrease in coordination number is found to be:

Change in coordination	Size contraction, percent
12 → 8	3
12 → 6	4
12 → 4	12

This means, for example, that the diameter of an iron atom is greater if the iron is dissolved in FCC copper than if it exists in a crystal of BCC α-iron. If it were dissolved in copper, its diameter would be approximately 2.48/0.97, or 2.56A.

The size of an atom in a crystal also depends on whether its binding is ionic, covalent, metallic, or van der Waals, and on its state of ionization. The more electrons are removed from a neutral atom the smaller it becomes, as shown strikingly for iron, whose atoms and ions Fe, Fe^{++}, Fe^{+++} have diameters of 2.48, 1.66, and 1.34A, respectively.

2–9 Crystal shape. We have said nothing so far about the shape of crystals, preferring to concentrate instead on their interior structure. However, the shape of crystals is, to the layman, perhaps their most characteristic property, and nearly everyone is familiar with the beautifully developed flat faces exhibited by natural minerals or crystals artificially grown from a supersaturated salt solution. In fact, it was with a study of these faces and the angles between them that the science of crystallography began.

Nevertheless, the shape of crystals is really a secondary characteristic, since it depends on, and is a consequence of, the interior arrangement of atoms. Sometimes the external shape of a crystal is rather obviously related to its smallest building block, the unit cell, as in the little cubical grains of ordinary table salt (NaCl has a cubic lattice) or the six-sided prisms of natural quartz crystals (hexagonal lattice). In many other cases, however, the crystal and its unit cell have quite different shapes; gold, for example, has a cubic lattice, but natural gold crystals are octahedral in form, i.e., bounded by eight planes of the form {111}.

An important fact about crystal faces was known long before there was any knowledge of crystal interiors. It is expressed as the *law of rational indices*, which states that the indices of naturally developed crystal faces are always composed of small whole numbers, rarely exceeding 3 or 4. Thus, faces of the form {100}, {111}, {1$\bar{1}$00}, {210}, etc., are observed but not such faces as {510}, {719}, etc. We know today that planes of low indices have the largest density of lattice points, and it is a law of crystal growth that such planes develop at the expense of planes with high indices and few lattice points.

To a metallurgist, however, crystals with well-developed faces are in the category of things heard of but rarely seen. They occur occasionally on the free surface of castings, in some electrodeposits, or under other conditions of no external constraint. To a metallurgist, a crystal is most usually a "grain," seen through a microscope in the company of many other grains on a polished section. If he has an isolated single crystal, it will have been artificially grown either from the melt, and thus have the shape of the crucible in which it solidified, or by recrystallization, and thus have the shape of the starting material, whether sheet, rod, or wire.

The shapes of the grains in a polycrystalline mass of metal are the result of several kinds of forces, all of which are strong enough to counteract the natural tendency of each grain to grow with well-developed flat faces. The result is a grain roughly polygonal in shape with no obvious aspect of crystallinity. Nevertheless, that grain is a crystal and just as "crystalline" as, for example, a well-developed prism of natural quartz, since the essence of crystallinity is a periodicity of inner atomic arrangement and not any regularity of outward form.

2–10 Twinned crystals. Some crystals have two parts symmetrically related to one another. These, called twinned crystals, are fairly common both in minerals and in metals and alloys.

The relationship between the two parts of a twinned crystal is described by the symmetry operation which will bring one part into coincidence with the other or with an extension of the other. Two main kinds of twinning are distinguished, depending on whether the symmetry operation is (a) 180° rotation about an axis, called the twin axis, or (b) reflection across a plane, called the twin plane. The plane on which the two parts of a twinned crystal are united is called the composition plane. In the case of a reflection twin, the composition plane may or may not coincide with the twin plane.

Of most interest to metallurgists, who deal mainly with FCC, BCC, and HCP structures, are the following kinds of twins:

(1) Annealing twins, such as occur in FCC metals and alloys (Cu, Ni, α-brass, Al, etc.), which have been cold-worked and then annealed to cause recrystallization.

(2) Deformation twins, such as occur in deformed HCP metals (Zn, Mg, Be, etc.) and BCC metals (α-Fe, W, etc.).

Annealing twins in FCC metals are rotation twins, in which the two parts are related by a 180° rotation about a twin axis of the form $\langle 111 \rangle$. Because of the high symmetry of the cubic lattice, this orientation relationship is also given by a 60° rotation about the twin axis or by reflection across the $\{111\}$ plane normal to the twin axis. In other words, FCC annealing twins may also be classified as reflection twins. The twin plane is also the composition plane.

Occasionally, annealing twins appear under the microscope as in Fig. 2–22(a), with one part of a grain (B) twinned with respect to the other part (A). The two parts are in contact on the composition plane (111) which makes a straight-line trace on the plane of polish. More common, however, is the kind shown in Fig. 2–22(b). The grain shown consists of three parts: two parts (A_1 and A_2) of identical orientation separated by a third part (B) which is twinned with respect to A_1 and A_2. B is known as a twin band.

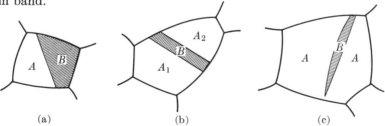

FIG. 2–22. Twinned grains: (a) and (b) FCC annealing twins; (c) HCP deformation twin.

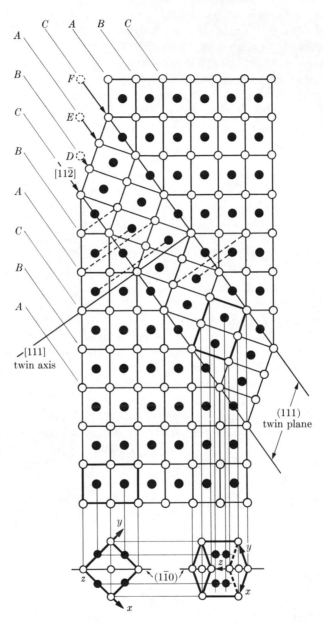

PLAN OF CRYSTAL   PLAN OF TWIN

FIG. 2–23. Twin band in FCC lattice. Plane of main drawing is $(1\bar{1}0)$.

Figure 2–23 illustrates the structure of an FCC twin band. The plane of the main drawing is (1$\bar{1}$0), the (111) twin plane is perpendicular to this plane, and the [111] twin axis lies in it. Open circles represent atoms in the plane of the drawing and filled circles those in the layers immediately above or below. The reflection symmetry across the twin plane is suggested by the dashed lines connecting several pairs of atoms.

The statement that a rotation twin of this kind is related to the parent crystal by a 180° rotation about the twin axis is merely an expression of the orientation relationship between the two and is not meant to suggest that a twin is formed by a physical rotation of one part of the crystal with respect to another. Actually, FCC annealing twins are formed by a change in the normal growth mechanism. Suppose that, during normal grain growth following recrystallization, a grain boundary is roughly parallel to (111) and is advancing in a direction approximately normal to this boundary, namely [111]. To say that the boundary is advancing is to say that atoms are leaving the lattice of the consumed grain and joining that of the growing grain. The grain is therefore growing by the addition of layers of atoms parallel to (111), and we already know that these layers are piled up in the sequence $A\,B\,C\,A\,B\,C$ ... in an FCC crystal. If, however, a mistake should occur and this sequence become altered to $C\,B\,A\,C\,B\,A$ ..., the crystal so formed would still be FCC but it would be a twin of the former. If a similar mistake occurred later, a crystal of the original orientation would start growing and a twin band would be formed. With this symbolism, we may indicate a twin band as follows:

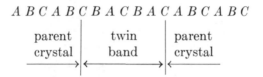

$$A\,B\,C\,A\,B\,C\,B\,A\,C\,B\,A\,C\,A\,B\,C\,A\,B\,C$$

| parent crystal | twin band | parent crystal |

In this terminology, the symbols themselves are imaged in the mirror C, the twin plane. At the left of Fig. 2–23 the positional symbols A, B, C are attached to various (111) planes to show the change in stacking which occurs at the boundaries of the twin band. Parenthetically, it should be remarked that twin bands visible under the light microscope are thousands of times thicker than the one shown in this drawing.

There is still another way of *describing* the orientation relationship between an FCC crystal and its twin: the (111) layers of the twin are in positions which would result from homogeneous shear in a [11$\bar{2}$] direction, each layer moving by an amount proportional to its distance from the twin plane. In Fig. 2–23, this shear is indicated by the arrows going from initial positions D, E, F to final positions in the twin. Although it has been frequently suggested that such twins are *formed* by deformation, no convincing evidence for this view has been advanced and it is generally held that annealing twins are the result of the growth process described above. Nevertheless, this hypothetical shear is sometimes a useful way of describing the orientation relationship between a crystal and its twin.

Deformation twins are found in both BCC and HCP lattices and are all that their name implies, since, in both cases, the cause of twinning is deformation. In each case, the orientation relationship between parent crystal and twin is that of reflection across a plane.

In BCC structures, the twin plane is (112) and the twinning shear is in the direction $[11\bar{1}]$. The only common example of such twins is in α-iron (ferrite) deformed by impact, where they occur as extremely narrow twin bands called Neumann bands. It should be noted that, in cubic lattices, both {112} and {111} reflection twinning produce the same orientation relationship; however, they differ in the interatomic distances produced, and an FCC lattice can twin by reflection on {111} with less distortion than on {112}, while for the same reason {112} is the preferred plane for BCC lattices.

In HCP metals, the twin plane is normally $(10\bar{1}2)$. The twinning shear is not well understood; in a gross sense, it takes place in the direction $[\bar{2}11]$ for metals with c/a ratios less than $\sqrt{3}$ (Be, Ti, Mg) and in the reverse direction $[21\bar{1}]$ for metals with c/a larger than $\sqrt{3}$ (Zn, Cd), but the direction of motion of individual atoms during shear is not definitely known. Figure 2–22(c) illustrates the usual form of a twin band in HCP metals, and it will be noted that the composition "plane," although probably parallel or nearly parallel to the twin plane, is not quite flat but often exhibits appreciable curvature. Figure 2–24 shows the structure of a twin band in cadmium ($c/a = 1.886$). The twin plane is perpendicular to the plane of the drawing $(\bar{1}2\bar{1}0)$, and the shear direction lies in it. Open and filled circles represent atoms in and immediately above or below this plane, respectively. While the over-all shear is not very large (0.17 for cadmium), it produces a drastic reorientation of the lattice, the c axis of the twin being almost at right angles to the c axis of the parent crystal. It is for this reason, incidentally, that slip in HCP metals is promoted by twinning; if a crystal is unfavorably oriented for slip on its basal planes, then the occurrence of twinning will produce a favorable orientation of the basal planes in the twinned part.

Twins, in general, can form on different planes in the same crystal. For example, there are four {111} planes of different orientation on which twinning can take place in an FCC crystal. Accordingly, in the microstructure of recrystallized copper, for example, one often sees twin bands running in more than one direction in the same grain.

A crystal may also twin repeatedly, producing several new orientations. If crystal A twins to form B, which twins to form C, etc., then B, C, etc.,

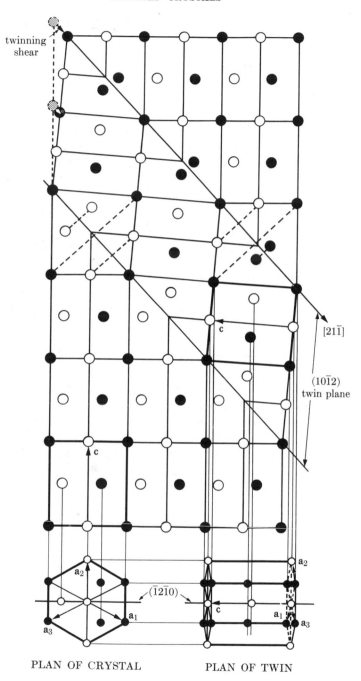

FIG. 2–24. Twin band in HCP lattice. Plane of main drawing is $(\bar{1}2\bar{1}0)$.

are said to be first-order, second-order, etc., twins of the parent crystal A. Not all these orientations are new. In Fig. 2–22(b), for example, B may be regarded as the first-order twin of A_1, and A_2 as the first order twin of B. A_2 is therefore the second-order twin of A_1 but has the same orientation as A_1.

2–11 The stereographic projection. Crystal drawings made in perspective or in the form of plan and elevation, while they have their uses, are not suitable for displaying the angular relationship between lattice planes and directions. But frequently we are more interested in these angular relationships than in any other aspect of the crystal, and we then need a kind of drawing on which the angles between planes can be accurately measured and which will permit graphical solution of problems involving such angles. The stereographic projection fills this need.

The orientation of any plane in a crystal can be just as well represented by the inclination of the normal to that plane relative to some reference plane as by the inclination of the plane itself. All the planes in a crystal can thus be represented by a set of plane normals radiating from some one point within the crystal. If a reference sphere is now described about this point, the plane normals will intersect the surface of the sphere in a set of points called *poles*. This procedure is illustrated in Fig. 2–25, which is restricted to the {100} planes of a cubic crystal. The pole of a plane represents, by its position on the sphere, the orientation of that plane.

A plane may also be represented by the trace the extended plane makes in the surface of the sphere, as illustrated in Fig. 2–26, where the trace $ABCDA$ represents the plane whose pole is P_1. This trace is a *great circle*, i.e., a circle of maximum diameter, if the plane passes through the center of the sphere. A plane not passing through the center will intersect the sphere in a *small circle*. On a ruled globe, for example, the longitude lines

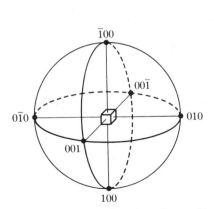

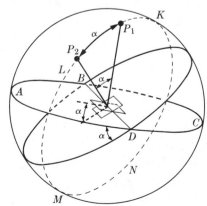

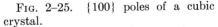

FIG. 2–25. {100} poles of a cubic crystal.   FIG. 2–26. Angle between two planes.

(meridians) are great circles, while the latitude lines, except the equator, are small circles.

The angle α between two planes is evidently equal to the angle between their great circles or to the angle between their normals (Fig. 2–26). But this angle, in degrees, can also be measured on the surface of the sphere along the great circle $KLMNK$ connecting the poles P_1 and P_2 of the two planes, if this circle has been divided into 360 equal parts. The measurement of an angle has thus been transferred from the planes themselves to the surface of the reference sphere.

Preferring, however, to measure angles on a flat sheet of paper rather than on the surface of a sphere, we find ourselves in the position of the

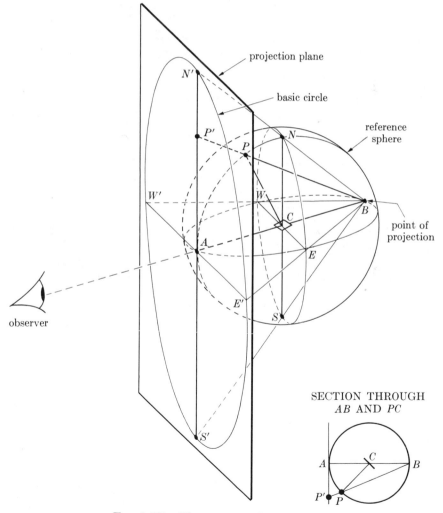

FIG. 2–27.   The stereographic projection.

geographer who wants to transfer a map of the world from a globe to a page of an atlas. Of the many known kinds of projections, he usually chooses a more or less equal-area projection so that countries of equal area will be represented by equal areas on the map. In crystallography, however, we prefer the equiangular stereographic projection since it preserves angular relationships faithfully although distorting areas. It is made by placing a plane of projection normal to the end of any chosen diameter of the sphere and using the other end of that diameter as the point of projection. In Fig. 2–27 the projection plane is normal to the diameter AB, and the projection is made from the point B. If a plane has its pole at P, then the stereographic projection of P is at P', obtained by drawing the line BP and producing it until it meets the projection plane. Alternately stated, the stereographic projection of the pole P is the shadow cast by P on the projection plane when a light source is placed at B. The observer, incidentally, views the projection from the side opposite the light source.

The plane $NESW$ is normal to AB and passes through the center C. It therefore cuts the sphere in half and its trace in the sphere is a great circle. This great circle projects to form the *basic circle* $N'E'S'W'$ on the projection, and all poles on the left-hand hemisphere will project within this basic circle. Poles on the right-hand hemisphere will project outside this basic circle, and those near B will have projections lying at very large distances from the center. If we wish to plot such poles, we move the point of projection to A and the projection plane to B and distinguish the new set of points so formed by minus signs, the previous set (projected from B) being marked with plus signs. Note that movement of the projection plane along AB or its extension merely alters the magnification; we usually make it tangent to the sphere, as illustrated, but we can also make it pass through the center of the sphere, for example, in which case the basic circle becomes identical with the great circle $NESW$.

A lattice plane in a crystal is several steps removed from its stereographic projection, and it may be worth-while at this stage to summarize these steps:

(1) The plane C is represented by its normal CP.

(2) The normal CP is represented by its pole P, which is its intersection with the reference sphere.

(3) The pole P is represented by its stereographic projection P'.

After gaining some familiarity with the stereographic projection, the student will be able mentally to omit these intermediate steps and he will then refer to the projected point P' as the pole of the plane C or, even more directly, as the plane C itself.

Great circles on the reference sphere project as circular arcs on the projection or, if they pass through the points A and B (Fig. 2–28), as straight lines through the center of the projection. Projected great circles always cut the basic circle in diametrically opposite points, since the locus of a great circle on the sphere is a set of diametrically opposite points. Thus the great circle $ANBS$ in Fig. 2–28 projects as the straight line $N'S'$ and $AWBE$ as $W'E'$; the great circle $NGSH$, which is inclined to the plane of projection, projects as the circle arc $N'G'S'$. If the half great circle WAE is divided into 18 equal parts and these points of division projected on $W'AE'$, we obtain a graduated scale, at 10° intervals, on the equator of the basic circle.

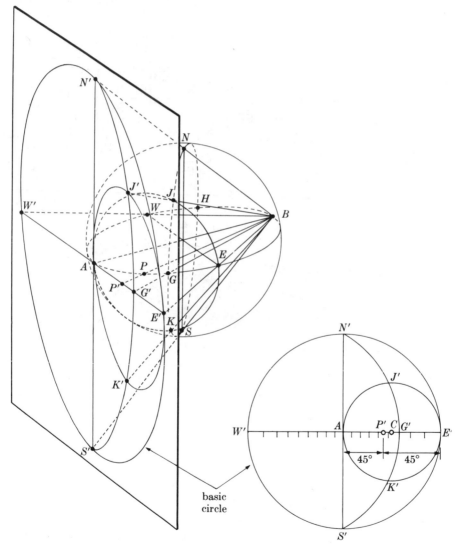

basic circle

Fig. 2–28. Stereographic projection of great and small circles.

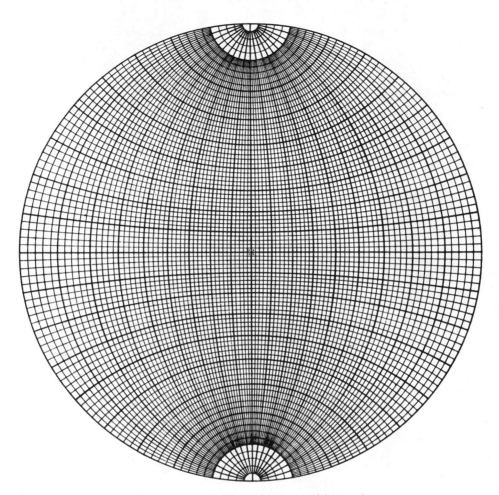

FIG. 2–29.   Wulff net drawn to 2° intervals.

Small circles on the sphere also project as circles, but their projected center does not coincide with their center on the projection. For example, the circle $AJEK$ whose center P lies on $AWBE$ projects as $AJ'E'K'$. Its center *on the projection* is at C, located at equal distances from A and E', but its *projected center* is at P', located an equal number of degrees (45° in this case) from A and E'.

The device most useful in solving problems involving the stereographic projection is the *Wulff net* shown in Fig. 2–29. It is the projection of a sphere ruled with parallels of latitude and longitude on a plane parallel to the north-south axis of the sphere. The latitude lines on a Wulff net are small circles extending from side to side and the longitude lines (meridians) are great circles connecting the north and south poles of the net.

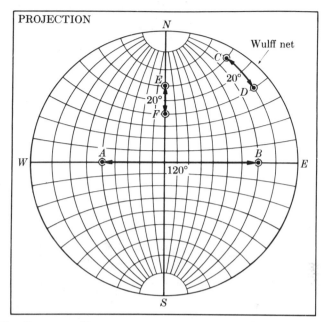

Fig. 2–30. Stereographic projection superimposed on Wulff net for measurement of angle between poles.

These nets are available in various sizes, one of 18-cm diameter giving an accuracy of about one degree, which is satisfactory for most problems; to obtain greater precision, either a larger net or mathematical calculation must be used. Wulff nets are used by making the stereographic projection on tracing paper and with the basic circle of the same diameter as that of the Wulff net; the projection is then superimposed on the Wulff net and pinned at the center so that it is free to rotate with respect to the net.

To return to our problem of the measurement of the angle between two crystal planes, we saw in Fig. 2–26 that this angle could be measured on the surface of the sphere along the great circle connecting the poles of the two planes. This measurement can also be carried out on the stereographic projection *if, and only if, the projected poles lie on a great circle*. In Fig. 2–30, for example, the angle between the planes* A and B or C and D can be measured directly, simply by counting the number of degrees separating them along the great circle on which they lie. Note that the angle C–D equals the angle E–F, there being the same difference in latitude between C and D as between E and F.

If the two poles do not lie on a great circle, then the projection is rotated relative to the Wulff net until they do lie on a great circle, where the de-

* We are here using the abbreviated terminology referred to above.

66

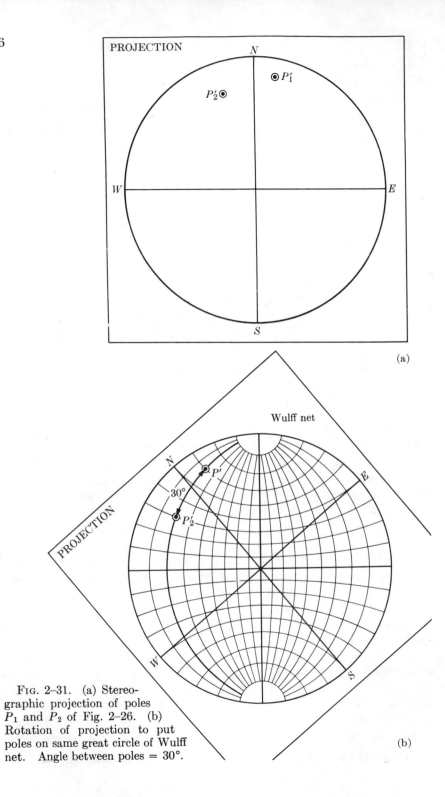

FIG. 2–31. (a) Stereo-
graphic projection of poles
P_1 and P_2 of Fig. 2–26. (b)
Rotation of projection to put
poles on same great circle of Wulff
net. Angle between poles = 30°.

sired angle measurement can then be made. Figure 2–31(a) is a projection of the two poles P_1 and P_2 shown in perspective in Fig. 2–26, and the angle between them is found by the rotation illustrated in Fig. 2–31(b). This rotation of the projection is equivalent to rotation of the poles on latitude circles of a sphere whose north-south axis is perpendicular to the projection plane.

As shown in Fig. 2–26, a plane may be represented by its trace in the reference sphere. This trace becomes a great circle in the stereographic projection. Since every point on this great circle is 90° from the pole of the plane, the great circle may be found by rotating the projection until the pole falls on the equator of the underlying Wulff net and tracing that meridian which cuts the equator 90° from the pole, as illustrated in Fig. 2–32. If this is done for two poles, as in Fig. 2–33, the angle between the corresponding planes may also be found from the angle of intersection of the two great circles corresponding to these poles; it is in this sense that the stereographic projection is said to be angle-true. This method of angle measurement is not as accurate, however, as that shown in Fig. 2–31(b).

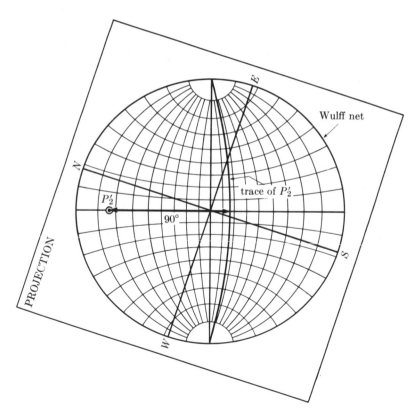

FIG. 2–32. Method of finding the trace of a pole (the pole P_2' in Fig. 2–31).

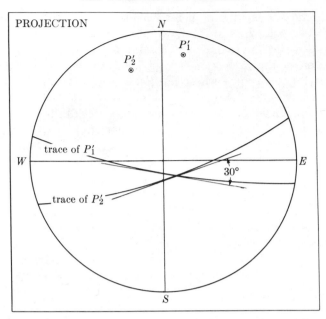

FIG. 2–33.   Measurement of an angle between two poles (P_1 and P_2 of Fig. 2–26) by measurement of the angle of intersection of the corresponding traces.

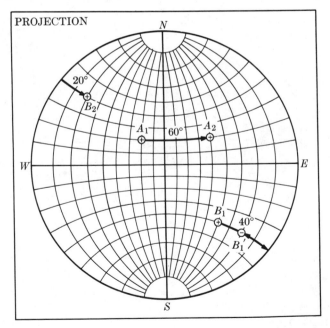

FIG. 2–34.   Rotation of poles about NS axis of projection.

We often wish to rotate poles around various axes. We have already seen that rotation about an axis normal to the projection is accomplished simply by rotation of the projection around the center of the Wulff net. Rotation about an axis lying in the plane of the projection is performed by, first, rotating the *axis* about the center of the Wulff net until it coincides with the north-south axis if it does not already do so, and, second, moving the poles involved along their respective latitude circles the required number of degrees. Suppose it is required to rotate the poles A_1 and B_1 shown in Fig. 2–34 by 60° about the NS axis, the direction of motion being from W to E on the projection. Then A_1 moves to A_2 along its latitude circle as shown. B_1, however, can rotate only 40° before finding itself at the edge of the projection; we must then imagine it to move 20° in from the edge to the point B_1' on the other side of the projection, staying always on its own latitude circle. The final position of this pole on the positive side of the projection is at B_2 diametrically opposite B_1'.

Rotation about an axis inclined to the plane of projection is accomplished by compounding rotations about axes lying in and perpendicular to the projection plane. In this case, the given axis must first be rotated into coincidence with one or the other of the two latter axes, the given rotation performed, and the axis then rotated back to its original position. Any movement of the given axis must be accompanied by a similar movement of all the poles on the projection.

For example, we may be required to rotate A_1 about B_1 by 40° in a clockwise direction (Fig. 2–35). In (a) the pole to be rotated A_1 and the rotation axis B_1 are shown in their initial position. In (b) the projection has been rotated to bring B_1 to the equator of a Wulff net. A rotation of 48° about the NS axis of the net brings B_1 to the point B_2 at the center of the net; at the same time A_1 must go to A_2 along a parallel of latitude. The rotation axis is now perpendicular to the projection plane, and the required rotation of 40° brings A_2 to A_3 along a circular path centered on B_2. The operations which brought B_1 to B_2 must now be reversed in order to return B_2 to its original position. Accordingly, B_2 is brought to B_3 and A_3 to A_4, by a 48° reverse rotation about the NS axis of the net. In (c) the projection has been rotated back to its initial position, construction lines have been omitted, and only the initial and final positions of the rotated pole are shown. During its rotation about B_1, A_1 moves along the small circle shown. This circle is centered at C on the projection and not at its projected center B_1. To find C we use the fact that all points on the circle must lie at equal *angular* distances from B_1; in this case, measurement on a Wulff net shows that both A_1 and A_4 are 76° from B_1. Accordingly, we locate any other point, such as D, which is 76° from B_1, and knowing three points on the required circle, we can locate its center C.

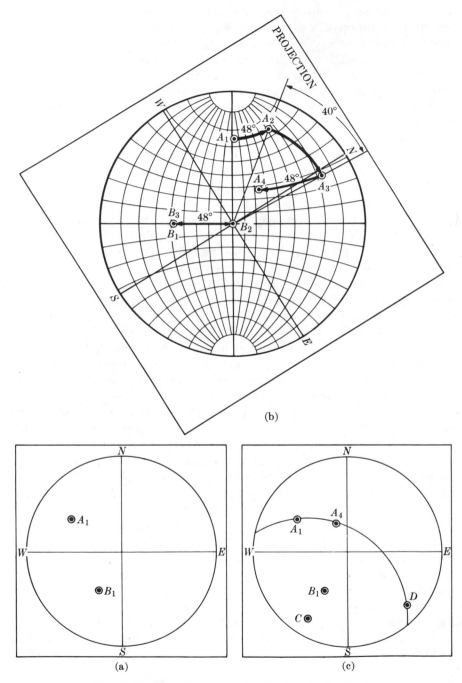

FIG. 2–35. Rotation of a pole about an inclined axis.

In dealing with problems of crystal orientation a *standard projection* is of very great value, since it shows at a glance the relative orientation of all the important planes in the crystal. Such a projection is made by selecting some important crystal plane of low indices as the plane of projection [e.g., (100), (110), (111), or (0001)] and projecting the poles of various crystal planes onto the selected plane. The construction of a standard projection of a crystal requires a knowledge of the interplanar angles for all the principal planes of the crystal. A set of values applicable to all crystals in the cubic system is given in Table 2–3, but those for crystals of other systems depend on the particular axial ratios involved and must be calculated for each case by the equations given in Appendix 1. Much time can be saved in making standard projections by making use of the zonal relation: the normals to all planes belonging to one zone are coplanar and at right angles to the zone axis. Consequently, the poles of planes of a zone will all lie on the same great circle on the projection, and the axis of the zone will be at 90° from this great circle. Furthermore, important planes usually belong to more than one zone and their poles are therefore located at the intersection of zone circles. It is also helpful to remember that important directions, which in the cubic system are normal to planes of the same indices, are usually the axes of important zones.

Figure 2–36(a) shows the principal poles of a cubic crystal projected on the (001) plane of the crystal or, in other words, a standard (001) projection. The location of the {100} cube poles follows immediately from Fig. 2–25. To locate the {110} poles we first note from Table 2–3 that they must lie at 45° from {100} poles, which are themselves 90° apart. In

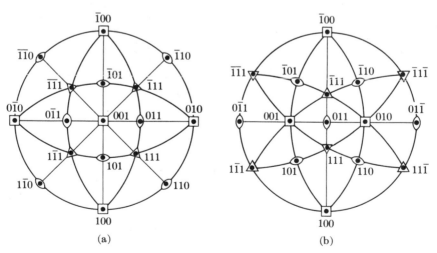

(a)   (b)

FIG. 2–36.   Standard projections of cubic crystals, (a) on (001) and (b) on (011).

TABLE 2–3

INTERPLANAR ANGLES (IN DEGREES) IN CUBIC CRYSTALS BETWEEN PLANES OF THE FORM $\{h_1k_1l_1\}$ AND $\{h_2k_2l_2\}$

$\{h_2k_2l_2\}$	$\{h_1k_1l_1\}$						
	100	110	111	210	211	221	310
100	0 90						
110	45 90	0 60 90					
111	54.7	35.3 90	0 70.5 109.5				
210	26.6 63.4 90	18.4 50.8 71.6	39.2 75.0	0 36.9 53.1			
211	35.3 65.9	30 54.7 73.2 90	19.5 61.9 90	24.1 43.1 56.8	0 33.6 48.2		
221	48.2 70.5	19.5 45 76.4 90	15.8 54.7 78.9	26.6 41.8 53.4	17.7 35.3 47.1	0 27.3 39.0	
310	18.4 71.6 90	26.6 47.9 63.4 77.1	43.1 68.6	8.1 58.1 45	25.4 49.8 58.9	32.5 42.5 58.2	0 25.9 36.9
311	25.2 72.5	31.5 64.8 90	29.5 58.5 80.0	19.3 47.6 66.1	10.0 42.4 60.5	25.2 45.3 59.8	17.6 40.3 55.1
320	33.7 56.3 90	11.3 54.0 66.9	61.3 71.3	7.1 29.8 41.9	25.2 37.6 55.6	22.4 42.3 49.7	15.3 37.9 52.1
321	36.7 57.7 74.5	19.1 40.9 55.5	22.2 51.9 72.0 90	17.0 33.2 53.3	10.9 29.2 40.2	11.5 27.0 36.7	21.6 32.3 40.5
331	46.5	13.1	22.0				
510	11.4						
511	15.6						
711	11.3						

Largely from R. M. Bozorth, *Phys. Rev.* **26**, 390 (1925); rounded off to the nearest 0.1°.

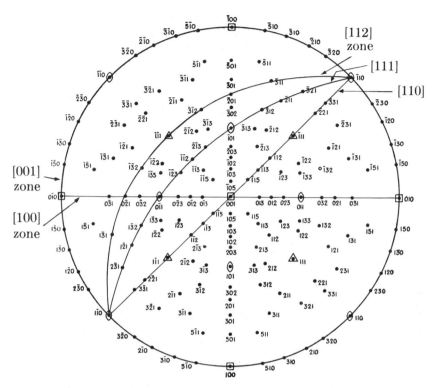

FIG. 2–37. Standard (001) projection of a cubic crystal. (From *Structure of Metals*, by C. S. Barrett, McGraw-Hill Book Company, Inc., 1952.)

this way we locate (011), for example, on the great circle joining (001) and (010) and at 45° from each. After all the {110} poles are plotted, we can find the {111} poles at the intersection of zone circles. Inspection of a crystal model or drawing or use of the zone relation given by Eq. (2–3) will show that (111), for example, belongs to both the zone [$\bar{1}$01] and the zone [0$\bar{1}$1]. The pole of (111) is thus located at the intersection of the zone circle through (0$\bar{1}$0), (101), and (010) and the zone circle through ($\bar{1}$00), (011), and (100). This location may be checked by measurement of its angular distance from (010) or (100), which should be 54.7°. The (011) standard projection shown in Fig. 2–36(b) is plotted in the same manner. Alternately, it may be constructed by rotating all the poles in the (001) projection 45° to the left about the *NS* axis of the projection, since this operation will bring the (011) pole to the center. In both of these projections symmetry symbols have been given each pole in conformity with Fig. 2–6(b), and it will be noted that the projection itself has the symmetry of the axis perpendicular to its plane, Figs. 2–36(a) and (b) having 4-fold and 2-fold symmetry, respectively.

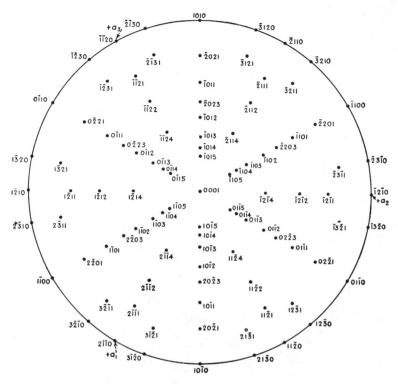

FIG. 2–38. Standard (0001) projection for zinc (hexagonal, $c/a = 1.86$). (From *Structure of Metals*, by C. S. Barrett, McGraw-Hill Book Company, Inc., 1952.)

Figure 2–37 is a standard (001) projection of a cubic crystal with considerably more detail and a few important zones indicated. A standard (0001) projection of a hexagonal crystal (zinc) is given in Fig. 2–38.

It is sometimes necessary to determine the *Miller indices of a given pole* on a crystal projection, for example the pole A in Fig. 2–39(a), which applies to a cubic crystal. If a detailed standard projection is available, the projection with the unknown pole can be superimposed on it and its indices will be disclosed by its coincidence with one of the known poles on the standard. Alternatively, the method illustrated in Fig. 2–39 may be used. The pole A defines a direction in space, normal to the plane (hkl) whose indices are required, and this direction makes angles ρ, σ, τ with the coordinate axes **a**, **b**, **c**. These angles are measured on the projection as shown in (a). Let the perpendicular distance between the origin and the (hkl) plane nearest the origin be d [Fig. 2–39(b)], and let the direction cosines of the line A be p, q, r. Therefore

$$p = \cos \rho = \frac{d}{a/h}, \qquad q = \cos \sigma = \frac{d}{b/k}, \qquad r = \cos \tau = \frac{d}{c/l},$$

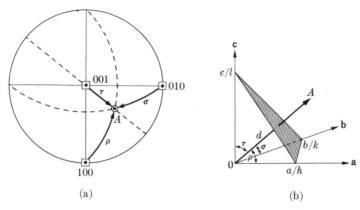

FIG. 2–39.   Determination of the Miller indices of a pole.

$$h:k:l = pa:qb:rc. \tag{2–8}$$

For the cubic system we have the simple result that the Miller indices required are in the same ratio as the direction cosines.

The lattice reorientation caused by *twinning* can be clearly shown on the stereographic projection.   In Fig. 2–40 the open symbols are the $\{100\}$ poles of a cubic crystal projected on the (001) plane.   If this crystal is FCC, then one of its possible twin planes is $(\overline{1}\overline{1}1)$, represented on the projection both by its pole and its trace.   The cube poles of the twin formed by reflection in this plane are shown as solid symbols; these poles are located by rotating the projection on a Wulff net until the pole of the twin plane lies on the equator, after which the cube poles of the crystal can be moved along latitude circles of the net to their final position.

The main principles of the stereographic projection have now been presented, and we will have occasion to use them later in dealing with various practical problems in x-ray metallography.   The student is reminded, however, that a mere reading of this section is not sufficient preparation for such problems.   In order to gain real familiarity with the stereographic projection, he must practice, with Wulff net and tracing paper, the operations described above and solve problems of the kind given below.   Only in this way will he be able to read and manipulate the stereographic projection with facility and think in three dimensions of what is represented in two.

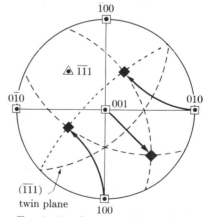

FIG. 2–40.   Stereographic projection of an FCC crystal and its twin.

Problems

2-1. Draw the following planes and directions in a tetragonal unit cell: (001), (011), (113), [110], [201], [$\bar{1}$01].

2-2. Show by means of a (1$\bar{1}$0) sectional drawing that [111] is perpendicular to (111) in the cubic system, but not, in general, in the tetragonal system.

2-3. In a drawing of a hexagonal prism, indicate the following planes and directions: (1$\bar{2}$10), (10$\bar{1}$2), ($\bar{1}$011), [110], [11$\bar{1}$], [021].

2-4. Derive Eq. (2-2) of the text.

2-5. Show that the planes (1$\bar{1}$0), (1$\bar{2}$1), and ($\bar{3}$12) belong to the zone [111].

2-6. Do the following planes all belong to the same zone: ($\bar{1}$10), ($\bar{3}$11), ($\bar{1}$32)? If so, what is the zone axis? Give the indices of any other plane belonging to this zone.

2-7. Prepare a cross-sectional drawing of an HCP structure which will show that all atoms do not have identical surroundings and therefore do not lie on a point lattice.

2-8. Show that c/a for hexagonal close packing of spheres is 1.633.

2-9. Show that the HCP structure (with $c/a = 1.633$) and the FCC structure are equally close-packed, and that the BCC structure is less closely packed than either of the former.

2-10. The unit cells of several orthorhombic crystals are described below. What is the Bravais lattice of each and how do you know?

(a) Two atoms of the same kind per unit cell located at $0\ \frac{1}{2}\ 0$, $\frac{1}{2}\ 0\ \frac{1}{2}$.

(b) Four atoms of the same kind per unit cell located at $0\ 0\ z$, $0\ \frac{1}{2}\ z$, $0\ \frac{1}{2}\ (\frac{1}{2} + z)$, $0\ 0\ (\frac{1}{2} + z)$.

(c) Four atoms of the same kind per unit cell located at $x\ y\ z$, $\bar{x}\ \bar{y}\ z$, $(\frac{1}{2} + x)$ $(\frac{1}{2} - y)\ \bar{z}$, $(\frac{1}{2} - x)\ (\frac{1}{2} + y)\ \bar{z}$.

(d) Two atoms of one kind A located at $\frac{1}{2}\ 0\ 0$, $0\ \frac{1}{2}\ \frac{1}{2}$; and two atoms of another kind B located at $0\ 0\ \frac{1}{2}$, $\frac{1}{2}\ \frac{1}{2}\ 0$.

2-11. Make a drawing, similar to Fig. 2-23, of a (112) twin in a BCC lattice and show the shear responsible for its formation. Obtain the magnitude of the shear strain graphically.

2-12. Construct a Wulff net, 18 cm in diameter and graduated at 30° intervals, by the use of compass, dividers, and straightedge only. Show all construction lines.

In some of the following problems, the coordinates of a point on a stereographic projection are given in terms of its latitude and longitude, measured from the center of the projection. Thus, the N pole is 90°N, 0°E, the E pole is 0°N, 90°E, etc.

2-13. Plane A is represented on a stereographic projection by a great circle passing through the N and S poles and the point 0°N, 70°W. The pole of plane B is located at 30°N, 50°W.

(a) Find the angle between the two planes.

(b) Draw the great circle of plane B and demonstrate that the stereographic projection is angle-true by measuring with a protractor the angle between the great circles of A and B.

2-14. Pole A, whose coordinates are 20°N, 50°E, is to be rotated about the axes described below. In each case, find the coordinates of the final position of pole A and show the path traced out during its rotation.

(a) 100° rotation about the NS axis, counterclockwise looking from N to S.

(b) 60° rotation about an axis normal to the plane of projection, clockwise to the observer.

(c) 60° rotation about an inclined axis B, whose coordinates are 10°S, 30°W, clockwise to the observer.

2-15. Draw a standard (111) projection of a cubic crystal, showing all poles of the form {100}, {110}, {111} and the important zone circles between them. Compare with Figs. 2–36(a) and (b).

2-16. Draw a standard (001) projection of white tin (tetragonal, $c/a = 0.545$), showing all poles of the form {001}, {100}, {110}, {011}, {111} and the important zone circles between them. Compare with Fig. 2–36(a).

2-17. Draw a standard (0001) projection of beryllium (hexagonal, $c/a = 1.57$), showing all poles of the form {2$\bar{1}\bar{1}$0}, {10$\bar{1}$0}, {2$\bar{1}\bar{1}$1}, {10$\bar{1}$1} and the important zone circles between them. Compare with Fig. 2–38.

2-18. On a standard (001) projection of a cubic crystal, in the orientation of Fig. 2–36(a), the pole of a certain plane has coordinates 53.3°S, 26.6°E. What are its Miller indices? Verify your answer by comparison of measured angles with those given in Table 2–3.

2-19. Duplicate the operations shown in Fig. 2–40 and thus find the locations of the cube poles of a ($\bar{1}\bar{1}$1) reflection twin in a cubic crystal. What are their coordinates?

2-20. Show that the twin orientation found in Prob. 2–19 can also be obtained by

(a) Reflection in a {112} plane. Which one?

(b) 180° rotation about a ⟨111⟩ axis. Which one?

(c) 60° rotation about a ⟨111⟩ axis. Which one?

In (c), show the paths traced out by the cube poles during their rotation.

CHAPTER 3

DIFFRACTION I: THE DIRECTIONS OF DIFFRACTED BEAMS

3–1 Introduction. After our preliminary survey of the physics of x-rays and the geometry of crystals, we can now proceed to fit the two together and discuss the phenomenon of x-ray diffraction, which is an interaction of the two. Historically, this is exactly the way this field of science developed. For many years, mineralogists and crystallographers had accumulated knowledge about crystals, chiefly by measurement of interfacial angles, chemical analysis, and determination of physical properties. There was little knowledge of interior structure, however, although some very shrewd guesses had been made, namely, that crystals were built up by periodic repetition of some unit, probably an atom or molecule, and that these units were situated some 1 or 2A apart. On the other hand, there were indications, but only indications, that x-rays might be electromagnetic waves about 1 or 2A in wavelength. In addition, the phenomenon of diffraction was well understood, and it was known that diffraction, as of visible light by a ruled grating, occurred whenever wave motion encountered a set of regularly spaced scattering objects, provided that the wavelength of the wave motion was of the same order of magnitude as the repeat distance between the scattering centers.

Such was the state of knowledge in 1912 when the German physicist von Laue took up the problem. He reasoned that, *if* crystals were composed of regularly spaced atoms which might act as scattering centers for x-rays, and *if* x-rays were electromagnetic waves of wavelength about equal to the interatomic distance in crystals, then it should be possible to diffract x-rays by means of crystals. Under his direction, experiments to test this hypothesis were carried out: a crystal of copper sulfate was set up in the path of a narrow beam of x-rays and a photographic plate was arranged to record the presence of diffracted beams, if any. The very first experiment was successful and showed without doubt that x-rays *were* diffracted by the crystal out of the primary beam to form a pattern of spots on the photographic plate. These experiments proved, at one and the same time, the wave nature of x-rays and the periodicity of the arrangement of atoms within a crystal. Hindsight is always easy and these ideas appear quite simple to us now, when viewed from the vantage point of more than forty years' development of the subject, but they were not at all obvious in 1912, and von Laue's hypothesis and its experimental verification must stand as a great intellectual achievement.

78

The account of these experiments was read with great interest by two English physicists, W. H. Bragg and his son W. L. Bragg. The latter, although only a young student at the time—it was still the year 1912—successfully analyzed the Laue experiment and was able to express the necessary conditions for diffraction in a somewhat simpler mathematical form than that used by von Laue. He also attacked the problem of crystal structure with the new tool of x-ray diffraction and, in the following year, solved the structures of NaCl, KCl, KBr, and KI, all of which have the NaCl structure; these were the first complete crystal-structure determinations ever made.

3–2 Diffraction. Diffraction is due essentially to the existence of certain phase relations between two or more waves, and it is advisable, at the start, to get a clear notion of what is meant by phase relations. Consider a beam of x-rays, such as beam **1** in Fig. 3–1, proceeding from left to right. For convenience only, this beam is assumed to be plane-polarized in order that we may draw the electric field vector **E** always in one plane. We may imagine this beam to be composed of two equal parts, ray **2** and ray **3**, each of half the amplitude of beam **1**. These two rays, on the wave front AA', are said to be completely *in phase* or in step; i.e., their electric-field vectors have the same magnitude and direction at the same instant at any point x measured along the direction of propagation of the wave. A *wave front* is a surface perpendicular to this direction of propagation.

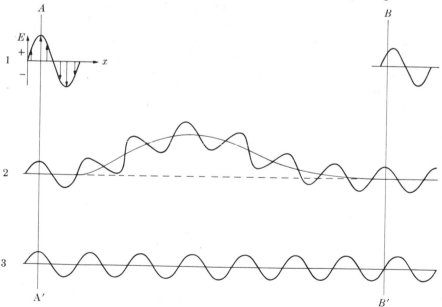

FIG. 3–1.   Effect of path difference on relative phase.

Now consider an imaginary experiment, in which ray **3** is allowed to continue in a straight line but ray **2** is diverted by some means into a curved path before rejoining ray **3**. What is the situation on the wave front BB' where both rays are proceeding in the original direction? On this front, the electric vector of ray **2** has its maximum value at the instant shown, but that of ray **3** is zero. The two rays are therefore *out of phase*. If we add these two imaginary components of the beam together, we find that beam **1** now has the form shown in the upper right of the drawing. If the amplitudes of rays **2** and **3** are each 1 unit, then the amplitude of beam **1** at the left is 2 units and that of beam **1** at the right is 1.4 units, if a sinusoidal variation of **E** with x is assumed.

Two conclusions may be drawn from this illustration:

(1) Differences in the length of the path traveled lead to differences in phase.

(2) The introduction of phase differences produces a change in amplitude.

The greater the path difference, the greater the difference in phase, since the path difference, measured in wavelengths, exactly equals the phase difference, also measured in wavelengths. If the diverted path of ray **2** in Fig. 3-1 were a quarter wavelength longer than shown, the phase difference would be a half wavelength. The two rays would then be completely out of phase on the wave front BB' and beyond, and they would therefore annul each other, since at any point their electric vectors would be either both zero or of the same magnitude and opposite in direction. If the difference in path length were made three quarters of a wavelength greater than shown, the two rays would be one complete wavelength out of phase, a condition indistinguishable from being completely in phase since in both cases the two waves would combine to form a beam of amplitude 2 units, just like the original beam. We may conclude that two rays are completely in phase whenever their path lengths differ either by zero or by a whole number of wavelengths.

Differences in the path length of various rays arise quite naturally when we consider how a crystal diffracts x-rays. Figure 3-2 shows a section of a crystal, its atoms arranged on a set of parallel planes A, B, C, D, ..., normal to the plane of the drawing and spaced a distance d' apart. Assume that a beam of perfectly parallel, perfectly monochromatic x-rays of wavelength λ is incident on this crystal at an angle θ, called the Bragg angle, where θ is measured between the incident beam and the particular crystal planes under consideration.

We wish to know whether this incident beam of x-rays will be diffracted by the crystal and, if so, under what conditions. *A diffracted beam may be defined as a beam composed of a large number of scattered rays mutually reinforcing one another.* Diffraction is, therefore, essentially a scattering phe-

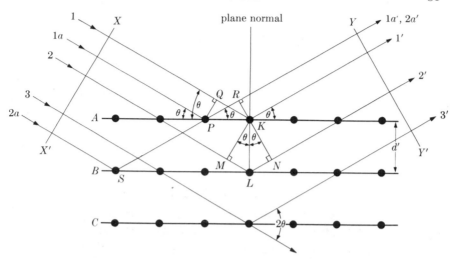

F<small>IG</small>. 3–2.　Diffraction of x-rays by a crystal.

nomenon and not one involving any "new" kind of interaction between x-rays and atoms. We saw in Sec. 1–5 that atoms scatter incident x-rays in all directions, and we shall see presently that in some of these directions the scattered beams will be completely in phase and so reinforce each other to form diffracted beams.

For the particular conditions described by Fig. 3–2 the only diffracted beam formed is that shown, namely one making an angle θ of reflection* equal to the angle θ of incidence. We will show this, first, for one plane of atoms and, second, for all the atoms making up the crystal. Consider rays **1** and **1a** in the incident beam; they strike atoms K and P in the first plane of atoms and are scattered in all directions. Only in the directions **1′** and **1a′**, however, are these scattered beams completely in phase and so capable of reinforcing one another; they do so because the difference in their length of path between the wave fronts XX' and YY' is equal to

$$QK - PR = PK \cos \theta - PK \cos \theta = 0.$$

Similarly, the rays scattered by all the atoms in the first plane in a direction parallel to **1′** are in phase and add their contributions to the diffracted beam. This will be true of all the planes separately, and it remains to find the condition for reinforcement of rays scattered by atoms in different planes. Rays **1** and **2**, for example, are scattered by atoms K and L, and

---

* Note that these angles are defined differently in x-ray diffraction and in general optics. In the latter, the angles of incidence and reflection are the angles which the incident and reflected beams make with the *normal* to the reflecting surface.

the path difference for rays $1K1'$ and $2L2'$ is

$$ML + LN = d' \sin \theta + d' \sin \theta.$$

This is also the path difference for the overlapping rays scattered by S and P in the direction shown, since in this direction there is no path difference between rays scattered by S and L or P and K. Scattered rays $1'$ and $2'$ will be completely in phase if this path difference is equal to a whole number n of wavelengths, or if

$$n\lambda = 2d' \sin \theta. \tag{3-1}$$

This relation was first formulated by W. L. Bragg and is known as the Bragg law. It states the essential condition which must be met if diffraction is to occur. n is called the order of reflection; it may take on any integral value consistent with $\sin \theta$ not exceeding unity and is equal to the number of wavelengths in the path difference between rays scattered by *adjacent* planes. Therefore, for fixed values of λ and d', there may be several angles of incidence θ_1, θ_2, θ_3 ... at which diffraction may occur, corresponding to $n = 1, 2, 3, \ldots$. In a first-order reflection ($n = 1$), the scattered rays $1'$ and $2'$ of Fig. 3-2 would differ in length of path (and in phase) by one wavelength, rays $1'$ and $3'$ by two wavelengths, rays $1'$ and $4'$ by three wavelengths, and so on throughout the crystal. The rays scattered by all the atoms in all the planes are therefore completely in phase and reinforce one another (constructive interference) to form a diffracted beam in the direction shown. In all other directions of space the scattered beams are out of phase and annul one another (destructive interference). The diffracted beam is rather strong compared to the sum of all the rays scattered in the same direction, simply because of the reinforcement which occurs,* but extremely weak compared to the incident beam since the atoms of a crystal scatter only a small fraction of the energy incident on them.

---

* If the scattering atoms were not arranged in a regular, periodic fashion but in some independent manner, then the rays scattered by them would have a random phase relationship to one another. In other words, there would be an equal probability of the phase difference between any two scattered rays having any value between zero and one wavelength. Neither constructive nor destructive interference takes place under these conditions, and the intensity of the beam scattered in a particular direction is simply the sum of the intensities of all the rays scattered in that direction. If there are N scattered rays each of amplitude A and therefore of intensity A^2 in arbitrary units, then the intensity of the scattered beam is NA^2. On the other hand, if the rays are scattered by the atoms of a crystal in a direction satisfying the Bragg law, then they are all in phase and the amplitude of the scattered beam is N times the amplitude A of each scattered ray, or NA. The intensity of the scattered beam is therefore N^2A^2, or N times as large as if reinforcement had not occurred. Since N is very large for the scattering of x-rays from even a small bit of crystal, the role of reinforcement in producing a strong diffracted beam is considerable.

We have here regarded a diffracted beam as being built up of rays scattered by successive planes of atoms within the crystal. It would be a mistake to assume, however, that a single plane of atoms A would diffract x-rays just as the complete crystal does but less strongly. Actually, the single plane of atoms would produce, not only the beam in the direction 1′ as the complete crystal does, but also additional beams in other directions, some of them not confined to the plane of the drawing. These additional beams do not exist in the diffraction from the complete crystal precisely because the atoms in the other planes scatter beams which destructively interfere with those scattered by the atoms in plane A, *except* in the direction 1′.

At first glance, the diffraction of x-rays by crystals and the reflection of visible light by mirrors appear very similar, since in both phenomena the angle of incidence is equal to the angle of reflection. It seems that we might regard the planes of atoms as little mirrors which "reflect" the x-rays. Diffraction and reflection, however, differ fundamentally in at least three aspects:

(1) The diffracted beam from a crystal is built up of rays scattered by all the atoms of the crystal which lie in the path of the incident beam. The reflection of visible light takes place in a thin surface layer only.

(2) The diffraction of monochromatic x-rays takes place only at those particular angles of incidence which satisfy the Bragg law. The reflection of visible light takes place at any angle of incidence.

(3) The reflection of visible light by a good mirror is almost 100 percent efficient. The intensity of a diffracted x-ray beam is extremely small compared to that of the incident beam.

Despite these differences, we often speak of "reflecting planes" and "reflected beams" when we really mean diffracting planes and diffracted beams. This is common usage and, from now on, we will frequently use these terms without quotation marks but with the tacit understanding that we really mean diffraction and not reflection.*

To sum up, diffraction is essentially a scattering phenomenon in which a large number of atoms cooperate. Since the atoms are arranged periodically on a lattice, the rays scattered by them have definite phase relations between them; these phase relations are such that destructive interference occurs in most directions of scattering, but in a few directions constructive interference takes place and diffracted beams are formed. The two essentials are a wave motion capable of interference (x-rays) and a set of periodically arranged scattering centers (the atoms of a crystal).

---

* For the sake of completeness, it should be mentioned that x-rays *can* be totally reflected by a solid surface, just like visible light by a mirror, but only at very small angles of incidence (below about one degree). This phenomenon is of little practical importance in x-ray metallography and need not concern us further.

3–3 The Bragg law.   Two geometrical facts are worth remembering:

(1) The incident beam, the normal to the reflecting plane, and the diffracted beam are always coplanar.

(2) The angle between the diffracted beam and the transmitted beam is always 2θ. This is known as the diffraction angle, and it is this angle, rather than θ, which is usually measured experimentally.

As previously stated, diffraction in general occurs only when the wavelength of the wave motion is of the same order of magnitude as the repeat distance between scattering centers. This requirement follows from the Bragg law. Since $\sin \theta$ cannot exceed unity, we may write

$$\frac{n\lambda}{2d'} = \sin \theta < 1. \tag{3–2}$$

Therefore, $n\lambda$ must be less than $2d'$. For diffraction, the smallest value of n is 1. ($n = 0$ corresponds to the beam diffracted in the same direction as the transmitted beam. It cannot be observed.) Therefore the condition for diffraction at any observable angle 2θ is

$$\lambda < 2d'. \tag{3–3}$$

For most sets of crystal planes d' is of the order of 3A or less, which means that λ cannot exceed about 6A. A crystal could not possibly diffract ultraviolet radiation, for example, of wavelength about 500A. On the other hand, if λ is very small, the diffraction angles are too small to be conveniently measured.

The Bragg law may be written in the form

$$\lambda = 2 \frac{d'}{n} \sin \theta. \tag{3–4}$$

Since the coefficient of λ is now unity, we can consider a reflection of any order as a first-order reflection from planes, real or fictitious, spaced at a distance $1/n$ of the previous spacing. This turns out to be a real convenience, so we set $d = d'/n$ and write the Bragg law in the form

$$\boxed{\lambda = 2d \sin \theta}. \tag{3–5}$$

This form will be used throughout this book.

This usage is illustrated by Fig. 3–3. Consider the second-order 100 reflection* shown in (a). Since it is second-order, the path difference ABC between rays scattered by adjacent (100) planes must be two whole wave-

---

* This means the reflection from the (100) planes. Conventionally, the Miller indices of a reflecting plane hkl, written without parentheses, stand for the reflected beam from the plane (hkl).

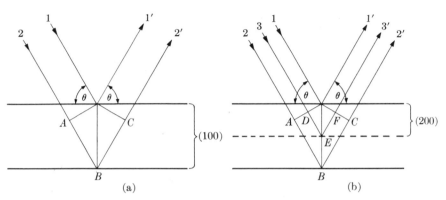

FIG. 3–3. Equivalence of (a) a second-order 100 reflection and (b) a first-order 200 reflection.

lengths. If there is no real plane of atoms between the (100) planes, we can always imagine one as in Fig. 3–3(b), where the dotted plane midway between the (100) planes forms part of the (200) set of planes. For the same reflection as in (a), the path difference DEF between rays scattered by adjacent (200) planes is now only one whole wavelength, so that this reflection can properly be called a first-order 200 reflection. Similarly, 300, 400, etc., reflections are equivalent to reflections of the third, fourth, etc., orders from the (100) planes. In general, an nth-order reflection from (hkl) planes of spacing d' may be considered as a first-order reflection from the $(nh\ nk\ nl)$ planes of spacing $d = d'/n$. Note that this convention is in accord with the definition of Miller indices since $(nh\ nk\ nl)$ are the Miller indices of planes parallel to the (hkl) planes but with $1/n$ the spacing of the latter.

3–4 X-ray spectroscopy. Experimentally, the Bragg law can be utilized in two ways. By using x-rays of known wavelength λ and measuring θ, we can determine the spacing d of various planes in a crystal: this is *structure analysis* and is the subject, in one way or another, of the greater part of this book. Alternatively, we can use a crystal with planes of known spacing d, measure θ, and thus determine the wavelength λ of the radiation used: this is *x-ray spectroscopy*.

The essential features of an x-ray spectrometer are shown in Fig. 3–4. X-rays from the tube T are incident on a crystal C which may be set at any desired angle to the incident

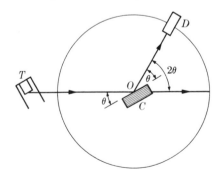

FIG. 3–4. The x-ray spectrometer.

beam by rotation about an axis through O, the center of the spectrometer circle. D is an ionization chamber or some form of counter which measures the intensity of the diffracted x-rays; it can also be rotated about O and set at any desired angular position. The crystal is usually cut or cleaved so that a particular set of reflecting planes of known spacing is parallel to its surface, as suggested by the drawing. In use, the crystal is positioned so that its reflecting planes make some particular angle θ with the incident beam, and D is set at the corresponding angle 2θ. The intensity of the diffracted beam is then measured and its wavelength calculated from the Bragg law, this procedure being repeated for various angles θ. It is in this way that curves such as Fig. 1–5 and the characteristic wavelengths tabulated in Appendix 3 were obtained. W. H. Bragg designed and used the first x-ray spectrometer, and the Swedish physicist Siegbahn developed it into an instrument of very high precision.

Except for one application, the subject of fluorescent analysis described in Chap. 15, we are here concerned with x-ray spectroscopy only in so far as it concerns certain units of wavelength. Wavelength measurements made in the way just described are obviously relative, and their accuracy is no greater than the accuracy with which the plane spacing of the crystal is known. For a cubic crystal this spacing can be obtained independently from a measurement of its density. For any crystal,

$$\text{Density} = \frac{\text{weight of atoms in unit cell}}{\text{volume of unit cell}},$$

$$\rho = \frac{\Sigma A}{NV}, \tag{3-6}$$

where ρ = density (gm/cm^3), ΣA = sum of the atomic weights of the atoms in the unit cell, N = Avogadro's number, and V = volume of unit cell (cm^3). NaCl, for example, contains four sodium atoms and four chlorine atoms per unit cell, so that

$$\Sigma A = 4(\text{at. wt Na}) + 4(\text{at. wt Cl}).$$

If this value is inserted into Eq. (3–6), together with Avogadro's number and the measured value of the density, the volume of the unit cell V can be found. Since NaCl is cubic, the lattice parameter a is given simply by the cube root of V. From this value of a and the cubic plane-spacing equation (Eq. 2–5), the spacing of any set of planes can be found.

In this way, Siegbahn obtained a value of 2.814A for the spacing of the (200) planes of rock salt, which he could use as a basis for wavelength measurements. However, he was able to measure wavelengths in terms of this spacing much more accurately than the spacing itself was known, in the sense that he could make relative wavelength measurements accurate to six significant figures whereas the spacing in absolute units (angstroms) was known only to four. It was therefore decided to define arbitrarily the (200) spacing of rock salt as 2814.00 X units (XU), this new unit being chosen to be as nearly as possible equal to 0.001A.

Once a particular wavelength was determined in terms of this spacing, the spacing of a given set of planes in any other crystal could be measured. Siegbahn thus measured the (200) spacing of calcite, which he found more suitable as a standard crystal, and thereafter based all his wavelength measurements on this spacing. Its value is 3029.45 XU. Later on, the kilo X unit (kX) was introduced, a thousand times as large as the X unit and nearly equal to an angstrom. The kX unit is therefore *defined* by the relation

$$1 \text{ kX} = \frac{(200) \text{ plane spacing of calcite}}{3.02945}. \tag{3-7}$$

On this basis, Siegbahn and his associates made very accurate measurements of wavelength in relative (kX) units and these measurements form the basis of most published wavelength tables.

It was found later that x-rays could be diffracted by a ruled grating such as is used in the spectroscopy of visible light, provided that the angle of incidence (the angle between the incident beam and the plane of the grating) is kept below the critical angle for total reflection. Gratings thus offer a means of making absolute wavelength measurements, independent of any knowledge of crystal structure. By a comparison of values so obtained with those found by Siegbahn from crystal diffraction, it was possible to calculate the following relation between the relative and absolute units:

$$\boxed{1 \text{ kX} = 1.00202\text{A}}. \tag{3-8}$$

This conversion factor was decided on in 1946 by international agreement, and it was recommended that, in the future, x-ray wavelengths and the lattice parameters of crystals be expressed in angstroms. If V in Eq. (3-6) for the density of a crystal is expressed in A^3 (*not* in kX^3) and the currently accepted value of Avogadro's number inserted, then the equation becomes

$$\rho = \frac{1.66020 \Sigma A}{V}. \tag{3-9}$$

The distinction between kX and A is unimportant if no more than about three significant figures are involved. In precise work, on the other hand, units must be correctly stated, and on this point there has been considerable confusion in the past. Some wavelength values published prior to about 1946 are stated to be in angstrom units but are actually in kX units. Some crystallographers have used such a value as the basis for a precise measurement of the lattice parameter of a crystal and the result has been stated, again incorrectly, in angstrom units. Many published parameters are therefore in error, and it is unfortunately not always easy to determine which ones are and which ones are not. The only safe rule to follow, in stating a precise parameter, is to give the wavelength of the radiation used in its determination. Similarly, any published table of wavelengths can be tested for the correctness of its units by noting the wavelength given for a particular characteristic line, Cu $K\alpha_1$ for example. The wavelength of this line is 1.54051A or 1.53740 kX.

3–5 Diffraction directions. What determines the possible directions, i.e., the possible angles 2θ, in which a given crystal can diffract a beam of monochromatic x-rays? Referring to Fig. 3–3, we see that various diffraction angles $2\theta_1$, $2\theta_2$, $2\theta_3$, ... can be obtained from the (100) planes by using a beam incident at the correct angle θ_1, θ_2, θ_3, ... and producing first-, second-, third-, ... order reflections. But diffraction can also be produced by the (110) planes, the (111) planes, the (213) planes, and so on. We obviously need a general relation which will predict the diffraction angle for *any* set of planes. This relation is obtained by combining the Bragg law and the plane-spacing equation (Appendix 1) applicable to the particular crystal involved.

For example, if the crystal is cubic, then

$$\lambda = 2d \sin \theta$$

and

$$\frac{1}{d^2} = \frac{(h^2 + k^2 + l^2)}{a^2}.$$

Combining these equations, we have

$$\sin^2 \theta = \frac{\lambda^2}{4a^2} (h^2 + k^2 + l^2). \tag{3–10}$$

This equation predicts, for a particular incident wavelength λ and a particular cubic crystal of unit cell size a, all the possible Bragg angles at which diffraction can occur from the planes (hkl). For (110) planes, for example, Eq. (3–10) becomes

$$\sin^2 \theta_{110} = \frac{\lambda^2}{2a^2}.$$

If the crystal is tetragonal, with axes a and c, then the corresponding general equation is

$$\sin^2 \theta = \frac{\lambda^2}{4} \left(\frac{h^2 + k^2}{a^2} + \frac{l^2}{c^2} \right), \tag{3–11}$$

and similar equations can readily be obtained for the other crystal systems.

These examples show that the directions in which a beam of given wavelength is diffracted by a given set of lattice planes is determined by the crystal system to which the crystal belongs and its lattice parameters. In short, *diffraction directions are determined solely by the shape and size of the unit cell.* This is an important point and so is its converse: all we can possibly determine about an unknown crystal by measurements of the *directions* of diffracted beams are the shape and size of its unit cell. We will find, in the next chapter, that the *intensities* of diffracted beams are determined by the positions of the atoms within the unit cell, and it follows that we must measure intensities if we are to obtain any information at all about atom positions. We will find, for many crystals, that there are particular atomic arrangements which reduce the intensities of some diffracted beams to zero. In such a case, there is simply no diffracted beam at the angle predicted by an equation of the type of Eqs. (3–10) and (3–11). It is in this sense that equations of this kind predict all *possible* diffracted beams.

3–6 Diffraction methods. Diffraction can occur whenever the Bragg law, $\lambda = 2d \sin \theta$, is satisfied. This equation puts very stringent conditions on λ and θ for any given crystal. With monochromatic radiation, an arbitrary setting of a single crystal in a beam of x-rays will not in general produce *any* diffracted beams. Some way of satisfying the Bragg law must be devised, and this can be done by continuously varying either λ or θ during the experiment. The ways in which these quantities are varied distinguish the three main diffraction methods:

	λ	θ
Laue method	Variable	Fixed
Rotating-crystal method	Fixed	Variable (in part)
Powder method	Fixed	Variable

The **Laue method** was the first diffraction method ever used, and it reproduces von Laue's original experiment. A beam of white radiation, the continuous spectrum from an x-ray tube, is allowed to fall on a fixed single crystal. The Bragg angle θ is therefore fixed for every set of planes in the crystal, and each set picks out and diffracts that particular wavelength which satisfies the Bragg law for the particular values of d and θ involved. Each diffracted beam thus has a different wavelength.

There are two variations of the Laue method, depending on the relative positions of source, crystal, and film (Fig. 3–5). In each, the film is flat and placed perpendicular to the incident beam. The film in the *transmission Laue method* (the original Laue method) is placed behind the crystal so as to record the beams diffracted in the forward direction. This

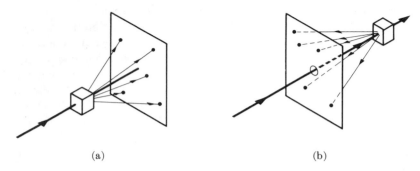

(a)   (b)

FIG. 3–5.   (a) Transmission and (b) back-reflection Laue methods.

method is so called because the diffracted beams are partially transmitted through the crystal.   In the *back-reflection Laue method* the film is placed between the crystal and the x-ray source, the incident beam passing through a hole in the film, and the beams diffracted in a backward direction are recorded.

In either method, the diffracted beams form an array of spots on the film as shown in Fig. 3–6.   This array of spots is commonly called a pattern, but the term is not used in any strict sense and does not imply any periodic arrangement of the spots.   On the contrary, the spots are seen to lie on certain curves, as shown by the lines drawn on the photographs.

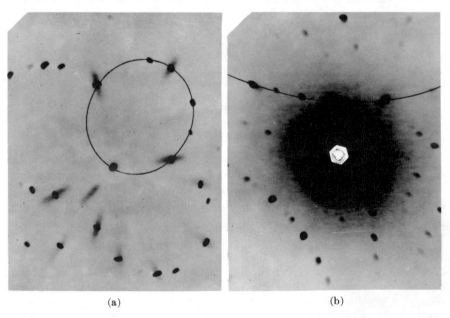

(a)   (b)

FIG. 3–6.   (a) Transmission and (b) back-reflection Laue patterns of an aluminum crystal (cubic).   Tungsten radiation, 30 kv, 19 ma.

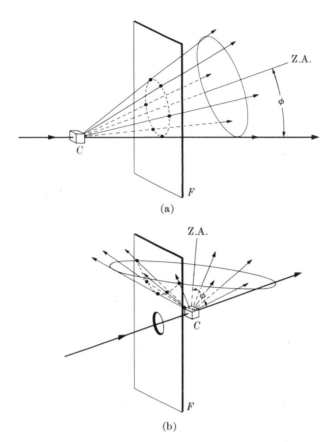

(a)

(b)

FIG. 3–7. Location of Laue spots (a) on ellipses in transmission method and (b) on hyperbolas in back-reflection method. (C = crystal, F = film, Z.A. = zone axis.)

These curves are generally ellipses or hyperbolas for transmission patterns [Fig. 3–6(a)] and hyperbolas for back-reflection patterns [Fig. 3–6(b)].

The spots lying on any one curve are reflections from planes belonging to one zone. This is due to the fact that the Laue reflections from planes of a zone all lie on the surface of an imaginary cone whose axis is the zone axis. As shown in Fig. 3–7(a), one side of the cone is tangent to the transmitted beam, and the angle of inclination ϕ of the zone axis (Z.A.) to the transmitted beam is equal to the semi-apex angle of the cone. A film placed as shown intersects the cone in an imaginary ellipse passing through the center of the film, the diffraction spots from planes of a zone being arranged on this ellipse. When the angle ϕ exceeds 45°, a film placed between the crystal and the x-ray source to record the back-reflection pattern will intersect the cone in a hyperbola, as shown in Fig. 3–7(b).

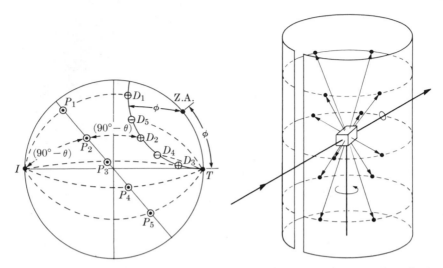

FIG. 3–8.   Stereographic projection   FIG. 3–9.   Rotating-crystal method.
of transmission Laue method.

The fact that the Laue reflections from planes of a zone lie on the surface of a cone can be nicely demonstrated with the stereographic projection. In Fig. 3–8, the crystal is at the center of the reference sphere, the incident beam I enters at the left, and the transmitted beam T leaves at the right. The point representing the zone axis lies on the circumference of the basic circle and the poles of five planes belonging to this zone, P_1 to P_5, lie on the great circle shown.   The direction of the beam diffracted by any one of these planes, for example the plane P_2, can be found as follows. I, P_2, D_2 (the diffraction direction required), and T are all coplanar.   Therefore D_2 lies on the great circle through I, P_2, and T.   The angle between I and P_2 is $(90° - \theta)$, and D_2 must lie at an equal angular distance on the other side of P_2, as shown.   The diffracted beams so found, D_1 to D_5, are seen to lie on a small circle, the intersection with the reference sphere of a cone whose axis is the zone axis.

The positions of the spots on the film, for both the transmission and the back-reflection method, depend on the orientation of the crystal relative to the incident beam, and the spots themselves become distorted and smeared out if the crystal has been bent or twisted in any way.   These facts account for the two main uses of the Laue methods: the determination of crystal orientation and the assessment of crystal perfection.

In the **rotating-crystal method** a single crystal is mounted with one of its axes, or some important crystallographic direction, normal to a monochromatic x-ray beam.   A cylindrical film is placed around it and the crystal is rotated about the chosen direction, the axis of the film coinciding with the axis of rotation of the crystal (Fig. 3–9).   As the crystal rotates,

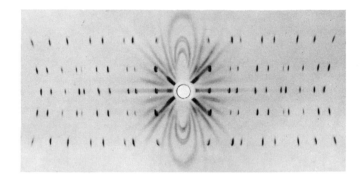

FIG. 3–10. Rotating-crystal pattern of a quartz crystal (hexagonal) rotated about its **c** axis. Filtered copper radiation. (The streaks are due to the white radiation not removed by the filter.) (Courtesy of B. E. Warren.)

a particular set of lattice planes will, for an instant, make the correct Bragg angle for reflection of the monochromatic incident beam, and at that instant a reflected beam will be formed. The reflected beams are again located on imaginary cones but now the cone axes coincide with the rotation axis. The result is that the spots on the film, when the film is laid out flat, lie on imaginary horizontal lines, as shown in Fig. 3–10. Since the crystal is rotated about only one axis, the Bragg angle does not take on all possible values between 0° and 90° for every set of planes. Not every set, therefore, is able to produce a diffracted beam; sets perpendicular or almost perpendicular to the rotation axis are obvious examples.

The chief use of the rotating-crystal method and its variations is in the determination of unknown crystal structures, and for this purpose it is the most powerful tool the x-ray crystallographer has at his disposal. However, the complete determination of complex crystal structures is a subject beyond the scope of this book and outside the province of the average metallurgist who uses x-ray diffraction as a laboratory tool. For this reason the rotating-crystal method will not be described in any further detail, except for a brief discussion in Appendix 15.

In the **powder method,** the crystal to be examined is reduced to a very fine powder and placed in a beam of monochromatic x-rays. Each particle of the powder is a tiny crystal oriented at random with respect to the incident beam. Just by chance, some of the particles will be correctly oriented so that their (100) planes, for example, can reflect the incident beam. Other particles will be correctly oriented for (110) reflections, and so on. The result is that every set of lattice planes will be capable of reflection. The mass of powder is equivalent, in fact, to a single crystal rotated, not about one axis, but about all possible axes.

Consider one particular hkl reflection. One or more particles of powder will, by chance, be so oriented that their (hkl) planes make the correct

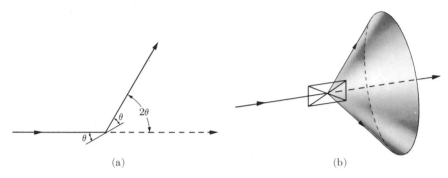

Fɪɢ. 3–11.   Formation of a diffracted cone of radiation in the powder method.

Bragg angle for reflection; Fig. 3–11(a) shows one plane in this set and the diffracted beam formed.   If this plane is now rotated about the incident beam as axis in such a way that θ is kept constant, then the reflected beam will travel over the surface of a cone as shown in Fig. 3–11(b), the axis of the cone coinciding with the transmitted beam.   This rotation does not actually occur in the powder method, but the presence of a large number of crystal particles having all possible orientations is equivalent to this rotation, since among these particles there will be a certain fraction whose (hkl) planes make the right Bragg angle with the incident beam and which at the same time lie in all possible rotational positions about the axis of the incident beam.   The hkl reflection from a stationary mass of powder thus has the form of a cone of diffracted radiation, and a separate cone is formed for each set of differently spaced lattice planes.

Figure 3–12 shows four such cones and also illustrates the most common powder-diffraction method.   In this, the Debye-Scherrer method, a narrow strip of film is curved into a short cylinder with the specimen placed on its axis and the incident beam directed at right angles to this axis.   The cones of diffracted radiation intersect the cylindrical strip of film in lines and, when the strip is unrolled and laid out flat, the resulting pattern has the appearance of the one illustrated in Fig. 3–12(b).   Actual patterns, produced by various metal powders, are shown in Fig. 3–13.   Each diffraction line is made up of a large number of small spots, each from a separate crystal particle, the spots lying so close together that they appear as a continuous line.   The lines are generally curved, unless they occur exactly at $2\theta = 90°$ when they will be straight.   From the measured position of a given diffraction line on the film, θ can be determined, and, knowing λ, we can calculate the spacing d of the reflecting lattice planes which produced the line.

Conversely, if the shape and size of the unit cell of the crystal are known, we can predict the position of all possible diffraction lines on the film.   The line of lowest 2θ value is produced by reflection from planes of the greatest

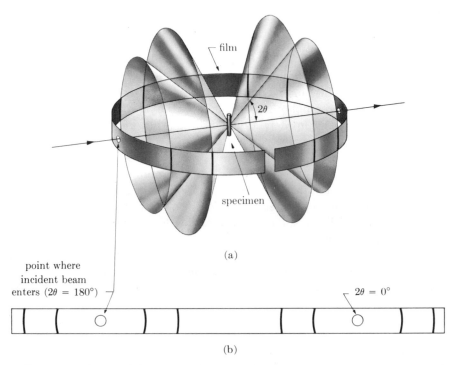

(a)

(b)

Fig. 3–12.   Debye-Scherrer powder method: (a) relation of film to specimen and incident beam; (b) appearance of film when laid out flat.

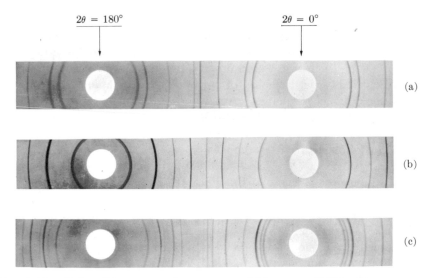

Fig. 3–13.   Debye-Scherrer powder patterns of (a) copper (FCC), (b) tungsten (BCC), and (c) zinc (HCP).   Filtered copper radiation, camera diameter = 5.73 cm.

spacing. In the cubic system, for example, d is a maximum when $(h^2 + k^2 + l^2)$ is a minimum, and the minimum value of this term is 1, corresponding to (hkl) equal to (100). The 100 reflection is accordingly the one of lowest 2θ value. The next reflection will have indices hkl corresponding to the next highest value of $(h^2 + k^2 + l^2)$, namely 2, in which case (hkl) equals (110), and so on.

The Debye-Scherrer and other variations of the powder method are very widely used, especially in metallurgy. The powder method is, of course, the only method that can be employed when a single crystal specimen is not available, and this is the case more often than not in metallurgical work. The method is especially suited for determining lattice parameters with high precision and for the identification of phases, whether they occur alone or in mixtures such as polyphase alloys, corrosion products, refractories, and rocks. These and other uses of the powder method will be fully described in later chapters.

Finally, the x-ray spectrometer can be used as a tool in diffraction analysis. This instrument is known as a **diffractometer** when it is used with x-rays of *known* wavelength to determine the *unknown* spacing of crystal planes, and as a spectrometer in the reverse case, when crystal planes of known spacing are used to determine unknown wavelengths. The diffractometer is always used with monochromatic radiation and measurements may be made on either single crystals or polycrystalline specimens; in the latter case, it functions much like a Debye-Scherrer camera in that the counter intercepts and measures only a short arc of any one cone of diffracted rays.

3–7 Diffraction under nonideal conditions. Before going any further, it is important to stop and consider with some care the derivation of the Bragg law given in Sec. 3–2 in order to understand precisely under what conditions it is strictly valid. In our derivation we assumed certain ideal conditions, namely a perfect crystal and an incident beam composed of perfectly parallel and strictly monochromatic radiation. These conditions never actually exist, so we must determine the effect on diffraction of various kinds of departure from the ideal.

In particular, the way in which destructive interference is produced in all directions except those of the diffracted beams is worth considering in some detail, both because it is fundamental to the theory of diffraction and because it will lead us to a method for estimating the size of very small crystals. We will find that only the infinite crystal is really perfect and that small size alone, of an otherwise perfect crystal, can be considered a crystal imperfection.

The condition for reinforcement used in Sec. 3–2 is that the waves involved must differ in path length, that is, in phase, by exactly an integral number of wavelengths. But suppose that the angle θ in Fig. 3–2 is such that the path difference for rays scattered by the first and second planes is only a quarter wavelength. These rays do not annul one another but, as we saw in Fig. 3–1, simply unite to form a beam of smaller amplitude than that formed by two rays which are completely in phase. How then does destructive interference take place? The answer lies in the contributions from planes deeper in the crystal. Under the assumed conditions, the rays scattered by the second and third planes would also be a quarter wavelength out of phase. But this means that the rays scattered by the first and third planes are exactly half a wavelength out of phase and would completely cancel one another. Similarly, the rays from the second and fourth planes, third and fifth planes, etc., throughout the crystal, are completely out of phase; the result is destructive interference and no diffracted beam. Destructive interference is therefore just as much a consequence of the periodicity of atom arrangement as is constructive interference.

This is an extreme example. If the path difference between rays scattered by the first two planes differs only slightly from an integral number of wavelengths, then the plane scattering a ray exactly out of phase with the ray from the first plane will lie deep within the crystal. If the crystal is so small that this plane does not exist, then complete cancellation of all the scattered rays will not result. It follows that there is a connection between the amount of "out-of-phaseness" that can be tolerated and the size of the crystal.

Suppose, for example, that the crystal has a thickness t measured in a direction perpendicular to a particular set of reflecting planes (Fig. 3–14). Let there be $(m + 1)$ planes in this set. We will regard the Bragg angle θ as a variable and call θ_B the angle which exactly satisfies the Bragg law for the particular values of λ and d involved, or

$$\lambda = 2d \sin \theta_B.$$

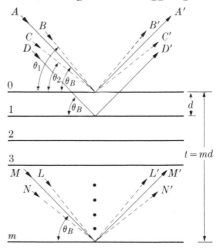

In Fig. 3–14, rays A, D, ..., M make exactly this angle θ_B with the reflecting planes. Ray D', scattered by the first plane below the surface, is therefore one wavelength out of phase with A'; and ray M', scattered by the mth plane below the surface, is m wavelengths out of phase with A'. Therefore, at a diffraction angle $2\theta_B$, rays A', D', ..., M' are completely in phase and unite to form a diffracted

FIG. 3–14. Effect of crystal size on diffraction.

beam of maximum amplitude, i.e., a beam of maximum intensity, since the intensity is proportional to the square of the amplitude.

When we consider incident rays that make Bragg angles only slightly different from θ_B, we find that destructive interference is not complete. Ray **B**, for example, makes a slightly larger angle θ_1, such that ray **L′** from the mth plane below the surface is $(m + 1)$ wavelengths out of phase with **B′**, the ray from the surface plane. This means that midway in the crystal there is a plane scattering a ray which is one-half (actually, an integer plus one-half) wavelength out of phase with ray **B′** from the surface plane. These rays cancel one another, and so do the other rays from similar pairs of planes throughout the crystal, the net effect being that rays scattered by the top half of the crystal annul those scattered by the bottom half. The intensity of the beam diffracted at an angle $2\theta_1$ is therefore zero. It is also zero at an angle $2\theta_2$ where θ_2 is such that ray **N′** from the mth plane below the surface is $(m - 1)$ wavelengths out of phase with ray **C′** from the surface plane. It follows that the diffracted intensity at angles near $2\theta_B$, but not greater than $2\theta_1$ or less than $2\theta_2$, is *not zero* but has a value intermediate between zero and the maximum intensity of the beam diffracted at an angle $2\theta_B$. The curve of diffracted intensity *vs.* 2θ will thus have the form of Fig. 3–15(a) in contrast to Fig. 3–15(b), which illustrates the hypothetical case of diffraction occurring only at the exact Bragg angle.

The width of the diffraction curve of Fig. 3–15(a) increases as the thickness of the crystal decreases. The width B is usually measured, in radians, at an intensity equal to half the maximum intensity. As a rough measure

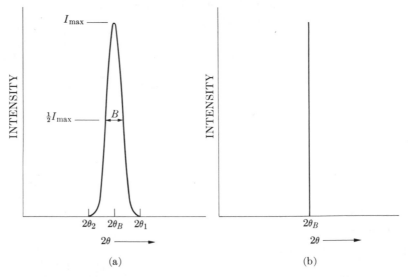

FIG. 3–15.   Effect of fine particle size on diffraction curves (schematic).

of B, we can take half the difference between the two extreme angles at which the intensity is zero, or

$$B = \tfrac{1}{2}(2\theta_1 - 2\theta_2) = \theta_1 - \theta_2.$$

The path-difference equations for these two angles are

$$2t \sin \theta_1 = (m + 1)\lambda,$$

$$2t \sin \theta_2 = (m - 1)\lambda.$$

By subtraction we find

$$t(\sin \theta_1 - \sin \theta_2) = \lambda,$$

$$2t \cos \left(\frac{\theta_1 + \theta_2}{2}\right) \sin \left(\frac{\theta_1 - \theta_2}{2}\right) = \lambda.$$

But θ_1 and θ_2 are both very nearly equal to θ_B, so that

$$\theta_1 + \theta_2 = 2\theta_B \quad \text{(approx.)}$$

and

$$\sin \left(\frac{\theta_1 - \theta_2}{2}\right) = \left(\frac{\theta_1 - \theta_2}{2}\right) \quad \text{(approx.).}$$

Therefore

$$2t \left(\frac{\theta_1 - \theta_2}{2}\right) \cos \theta_B = \lambda,$$

$$t = \frac{\lambda}{B \cos \theta_B}. \tag{3–12}$$

A more exact treatment of the problem gives

$$t = \frac{0.9\lambda}{B \cos \theta_B}, \tag{3–13}$$

which is known as the Scherrer formula. It is used to estimate the *particle size* of very small crystals from the measured width of their diffraction curves. What is the order of magnitude of this effect? Suppose $\lambda = 1.5\text{A}$, $d = 1.0\text{A}$, and $\theta = 49°$. Then for a crystal 1 mm in diameter the breadth B, due to the small crystal effect alone, would be about 2×10^{-7} radian (0.04 sec), or too small to be observable. Such a crystal would contain some 10^7 parallel lattice planes of the spacing assumed above. However, if the crystal were only 500A thick, it would contain only 500 planes, and the diffraction curve would be relatively broad, namely about 4×10^{-3} radian (0.2°).

Nonparallel incident rays, such as **B** and **C** in Fig. 3–14, actually exist in any real diffraction experiment, since the "perfectly parallel beam" assumed in Fig. 3–2 has never been produced in the laboratory. As will be shown in Sec. 5–4, any actual beam of x-rays contains divergent and convergent rays as well as parallel rays, so that the phenomenon of diffraction at angles not exactly satisfying the Bragg law actually takes place.

Neither is any real beam ever strictly monochromatic. The usual "monochromatic" beam is simply one containing the strong $K\alpha$ component superimposed on the continuous spectrum. But the $K\alpha$ line itself has a width of about 0.001A and this narrow range of wavelengths in the nominally monochromatic beam is a further cause of line broadening, i.e., of measurable diffraction at angles close, but not equal, to $2\theta_B$, since for each value of λ there is a corresponding value of θ. (Translated into terms of diffraction line width, a range of wavelengths extending over 0.001A leads to an increase in line width, for $\lambda = 1.5$A and $\theta = 45°$, of about 0.08° over the width one would expect if the incident beam were strictly monochromatic.) Line broadening due to this natural "spectral width" is proportional to $\tan \theta$ and becomes quite noticeable as θ approaches 90°.

Finally, there is a kind of crystal imperfection known as *mosaic structure* which is possessed by all real crystals to a greater or lesser degree and which has a decided effect on diffraction phenomena. It is a kind of substructure into which a "single" crystal is broken up and is illustrated in Fig. 3–16 in an enormously exaggerated fashion. A crystal with mosaic structure does not have its atoms arranged on a perfectly regular lattice extending from one side of the

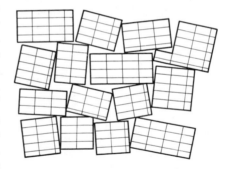

FIG. 3–16. The mosaic structure of a real crystal.

crystal to the other; instead, the lattice is broken up into a number of tiny blocks, each slightly disoriented one from another. The size of these blocks is of the order of 1000A, while the maximum angle of disorientation between them may vary from a very small value to as much as one degree, depending on the crystal. If this angle is ϵ, then diffraction of a parallel monochromatic beam from a "single" crystal will occur not only at an angle of incidence θ_B but at all angles between θ_B and $\theta_B + \epsilon$. Another effect of mosaic structure is to increase the intensity of the reflected beam relative to that theoretically calculated for an ideally perfect crystal.

These, then, are some examples of diffraction under nonideal conditions, that is, of diffraction as it actually occurs. We should not regard these as "deviations" from the Bragg law, and we will not as long as we remember that this law is derived for certain ideal conditions and that diffraction is

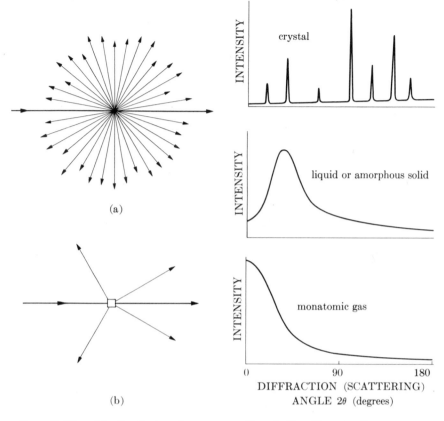

FIG. 3–17. (a) Scattering by an atom. (b) Diffraction by a crystal.

FIG. 3–18. Comparative x-ray scattering by crystalline solids, amorphous solids, liquids, and monatomic gases (schematic).

only a special kind of scattering. This latter point cannot be too strongly emphasized. A single atom scatters an incident beam of x-rays in all directions in space, but a large number of atoms arranged in a perfectly periodic array in three dimensions to form a crystal scatters (diffracts) x-rays in relatively few directions, as illustrated schematically in Fig. 3–17. It does so precisely because the periodic arrangement of atoms causes destructive interference of the scattered rays in all directions *except* those predicted by the Bragg law, and in these directions constructive interference (reinforcement) occurs. It is not surprising, therefore, that measurable diffraction (scattering) occurs at non-Bragg angles whenever any crystal imperfection results in the partial absence of one or more of the necessary conditions for perfect destructive interference at these angles.

These imperfections are generally slight compared to the over-all regularity of the lattice, with the result that diffracted beams are confined to very narrow angular ranges centered on the angles predicted by the Bragg law for ideal conditions.

This relation between destructive interference and structural periodicity can be further illustrated by a comparison of x-ray scattering by solids, liquids, and gases (Fig. 3–18). The curve of scattered intensity *vs.* 2θ for a crystalline solid is almost zero everywhere except at certain angles where high sharp maxima occur: these are the diffracted beams. Both amorphous solids and liquids have structures characterized by an almost complete lack of periodicity and a tendency to "order" only in the sense that the atoms are fairly tightly packed together and show a statistical preference for a particular interatomic distance; the result is an x-ray scattering curve showing nothing more than one or two broad maxima. Finally, there are the monatomic gases, which have no structural periodicity whatever; in such gases, the atoms are arranged perfectly at random and their relative positions change constantly with time. The corresponding scattering curve shows no maxima, merely a regular decrease of intensity with increase in scattering angle.

PROBLEMS

3–1. Calculate the "x-ray density" [the density given by Eq. (3–9)] of copper to four significant figures.

3–2. A transmission Laue pattern is made of a cubic crystal having a lattice parameter of 4.00A. The x-ray beam is horizontal. The [0$\bar{1}$0] axis of the crystal points along the beam towards the x-ray tube, the [$\bar{1}$00] axis points vertically upward, and the [001] axis is horizontal and parallel to the photographic film. The film is 5.00 cm from the crystal.

(*a*) What is the wavelength of the radiation diffracted from the ($\bar{3}$10) planes?

(*b*) Where will the $\bar{3}$10 reflection strike the film?

3–3. A back-reflection Laue pattern is made of a cubic crystal in the orientation of Prob. 3–2. By means of a stereographic projection similar to Fig. 3–8, show that the beams diffracted by the planes ($\bar{1}$20), ($\bar{1}\bar{2}$3), and (121), all of which belong to the zone [$\bar{2}$10], lie on the surface of a cone whose axis is the zone axis. What is the angle ϕ between the zone axis and the transmitted beam?

3–4. Determine the values of 2θ and (*hkl*) for the first three lines (those of lowest 2θ values) on the powder patterns of substances with the following structures, the incident radiation being Cu $K\alpha$:

(*a*) Simple cubic ($a = 3.00$A)

(*b*) Simple tetragonal ($a = 2.00$A, $c = 3.00$A)

(*c*) Simple tetragonal ($a = 3.00$A, $c = 2.00$A)

(*d*) Simple rhombohedral ($a = 3.00$A, $\alpha = 80°$)

3–5. Calculate the breadth B (in degrees of 2θ), due to the small crystal effect alone, of the powder pattern lines of particles of diameter 1000, 750, 500, and 250A. Assume $\theta = 45°$ and $\lambda = 1.5$A. For particles 250A in diameter, calculate the breadth B for $\theta = 10, 45,$ and $80°$.

3–6. Check the value given in Sec. 3–7 for the increase in breadth of a diffraction line due to the natural width of the $K\alpha$ emission line. (*Hint:* Differentiate the Bragg law and find an expression for the rate of change of 2θ with λ.)

CHAPTER 4

DIFFRACTION II: THE INTENSITIES OF DIFFRACTED BEAMS

4–1 Introduction. As stated earlier, the positions of the atoms in the unit cell affect the intensities but not the directions of the diffracted beams. That this must be so may be seen by considering the two structures shown in Fig. 4–1. Both are orthorhombic with two atoms of the same kind per unit cell, but the one on the left is base-centered and the one on the right body-centered. Either is derivable from the other by a simple shift of one atom by the vector $\frac{1}{2}c$.

Consider reflections from the (001) planes which are shown in profile in Fig. 4–2. For the base-centered lattice shown in (a), suppose that the Bragg law is satisfied for the particular values of λ and θ employed. This means that the path difference ABC between rays **1'** and **2'** is one wavelength, so that rays **1'** and **2'** are in phase and diffraction occurs in the direction shown. Similarly, in the body-centered lattice shown in (b), rays **1'** and **2'** are in phase, since their path difference ABC is one wavelength. However, in this case, there is another plane of atoms midway between the (001) planes, and the path difference DEF between rays **1'** and **3'** is exactly half of ABC, or one half wavelength. Thus rays **1'** and **3'** are completely out of phase and annul each other. Similarly, ray **4'** from the next plane down (not shown) annuls ray **2'**, and so on throughout the crystal. There is no 001 reflection from the body-centered lattice.

This example shows how a simple rearrangement of atoms within the unit cell can eliminate a reflection completely. More generally, the intensity of a diffracted beam is changed, not necessarily to zero, by any change in atomic positions, and, conversely, we can only determine atomic positions by observations of diffracted intensities. To establish an exact relation between atom position and intensity is the main purpose of this chapter. The problem is complex because of the many variables involved, and we will have to proceed step by step: we will consider how x-rays are scattered first by a single electron, then by an atom, and finally by all the

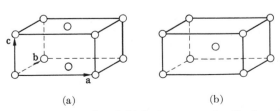

(a)   (b)

Fig. 4–1.   (a) Base-centered and (b) body-centered orthorhombic unit cells.

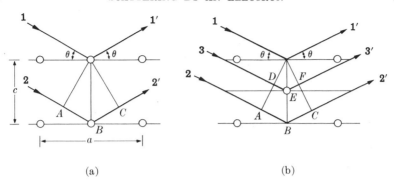

FIG. 4–2. Diffraction from the (001) planes of (a) base-centered and (b) body-centered orthorhombic lattices.

atoms in the unit cell. We will apply these results to the powder method of x-ray diffraction only, and, to obtain an expression for the intensity of a powder pattern line, we will have to consider a number of other factors which affect the way in which a crystalline powder diffracts x-rays.

4–2 Scattering by an electron. We have seen in Chap. 1 that an x-ray beam is an electromagnetic wave characterized by an electric field whose strength varies sinusoidally with time at any one point in the beam. Since an electric field exerts a force on a charged particle such as an electron, the oscillating electric field of an x-ray beam will set any electron it encounters into oscillatory motion about its mean position.

Now an accelerating or decelerating electron emits an electromagnetic wave. We have already seen an example of this phenomenon in the x-ray tube, where x-rays are emitted because of the rapid deceleration of the electrons striking the target. Similarly, an electron which has been set into oscillation by an x-ray beam is continuously accelerating and decelerating during its motion and therefore emits an electromagnetic wave. In this sense, an electron is said to *scatter* x-rays, the scattered beam being simply the beam radiated by the electron under the action of the incident beam. The scattered beam has the same wavelength and frequency as the incident beam and is said to be *coherent* with it, since there is a definite relationship between the phase of the scattered beam and that of the incident beam which produced it.

Although x-rays are scattered in all directions by an electron, the intensity of the scattered beam depends on the angle of scattering, in a way which was first worked out by J. J. Thomson. He found that the intensity I of the beam scattered by a single electron of charge e and mass m, at a distance r from the electron, is given by

$$I = I_0 \frac{e^4}{r^2 m^2 c^4} \sin^2 \alpha, \qquad (4–1)$$

where I_0 = intensity of the incident beam, c = velocity of light, and α = angle between the scattering direction and the direction of acceleration of the electron. Suppose the incident beam is traveling in the direction Ox (Fig. 4–3) and encounters an electron at O. We wish to know the scattered intensity at P in the xz plane where OP is inclined at a scattering angle of 2θ to the incident beam. An unpolarized incident beam, such as that issuing from an x-ray tube, has its electric vector $\mathbf{E}$ in a random direction in the yz plane. This beam may be resolved into two plane-polarized components, having electric vectors $\mathbf{E}_y$ and $\mathbf{E}_z$ where

$$\mathbf{E}^2 = \mathbf{E}_y{}^2 + \mathbf{E}_z{}^2.$$

On the average, $\mathbf{E}_y$ will be equal to $\mathbf{E}_z$, since the direction of $\mathbf{E}$ is perfectly random. Therefore

$$\mathbf{E}_y{}^2 = \mathbf{E}_z{}^2 = \tfrac{1}{2}\mathbf{E}^2.$$

The intensity of these two components of the incident beam is proportional to the square of their electric vectors, since $\mathbf{E}$ measures the amplitude of the wave and the intensity of a wave is proportional to the square of its amplitude. Therefore

$$I_{0y} = I_{0z} = \tfrac{1}{2}I_0.$$

The y component of the incident beam accelerates the electron in the direction Oy. It therefore gives rise to a scattered beam whose intensity at P is found from Eq. (4–1) to be

$$I_{Py} = I_{0y}\frac{e^4}{r^2 m^2 c^4},$$

since $\alpha = \measuredangle yOP = \pi/2$. Similarly, the intensity of the scattered z component is given by

$$I_{Pz} = I_{0z}\frac{e^4}{r^2 m^2 c^4}\cos^2 2\theta,$$

since $\alpha = \pi/2 - 2\theta$. The total scattered intensity at P is obtained by summing the intensities of these two scattered components:

$$I_P = I_{Py} + I_{Pz}$$

$$= \frac{e^4}{r^2 m^2 c^4}\left(I_{0y} + I_{0z}\cos^2 2\theta\right)$$

$$= \frac{e^4}{r^2 m^2 c^4}\left(\frac{I_0}{2} + \frac{I_0}{2}\cos^2 2\theta\right)$$

$$= I_0\frac{e^4}{r^2 m^2 c^4}\left(\frac{1 + \cos^2 2\theta}{2}\right). \tag{4–2}$$

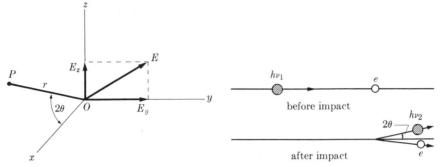

FIG. 4–3. Coherent scattering of x-rays by a single electron.　　　FIG. 4–4. Elastic collision of photon and electron (Compton effect).

This is the Thomson equation for the scattering of an x-ray beam by a single electron. If the values of the constants e, r, m, and c are inserted into this equation, it will be found that the intensity of the scattered beam is only a minute fraction of the intensity of the incident beam. The equation also shows that the scattered intensity decreases as the inverse square of the distance from the scattering electron, as one would expect, and that the scattered beam is stronger in forward or backward directions than in a direction at right angles to the incident beam.

The Thomson equation gives the absolute intensity (in ergs/sq cm/sec) of the scattered beam in terms of the absolute intensity of the incident beam. These absolute intensities are both difficult to measure and difficult to calculate, so it is fortunate that relative values are sufficient for our purposes in practically all diffraction problems. In most cases, all factors in Eq. (4–2) except the last are constant during the experiment and can be omitted. This last factor, $\frac{1}{2}(1 + \cos^2 2\theta)$, is called the *polarization factor;* this is a rather unfortunate term because, as we have just seen, this factor enters the equation simply because the incident beam is unpolarized. The polarization factor is common to all intensity calculations, and we will use it later in our equation for the intensity of a beam diffracted by a crystalline powder.

There is another and quite different way in which an electron can scatter x-rays, and that is manifested in the *Compton effect.* This effect, discovered by A. H. Compton in 1923, occurs whenever x-rays encounter loosely bound or free electrons and can be best understood by considering the incident beam, not as a wave motion, but as a stream of x-ray quanta or photons, each of energy $h\nu_1$. When such a photon strikes a loosely bound electron, the collision is an elastic one like that of two billiard balls (Fig. 4–4). The electron is knocked aside and the photon is deviated through an angle 2θ. Since some of the energy of the incident photon is used in providing kinetic energy for the electron, the energy $h\nu_2$ of the photon after impact is less than its energy $h\nu_1$ before impact. The wavelength λ_2 of the scattered radiation is thus slightly greater than the wavelength λ_1 of the incident beam, the magnitude of the change being given by the equation

$$\Delta\lambda(A) = \lambda_2 - \lambda_1 = 0.0243\ (1 - \cos 2\theta). \qquad (4\text{--}3)$$

The increase in wavelength depends only on the scattering angle, and it varies from zero in the forward direction ($2\theta = 0$) to 0.05A in the extreme backward direction ($2\theta = 180°$).

Radiation so scattered is called Compton modified radiation, and, besides having its wavelength increased, it has the important characteristic that *its phase has no fixed relation to the phase of the incident beam*. For this reason it is also known as incoherent radiation. It cannot take part in diffraction because its phase is only randomly related to that of the incident beam and cannot therefore produce any interference effects. Compton modified scattering cannot be prevented, however, and it has the undesirable effect of darkening the background of diffraction patterns.

(It should be noted that the quantum theory can account for both the coherent and the incoherent scattering, whereas the wave theory is only applicable to the former. In terms of the quantum theory, coherent scattering occurs when an incident photon bounces off an electron which is so tightly bound that the photon receives no momentum from the impact. The scattered photon therefore has the same energy, and hence wavelength, as it had before.)

4–3 Scattering by an atom. When an x-ray beam encounters an atom, each electron in it scatters part of the radiation coherently in accordance with the Thomson equation. One might also expect the nucleus to take part in the coherent scattering, since it also bears a charge and should be capable of oscillating under the influence of the incident beam. However, the nucleus has an extremely large mass relative to that of the electron and cannot be made to oscillate to any appreciable extent; in fact, the Thomson equation shows that the intensity of coherent scattering is inversely proportional to the square of the mass of the scattering particle. The net effect is that coherent scattering by an atom is due only to the electrons contained in that atom.

The following question then arises: is the wave scattered by an atom simply the sum of the waves scattered by its component electrons? More precisely, does an atom of atomic number Z, i.e., an atom containing Z electrons, scatter a wave whose amplitude is Z times the amplitude of the wave scattered by a single electron? The answer is yes, if the scattering is in the forward direction ($2\theta = 0$), because the waves scattered by all the electrons of the atom are then in phase and the amplitudes of all the scattered waves can be added directly.

This is not true for other directions of scattering. The fact that the electrons of an atom are situated at different points in space introduces differences in phase between the waves scattered by different electrons. Consider Fig. 4–5, in which, for simplicity, the electrons are shown as points arranged around the central nucleus. The waves scattered in the forward direction by electrons A and B are exactly in phase on a wave front such as XX', because each wave has traveled the same distance before and after scattering. The other scattered waves shown in the figure, however, have a path difference equal to $(CB - AD)$ and are thus somewhat out of phase along a wave front such as YY', the path difference being less than one wavelength. Partial interference occurs between the waves scattered by A and B, with the result that the net amplitude of the wave scattered in this direction is less than that of the wave scattered by the same electrons in the forward direction.

A quantity f, *the atomic scattering factor*, is used to describe the "efficiency" of scattering of a given atom in a given direction. It is defined as a ratio of amplitudes:

$$f = \frac{\text{amplitude of the wave scattered by an atom}}{\text{amplitude of the wave scattered by one electron}}.$$

From what has been said already, it is clear that $f = Z$ for any atom scattering in the forward direction. As θ increases, however, the waves scattered by individual electrons become more and more out of phase and f decreases. The atomic scattering factor also depends on the wavelength of the incident beam: at a fixed value of θ, f will be smaller the shorter the

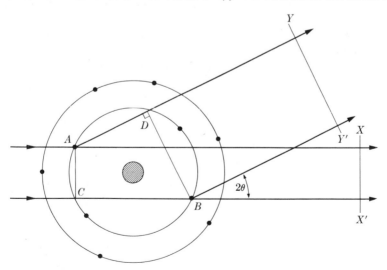

FIG. 4–5. X-ray scattering by an atom.

wavelength, since the path differences will be larger relative to the wavelength, leading to greater interference between the scattered beams. The actual calculation of f involves $\sin \theta$ rather than θ, so that the net effect is that f decreases as the quantity $(\sin \theta)/\lambda$ increases.

Calculated values of f for various atoms and various values of $(\sin \theta)/\lambda$ are tabulated in Appendix 8, and a curve showing the typical variation of f, in this case for copper, is given in Fig. 4–6. Note again that the curve begins at the atomic number of copper, 29, and decreases to very low values for scattering in the backward direction (θ near 90°) or for

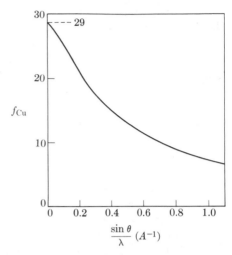

FIG. 4–6. The atomic scattering factor of copper.

very short wavelengths. Since the intensity of a wave is proportional to the square of its amplitude, a curve of scattered intensity from an atom can be obtained simply by squaring the ordinates of a curve such as Fig. 4–6. (The resulting curve closely approximates the observed scattered intensity per atom of a monatomic gas, as shown in Fig. 3–18.)

The scattering just discussed, whose amplitude is expressed in terms of the atomic scattering factor, is coherent, or unmodified, scattering, which is the only kind capable of being diffracted. On the other hand, incoherent, or Compton modified, scattering is occurring at the same time. Since the latter is due to collisions of quanta with loosely bound electrons, its intensity relative to that of the unmodified radiation increases as the proportion of loosely bound electrons increases. The intensity of Compton modified radiation thus increases as the atomic number Z decreases. It is for this reason that it is difficult to obtain good diffraction photographs of organic materials, which contain light elements such as carbon, oxygen, and hydrogen, since the strong Compton modified scattering from these substances darkens the background of the photograph and makes it difficult to see the diffraction lines formed by the unmodified radiation. It is also found that the intensity of the modified radiation increases as the quantity $(\sin \theta)/\lambda$ increases. The intensities of modified scattering and of unmodified scattering therefore vary in opposite ways with Z and with $(\sin \theta)/\lambda$.

To summarize, when a monochromatic beam of x-rays strikes an atom, two scattering processes occur. Tightly bound electrons are set into oscillation and radiate x-rays of the same wavelength as that of the incident

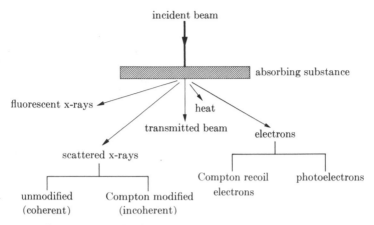

Fɪɢ. 4–7. Effects produced by the passage of x-rays through matter. (After N. F. M. Henry, H. Lipson, and W. A. Wooster, *The Interpretation of X-Ray Diffraction Photographs*, Macmillan, London, 1951.)

beam. More loosely bound electrons scatter part of the incident beam and slightly increase its wavelength in the process, the exact amount of increase depending on the scattering angle. The former is called coherent or unmodified scattering and the latter incoherent or modified; both kinds occur simultaneously and in all directions. If the atom is a part of a large group of atoms arranged in space in a regular periodic fashion as in a crystal, then another phenomenon occurs. The coherently scattered radiation from all the atoms undergoes reinforcement in certain directions and cancellation in other directions, thus producing diffracted beams. Diffraction is, essentially, reinforced coherent scattering.

We are now in a position to summarize, from the preceding sections and from Chap. 1, the chief effects associated with the passage of x-rays through matter. This is done schematically in Fig. 4–7. The incident x-rays are assumed to be of high enough energy, i.e., of short enough wavelength, to cause the emission of photoelectrons and characteristic fluorescent radiation. The Compton recoil electrons shown in the diagram are the loosely bound electrons knocked out of the atom by x-ray quanta, the interaction giving rise to Compton modified radiation.

4–4 Scattering by a unit cell. To arrive at an expression for the intensity of a diffracted beam, we must now restrict ourselves to a consideration of the coherent scattering, not from an isolated atom, but from all the atoms making up the crystal. The mere fact that the atoms are arranged in a periodic fashion in space means that the scattered radiation is now severely limited to certain definite directions and is now referred to as a set of diffracted beams. The directions of these beams are fixed by

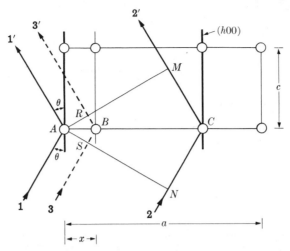

Fig. 4–8.   The effect of atom position on the phase difference between diffracted rays.

the Bragg law, which is, in a sense, a negative law.   If the Bragg law is not satisfied, no diffracted beam can occur; however, the Bragg law may be satisfied for a certain set of atomic planes and yet no diffraction may occur, as in the example given at the beginning of this chapter, because of a particular arrangement of atoms within the unit cell [Fig. 4–2(b)].

Assuming that the Bragg law is satisfied, we wish to find the intensity of the beam diffracted by a crystal as a function of atom position.   Since the crystal is merely a repetition of the fundamental unit cell, it is enough to consider the way in which the arrangement of atoms within a single unit cell affects the diffracted intensity.

Qualitatively, the effect is similar to the scattering from an atom, discussed in the previous section.   There we found that phase differences occur in the waves scattered by the individual electrons, for any direction of scattering except the extreme forward direction.   Similarly, the waves scattered by the individual atoms of a unit cell are not necessarily in phase except in the forward direction, and we must now determine how the phase difference depends on the arrangement of the atoms.

This problem is most simply approached by finding the phase difference between waves scattered by an atom at the origin and another atom whose position is variable in the x direction only.   For convenience, consider an orthogonal unit cell, a section of which is shown in Fig. 4–8.   Take atom A as the origin and let diffraction occur from the $(h00)$ planes shown as heavy lines in the drawing.   This means that the Bragg law is satisfied for this reflection and that $\delta_{2'1'}$, the path difference between ray **2'** and ray **1'**, is given by

$$\delta_{2'1'} = MCN = 2d_{h00} \sin \theta = \lambda.$$

From the definition of Miller indices,

$$d_{h00} = AC = \frac{a}{h}.$$

How is this reflection affected by x-rays scattered in the same direction by atom B, located at a distance x from A? Note that only this direction need be considered since only in this direction is the Bragg law satisfied for the $h00$ reflection. Clearly, the path difference between ray **3'** and ray **1'**, $\delta_{3'1'}$, will be less than λ; by simple proportion it is found to be

$$\delta_{3'1'} = RBS = \frac{AB}{AC}(\lambda) = \frac{x}{a/h}(\lambda).$$

Phase differences may be expressed in angular measure as well as in wavelength: two rays, differing in path length by one whole wavelength, are said to differ in phase by 360°, or 2π radians. If the path difference is δ, then the phase difference ϕ in radians is given by

$$\phi = \frac{\delta}{\lambda}(2\pi).$$

The use of angular measure is convenient because it makes the expression of phase differences independent of wavelength, whereas the use of a path difference to describe a phase difference is meaningless unless the wavelength is specified.

The phase difference, then, between the wave scattered by atom B and that scattered by atom A at the origin is given by

$$\phi_{3'1'} = \frac{\delta_{3'1'}}{\lambda}(2\pi) = \frac{2\pi h x}{a}.$$

If the position of atom B is specified by its fractional coordinate $u = \frac{x}{a}$, then the phase difference becomes

$$\phi_{3'1'} = 2\pi h u.$$

This reasoning may be extended to three dimensions, as in Fig. 4–9, in which atom B has actual coordinates $x\ y\ z$ or fractional coordinates $\frac{x}{a}\frac{y}{b}\frac{z}{c}$ equal to $u\ v\ w$, respectively. We then arrive at the following important relation for the phase difference between the wave scattered by atom B and that scattered by atom A at the origin, for the hkl reflection:

$$\phi = 2\pi(hu + kv + lw). \qquad (4\text{--}4)$$

This relation is general and applicable to a unit cell of any shape.

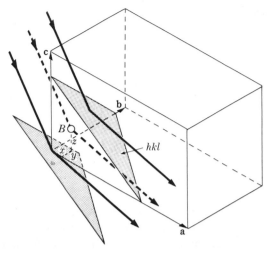

Fig. 4–9.   The three-dimensional analogue of Fig. 4–8.

These two waves may differ, not only in phase, but also in amplitude if atom B and the atom at the origin are of different kinds.   In that case, the amplitudes of these waves are given, relative to the amplitude of the wave scattered by a single electron, by the appropriate values of f, the atomic scattering factor.

We now see that the problem of scattering from a unit cell resolves itself into one of adding waves of different phase and amplitude in order to find the resultant wave.   Waves scattered by all the atoms of the unit cell, including the one at the origin, must be added.   The most convenient way of carrying out this summation is by expressing each wave as a complex exponential function.

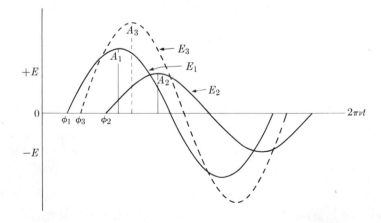

Fig. 4–10.   The addition of sine waves of different phase and amplitude.

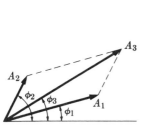

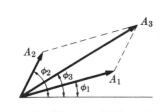

FIG. 4–11. Vector addition of waves.   FIG. 4–12. A wave vector in the complex plane.

The two waves shown as full lines in Fig. 4–10 represent the variations in electric field intensity $\mathbf{E}$ with time t of two rays on any given wave front in a diffracted x-ray beam. Their equations may be written

$$\mathbf{E}_1 = A_1 \sin (2\pi\nu t - \phi_1), \tag{4–5}$$

$$\mathbf{E}_2 = A_2 \sin (2\pi\nu t - \phi_2). \tag{4–6}$$

These waves are of the same frequency ν and therefore of the same wavelength λ, but differ in amplitude A and in phase ϕ. The dotted curve shows their sum $\mathbf{E}_3$, which is also a sine wave, but of different amplitude and phase.

Waves differing in amplitude and phase may also be added by representing them as vectors. In Fig. 4–11, each component wave is represented by a vector whose length is equal to the amplitude of the wave and which is inclined to the x-axis at an angle equal to the phase angle. The amplitude and phase of the resultant wave is then found simply by adding the vectors by the parallelogram law.

This geometrical construction may be avoided by use of the following analytical treatment, in which complex numbers are used to represent the vectors. A complex number is the sum of a real and an imaginary number, such as $(a + bi)$, where a and b are real and $i = \sqrt{-1}$ is imaginary. Such numbers may be plotted in the "complex plane," in which real numbers are plotted as abscissae and imaginary numbers as ordinates. Any point in this plane or the vector drawn from the origin to this point then represents a particular complex number $(a + bi)$.

To find an analytical expression for a vector representing a wave, we draw the wave vector in the complex plane as in Fig. 4–12. Here again the amplitude and phase of the wave is given by A, the length of the vector, and ϕ, the angle between the vector and the axis of real numbers. The analytical expression for the wave is now the complex number $(A \cos \phi + iA \sin \phi)$, since these two terms are the horizontal and vertical components

OM and *ON* of the vector. Note that multiplication of a vector by i rotates it counterclockwise by 90°; thus multiplication by i converts the horizontal vector 2 into the vertical vector $2i$. Multiplication twice by i, that is, by $i^2 = -1$, rotates a vector through 180° or reverses its sense; thus multiplication twice by i converts the horizontal vector 2 into the horizontal vector -2 pointing in the opposite direction.

If we write down the power-series expansions of e^{ix}, $\cos x$, and $\sin x$, we find that

$$e^{ix} = \cos x + i \sin x \qquad (4\text{--}7)$$

or

$$A e^{i\phi} = A \cos \phi + A i \sin \phi. \qquad (4\text{--}8)$$

Thus the wave vector may be expressed analytically by either side of Eq. (4–8). The expression on the left is called a complex exponential function.

Since the intensity of a wave is proportional to the square of its amplitude, we now need an expression for A^2, the square of the absolute value of the wave vector. When a wave is expressed in complex form, this quantity is obtained by multiplying the complex expression for the wave by its complex conjugate, which is obtained simply by replacing i by $-i$. Thus, the complex conjugate of $A e^{i\phi}$ is $A e^{-i\phi}$. We have

$$\left| A e^{i\phi} \right|^2 = A e^{i\phi} A e^{-i\phi} = A^2, \qquad (4\text{--}9)$$

which is the quantity desired. Or, using the other form given by Eq. (4–8), we have

$$A (\cos \phi + i \sin \phi) A (\cos \phi - i \sin \phi) = A^2 (\cos^2 \phi + \sin^2 \phi) = A^2.$$

We return now to the problem of adding the scattered waves from each of the atoms in the unit cell. The amplitude of each wave is given by the appropriate value of f for the scattering atom considered and the value of $(\sin \theta)/\lambda$ involved in the reflection. The phase of each wave is given by Eq. (4–4) in terms of the *hkl* reflection considered and the *uvw* coordinates of the atom. Using our previous relations, we can then express any scattered wave in the complex exponential form

$$A e^{i\phi} = f e^{2\pi i (hu + kv + lw)}. \qquad (4\text{--}10)$$

The resultant wave scattered by all the atoms of the unit cell is called the *structure factor* and is designated by the symbol F. It is obtained by simply adding together all the waves scattered by the individual atoms. If a unit cell contains atoms 1, 2, 3, $\ldots$, N, with fractional coordinates $u_1 v_1 w_1$, $u_2 v_2 w_2$, $u_3 v_3 w_3$, $\ldots$ and atomic scattering factors $f_1, f_2, f_3, \ldots$, then the structure factor for the *hkl* reflection is given by

$$F = f_1 e^{2\pi i (hu_1 + kv_1 + lw_1)} + f_2 e^{2\pi i (hu_2 + kv_2 + lw_2)} + f_3 e^{2\pi i (hu_3 + kv_3 + lw_3)} + \cdots.$$

This equation may be written more compactly as

$$F_{hkl} = \sum_{1}^{N} f_n e^{2\pi i(hu_n + kv_n + lw_n)},$$ (4–11)

the summation extending over all the atoms of the unit cell.

F is, in general, a complex number, and it expresses both the amplitude and phase of the resultant wave. Its absolute value $|F|$ gives the amplitude of the resultant wave in terms of the amplitude of the wave scattered by a single electron. Like the atomic scattering factor f, $|F|$ is defined as a ratio of amplitudes:

$$|F| = \frac{\text{amplitude of the wave scattered by all the atoms of a unit cell}}{\text{amplitude of the wave scattered by one electron}}.$$

The intensity of the beam diffracted by all the atoms of the unit cell in a direction predicted by the Bragg law is proportional simply to $|F|^2$, the square of the amplitude of the resultant beam, and $|F|^2$ is obtained by multiplying the expression given for F in Eq. (4–11) by its complex conjugate. Equation (4–11) is therefore a very important relation in x-ray crystallography, since it permits a calculation of the intensity of any hkl reflection from a knowledge of the atomic positions.

We have found the resultant scattered wave by adding together waves, differing in phase, scattered by individual atoms in the unit cell. Note that the phase difference between rays scattered by any two atoms, such as A and B in Fig. 4–8, is *constant* for every unit cell. There is no question here of these rays becoming increasingly out of phase as we go deeper in the crystal as there was when we considered diffraction at angles not exactly equal to the Bragg angle θ_B. In the direction predicted by the Bragg law, the rays scattered by all the atoms A in the crystal are exactly in phase and so are the rays scattered by all the atoms B, but between these two sets of rays there is a definite phase difference which depends on the relative positions of atoms A and B in the unit cell and which is given by Eq. (4–4).

Although it is more unwieldy, the following trigonometric equation may be used instead of Eq. (4–11):

$$F = \sum_{1}^{N} f_n[\cos 2\pi(hu_n + kv_n + lw_n) + i \sin 2\pi(hu_n + kv_n + lw_n)].$$

One such term must be written down for each atom in the unit cell. In general, the summation will be a complex number of the form

$$F = a + ib,$$

where

$$a = \sum_{1}^{N} f_n \cos 2\pi(hu_n + kv_n + lw_n),$$

$$b = \sum_{1}^{N} f_n \sin 2\pi(hu_n + kv_n + lw_n),$$

$$|F|^2 = (a + ib)(a - ib) = a^2 + b^2.$$

Substitution for a and b gives the final form of the equation:

$$|F|^2 = [f_1 \cos 2\pi(hu_1 + kv_1 + lw_1) + f_2 \cos 2\pi(hu_2 + kv_2 + lw_2) + \cdots]^2$$

$$+ [f_1 \sin 2\pi(hu_1 + kv_1 + lw_1) + f_2 \sin 2\pi(hu_2 + kv_2 + lw_2) + \cdots]^2.$$

Equation (4–11) is much easier to manipulate, compared to this trigonometric form, particularly if the structure is at all complicated, since the exponential form is more compact.

4–5 Some useful relations. In calculating structure factors by complex exponential functions, many particular relations occur often enough to be worthwhile stating here. They may be verified by means of Eq. (4–7).

(a) $$e^{\pi i} = e^{3\pi i} = e^{5\pi i} = -1,$$

(b) $$e^{2\pi i} = e^{4\pi i} = e^{6\pi i} = +1,$$

(c) In general, $e^{n\pi i} = (-1)^n$, where n is any integer,

(d) $$e^{n\pi i} = e^{-n\pi i}, \text{ where } n \text{ is any integer,}$$

(e) $$e^{ix} + e^{-ix} = 2 \cos x.$$

4–6 Structure-factor calculations. Facility in the use of Eq. (4–11) can be gained only by working out some actual examples, and we shall consider a few such problems here and again in Chap. 10.

(a) The simplest case is that of a unit cell containing only one atom at the origin, i.e., having fractional coordinates 0 0 0. Its structure factor is

$$F = fe^{2\pi i(0)} = f$$

and

$$F^2 = f^2.$$

F^2 is thus independent of h, k, and l and is the same for all reflections.

(b) Consider now the base-centered cell discussed at the beginning of this chapter and shown in Fig. 4–1(a). It has two atoms of the same kind per unit cell located at 0 0 0 and $\frac{1}{2} \frac{1}{2} 0$.

$$F = fe^{2\pi i(0)} + fe^{2\pi i(h/2+k/2)}$$

$$= f[1 + e^{\pi i(h+k)}].$$

This expression may be evaluated without multiplication by the complex conjugate, since $(h + k)$ is always integral, and the expression for F is thus real and not complex. If h and k are both even or both odd, i.e., "unmixed," then their sum is always even and $e^{\pi i(h+k)}$ has the value 1. Therefore

$$F = 2f \quad \text{for } h \text{ and } k \text{ unmixed};$$

$$F^2 = 4f^2.$$

On the other hand, if h and k are one even and one odd, i.e., "mixed," then their sum is odd and $e^{\pi i(h+k)}$ has the value -1. Therefore

$$F = 0 \quad \text{for } h \text{ and } k \text{ mixed};$$

$$F^2 = 0.$$

Note that, in either case, the value of the l index has no effect on the structure factor. For example, the reflections 111, 112, 113, and 021, 022, 023 all have the same value of F, namely $2f$. Similarly, the reflections 011, 012, 013, and 101, 102, 103 all have a zero structure factor.

(c) The structure factor of the body-centered cell shown in Fig. 4–1(b) may also be calculated. This cell has two atoms of the same kind located at $0\,0\,0$ and $\frac{1}{2}\,\frac{1}{2}\,\frac{1}{2}$.

$$F = fe^{2\pi i(0)} + fe^{2\pi i(h/2+k/2+l/2)}$$

$$= f[1 + e^{\pi i(h+k+l)}].$$

$$F = 2f \quad \text{when } (h + k + l) \text{ is even};$$

$$F^2 = 4f^2.$$

$$F = 0 \quad \text{when } (h + k + l) \text{ is odd};$$

$$F^2 = 0.$$

We had previously concluded from geometrical considerations that the base-centered cell would produce a 001 reflection but that the body-centered cell would not. This result is in agreement with the structure-factor equations for these two cells. A detailed examination of the geometry of all possible reflections, however, would be a very laborious process compared to the straightforward calculation of the structure factor, a calculation that yields a set of rules governing the value of F^2 for all possible values of plane indices.

(d) A face-centered cubic cell, such as that shown in Fig. 2–14, may now be considered. Assume it to contain four atoms of the same kind, located at $0\,0\,0$, $\frac{1}{2}\,\frac{1}{2}\,0$, $\frac{1}{2}\,0\,\frac{1}{2}$, and $0\,\frac{1}{2}\,\frac{1}{2}$.

$$F = fe^{2\pi i(0)} + fe^{2\pi i(h/2+k/2)} + fe^{2\pi i(h/2+l/2)} + fe^{2\pi i(k/2+l/2)}$$

$$= f[1 + e^{\pi i(h+k)} + e^{\pi i(h+l)} + e^{\pi i(k+l)}].$$

If h, k, and l are unmixed, then all three sums $(h + k)$, $(h + l)$, and $(k + l)$ are even integers, and each term in the above equation has the value 1.

$$F = 4f \qquad \text{for unmixed indices;}$$

$$F^2 = 16f^2.$$

If h, k, and l are mixed, then the sum of the three exponentials is -1, whether two of the indices are odd and one even, or two even and one odd. Suppose for example, that h and l are even and k is odd, e.g., 012. Then $F = f(1 - 1 + 1 - 1) = 0$, and no reflection occurs.

$$F = 0 \quad \text{for mixed indices;}$$

$$F^2 = 0$$

Thus, reflections will occur for such planes as (111), (200), and (220) but not for the planes (100), (210), (112), etc.

The reader may have noticed in the previous examples that some of the information given was not used in the calculations. In (a), for example, the cell was said to contain only one atom, but the shape of the cell was not specified; in (b) and (c), the cells were described as orthorhombic and in (d) as cubic, but this information did not enter into the structure-factor calculations. This illustrates the important point that *the structure factor is independent of the shape and size of the unit cell.* For example, *any* body-centered cell will have missing reflections for those planes which have $(h + k + l)$ equal to an odd number, whether the cell is cubic, tetragonal, or orthorhombic. The rules we have derived in the above examples are therefore of wider applicability than would at first appear and demonstrate the close connection between the Bravais lattice of a substance and its diffraction pattern. They are summarized in Table 4–1. These rules are subject to some qualification, since some cells may contain more atoms than the ones given in examples (a) through (d), and these atoms may be in such positions that reflections normally present are now missing. For example, diamond has a face-centered cubic lattice, but it contains eight

TABLE 4–1

Bravais lattice	Reflections present	Reflections absent
Simple	all	none
Base–centered	h and k unmixed[*]	h and k mixed[*]
Body–centered	$(h + k + l)$ even	$(h + k + l)$ odd
Face–centered	h, k, and l unmixed	h, k, and l mixed

* These relations apply to a cell centered on the C face. If reflections are present only when h and l are unmixed, or when k and l are unmixed, then the cell is centered on the B or A face, respectively.

carbon atoms per unit cell. All the reflections present have unmixed indices, but reflections such as 200, 222, 420, etc., are missing. The fact that the only reflections *present* have unmixed indices proves that the lattice is face-centered, while the extra missing reflections are a clue to the actual atom arrangement in this crystal.

(e) This point may be further illustrated by the structure of NaCl (Fig. 2–18). This crystal has a cubic lattice with 4 Na and 4 Cl atoms per unit cell, located as follows:

$$\text{Na} \quad\quad 0\,0\,0 \quad\quad \tfrac{1}{2}\,\tfrac{1}{2}\,0 \quad\quad \tfrac{1}{2}\,0\,\tfrac{1}{2} \quad\quad 0\,\tfrac{1}{2}\,\tfrac{1}{2}$$

$$\text{Cl} \quad\quad \tfrac{1}{2}\,\tfrac{1}{2}\,\tfrac{1}{2} \quad\quad 0\,0\,\tfrac{1}{2} \quad\quad 0\,\tfrac{1}{2}\,0 \quad\quad \tfrac{1}{2}\,0\,0$$

In this case, the proper atomic scattering factors for each atom must be inserted in the structure-factor equation:

$$F = f_{\text{Na}}e^{2\pi i(0)} + f_{\text{Na}}e^{2\pi i(h/2+k/2)} + f_{\text{Na}}e^{2\pi i(h/2+l/2)} + f_{\text{Na}}e^{2\pi i(k/2+l/2)}$$

$$+ f_{\text{Cl}}e^{2\pi i(h/2+k/2+l/2)} + f_{\text{Cl}}e^{2\pi i(l/2)} + f_{\text{Cl}}e^{2\pi i(k/2)} + f_{\text{Cl}}e^{2\pi i(h/2)},$$

$$F = f_{\text{Na}}[1 + e^{\pi i(h+k)} + e^{\pi i(h+l)} + e^{\pi i(k+l)}]$$

$$+ f_{\text{Cl}}[e^{\pi i(h+k+l)} + e^{\pi il} + e^{\pi ik} + e^{\pi ih}].$$

As discussed in Sec. 2–7, the sodium-atom positions are related by the face-centering translations and so are the chlorine-atom positions. Whenever a lattice contains common translations, the corresponding terms in the structure-factor equation can always be factored out, leading to considerable simplification. In this case we proceed as follows:

$$F = f_{\text{Na}}[1 + e^{\pi i(h+k)} + e^{\pi i(h+l)} + e^{\pi i(k+l)}]$$

$$+ f_{\text{Cl}}e^{\pi i(h+k+l)}[1 + e^{\pi i(-h-k)} + e^{\pi i(-h-l)} + e^{\pi i(-k-l)}].$$

The signs of the exponents in the second bracket may be changed, by relation (d) of Sec. 4–5. Therefore

$$F = [1 + e^{\pi i(h+k)} + e^{\pi i(h+l)} + e^{\pi i(k+l)}][f_{\text{Na}} + f_{\text{Cl}}e^{\pi i(h+k+l)}].$$

Here the terms corresponding to the face-centering translations appear in the first factor. These terms have already appeared in example (d), and they were found to have a total value of zero for mixed indices and 4 for unmixed indices. This shows at once that NaCl has a face-centered lattice and that

$$F = 0 \quad \text{for mixed indices;}$$

$$F^2 = 0.$$

For unmixed indices,

$$F = 4[f_{Na} + f_{Cl}e^{\pi i(h+k+l)}].$$

$$F = 4(f_{Na} + f_{Cl}) \quad \text{if } (h + k + l) \text{ is even;}$$

$$F^2 = 16(f_{Na} + f_{Cl})^2.$$

$$F = 4(f_{Na} - f_{Cl}) \quad \text{if } (h + k + l) \text{ is odd;}$$

$$F^2 = 16(f_{Na} - f_{Cl})^2.$$

In this case, there are more than four atoms per unit cell, but the lattice is still face-centered. The introduction of additional atoms has not eliminated any reflections present in the case of the four-atom cell, but it has decreased some in intensity. For example, the 111 reflection now involves the difference, rather than the sum, of the scattering powers of the two atoms.

(f) One other example of structure factor calculation will be given here. The close-packed hexagonal cell shown in Fig. 2–15 has two atoms of the same kind located at $0\ 0\ 0$ and $\frac{1}{3}\ \frac{2}{3}\ \frac{1}{2}$.

$$F = fe^{2\pi i(0)} + fe^{2\pi i(h/3+2k/3+l/2)}$$

$$= f[1 + e^{2\pi i[(h+2k)/3+l/2]}].$$

For convenience, put $[(h + 2k)/3 + l/2] = g$.

$$F = f(1 + e^{2\pi ig}).$$

Since g may have fractional values, such as $\frac{1}{3}$, $\frac{2}{3}$, $\frac{5}{6}$, etc., this expression is still complex. Multiplication by the complex conjugate, however, will give the square of the absolute value of the resultant wave amplitude F.

$$|F|^2 = f^2(1 + e^{2\pi ig})(1 + e^{-2\pi ig})$$

$$= f^2(2 + e^{2\pi ig} + e^{-2\pi ig}).$$

By relation (e) of Sec. 4–5, this becomes

$$|F|^2 = f^2(2 + 2\cos 2\pi g)$$

$$= f^2[2 + 2(2\cos^2 \pi g - 1)]$$

$$= f^2(4\cos^2 \pi g)$$

$$= 4f^2 \cos^2 \pi \left(\frac{h + 2k}{3} + \frac{l}{2}\right)$$

$$= 0 \quad \text{when } (h + 2k) \text{ is a multiple of 3 and } l \text{ is odd.}$$

It is by these missing reflections, such as $11 \cdot 1$, $11 \cdot 3$, $22 \cdot 1$, $22 \cdot 3$, that a hexagonal structure is recognized as being close-packed. Not all the reflections present have the same structure factor. For example, if $(h + 2k)$ is a multiple of 3 and l is even, then

$$\left(\frac{h + 2k}{3} + \frac{l}{2} \right) = n, \quad \text{where } n \text{ is an integer;}$$

$$\cos \pi n = \pm 1,$$

$$\cos^2 \pi n = 1,$$

$$|F|^2 = 4f^2.$$

When all possible values of h, k, and l are considered, the results may be summarized as follows:

$h + 2k$	l	$|F|^2$
$3n$	odd	0
$3n$	even	$4f^2$
$3n \pm 1$	odd	$3f^2$
$3n \pm 1$	even	f^2

4–7 Application to powder method. Any calculation of the intensity of a diffracted beam must always begin with the structure factor. The remainder of the calculation, however, varies with the particular diffraction method involved. For the Laue method, intensity calculations are so difficult that they are rarely made, since each diffracted beam has a different wavelength and blackens the film by a variable amount, depending on both the intensity and the film sensitivity for that particular wavelength. The factors governing diffracted intensity in the rotating-crystal and powder methods are somewhat similar, in that monochromatic radiation is used in each, but they differ in detail. The remainder of this chapter will be devoted to the powder method, since it is of most general utility in metallurgical work.

There are six factors affecting the relative intensity of the diffraction lines on a powder pattern:

(1) polarization factor,
(2) structure factor,
(3) multiplicity factor,
(4) Lorentz factor,
(5) absorption factor,
(6) temperature factor.

The first two of these have already been described, and the others will be discussed in the following sections.

4–8 Multiplicity factor. Consider the 100 reflection from a cubic lattice. In the powder specimen, some of the crystals will be so oriented that reflection can occur from their (100) planes. Other crystals of different orientation may be in such a position that reflection can occur from their (010) or (001) planes. Since all these planes have the same spacing, the beams diffracted by them all form part of the same cone. Now consider the 111 reflection. There are four sets of planes of the form {111} which have the same spacing but different orientation, namely, (111), (11$\bar{1}$), (1$\bar{1}\bar{1}$), and (1$\bar{1}$1), whereas there are only three sets of the form {100}. Therefore, the probability that {111} planes will be correctly oriented for reflection is $\frac{4}{3}$ the probability that {100} planes will be correctly oriented. It follows that the intensity of the 111 reflection will be $\frac{4}{3}$ that of the 100 reflection, other things being equal.

This relative proportion of planes contributing to the same reflection enters the intensity equation as the quantity p, the *multiplicity factor*, which may be defined as the number of different planes in a form having the same spacing. Parallel planes with different Miller indices, such as (100) and ($\bar{1}$00), are counted separately as different planes, yielding numbers which are double those given in the preceding paragraph. Thus the multiplicity factor for the {100} planes of a cubic crystal is 6 and for the {111} planes 8.

The value of p depends on the crystal system: in a tegragonal crystal, the (100) and (001) planes do not have the same spacing, so that the value of p for {100} planes is reduced to 4 and the value for {001} planes to 2. Values of the multiplicity factor as a function of hkl and crystal system are given in Appendix 9.

4–9 Lorentz factor. We must now consider certain trigonometrical factors which influence the intensity of the reflected beam. Suppose there is incident on a crystal [Fig. 4–13(a)] a narrow beam of parallel monochromatic rays, and let the crystal be rotated at a uniform angular velocity about an axis through O and normal to the drawing, so that a particular set of reflecting planes, assumed for convenience to be parallel to the crystal surface, passes through the angle θ_B, at which the Bragg law is exactly satisfied. As mentioned in Sec. 3–7, the intensity of reflection is greatest at the exact Bragg angle but still appreciable at angles deviating slightly from the Bragg angle, so that a curve of intensity *vs.* 2θ is of the form shown in Fig. 4–13(b). If all the diffracted beams sent out by the crystal as it rotates through the Bragg angle are received on a photographic film or in a counter, the total energy of the diffracted beam can be measured. This energy is called the *integrated intensity* of the reflection and is given by the area under the curve of Fig. 4–13(b). The integrated intensity is of much more interest than the maximum intensity, since the former is

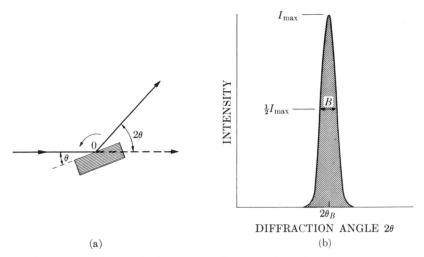

(a)   (b)

FIG. 4–13. Diffraction by a crystal rotated through the Bragg angle.

characteristic of the specimen while the latter is influenced by slight adjust-ments of the experimental apparatus. Moreover, in the visual comparison of the intensities of diffraction lines, it is the integrated intensity of the line rather than the maximum intensity which the eye evaluates.

The integrated intensity of a reflection depends on the particular value of θ_B involved, even though all other variables are held constant. We can find this dependence by considering, separately, two aspects of the diffraction curve: the maximum intensity and the breadth. When the reflecting planes make an angle θ_B with the incident beam, the Bragg law is exactly satisfied and the intensity diffracted in the direction $2\theta_B$ is a maximum. But some energy is still diffracted in this direction when the angle of incidence differs slightly from θ_B, and the total energy diffracted in the direction $2\theta_B$ as the crystal is rotated through the Bragg angle is given by the value of I_{max} of the curve of Fig. 4–13(b). The value of I_{max} therefore depends on the angular range of crystal rotation over which the energy diffracted in the direction $2\theta_B$ is appreciable. In Fig. 4–14(a), the dashed lines show the position of the crystal after rotation through a small angle

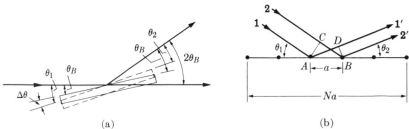

(a)   (b)

FIG. 4–14. Scattering in a fixed direction during crystal rotation.

$\Delta\theta$ from the Bragg position. The incident beam and the diffracted beam under consideration now make unequal angles with the reflecting planes, the former making an angle $\theta_1 = \theta_B + \Delta\theta$ and the latter an angle $\theta_2 = \theta_B - \Delta\theta$. The situation on an atomic scale is shown in Fig. 4–14(b). Here we need only consider a single plane of atoms, since the rays scattered by all other planes are in phase with the corresponding rays scattered by the first plane. Let a equal the atom spacing in the plane and Na the total length* of the plane. The difference in path length for rays **1'** and **2'** scattered by adjacent atoms is given by

$$\delta_{1'2'} = AD - CB$$

$$= a \cos \theta_2 - a \cos \theta_1$$

$$= a[\cos (\theta_B - \Delta\theta) - \cos (\theta_B + \Delta\theta)].$$

By expanding the cosine terms and setting $\sin \Delta\theta$ equal to $\Delta\theta$, since the latter is small, we find:

$$\delta_{1'2'} = 2a\Delta\theta \sin \theta_B,$$

and the path difference between the rays scattered by atoms at either end of the plane is simply N times this quantity. When the rays scattered by the two end atoms are one wavelength out of phase, the diffracted intensity will be zero. (The argument here is exactly analogous to that used in Sec. 3–7.) The condition for zero diffracted intensity is therefore

$$2Na\Delta\theta \sin \theta_B = \lambda,$$

or

$$\Delta\theta = \frac{\lambda}{2Na \sin \theta_B}.$$

This equation gives the maximum angular range of crystal rotation over which appreciable energy will be diffracted in the direction $2\theta_B$. Since I_{max} depends on this range, we can conclude that I_{max} is proportional to $1/\sin \theta_B$. Other things being equal, I_{max} is therefore large at low scattering angles and small in the back-reflection region.

The breadth of the diffraction curve varies in the opposite way, being larger at large values of $2\theta_B$, as was shown in Sec. 3–7, where the half-maximum breadth B was found to be proportional to $1/\cos \theta_B$. The integrated intensity of the reflection is given by the area under the diffraction curve and is therefore proportional to the product $I_{max}B$, which is in turn proportional to $(1/\sin \theta_B)(1/\cos \theta_B)$ or to $1/\sin 2\theta_B$. Thus, as a crystal is rotated through the Bragg angle, the integrated intensity of a reflection, which is the quantity of most experimental interest, turns out to be greater

---

* If the crystal is larger than the incident beam, then Na is the irradiated length of the plane; if it is smaller, Na is the actual length of the plane.

for large and small values of $2\theta_B$ than for intermediate values, other things being equal.

The preceding remarks apply just as well to the powder method as they do to the case of a rotating crystal, since the range of orientations available among the powder particles, some satisfying the Bragg law exactly, some not so exactly, are the equivalent of single-crystal rotation.

However, in the powder method, a second geometrical factor arises when we consider that the integrated intensity of a reflection at any particular Bragg angle depends on the number of particles oriented at or near that angle. This number is not constant even though the particles are oriented completely at random. In Fig. 4–15 a reference sphere of radius r is drawn around the powder specimen located at O. For the particular hkl reflection shown, ON is the normal to this set of planes in one particle of the powder. Suppose that the range of angles near the Bragg angle over which reflection is appreciable is $\Delta\theta$. Then, for this particular reflection, only those particles will be in a reflecting position which have the ends of their plane normals lying in a band of width $r\Delta\theta$ on the surface of the sphere. Since the particles are assumed to be oriented at random, the ends of their plane normals will be uniformly distributed over the surface of the sphere; the fraction favorably oriented for a reflection will be given by the ratio of the area of the strip to that of the whole sphere. If ΔN is the number of such particles and N the total number, then

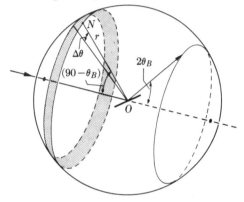

FIG. 4–15. The distribution of plane normals for a particular cone of reflected rays.

$$\frac{\Delta N}{N} = \frac{r\Delta\theta \cdot 2\pi r \sin\,(90° - \theta_B)}{4\pi r^2} = \frac{\Delta\theta \cos \theta_B}{2}.$$

The number of particles favorably oriented for reflection is thus proportional to $\cos \theta_B$ and is quite small for reflections in the backward direction.

In assessing relative intensities, we do not compare the total diffracted energy in one cone of rays with that in another but rather the integrated intensity per unit length of one diffraction line with that of another. For example, in the most common arrangement of specimen and film, the Debye-Scherrer method, shown in Fig. 4–16, the film obviously receives a greater proportion of a diffraction cone when the reflection is in the forward or backward direction than it does near $2\theta = 90°$. Inclusion of this effect

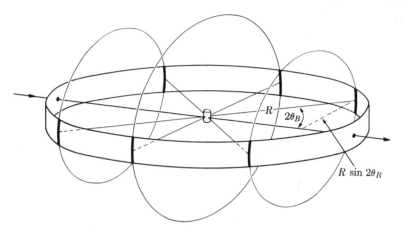

FIG. 4–16.   Intersection of cones of diffracted rays with Debye-Scherrer film.

thus leads to a third geometrical factor affecting the intensity of a reflection.   The length of any diffraction line being $2\pi R \sin 2\theta_B$, where R is the radius of the camera, the relative intensity per unit length of line is proportional to $1/\sin 2\theta_B$.

In intensity calculations, the three factors just discussed are combined into one and called the Lorentz factor.   Dropping the subscript on the Bragg angle, we have:

$$\text{Lorentz factor} = \left(\frac{1}{\sin 2\theta}\right)\left(\cos \theta\right)\left(\frac{1}{\sin 2\theta}\right) = \frac{\cos \theta}{\sin^2 2\theta} = \frac{1}{4 \sin^2 \theta \cos \theta}.$$

This in turn is combined with the polarization factor $\frac{1}{2}(1 + \cos^2 2\theta)$ of Sec. 4–2 to give the combined Lorentz-polarization factor which, with a constant factor of $\frac{1}{8}$ omitted, is given by

Lorentz-polarization factor $=$

$$\frac{1 + \cos^2 2\theta}{\sin^2 \theta \cos \theta}.$$

Values of this factor are given in Appendix 10 and plotted in Fig. 4–17 as a function of θ.   The over-all effect of these geometrical factors is to decrease the intensity of reflections at intermediate angles compared to those in forward or backward directions.

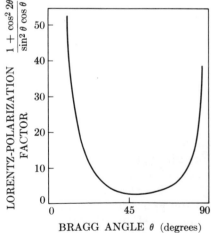

FIG. 4–17.   Lorentz-polarization factor.

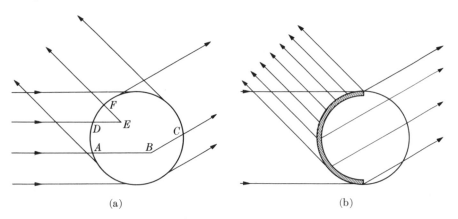

Fig. 4–18.   Absorption in Debye-Scherrer specimens: (a) general case, (b) highly absorbing specimen.

4–10 Absorption factor.   Still another factor affecting the intensities of the diffracted rays must be considered, and that is the absorption which takes place in the specimen itself.   The specimen in the Debye-Scherrer method has the form of a very thin cylinder of powder placed on the camera axis, and Fig. 4–18(a) shows the cross section of such a specimen.   For the low-angle reflection shown, absorption of a particular ray in the incident beam occurs along a path such as AB; at B a small fraction of the incident energy is diffracted by a powder particle, and absorption of this diffracted beam occurs along the path BC.   Similarly, for a high-angle reflection, absorption of both the incident and diffracted beams occurs along a path such as $(DE + EF)$.   The net result is that the diffracted beam is of lower intensity than one would expect for a specimen of no absorption.

A calculation of this effect shows that the relative absorption increases as θ decreases, for any given cylindrical specimen.   That this must be so can be seen from Fig. 4–18(b) which applies to a specimen (for example, tungsten) of very high absorption.   The incident beam is very rapidly absorbed, and most of the diffracted beams originate in the thin surface layer on the left side of the specimen; backward-reflected beams then undergo very little absorption, but forward-reflected beams have to pass through the whole specimen and are greatly absorbed.   Actually, the forward-reflected beams in this case come almost entirely from the top and bottom edges of the specimen.*   This difference in absorption between

---

* The powder patterns reproduced in Fig. 3–13 show this effect.   The lowest-angle line in each pattern is split in two, because the beam diffracted through the center of the specimen is so highly absorbed.   It is important to keep the possibility of this phenomenon in mind when examining Debye-Scherrer photographs, or split low-angle lines may be incorrectly interpreted as separate diffraction lines from two different sets of planes.

high-θ and low-θ reflections decreases as the linear absorption coefficient of the specimen decreases, but the absorption is always greater for the low-θ reflections. (These remarks apply only to the cylindrical specimen used in the Debye-Scherrer method. The absorption factor has an entirely different form for the flat-plate specimen used in a diffractometer, as will be shown in Sec. 7–4.)

Exact calculation of the absorption factor for a cylindrical specimen is often difficult, so it is fortunate that this effect can usually be neglected in the calculation of diffracted intensities, when the Debye-Scherrer method is used. Justification of this omission will be found in the next section.

4–11 Temperature factor. So far we have considered a crystal as a collection of atoms located at fixed points in the lattice. Actually, the atoms undergo thermal vibration about their mean positions even at the absolute zero of temperature, and the amplitude of this vibration increases as the temperature increases. In aluminum at room temperature, the average displacement of an atom from its mean position is about 0.17A, which is by no means negligible, being about 6 percent of the distance of closest approach of the mean atom positions in this crystal.

Thermal agitation decreases the intensity of a diffracted beam because it has the effect of smearing out the lattice planes; atoms can be regarded as lying no longer on mathematical planes but rather in platelike regions of ill-defined thickness. Thus the reinforcement of waves scattered at the Bragg angle by various parallel planes, the reinforcement which is called a diffracted beam, is not as perfect as it is for a crystal with fixed atoms. This reinforcement requires that the path difference, which is a function of the plane spacing d, between waves scattered by adjacent planes be an integral number of wavelengths. Now the thickness of the platelike "planes" in which the vibrating atoms lie is, on the average, $2u$, where u is the average displacement of an atom from its mean position. Under these conditions reinforcement is no longer perfect, and it becomes more imperfect as the ratio u/d increases, i.e., as the temperature increases, since that increases u, or as θ increases, since high-θ reflections involve planes of low d value. Thus the intensity of a diffracted beam decreases as the temperature is raised, and, for a constant temperature, thermal vibration causes a greater decrease in the reflected intensity at high angles than at low angles.

The temperature effect and the previously discussed absorption effect in cylindrical specimens therefore depend on angle in opposite ways and, to a first approximation, cancel each other. In back reflection, for example, the intensity of a diffracted beam is decreased very little by absorption but very greatly by thermal agitation, while in the forward direction the reverse is true. The two effects do not exactly cancel one other at all angles; however, if the comparison of line intensities is restricted to lines not differing too greatly in θ values, the absorption and temperature effects can be safely ignored. This is a fortunate circumstance, since both of these effects are rather difficult to calculate exactly.

It should be noted here that thermal vibration of the atoms of a crystal does not cause any broadening of the diffraction lines; they remain sharp right up to the melting point, but their maximum intensity gradually decreases. It is also worth noting that the mean amplitude of atomic vibration is not a function of the temperature alone but depends also on the elastic constants of the crystal. At any given temperature, the less "stiff" the crystal, the greater the vibration amplitude u. This means that u is much greater at any one temperature for a soft, low-melting-point metal like lead than it is for, say, tungsten. Substances with low melting points have quite large values of u even at room temperature and therefore yield rather poor back-reflection photographs.

The thermal vibration of atoms has another effect on diffraction patterns. Besides decreasing the intensity of diffraction lines, it causes some general coherent scattering in all directions. This is called *temperature-diffuse scattering;* it contributes only to the general background of the pattern and its intensity gradually increases with 2θ. Contrast between lines and background naturally suffers, so this effect is a very undesirable one, leading in extreme cases to diffraction lines in the back-reflection region scarcely distinguishable from the background.

In the phenomenon of temperature-diffuse scattering we have another example, beyond those alluded to in Sec. 3–7, of scattering at non-Bragg angles. Here again it is not surprising that such scattering should occur, since the displacement of atoms from their mean positions constitutes a kind of crystal imperfection and leads to a partial breakdown of the conditions necessary for perfect destructive interference between rays scattered at non-Bragg angles.

The effect of thermal vibration also illustrates what has been called "the approximate law of conservation of diffracted energy." This law states that the total energy diffracted by a particular specimen under particular experimental conditions is roughly constant. Therefore, anything done to alter the physical condition of the specimen does not alter the total amount of diffracted energy but only its distribution in space. This "law" is not at all rigorous, but it does prove helpful in considering many diffraction phenomena. For example, at low temperatures there is very little background scattering due to thermal agitation and the diffraction lines are relatively intense; if the specimen is now heated to a high temperature, the lines will become quite weak and the energy which is lost from the lines will appear in a spread-out form as temperature-diffuse scattering.

4–12 Intensities of powder pattern lines. We are now in a position to gather together the factors discussed in preceding sections into an equation for the relative intensity of powder pattern lines:

$$I = |F|^2 p \left(\frac{1 + \cos^2 2\theta}{\sin^2 \theta \cos \theta} \right), \tag{4–12}$$

where I = relative integrated intensity (arbitrary units), F = structure factor, p = multiplicity factor, and θ = Bragg angle. In arriving at this equation, we have omitted factors which are constant for all lines of the pattern. For example, all that is retained of the Thomson equation (Eq. 4–2) is the polarization factor $(1 + \cos^2 2\theta)$, with constant factors, such as the intensity of the incident beam and the charge and mass of the electron, omitted. The intensity of a diffraction line is also directly proportional to the irradiated volume of the specimen and inversely proportional to the camera radius, but these factors are again constant for all diffraction lines and may be neglected. Omission of the temperature and absorption factors means that Eq. (4–12) is valid only for the Debye-Scherrer method and then only for lines fairly close together on the pattern; this latter restriction is not as serious as it may sound. Equation (4–12) is also restricted to the Debye-Scherrer method because of the particular way in which the Lorentz factor was determined; other methods, such as those involving focusing cameras, will require a modification of the Lorentz factor given here. In addition, the individual crystals making up the powder specimen must have completely random orientations if Eq. (4–12) is to apply. Finally, it should be remembered that this equation gives the relative *integrated* intensity, i.e., the relative area under the curve of intensity *vs.* 2θ.

It should be noted that "integrated intensity" is not really *intensity*, since intensity is expressed in terms of energy crossing unit area per unit of time. A beam diffracted by a powder specimen carries a certain amount of energy per unit time and one could quite properly refer to the total *power* of the diffracted beam. If this beam is then incident on a measuring device, such as photographic film, for a certain length of time and if a curve of diffracted intensity *vs.* 2θ is constructed from the measurements, then the area under this curve gives the total *energy* in the diffracted beam. This is the quantity commonly referred to as integrated intensity. A more descriptive term would be "total diffracted energy," but the term "integrated intensity" has been too long entrenched in the vocabulary of x-ray diffraction to be changed now.

4–13 Examples of intensity calculations. The use of Eq. (4–12) will be illustrated by the calculation of the position and relative intensities of the diffraction lines on a powder pattern of copper, made with Cu $K\alpha$ radiation. The calculations are most readily carried out in tabular form, as in Table 4–2.

TABLE 4–2

1	2	3	4	5	6	7	8
Line	hkl	$h^2 + k^2 + l^2$	$\sin^2\theta$	$\sin\theta$	θ	$\dfrac{\sin\theta}{\lambda}$ (A^{-1})	f_{Cu}
1	111	3	0.1365	0.369	21.7°	0.240	20.0
2	200	4	0.1820	0.426	25.2	0.277	18.7
3	220	8	0.364	0.602	37.0	0.391	15.6
4	311	11	0.500	0.706	44.9	0.459	14.0
5	222	12	0.546	0.738	47.6	0.479	13.7
6	400	16	0.728	0.851	58.3	0.553	12.4
7	331	19	0.865	0.929	68.3	0.604	11.7
8	420	20	0.910	0.951	72.0	0.618	11.4

1	9	10	11	12	13	14
Line	F^2	p	$\dfrac{1 + \cos^2 2\theta}{\sin^2\theta\cos\theta}$	Relative integrated intensity		
				Calc.	Calc.	Obs.
1	6400	8	12.10	6.20×10^5	10.0	s
2	5600	6	8.50	2.86	4.6	m
3	3890	12	3.75	1.75	2.8	m
4	3140	24	2.87	2.16	3.5	s
5	3000	8	2.75	0.66	1.1	w
6	2460	6	3.18	0.47	0.8	w
7	2190	24	4.75	2.50	4.0	vs
8	2080	24	5.92	2.96	4.8	vs

Remarks:

Column 2: Since copper is face-centered cubic, F is equal to $4f_{Cu}$ for lines of unmixed indices and zero for lines of mixed indices. The reflecting plane indices, all unmixed, are written down in this column in order of increasing values of $(h^2 + k^2 + l^2)$, from Appendix 6.

Column 4: For a cubic crystal, values of $\sin^2\theta$ are given by Eq. (3–10):

$$\sin^2\theta = \frac{\lambda^2}{4a^2}(h^2 + k^2 + l^2).$$

In this case, $\lambda = 1.542A$ (Cu $K\alpha$) and $a = 3.615A$ (lattice parameter of copper). Therefore, multiplication of the integers in column 3 by $\lambda^2/4a^2 = 0.0455$ gives the values of $\sin^2\theta$ listed in column 4. In this and similar calculations, slide-rule accuracy is ample.

Column 6: Needed to determine the Lorentz-polarization factor and $(\sin\theta)/\lambda$.

Column 7: Obtained from Appendix 7. Needed to determine f_{Cu}.

Column 8: Read from the curve of Fig. 4–6.

Column 9: Obtained from the relation $F^2 = 16f_{Cu}^2$.

Column 10: Obtained from Appendix 9.

Column 11: Obtained from Appendix 10.

Column 12: These values are the product of the values in columns 9, 10, and 11.

Column 13: Values from column 12 recalculated to give the first line an arbitrary intensity of 10.

Column 14: These entries give the observed intensities, visually estimated according to the following simple scale, from the pattern shown in Fig. 3–13(a) (vs = very strong, s = strong, m = medium, w = weak).

The agreement obtained here between observed and calculated intensities is satisfactory. For example, lines 1 and 2 are observed to be of strong and medium intensity, their respective calculated intensities being 10 and 4.6. Similar agreement can be found by comparing the intensities of any pair of neighboring lines in the pattern. Note, however, that the comparison must be made between lines which are not too far apart: for example, the calculated intensity of line 2 is greater than that of line 4, whereas line 4 is observed to be stronger than line 2. Similarly, the strongest lines on the pattern are lines 7 and 8, while calculations show line 1 to be strongest. Errors of this kind arise from the omission of the absorption and temperature factors from the calculation.

A more complicated structure may now be considered, namely that of the zinc-blende form of ZnS, shown in Fig. 2–19(b). This form of ZnS is cubic and has a lattice parameter of 5.41A. We will calculate the relative intensities of the first six lines on a pattern made with Cu $K\alpha$ radiation.

As always, the first step is to work out the structure factor. ZnS has four zinc and four sulfur atoms per unit cell, located in the following positions:

$$\text{Zn:} \tfrac{1}{4} \tfrac{1}{4} \tfrac{1}{4} + \text{face-centering translations,}$$

$$\text{S:} 0\,0\,0 + \text{face-centering translations.}$$

Since the structure is face-centered, we know that the structure factor will be zero for planes of mixed indices. We also know, from example (*e*) of Sec. 4–6, that the terms in the structure-factor equation corresponding to the face-centering translations can be factored out and the equation for unmixed indices written down at once:

$$F = 4[f_S + f_{Zn}e^{(\pi i/2)(h+k+l)}].$$

$|F|^2$ is obtained by multiplication of the above by its complex conjugate:

$$|F|^2 = 16[f_S + f_{Zn}e^{(\pi i/2)(h+k+l)}][f_S + f_{Zn}e^{-(\pi i/2)(h+k+l)}].$$

This equation reduces to the following form:

$$|F|^2 = 16\left[f_S^2 + f_{Zn}^2 + 2f_S f_{Zn} \cos\frac{\pi}{2}(h+k+l)\right].$$

Further simplification is possible for various special cases:

$$|F|^2 = 16(f_S^2 + f_{Zn}^2) \quad \text{when } (h + k + l) \text{ is odd;} \tag{4–13}$$

$$|F|^2 = 16(f_S - f_{Zn})^2 \quad \text{when } (h + k + l) \text{ is an odd multiple of 2;} \tag{4–14}$$

$$|F|^2 = 16(f_S + f_{Zn})^2 \quad \text{when } (h + k + l) \text{ is an even multiple of 2.} \tag{4–15}$$

The intensity calculations are carried out in Table 4–3, with some columns omitted for the sake of brevity.

TABLE 4–3

1	2	3	4	5	6
Line	hkl	θ	$\dfrac{\sin\theta}{\lambda}$ (A^{-1})	f_S	f_{Zn}
1	111	14.3°	0.161	11.5	24.2
2	200	16.6	0.185	11.0	23.2
3	220	23.8	0.262	9.5	20.0
4	311	28.2	0.307	8.9	18.5
5	222	29.6	0.321	8.6	18.0
6	400	34.8	0.370	8.1	16.7

1	7	8	9	10	11
Line	$|F|^2$	p	$\dfrac{1 + \cos^2 2\theta}{\sin^2\theta \cos\theta}$	Relative intensity Calc.	Obs.
1	11490	8	30.1	10.0	vs
2	2380	6	21.9	1.1	w
3	13940	12	9.72	5.9	vs
4	6750	24	6.65	3.9	vs
5	1410	8	6.00	0.2	vw
6	9850	6	4.24	0.9	w

Remarks:

Columns 5 and 6: These values are read from scattering-factor curves plotted from the data of Appendix 8.

Column 7: $|F|^2$ is obtained by the use of Eq. (4–13), (4–14), or (4–15), depending on the particular values of hkl involved. Thus, Eq. (4–13) is used for the 111 reflection and Eq. (4–15) for the 220 reflection.

Columns 10 and 11: The agreement obtained here between calculated and observed intensities is again satisfactory. In this case, the agreement is good when any pair of lines is compared, because of the limited range of θ values involved.

One further remark on intensity calculations is necessary. In the powder method, two sets of planes with different Miller indices can reflect to the same point on the film: for example, the planes (411) and (330) in the cubic system, since they have the same value of $(h^2 + k^2 + l^2)$ and hence the same spacing, or the planes (501) and (431) of the tetragonal system, since they have the same values of $(h^2 + k^2)$ and l^2. In such a case, the intensity of each reflection must be calculated separately, since in general the two will have different multiplicity and structure factors, and then added to find the total intensity of the line.

4-14 Measurement of x-ray intensity. In the examples just given, the observed intensity was estimated simply by visual comparison of one line with another. Although this simple procedure is satisfactory in a surprisingly large number of cases, there are problems in which a more precise measurement of diffracted intensity is necessary. Two methods are in general use today for making such measurements, one dependent on the photographic effect of x-rays and the other on the ability of x-rays to ionize gases and cause fluorescence of light in crystals. These methods have already been mentioned briefly in Sec. 1-8 and will be described more fully in Chaps. 6 and 7, respectively.

PROBLEMS

4-1. By adding Eqs. (4-5) and (4-6) and simplifying the sum, show that $\mathbf{E_3}$, the resultant of these two sine waves, is also a sine wave, of amplitude

$$A_3 = [A_1{}^2 + A_2{}^2 + 2A_1A_2 \cos (\phi_1 - \phi_2)]^{\frac{1}{2}}$$

and of phase

$$\phi_3 = \tan^{-1} \frac{A_1 \sin \phi_1 + A_2 \sin \phi_2}{A_1 \cos \phi_1 + A_2 \cos \phi_2}.$$

4-2. Obtain the same result by solving the vector diagram of Fig. 4-11 for the right-angle triangle of which A_3 is the hypotenuse.

4-3. Derive simplified expressions for F^2 for diamond, including the rules governing observed reflections. This crystal is cubic and contains 8 carbon atoms per unit cell, located in the following positions:

$$0\,0\,0 \qquad \tfrac{1}{2}\,\tfrac{1}{2}\,0 \qquad \tfrac{1}{2}\,0\,\tfrac{1}{2} \qquad 0\,\tfrac{1}{2}\,\tfrac{1}{2}$$
$$\tfrac{1}{4}\,\tfrac{1}{4}\,\tfrac{1}{4} \qquad \tfrac{3}{4}\,\tfrac{3}{4}\,\tfrac{1}{4} \qquad \tfrac{3}{4}\,\tfrac{1}{4}\,\tfrac{3}{4} \qquad \tfrac{1}{4}\,\tfrac{3}{4}\,\tfrac{3}{4}$$

4-4. A certain tetragonal crystal has four atoms of the same kind per unit cell, located at $0\,\tfrac{1}{2}\,\tfrac{1}{4}, \tfrac{1}{2}\,0\,\tfrac{1}{4}, \tfrac{1}{2}\,0\,\tfrac{3}{4}, 0\,\tfrac{1}{2}\,\tfrac{3}{4}$.

(a) Derive simplified expressions for F^2.
(b) What is the Bravais lattice of this crystal?
(c) What are the values of F^2 for the 100, 002, 111, and 011 reflections?

4-5. Derive simplified expressions for F^2 for the wurtzite form of ZnS, including the rules governing observed reflections. This crystal is hexagonal and contains 2 ZnS per unit cell, located in the following positions:

$$\text{Zn: } 0\,0\,0,\ \tfrac{1}{3}\,\tfrac{2}{3}\,\tfrac{1}{2},$$
$$\text{S: } 0\,0\,\tfrac{3}{8},\ \tfrac{1}{3}\,\tfrac{2}{3}\,\tfrac{7}{8}.$$

Note that these positions involve a common translation, which may be factored out of the structure-factor equation.

4–6. In Sec. 4–9, in the part devoted to scattering when the incident and scattered beams make unequal angles with the reflecting planes, it is stated that "rays scattered by all other planes are in phase with the corresponding rays scattered by the first plane." Prove this.

4–7. Calculate the position (in terms of θ) and the integrated intensity (in relative units) of the first five lines on the Debye pattern of silver made with Cu $K\alpha$ radiation. Ignore the temperature and absorption factors.

4–8. A Debye-Scherrer pattern of tungsten (BCC) is made with Cu $K\alpha$ radiation. The first four lines on this pattern were observed to have the following θ values:

Line	θ
1	20.3°
2	29.2
3	36.7
4	43.6

Index these lines (i.e., determine the Miller indices of each reflection by the use of Eq. (3–10) and Appendix 6) and calculate their relative integrated intensities.

4–9. A Debye-Scherrer pattern is made of gray tin, which has the same structure as diamond, with Cu $K\alpha$ radiation. What are the indices of the first two lines on the pattern, and what is the ratio of the integrated intensity of the first to that of the second?

4–10. A Debye-Scherrer pattern is made of the intermediate phase InSb with Cu $K\alpha$ radiation. This phase has the zinc-blende structure and a lattice parameter of 6.46A. What are the indices of the first two lines on the pattern, and what is the ratio of the integrated intensity of the first to the second?

4–11. Calculate the relative integrated intensities of the first six lines of the Debye-Scherrer pattern of zinc, made with Cu $K\alpha$ radiation. The indices and observed θ values of these lines are:

Line	hkl	θ
1	00·2	18.8°
2	10·0	20.2
3	10·1	22.3
4	10·2	27.9
5	11·0, 10·3	36.0
6	00·4	39.4

(Line 5 is made up of two unresolved lines from planes of very nearly the same spacing.) Compare your results with the intensities observed in the pattern shown in Fig. 3–13(c).

CHAPTER 5

LAUE PHOTOGRAPHS

5–1 Introduction. The experimental methods used in obtaining diffraction patterns will be described in this chapter and the two following ones. Here we are concerned with the Laue method only from the experimental viewpoint; its main applications will be dealt with in Chap. 8.

Laue photographs are the easiest kind of diffraction pattern to make and require only the simplest kind of apparatus. White radiation is necessary, and the best source is a tube with a heavy-metal target, such as tungsten, since the intensity of the continuous spectrum is proportional to the atomic number of the target metal. Good patterns can also be obtained with radiation from other metals, such as molybdenum or copper. Ordinarily, the presence of strong characteristic components, such as W $L\alpha_1$, Cu $K\alpha$, Mo $K\alpha$, etc., in the radiation used, does not complicate the diffraction pattern in any way or introduce difficulties in its interpretation. Such a component will only be reflected if a set of planes in the crystal happens to be oriented in just such a way that the Bragg law is satisfied for that component, and then the only effect will be the formation of a Laue spot of exceptionally high intensity.

The specimen used in the Laue method is a single crystal. This may mean an isolated single crystal or one particular crystal grain, not too small, in a polycrystalline aggregate. The only restriction on the size of a crystal in a polycrystalline mass is that it must be no smaller than the incident x-ray beam, if the pattern obtained is to correspond to that crystal alone.

Laue spots are often formed by overlapping reflections of different orders. For example, the 100, 200, 300, . . . reflections are all superimposed since the corresponding planes, (100), (200), (300), . . . are all parallel. The first-order reflection is made up of radiation of wavelength λ, the second-order of $\lambda/2$, the third-order of $\lambda/3$, etc., down to λ_{SWL}, the short-wavelength limit of the continuous spectrum.

The position of any Laue spot is unaltered by a change in plane spacing, since the only effect of such a change is to alter the wavelength of the diffracted beam. It follows that two crystals of the same orientation and crystal structure, but of different lattice parameter, will produce identical Laue patterns.

5–2 Cameras. Laue cameras are so simple to construct that homemade models are found in a great many laboratories. Figure 5–1 shows a typical **transmission camera,** in this case a commercial unit, and Fig.

FIG. 5–1. Transmission Laue camera. Specimen holder not shown. (Courtesy of General Electric Co., X-Ray Department.)

5–2 illustrates its essential parts. A is the collimator, a device used to produce a narrow incident beam made up of rays as nearly parallel as possible; it usually consists of two pinholes in line, one in each of two lead disks set into the ends of the collimator tube. C is the single-crystal specimen supported on the holder B. F is the light-tight film holder, or *cassette*, made of a frame, a removable metal back, and a sheet of opaque paper; the film, usually 4 by 5 in. in size, is sandwiched between the metal back and the paper. S is the beam stop, designed to prevent the transmitted beam from striking the film and causing excessive blackening. A

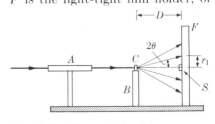

FIG. 5–2. Transmission Laue camera.

small copper disk, about 0.5 mm thick, cemented on the paper film cover serves very well for this purpose: it stops all but a small fraction of the beam transmitted through the crystal, while this small fraction serves to record the position of this beam on the film. The shadow of a beam stop of this kind can be seen in Fig. 3–6(a).

The Bragg angle θ corresponding to any transmission Laue spot is found very simply from the relation

$$\tan 2\theta = \frac{r_1}{D}, \tag{5–1}$$

where r_1 = distance of spot from center of film (point of incidence of transmitted beam) and D = specimen-to-film distance (usually 5 cm). Adjustment of the specimen-to-film distance is best made by using a feeler gauge of the correct length.

The voltage applied to the x-ray tube has a decided effect on the appearance of a transmission Laue pattern. It is of course true that the higher the tube voltage, the more intense the spots, other variables, such as tube current and exposure time, being held constant. But there is still another effect due to the fact that the continuous spectrum is cut off sharply on the short-wavelength side at a value of the wavelength which varies inversely as the tube voltage [Eq. (1–4)]. Laue spots near the center of a transmission pattern are caused by first-order reflections from planes inclined at very small Bragg angles to the incident beam. Only short-wavelength radiation can satisfy the Bragg law for such planes, but if the tube voltage is too low to produce the wavelength required, the corresponding Laue spot will not appear on the pattern. It therefore follows that there is a region near the center of the pattern which is devoid of Laue spots and that the size of this region increases as the tube voltage decreases. The tube voltage therefore affects not only the intensity of each spot, but also the number of spots. This is true also of spots far removed from the center of the pattern; some of these are due to planes so oriented and of such a spacing that they reflect radiation of wavelength close to the short-wavelength limit, and such spots will be eliminated by a decrease in tube voltage no matter how long the exposure.

A **back-reflection camera** is illustrated in Figs. 5–3 and 5–4.. Here the cassette supports both the film and the collimator. The latter has a reduced section at one end which screws into the back plate of the cassette and projects a short distance in front of the cassette through holes punched in the film and its paper cover.

The Bragg angle θ for any spot on a back-reflection pattern may be found from the relation

$$\tan (180° - 2\theta) = \frac{r_2}{D}, \tag{5–2}$$

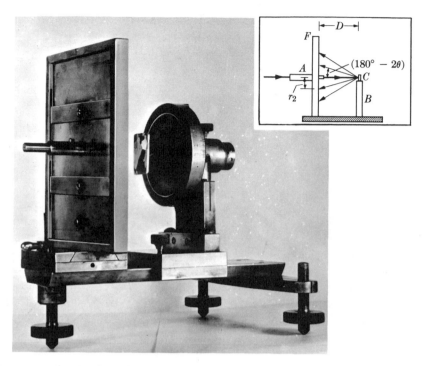

FIG. 5–3. Back-reflection Laue camera. The specimen holder shown permits vertical adjustment of the specimen, as well as rotation about an axis parallel to the incident beam. The specimen shown is a coarse-grained polycrystalline one, positioned so that only a single, selected grain will be struck by the incident beam.

FIG. 5–4. Back-reflection Laue camera (schematic).

where r_2 = distance of spot from center of film and D = specimen-to-film distance (usually 3 cm). In contrast to transmission patterns, back-reflection patterns may have spots as close to the center of the film as the size of the collimator permits. Such spots are caused by high-order overlapping reflections from planes almost perpendicular to the incident beam. Since each diffracted beam is formed of a number of wavelengths, the only effect of a decrease in tube voltage is to remove one or more short-wavelength components from some of the diffracted beams. The longer wavelengths will still be diffracted, and the decrease in voltage will not, in general, remove any spots from the pattern.

Transmission patterns can usually be obtained with much shorter exposures than back-reflection patterns. For example, with a tungsten-target tube operating at 30 kv and 20 ma and an aluminum crystal about 1 mm thick, the required exposure is about 5 min in transmission and 30 min in back reflection. This difference is due to the fact that the atomic scattering factor f decreases as the quantity $(\sin \theta)/\lambda$ increases, and this quantity is much larger in back reflection than in transmission. Transmission patterns are also clearer, in the sense of having greater contrast between the diffraction spots and the background, since the coherent scattering, which forms the spots, and the incoherent (Compton modified) scattering, which contributes to the background, vary in opposite ways with $(\sin \theta)/\lambda$. The incoherent scattering reaches its maximum value in the back-reflection region, as shown clearly in Fig. 3–6(a) and (b); it is in this region also that the temperature-diffuse scattering is most intense. In both Laue methods, the short-wavelength radiation in the incident beam will cause most specimens to emit K fluorescent radiation. If this becomes troublesome in back reflection, it may be minimized by placing a filter of aluminum sheet 0.01 in. thick in front of the film.

If necessary, the intensity of a Laue spot may be increased by means of an *intensifying screen*, as used in radiography. This resembles a fluorescent screen in having an active material coated on an inert backing such as cardboard, the active material having the ability to fluoresce in the visible region under the action of x-rays. When such a screen is placed with its active face in contact with the film (Fig. 5–5), the film is blackened not only by the incident x-ray beam but also by the visible light which the screen emits under the action of the beam. Whereas fluorescent screens emit yellow light, intensifying screens are designed to emit blue light, which is more effective than yellow in blackening the film. Two kinds of intensifying screens are in use today, one containing calcium tungstate and the other zinc sulfide with a trace of silver; the former is most effective at short x-ray wavelengths (about 0.5A or less), while the latter can be used at longer wavelengths.

An intensifying screen should not be used if it is important to record fine detail in the Laue spots, as in some studies of crystal distortion, since the presence of the screen will cause the spots to become more diffuse than

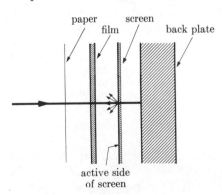

FIG. 5–5. Arrangement of film and intensifying screen (exploded view).

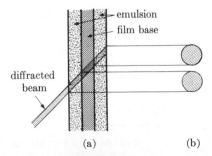

FIG. 5–6. Effect of double-coated film on appearance of Laue spot: (a) section through diffracted beam and film; (b) front view of doubled spot on film.

they would ordinarily be. Each particle of the screen which is struck by x-rays emits light in *all* directions and therefore blackens the film outside the region blackened by the diffracted beam itself, as suggested in Fig. 5–5. This effect is aggravated by the fact that most x-ray film is double-coated, the two layers of emulsion being separated by an appreciable thickness of film base. Even when an intensifying screen is not used, double-coated film causes the size of a diffraction spot formed by an obliquely incident beam to be larger than the cross section of the beam itself; in extreme cases, an apparent doubling of the diffraction spot results, as shown in Fig. 5–6.

5–3 Specimen holders. Before going into the question of specimen holders, we might consider the specimen itself. Obviously, a specimen for the transmission method must have low enough absorption to transmit the diffracted beams; in practice, this means that relatively thick specimens of a light element like aluminum may be used but that the thickness of a fairly heavy element like copper must be reduced, by etching, for example, to a few thousandths of an inch. On the other hand, the specimen must not be too thin or the diffracted intensity will be too low, since the intensity of a diffracted beam is proportional to the volume of diffracting material. In the back-reflection method, there is no restriction on the specimen thickness and quite massive specimens may be examined, since the diffracted beams originate in only a thin surface layer of the specimen. This difference between the two methods may be stated in another way and one which is well worth remembering: any information about a thick specimen obtained by the back-reflection method applies only to a thin surface layer of that specimen, whereas information recorded on a transmission pattern is representative of the complete thickness of the specimen, simply because the transmission specimen must necessarily be thin enough to transmit diffracted beams from all parts of its cross section.*

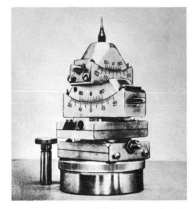

FIG. 5–7. Goniometer with three rotation axes. (Courtesy of Charles Supper Co.)

There is a large variety of specimen holders in use, each suited to some particular purpose. The simplest consists of a fixed post to which the specimen is attached with wax or plasticine. A more elaborate holder is required when it is necessary to set a crystal in some particular orientation

---

* See Sec. 9–5 for further discussion of this point.

relative to the x-ray beam. In this case, a three-circle goniometer is used (Fig. 5–7); it has three mutually perpendicular axes of rotation, two horizontal and one vertical, and is so constructed that the crystal, cemented to the tip of the short metal rod at the top, is not displaced in space by any of the three possible rotations.

In the examination of sheet specimens, it is frequently necessary to obtain diffraction patterns from various points on the surface, and this requires movement of the specimen, between exposures, in two directions at right angles in the plane of the specimen surface, this surface being perpendicular to the incident x-ray beam. The mechanical stage from a microscope can be easily converted to this purpose.

It is often necessary to know exactly where the incident x-ray beam strikes the specimen, as, for example, when one wants to obtain a pattern from a particular grain, or a particular part of a grain, in a polycrystalline mass. This is sometimes a rather difficult matter in a back-reflection camera because of the short distance between the film and the specimen. One method is to project a light beam through the collimator and observe its point of incidence on the specimen with a mirror or prism held near the collimator. An even simpler method is to push a stiff straight wire through the collimator and observe where it touches the specimen with a small mirror, of the kind used by dentists, fixed at an angle to the end of a rod.

5–4 Collimators. Collimators of one kind or another are used in all varieties of x-ray cameras, and it is therefore important to understand their function and to know what they can and cannot do. To "collimate" means, literally, to "render parallel," and the perfect collimator would produce a beam composed of perfectly parallel rays. Such a collimator does not exist, and the reason, essentially, lies in the source of the radiation, since every source emits radiation in all possible directions.

Consider the simplest kind of collimator (Fig. 5–8), consisting of two circular apertures of diameter d separated by a distance u, where u is large compared to d. If there is a point source of radiation at S, then all the rays in the beam from the collimator are nonparallel, and the beam is conical in shape with a maximum angle of divergence β_1 given by the

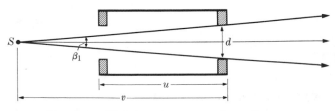

Fig. 5–8.   Pinhole collimator and small source.

equation

$$\tan \frac{\beta_1}{2} = \frac{d/2}{v},$$

where v is the distance of the exit pinhole from the source. Since β_1 is always very small, this relation can be closely approximated by the equation

$$\beta_1 = \frac{d}{v} \text{ radian.} \tag{5–3}$$

Whatever we do to decrease β_1 and therefore render the beam more nearly parallel will at the same time decrease the energy of the beam. We note also that the entrance pinhole serves no function when the source is very small, and may be omitted.

No actual source is a mathematical point, and, in practice, we usually have to deal with x-ray tubes which have focal spots of finite size, usually rectangular in shape. The projected shape of such a spot, at a small target-to-beam angle, is either a small square or a very narrow line (Fig. 1–16), depending on the direction of projection. Such sources produce beams having parallel, divergent, and convergent rays.

Figure 5–9 illustrates the case when the projected source shape is square and of such a height h that convergent rays from the edges of the source cross at the center of the collimator and then diverge. The maximum divergence angle is now given by

$$\beta_2 = \frac{2d}{u} \text{ radian,} \tag{5–4}$$

and the center of the collimator may be considered as the virtual source of these divergent rays. The beam issuing from the collimator contains not only parallel and divergent rays but also convergent ones, the maximum angle of convergence being given by

$$\alpha = \frac{d}{u + w} \text{ radian,} \tag{5–5}$$

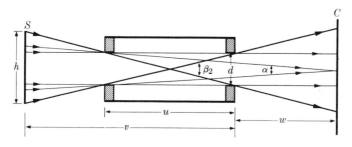

FIG. 5–9.   Pinhole collimator and large source. S = source, C = crystal.

where w is the distance of the crystal from the exit pinhole. The size of the source shown in Fig. 5–9 is given by

$$h = d \left(\frac{2v}{u} - 1 \right). \qquad (5\text{–}6)$$

In practice, v is very often about twice as large as u, which means that the conditions illustrated in Fig. 5–9 are achieved when the pinholes are about one-third the size of the projected source. If the value of h is smaller than that given by Eq. (5–6), then conditions will be intermediate between those shown in Figs. 5–8 and 5–9; as h approaches zero, the maximum divergence angle decreases from the value given by Eq. (5–4) to that given by Eq. (5–3) and the proportion of parallel rays in the beam and the maximum convergence angle both approach zero. When h exceeds the value given by Eq. (5–6), none of the conditions depicted in Fig. 5–9 are changed, and the increase in the size of the source merely represents wasted energy.

When the shape of the projected source is a fine line, the geometry of the beam varies between two extremes in two mutually perpendicular planes. In a plane at right angles to the line source, the shape is given by Fig. 5–8, and in a plane parallel to the source by Fig. 5–9. Aside from the component which diverges in the plane of the source, the resulting beam is shaped somewhat like a wedge. Since the length of the line source greatly exceeds the value given by Eq. (5–6), a large fraction of the x-ray energy is wasted with this arrangement of source and collimator.

The extent of the nonparallelism of actual x-ray beams may be illustrated by taking, as typical values, $d = 0.5$ mm, $u = 5$ cm, and $w = 3$ cm. Then Eq. (5–4) gives $\beta_2 = 1.15°$ and Eq. (5–5) gives $\alpha = 0.36°$. These values may of course be reduced by decreasing the size of the pinholes, for example, but this reduction will be obtained at the expense of decreased energy in the beam and increased exposure time.

5–5 The shapes of Laue spots. We will see later that Laue spots become smeared out if the reflecting crystal is distorted. Here, however, we are concerned with the shapes of spots obtained from perfect, undistorted crystals. These shapes are greatly influenced by the nature of the incident beam, i.e., by its convergence or divergence, and it is important to realize this fact, or Laue spots of "unusual" shape may be erroneously taken as evidence of crystal distortion.

Consider the transmission case first, and assume that the crystal is thin and larger than the cross section of the primary beam at the point of incidence. If this beam is mainly divergent, which is the usual case in practice (Fig. 5–8 or 5–9), then a focusing action takes place on diffraction. Figure 5–10 is a section through the incident beam and any diffracted beam; the incident beam, whose cross section at any point is circular, is shown issuing

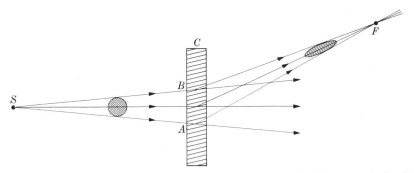

Fig. 5–10. Focusing of diffracted beam in the transmission Laue method. S = source, C = crystal, F = focal point.

from a small source, real or virtual. Each ray of the incident beam which lies in the plane of the drawing strikes the reflecting lattice planes of the crystal at a slightly different Bragg angle, this angle being a maximum at A and decreasing progressively toward B. The lowermost rays are therefore deviated through a greater angle 2θ than the upper ones, with the result that the diffracted beam converges to a focus at F. This is true only of the rays in the plane of the drawing; those in a plane at right angles continue to diverge after diffraction, with the result that the diffracted beam is elliptical in cross section. The film intersects different diffracted beams at different distances from the crystal, so elliptical spots of various sizes are observed, as shown in Fig. 5–11. This is not a sketch of a Laue pattern but an illustration of spot size and shape as a function of spot position in one quadrant of the film. Note that the spots are all elliptical with their minor axes aligned in a radial direction and that spots near the center and edge of the pattern are thicker than those in intermediate positions, the latter being formed by beams near their focal point. Spots having the shapes illustrated are fairly common, and Fig. 3–6(a) is an example.

In back reflection, no focusing occurs and a divergent incident beam continues to diverge in all directions after diffraction. Back-reflection Laue spots are therefore more or less circular near the center of the pattern, and they become increasingly elliptical toward the edge, due to the oblique incidence of the rays on the film, the major axes of the ellipses being approximately radial. Figure 3–6(b) is typical.

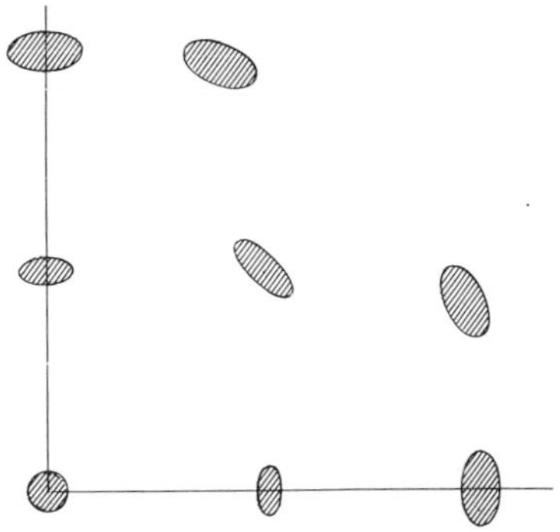

Fig. 5–11. Shape of transmission Laue spots as a function of position.

PROBLEMS

5–1. A transmission Laue pattern is made of an aluminum crystal with 40-kv tungsten radiation. The film is 5 cm from the crystal. How close to the center of the pattern can Laue spots be formed by reflecting planes of maximum spacing, namely (111), and those of next largest spacing, namely (200)?

5–2. A transmission Laue pattern is made of an aluminum crystal with a specimen-to-film distance of 5 cm. The (111) planes of the crystal make an angle of 3° with the incident beam. What minimum tube voltage is required to produce a 111 reflection?

5–3. (a) A back-reflection Laue pattern is made of an aluminum crystal at 50 kv. The (111) planes make an angle of 88° with the incident beam. What orders of reflection are present in the beam diffracted by these planes? (Assume that wavelengths larger than 2.0A are too weak and too easily absorbed by air to register on the film.)

(b) What orders of the 111 reflection are present if the tube voltage is reduced to 40 kv?

CHAPTER 6

POWDER PHOTOGRAPHS

6–1 Introduction. The powder method of x-ray diffraction was devised independently in 1916 by Debye and Scherrer in Germany and in 1917 by Hull in the United States. It is the most generally useful of all diffraction methods and, when properly employed, can yield a great deal of structural information about the material under investigation. Basically, this method involves the diffraction of monochromatic x-rays by a powder specimen. In this connection, "monochromatic" usually means the strong K characteristic component of the general radiation from an x-ray tube operated above the K excitation potential of the target material. "Powder" can mean either an actual, physical powder held together with a suitable binder or any specimen in polycrystalline form. The method is thus eminently suited for metallurgical work, since single crystals are not always available to the metallurgist and such materials as polycrystalline wire, sheet, rod, etc., may be examined nondestructively without any special preparation.

There are three main powder methods in use, differentiated by the relative position of the specimen and film:

(1) *Debye-Scherrer method.* The film is placed on the surface of a cylinder and the specimen on the axis of the cylinder.

(2) *Focusing method.* The film, specimen, and x-ray source are all placed on the surface of a cylinder.

(3) *Pinhole method.* The film is flat, perpendicular to the incident x-ray beam, and located at any convenient distance from the specimen.

In all these methods, the diffracted beams lie on the surfaces of cones whose axes lie along the incident beam or its extension; each cone of rays is diffracted from a particular set of lattice planes. In the Debye-Scherrer and focusing methods, only a narrow strip of film is used and the recorded diffraction pattern consists of short lines formed by the intersections of the cones of radiation with the film. In the pinhole method, the whole cone intersects the film to form a circular diffraction ring.

6–2 Debye-Scherrer method. A typical Debye camera is shown in Fig. 6–1. It consists essentially of a cylindrical chamber with a light-tight cover, a collimator to admit and define the incident beam, a beam stop to confine and stop the transmitted beam, a means for holding the film tightly against the inside circumference of the camera, and a specimen holder that can be rotated.

149

FIG. 6-1. Debye-Scherrer camera, with cover plate removed. (Courtesy of North American Philips Company, Inc.)

Camera diameters vary from about 5 to about 20 cm. The greater the diameter, the greater the resolution or separation of a particular pair of lines on the film. In spectroscopy, resolving power is the power of distinguishing between two components of radiation which have wavelengths very close together and is given by $\lambda/\Delta\lambda$, where $\Delta\lambda$ is the difference between the two wavelengths and λ is their mean value; in crystal-structure analysis, we may take resolving power as the ability to separate diffraction lines from sets of planes of very nearly the same spacing, or as the value of $d/\Delta d$.* Thus, if S is the distance measured on the film from a particular diffraction line to the point where the transmitted beam would strike the film (Fig. 6-2), then

$$S = 2\theta R$$

---

* Resolving power is often defined by the quantity $\Delta\lambda/\lambda$, which is the reciprocal of that given above. However, the *power* of resolving two wavelengths which are nearly alike is a quantity which should logically *increase* as $\Delta\lambda$, the difference between the two wavelengths to be separated, decreases. This is the reason for the definition given in the text. The same argument applies to interplanar spacings d.

and
$$\Delta S = R\Delta 2\theta, \tag{6–1}$$

where R is the radius of the camera. Two sets of planes of very nearly the same spacing will give rise to two diffracted beams separated by a small angle $\Delta 2\theta$; for a given value of $\Delta 2\theta$, Eq. (6–1) shows that ΔS, the separation of the lines on the film, increases with R. The resolving power may be obtained by differentiating the Bragg law:*

$$\lambda = 2d \sin \theta$$

$$\frac{d\theta}{dd} = \frac{-1}{d} \tan \theta. \tag{6–2}$$

But

$$d\theta = \frac{dS}{2R}.$$

Therefore

$$\frac{dS}{dd} = \frac{-2R}{d} \tan \theta$$

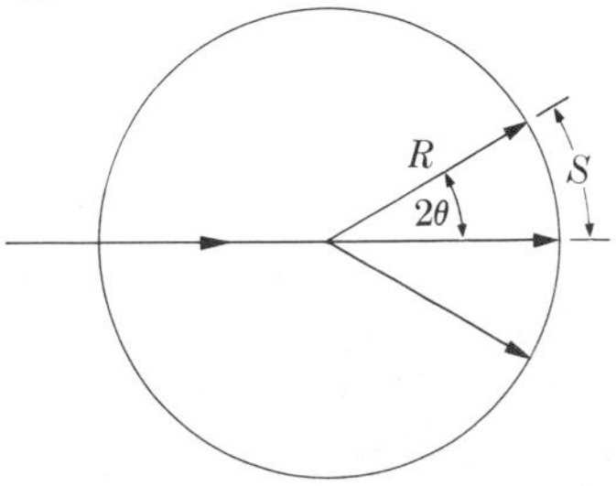

FIG. 6–2. Geometry of the Debye-Scherrer method. Section through film and one diffraction cone.

$$\text{Resolving power} = \frac{d}{\Delta d} = \frac{-2R}{\Delta S} \tan \theta, \tag{6–3}$$

where d is the mean spacing of the two sets of planes, Δd the difference in their spacings, and ΔS the separation of two diffraction lines which appear just resolved on the film. Equation (6–3) shows that the resolving power increases with the size of the camera; this increased resolution is obtained, however, at the cost of increased exposure time, and the smaller cameras are usually preferred for all but the most complicated patterns. A camera diameter of 5.73 cm is often used and will be found suitable for most work. This particular diameter, equal to 1/10 the number of degrees in a radian, facilitates calculation, since θ (in degrees) is obtained simply by multiplication of S (in cm) by 10, except for certain corrections necessary in precise work. Equation (6–3) also shows that the resolving power of a given camera increases with θ, being directly proportional to $\tan \theta$.

The increased exposure time required by an increase in camera diameter is due not only to the decrease in intensity of the diffracted beam with increased distance from the specimen, but also to the partial absorption of both the incident and diffracted beams by the air in the camera. For example, Prob. 1–7 and the curves of Fig. 6–3 show that, in a camera of 19 cm diameter (about the largest in common use), the decrease in intensity due to air absorption is about 20 percent for Cu $K\alpha$ radiation and about 52 percent for Cr $K\alpha$ radiation. This decrease in intensity may be

---

* A lower-case roman d is used throughout this book for differentials in order to avoid confusion with the symbol d for distance between atomic planes.

avoided by evacuating the camera or by filling it with a light gas such as hydrogen or helium during the exposure.

Correct design of the pinhole system which collimates the incident beam is important, especially when weak diffracted beams must be recorded. The exit pinhole scatters x-rays in all directions, and these scattered rays, if not prevented from striking the film, can seriously increase the intensity of the background. A "guarded-pinhole" assembly which practically eliminates this effect is shown in Fig. 6–4, where the divergent and convergent rays in the incident beam are ignored and only the parallel component is shown. The collimator tube is extended a considerable distance beyond the exit pinhole and constricted so that the end A is close enough to the main beam to confine the radiation scattered by the exit pinhole to a very narrow angular range and yet not close enough to touch the main beam and be itself a cause of further scattering. The beam stop is usually a thick piece of lead glass placed behind a fluorescent screen, the combination allowing the transmitted beam to be viewed with safety when adjusting the camera in front of the x-ray tube. Back scatter from the stop is minimized by extending the beam-stop tube backward and constricting its end B. Another reason for extending the collimator and beam-stop tubes as close to the specimen as possible is to minimize the extent to which the primary beam is scattered by air, as it passes through the camera. Both tubes are tapered to interfere as little as possible with low-angle and high-angle diffracted beams.

Some cameras employ rectangular slits rather than pinholes to define the beam, the long edges of the slits being parallel to the axis of the speci-

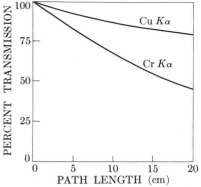

FIG. 6–3. Absorption of Cu $K\alpha$ and Cr $K\alpha$ radiation by air.

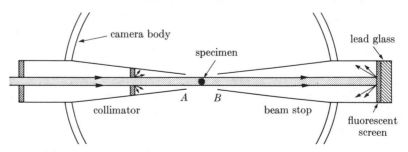

FIG. 6–4. Design of collimator and beam stop (schematic).

men. The use of slits instead of pinholes decreases exposure time by increasing the irradiated volume of the specimen, but requires more accurate positioning of the camera relative to the source and produces diffraction lines which are sharp only along the median line of the film.

6–3 Specimen preparation. Metals and alloys may be converted to powder by filing or, if they are sufficiently brittle, by grinding in a small agate mortar. In either case, the powder should be filed or ground as fine as possible, preferably to pass a 325-mesh screen, in order to produce smooth, continuous diffraction lines. The screened powder is usually annealed in evacuated glass or quartz capsules in order to relieve the strains due to filing or grinding.

Special precautions are necessary in screening two-phase alloys. If a small, representative sample is selected from an ingot for x-ray analysis, then that entire sample must be ground or filed to pass through the screen. The common method of grinding until an amount sufficient for the x-ray specimen has passed the screen, the oversize being rejected, may lead to very erroneous results. One phase of the alloy is usually more brittle than the other, and that phase will more easily be ground into fine particles; if the grinding and screening are interrupted at any point, then the material remaining on the screen will contain less of the more brittle phase than the original sample while the undersize will contain more, and neither will be representative.

The final specimen for the Debye camera should be in the form of a thin rod, 0.5 mm or less in diameter and about 1 cm long. There are various ways of preparing such a specimen, one of the simplest being to coat the powder on the surface of a fine glass fiber with a small amount of glue or petroleum jelly. Other methods consist in packing the powder into a thin-walled tube made of a weakly absorbing substance such as cellophane or lithium borate glass, or in extruding a mixture of powder and binder through a small hole. Polycrystalline wires may be used directly, but since they usually exhibit some preferred orientation, the resulting diffraction pattern must be interpreted with that fact in mind (Chap. 9). Strongly absorbing substances may produce split low-angle lines (see Sec. 4–10); if this effect becomes troublesome, it may be eliminated by diluting the substance involved with some weakly absorbing substance, so that the absorption coefficient of the composite specimen is low. Both flour and cornstarch have been used for this purpose. The diluent chosen should not produce any strong diffraction lines of its own and too much of it should not be used, or the lines from the substance being examined will become spotty.

After the specimen rod is prepared, it is mounted in its holder so that it will lie accurately along the axis of the camera when the specimen holder

is rotated. Rotation of the specimen during the exposure is common practice but not an intrinsic part of the powder method; its only purpose is to
produce continuous, rather than spotty, diffraction lines by increasing the
number of powder particles in reflecting positions.

6–4 Film loading. Figure 6–5 illustrates three methods of arranging
the film strip in the Debye method. The small sketches on the right show
the loaded film in relation to the incident beam, while the films laid out
flat are indicated on the left. In (a), a hole is punched in the center of the
film so that the film may be slipped over the beam stop; the transmitted
beam thus *leaves* through the hole in the film. The pattern is symmetrical
on either side, and the θ value of a particular reflection is obtained by
measuring U, the distance apart of two diffraction lines formed by the
same cone of radiation, and using the relation

$$4\theta R = U.$$

Photographic film always shrinks slightly during processing and drying,
and this shrinkage effectively changes the camera radius. The film-shrinkage error may be allowed for by slipping the ends of the film under metal
knife-edges which cast a sharp shadow near each end of the film. In this
way, a standard distance is impressed on the film which will shrink in the
same proportion as the distance between a given pair of diffraction lines.
If the angular separation $4\theta_K$ of the knife-edges in the camera is known,
either by direct measurement or by calibration with a substance of known
lattice parameter, then the value of θ for a particular reflection may be
obtained by simple proportion:

$$\frac{\theta}{\theta_K} = \frac{U}{U_K},$$

where U_K is the distance apart of the knife-edge shadows on the film.

Figure 6–5(b) illustrates a method of loading the film which is just the
reverse of the previous one. Here the incident beam *enters* through the
hole in the film, and θ is obtained from the relation

$$(2\pi - 4\theta)R = V.$$

Knife-edges may also be used in this case as a basis for film-shrinkage corrections.

The unsymmetrical, or Straumanis, method of film loading is shown in
Fig. 6–5(c). Two holes are punched in the film so that it may be slipped
over both the entrance collimator and the beam stop. Since it is possible
to determine from measurements on the film where the incident beam entered the film circle and where the transmitted beam left it, no knife-edges
are required to make the film-shrinkage correction. The point X ($2\theta =$

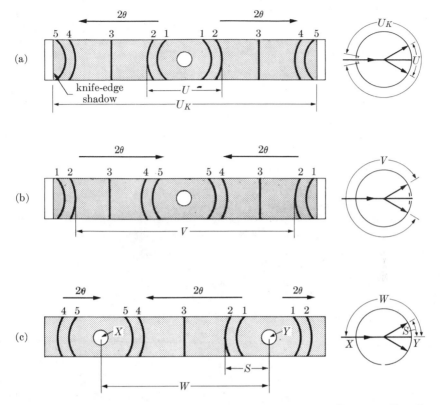

Fɪɢ. 6–5. Methods of film loading in Debye cameras. Corresponding lines have the same numbers in all films.

180°), where the incident beam entered, is halfway between the measured positions of lines 5,5; similarly, the point Y $(2\theta = 0°)$, where the transmitted beam left, is halfway between lines 1,1. The difference between the positions of X and Y gives W, and θ is found by proportion:

$$\frac{2\theta}{\pi} = \frac{S}{W}.$$

Unsymmetrical loading thus provides for the film-shrinkage correction without calibration of the camera or knowledge of any camera dimension.

The shapes of the diffraction lines in Fig. 6–5 should be noted. The low-angle lines are strongly curved because they are formed by cones of radiation which have a small apex angle 4θ. The same is true of the high-angle lines, although naturally they are curved in the opposite direction. Lines for which 4θ is nearly equal to 180° are practically straight. This change of line shape with change in θ may also be seen in the powder photographs shown in Fig. 3–13.

6–5 Cameras for high and low temperatures. Metallurgical investigations frequently require that the crystal structure of a phase stable only at high temperature be determined. In many cases, this can be accomplished by quenching the specimen at a high enough rate to suppress the decomposition of the high-temperature phase and then examining the specimen in an ordinary camera at room temperature. In other cases, the transformation into the phases stable at room temperature cannot be suppressed, and a high-temperature camera is necessary in order that the specimen may be examined at the temperature at which the phase in question is stable.

The design of high-temperature Debye cameras varies almost from laboratory to laboratory. They all involve a small furnace, usually of the electric-resistance type, to heat the specimen and a thermocouple to measure its temperature. The main design problem is to keep the film cool without too great an increase in the camera diameter; this requires water-cooling of the body of the camera and/or the careful placing of radiation shields between the furnace and the film, shields so designed that they will not interfere with the diffracted x-ray beams. The furnace which surrounds the specimen must also be provided with a slot of some kind to permit the passage of the incident and diffracted beams. If the specimen is susceptible to oxidation at high temperatures, means of evacuating the camera or of filling it with an inert gas must be provided; alternately, the powder specimen may be sealed in a thin-walled silica tube. Because of the small size of the furnace in a high-temperature camera, the temperature gradients in it are usually quite steep, and special care must be taken to ensure that the temperature recorded by the thermocouple is actually that of the specimen itself. Since the intensity of any reflection is decreased by an increase in temperature, the exposure time required for a high-temperature diffraction pattern is normally rather long.

Debye cameras are also occasionally required for work at temperatures below room temperature. Specimen cooling is usually accomplished by running a thin stream of coolant, such as liquid air, over the specimen throughout the x-ray exposure. The diffraction pattern of the coolant will also be recorded but this is easily distinguished from that of a crystalline solid, because the typical pattern of a liquid contains only one or two very diffuse maxima in contrast to the sharp diffraction lines from a solid. Scattering from the liquid will, however, increase the background blackening of the photograph.

6–6 Focusing cameras. Cameras in which diffracted rays originating from an extended region of the specimen all converge to one point on the film are called focusing cameras. The design of all such cameras is based on the following geometrical theorem (Fig. 6–6): all angles inscribed in a

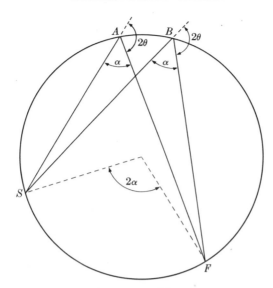

FIG. 6–6.   Geometry of focusing cameras.

circle and based on the same arc SF are equal to one another and equal to half the angle subtended at the center by the same arc. Suppose that x-rays proceeding in the directions SA and SB encounter a powder specimen located on the arc AB. Then the rays diffracted by the (hkl) planes at points A and B will be deviated through the same angle 2θ. But these deviation angles 2θ are each equal to $(180° - \alpha)$, which means that the diffracted rays must proceed along AF and BF, and come to a focus at F on a film placed along the circumference of the circle.

6–7 Seemann-Bohlin camera. This focusing principle is utilized in the Seemann-Bohlin camera shown in Fig. 6–7. The slit S acts as a virtual line source of x-rays, the actual source being the extended focal spot on the target T of the x-ray tube. Only converging rays from the target can enter this slit and, after passing it, they diverge to the specimen AB. (Alternatively, if a tube with a fine-line focal spot is available, the slit may be eliminated and exposure time shortened by designing the camera to use the focal spot itself as a source of divergent radiation.) For a particular hkl reflection, each ray is then diffracted through the same angle 2θ, with the result that all diffracted rays from various parts of the specimen converge to a focus at F. As in any powder method, the diffracted beams lie on the surfaces of cones whose axes are coincident with the incident beam; in this case, a number of incident beams contribute to each reflection and a diffraction line is formed by the intersection of a number of cones with the film. As in the Debye-Scherrer method, a diffraction line is in general curved, the amount of curvature depending on the par-

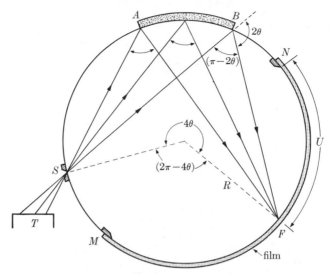

FIG. 6–7. Seemann-Bohlin focusing camera. Only one *hkl* reflection is shown.

ticular value of θ involved. Figure 6–8 shows a typical powder pattern made with this camera.

The ends of the film strip are covered by knife-edges M and N, which cast reference shadows on the film. The value of θ for any diffraction line may be found from the distance U, measured on the film, from the line to the shadow of the low-angle knife-edge N, by use of the relation

$$4\theta R = U + \text{arc } SABN. \qquad (6–4)$$

In practice, θ is found by calibrating the camera with a standard substance of known lattice parameter, such as NaCl, rather than by the use of Eq. (6–4). Several patterns are prepared of the same standard with radiations of different wavelength, in order to obtain diffraction lines at a large number of 2θ positions. Line positions are measured on each film, as well as the total length of the film between the knife-edge shadows M and N. Because of variable film shrinkage, these films will generally have unequal lengths. The length of one is taken as a standard, and a multiplying factor is found for each of the other films which will make its length equal to the standard length. This factor is then applied to the U value of each diffraction line. The corrected values of U are then plotted against calculated values of θ to obtain a calibration curve for the camera.

FIG. 6–8. Powder pattern of tungsten, made in a Seemann-Bohlin camera, 8.4 cm in diameter. This camera covers a 2θ range of 92 to 166°. High-angle end of film at left. Filtered copper radiation. (Courtesy of John T. Norton.)

A similar procedure is then followed when an "unknown" specimen is being examined. A correction factor is found which will convert the measured film length of the unknown to the standard length. This factor is then applied to each measured U value before finding the corresponding θ value from the calibration curve.

If more accuracy is desired than this graphical method can give, the calibration data can be handled analytically. Equation (6–4) is written in the form

$$\theta = K_1 U + K_2,$$

where K_1 and K_2 are constants. The values of these constants are then determined by the method of least squares (see Sec. 11–6). Once the constants are known, this equation can be used to calculate θ, or a table of corresponding θ and U values can be constructed.

By differentiating Eq. (6–4), we obtain

$$d\theta = \frac{dU}{4R}.$$

This relation may be combined with Eq. (6–2) to give

$$\frac{dU}{dd} = -\frac{4R}{d} \tan \theta.$$

$$\text{Resolving power} = \frac{d}{\Delta d} = -\frac{4R}{\Delta U} \tan \theta. \tag{6–5}$$

The resolving power, or ability to separate diffraction lines from planes of almost the same spacing, is therefore twice that of a Debye-Scherrer camera of the same radius. In addition, the exposure time is much shorter, because of the fact that a much larger specimen is used (the arc AB of Fig. 6–7 is of the order of 1 cm) and diffracted rays from a considerable volume of material are all brought to one focus. The Seemann-Bohlin camera is, therefore, very useful in studying complex diffraction patterns, whether they are due to a single phase or to a mixture of phases such as occur in alloy systems.

For metallurgical work, this camera has the further advantage that a massive polycrystalline specimen may be used as well as a powder. For example, a metallographic specimen, mounted in the usual 1-in. diameter bakelite mount for microscopic examination, can be fastened to the circumference of the camera and used directly. When a flat specimen placed tangentially to the camera circle is substituted for a curved specimen, the focusing action of the camera is slightly decreased but not objectionably so, while the advantage of being able to examine the same area of the specimen both with the microscope and with x-rays is obvious. It is worth noting also that both methods of examination, the optical and the x-ray, provide information only about the surface layer of the specimen, since the x-ray method here involved is of the reflection, and not the transmission, type.

A powder specimen may also be used in this camera by fixing a thin layer of the powder to a piece of paper with glue or petroleum jelly. The paper is then curved and held against the camera circumference by an attachment provided with the camera. Whether the specimen is in the massive or powder form, smoother diffraction lines can be obtained by oscillating the specimen about the camera axis.

On the debit side, the Seemann-Bohlin camera has the disadvantage that the reflections registered on the film cover only a limited range of 2θ values, particularly on the low-angle side; for this reason, it is better to make a preliminary survey of the whole pattern with a Debye camera, reserving the focusing camera for a closer study of certain portions. Some investigators use a set of three Seemann-Bohlin cameras, designed to cover practically the whole range of 2θ values in overlapping angular ranges.

Diffraction lines formed in a Seemann-Bohlin camera are normally broader than those in a Debye-Scherrer pattern. The focused line is, in a sense, an image of the slit, and decreasing the slit opening will decrease the line breadth but increase the exposure time. The line breadth increases as 2θ becomes smaller, since at low 2θ values the diffracted rays strike the film at a very low angle. This effect is aggravated by the double-emulsion film normally used for x-ray diffraction. In special cases, it may pay to use single-emulsion film at the cost of increased exposure time.

6–8 Back-reflection focusing cameras. The most precise measurement of lattice parameter is made in the back-reflection region, as discussed in greater detail in Chap. 11. The most suitable camera for such measurements is the symmetrical back-reflection focusing camera illustrated in Fig. 6–9.

It employs the same focusing principle as the Seemann-Bohlin camera, but the film straddles the slit and the specimen is placed diametrically opposite the slit. Means are usually provided for slowly oscillating the specimen through a few degrees about the camera axis in order to produce smooth diffraction lines. A typical film, punched in the center to allow the passage of the incident beam, is shown in Fig. 6–10. The value of θ for any diffraction line may be calculated from the relation

$$(4\pi - 8\theta)R = V, \tag{6–6}$$

where V is the distance on the film between corresponding diffraction lines on either side of the entrance slit.

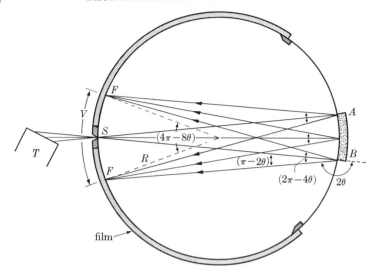

Fig. 6-9. Symmetrical back-reflection focusing camera. Only one *hkl* reflection is shown.

Differentiation of Eq. (6-6) gives

$$\Delta\theta = \frac{-1}{4R}\,\Delta\left(\frac{V}{2}\right), \tag{6-7}$$

where $\Delta(V/2)$ is the separation on the film of two reflections differing in Bragg angle by $\Delta\theta$. Combination of this equation with Eq. (6-2) shows that

$$\text{Resolving power} = \frac{d}{\Delta d} = \frac{4R}{\Delta(V/2)}\,\tan\theta.$$

The resolving power of this camera is therefore the same as that of a Seemann-Bohlin camera of the same diameter.

In the pattern shown in Fig. 6-10, two pairs of closely spaced lines can be seen, lines 1 and 2 and lines 4 and 5. Each pair is a doublet formed by

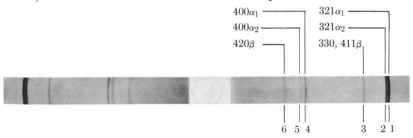

Fig. 6-10. Powder photograph of tungsten made in a symmetrical back-reflection focusing camera, 4.00 in. in diameter. Unfiltered copper radiation.

reflection from one set of planes of the two components, $K\alpha_1$ and $K\alpha_2$, which make up $K\alpha$ radiation. These component lines are commonly found to be resolved, or separated, in the back-reflection region. (The β lines in this photograph are not resolved since $K\beta$ radiation consists only of a single wavelength.) To determine the conditions under which a given camera can separate two components of radiation which have almost the same wavelength, we must use the spectroscopic definition of resolving power, namely $\lambda/\Delta\lambda$, where $\Delta\lambda$ is the difference between the two wavelengths and λ is their mean value. For Cu $K\alpha$ radiation, these wavelengths are:

$$\lambda(\text{Cu } K\alpha_2) = 1.54433\text{A}$$

$$\lambda(\text{Cu } K\alpha_1) = \underline{1.54051\text{A}}$$

$$\Delta\lambda = 0.00382\text{A}$$

Therefore

$$\frac{\lambda}{\Delta\lambda} = \frac{1.542}{0.00382} = 404.$$

The resolving power of the camera must exceed this value, for the particular reflection considered, if the component lines are to be separated on the film.

By differentiating the Bragg law, we obtain

$$\lambda = 2d \sin \theta,$$

$$\frac{d\theta}{d\lambda} = \frac{1}{2d \cos \theta} = \frac{\tan \theta}{2d \sin \theta} = \frac{\tan \theta}{\lambda},$$

$$\frac{\lambda}{\Delta\lambda} = \frac{\tan \theta}{\Delta\theta}. \tag{6-8}$$

Substitution of Eq. (6–7) gives

$$\text{Resolving power} = \frac{\lambda}{\Delta\lambda} = \frac{-4R \tan \theta}{\Delta(V/2)}. \tag{6-9}$$

The negative sign here can be disregarded; it merely means that an increase in λ causes a decrease in $V/2$, since the latter is measured from the center of the film. Equation (6–9) demonstrates that the resolving power increases with the camera radius and with θ, becoming very large near 90°. This latter point is clearly evident in Fig. 6–10, which shows a greater separation of the higher-angle 400 reflections as compared to the 321 reflections.

By use of Eq. (6–9), we can calculate the resolving power, for the 321 reflections, of the camera used to obtain Fig. 6–10. The camera radius is

2.00 in., and the mean θ value for these reflections is about 65.7°. The line breadth at half maximum intensity is about 0.04 cm. The two component lines of the doublet will be clearly resolved on the film if their separation is twice their breadth. Therefore

$$\Delta \left(\frac{V}{2}\right) = 2(0.04) = 0.08 \text{ cm},$$

$$\frac{\lambda}{\Delta\lambda} = \frac{(4)(2.00)(2.54)(\tan 65.7°)}{(0.08)} = 563.$$

Since this value exceeds the resolving power of 404, found above to be necessary for resolution of the Cu $K\alpha$ doublet, we would expect this doublet to be resolved for the 321 reflection, and such is seen to be the case in Fig. 6–10. At some lower angle, this would not be true and the two components would merge into a single, unresolved line. The fact that resolution of the $K\alpha$ doublet normally occurs only in the back-reflection region can be seen from the Debye photographs reproduced in Fig. 3–13.

6–9 Pinhole photographs. When monochromatic radiation is used to examine a polycrystalline specimen in a Laue camera, the result is called, for no particularly good reason, a pinhole photograph. Either a transmission or a back-reflection camera may be used. A typical transmission photograph, made of fine-grained aluminum sheet, is shown in Fig. 6–11.

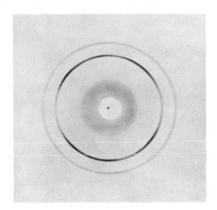

The pinhole method has the advantage that an entire Debye ring, and not just a part of it, is recorded on the film. On the other hand, the range of θ values which are recorded is rather limited: either low-angle or high-angle reflections may be obtained, but not those in the median

FIG. 6–11. Transmission pinhole photograph of an aluminum sheet specimen. Filtered copper radiation. (The diffuse circular band near the center is caused by white radiation. The nonuniform blackening of the Debye rings is due to preferred orientation in the specimen; see Chap. 9.)

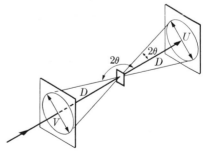

FIG. 6–12. Angular relationships in the pinhole method.

range of θ (see Fig. 6–12).   In the transmission method, the value of θ for a particular reflection is found from the relation

$$\tan 2\theta = \frac{U}{2D},\qquad (6\text{–}10)$$

where U = diameter of the Debye ring and D = specimen-to-film distance.   The corresponding relation for the back-reflection method is

$$\tan (\pi - 2\theta) = \frac{V}{2D},\qquad (6\text{–}11)$$

where V = diameter of the Debye ring.   The distance D is usually of the order of 3 to 5 cm.

Powder specimens may be prepared simply by spreading a bit of the powder mixed with a binder on a glass slide or a small piece of paper. However, the greatest utility of the pinhole method in metallurgical work lies in the fact that massive, polycrystalline specimens may be used.   In back reflection, mounted metallographic specimens may be examined directly, while the transmission method is of course restricted to wire and sheet specimens which are not too highly absorbing.

There is an optimum specimen thickness for the transmission method, because the diffracted beams will be very weak or entirely absent if the specimen is either too thin (insufficient volume of diffracting material) or too thick (excessive absorption).   As will be shown in Sec. 9–9, the specimen thickness which produces the maximum diffracted intensity is given by $1/\mu$, where μ is the linear absorption coefficient of the specimen.   Inspection of Eq. (1–10) shows that this condition can also be stated as follows: a transmission specimen is of optimum thickness when the intensity of the beam transmitted through the specimen is $1/e$, or about $\frac{1}{3}$, of the intensity of the incident beam.   Normally this optimum thickness is of the order of a few thousandths of an inch.   There is one way, however, in which a partial transmission pattern can be obtained from a thick specimen and that is by diffraction from an edge (Fig. 6–13).   Only the upper half of the pattern is recorded on the film, but that is all that is necessary in many applications.   The same technique has also been used in some Debye-Scherrer cameras.

The pinhole method is used in studies of preferred orientation, grain size, and crystal perfection.   With a back-reflection camera, fairly precise parameter measurements can be made by this method.   Precise knowledge of the specimen-to-film distance D is not necessary, provided the proper extrapolation equation is used (Chap. 11) or the camera is calibrated.   The calibration is usually performed for each exposure, simply by smearing a thin layer of the calibrating powder over the surface of the specimen; in this way, reference lines of known θ value are formed on each film.

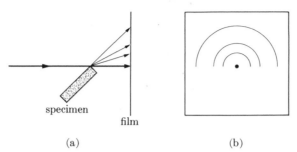

(a)   (b)

FIG. 6–13. Transmission pinhole method for thick specimens: (a) section through incident beam; (b) partial pattern obtained.

When the pinhole method is used for parameter measurements, the film or specimen, or both, is moved during the exposure to produce smooth, continuous diffraction lines. By rotating or oscillating the film about the axis of the incident beam, the reflections from each reflecting particle or grain are smeared out along the Debye ring. The specimen itself may be rotated about the incident beam axis or about any axis parallel to the incident beam, or translated back and forth in any direction in a plane parallel to the specimen surface. Such movements increase the number of grains in reflecting positions and allow a greater proportion of the total specimen surface to take part in diffraction, thus ensuring that the information recorded on the film is representative of the surface as a whole. Any camera in which the specimen can be so moved during the exposure that the incident beam traverses a large part of its surface is called an *integrating camera*.

6–10 Choice of radiation. With any of the powder methods described above, the investigator must choose the radiation best suited to the problem at hand. In making this choice, the two most important considerations are:

(1) The characteristic wavelength used should not be shorter than the K absorption edge of the specimen, or the fluorescent radiation produced will badly fog the film. In the case of alloys or compounds, it may be difficult or impossible to satisfy this condition for every element in the specimen.

(2) The Bragg law shows that the shorter the wavelength, the smaller the Bragg angle for planes of a given spacing. Decreasing the wavelength will therefore shift every diffraction line to lower Bragg angles and increase the total number of lines on the film, while increasing the wavelength will have the opposite effect. The choice of a short or a long wavelength depends on the particular problem involved.

The characteristic radiations usually employed in x-ray diffraction are the following:

Mo $K\alpha$:	0.711A
Cu $K\alpha$:	1.542
Co $K\alpha$:	1.790
Fe $K\alpha$:	1.937
Cr $K\alpha$:	2.291

In each case, the appropriate filter is used to suppress the $K\beta$ component of the radiation. All in all, Cu $K\alpha$ radiation is generally the most useful. It cannot be employed with ferrous materials, however, since it will cause fluorescent radiation from the iron in the specimen; instead, Co $K\alpha$, Fe $K\alpha$ or Cr $K\alpha$ radiation should be used.

Precise lattice-parameter measurements require that there be a number of lines in the back-reflection region, while some specimens may yield only one or two. This difficulty may be avoided by using unfiltered radiation, in order to have $K\beta$ as well as $K\alpha$ lines present, and by using an alloy target. For example, if a 50 atomic percent Fe-Co alloy is used as a target, and no filter is used in the x-ray beam, the radiation will contain the Fe $K\alpha$, Fe $K\beta$, Co $K\alpha$, and Co $K\beta$ wavelengths, since each element will emit its characteristic radiation independently. Of course, special targets can be used only with demountable x-ray tubes.

6–11 Background radiation. A good powder photograph has sharp intense lines superimposed on a background of minimum intensity. However, the diffraction lines themselves vary in intensity, because of the structure of the crystal itself, and an appreciable background intensity may exist, due to a number of causes. The two effects together may cause the weakest diffraction line to be almost invisible in relation to the background.

This background intensity is due to the following causes:

(1) *Fluorescent radiation emitted by the specimen.* It cannot be too strongly emphasized that the characteristic wavelength used should be longer than the K absorption edge of the specimen, in order to prevent the emission of fluorescent radiation. Incident radiation so chosen, however, will not completely eliminate fluorescence, since the short-wavelength components of the continuous spectrum will also excite K radiation in the specimen. For example, suppose a copper specimen is being examined with Cu $K\alpha$ radiation of wavelength 1.542A from a tube operated at 30 kv. Under these conditions the short-wavelength limit is 0.413A. The K absorption edge of copper is at 1.380A. The $K\alpha$ component of the incident radiation will not cause fluorescence, but all wavelengths between 0.413 and 1.380A will. If a nickel filter is used to suppress the $K\beta$ component of the incident beam, it will also have the desirable effect of reducing

the intensity of some of the short wavelengths which cause fluorescence, but it will not, of course, eliminate them completely, particularly in the wavelength region near 0.6A, where the intensity of the continuous spectrum is high and the absorption coefficient of nickel rather low.

It is sometimes possible to filter part of the fluorescent radiation from the specimen by placing the proper filter over the *film*. For example, if a steel specimen is examined with copper radiation, which is not generally advisable, the situation may be improved by covering the film with aluminum foil, because aluminum has a greater absorption for the fluorescent Fe $K\alpha$ radiation contributing to the background than for the Cu $K\alpha$ radiation forming the diffraction lines. In fact, the following is a good general rule to follow: if it is impossible to use a wavelength longer than the K absorption edge of the specimen, choose one which is considerably shorter and cover the film with a filter. Sometimes the air itself will provide sufficient filtration. Thus excellent patterns of aluminum can be obtained with Cu $K\alpha$ radiation, even though this wavelength (1.54A) is much shorter than the K absorption edge of aluminum (6.74A), simply because the Al $K\alpha$ radiation excited has such a long wavelength (8.34A) that it is almost completely absorbed in a few centimeters of air.

(2) *Diffraction of the continuous spectrum.* Each crystal in a powder specimen forms a weak Laue pattern, because of the continuous radiation component of the incident beam. This is of course true whether or not that particular crystal is in the correct position to reflect the characteristic component into the Debye ring. Many crystals in the specimen are therefore contributing only to the background of the photograph and not to the diffraction ring, and the totality of the Laue patterns from all the crystals is a continuous distribution of background radiation. If the incident radiation has been so chosen that very little fluorescent radiation is emitted, then diffraction of the continuous spectrum is the largest single cause of high background intensity in powder photographs.

(3) *Diffuse scattering from the specimen itself.*
   (*a*) Incoherent (Compton modified) scattering. This kind of scattering becomes more intense as the atomic number of the specimen decreases.
   (*b*) Coherent scattering.
      (i) Temperature-diffuse scattering. This form is more intense with soft materials of low melting point.
      (ii) Diffuse scattering due to various kinds of imperfection in the crystals. Any kind of randomness or strain will cause such scattering.
(4) *Diffraction and scattering from other than the specimen material.*
   (*a*) Collimator and beam stop. This kind of scattering can be minimized by correct camera design, as discussed in Sec. 6–2.

(b) Specimen binder, support, or enclosure. The glue or other adhesive used to compact the powder specimen, the glass fiber to which the powder is attached, or the glass or fused-quartz tube in which it is enclosed all contribute to the background of the photograph, since these are all amorphous substances. The amount of these materials should be kept to the absolute minimum.

(c) Air. Diffuse scattering from the air may be avoided by evacuating the camera or filling it with a light gas such as hydrogen or helium.

6–12 Crystal monochromators. The purest kind of radiation to use in a diffraction experiment is radiation which has itself been diffracted, since it is entirely monochromatic.* If a single crystal is set to reflect the strong $K\alpha$ component of the general radiation from an x-ray tube and this reflected beam is used as the incident beam in a diffraction camera, then the causes of background radiation listed under (1) and (2) above can be completely eliminated. Since the other causes of background scattering are less serious, the use of crystal-monochromated radiation produces diffraction photographs of remarkable clarity. There are two kinds of monochromators in use, depending on whether the reflecting crystal is unbent or bent and cut.

An unbent crystal is not a very efficient reflector, as can be seen from Fig. 6–14. The beam from an x-ray tube is never composed only of parallel rays, even when defined by a slit or collimator, but contains a large proportion of convergent and divergent radiation. When the crystal is set at the correct Bragg angle for the parallel component of the incident beam, it can reflect only that component and none of the other rays, with the

---

* This statement requires some qualification. When a crystal monochromator is set to diffract radiation of wavelength λ from a particular set of planes, then these same planes will also diffract radiation of wavelength $\lambda/2$ and $\lambda/3$ in the second and third order, respectively, and at exactly the same angle 2θ. These components of submultiple wavelength are of relatively low intensity when the main component is $K\alpha$ characteristic radiation but, even so, their presence is undesirable whenever precise calculations of the intensity diffracted by the *specimen* must be made. The submultiple components may be eliminated from the beam from the monochromator by reducing the tube voltage to the point where these wavelengths are not produced. If the main component is Cu $K\alpha$ radiation, this procedure is usually impractical because of the decrease in intensity attendant on a reduction in tube voltage to 16 kv (necessary to eliminate the $\lambda/2$ and $\lambda/3$ components). Usually, a compromise is made by operating at a voltage just insufficient to generate the $\lambda/3$ component (24 kv for copper radiation) and by using a crystal which has, for a certain set of planes, a negligible reflecting power for the $\lambda/2$ component. Fluorite (CaF_2) is such a crystal, the structure factor for the 222 reflection being much less than for the 111. The diamond cubic crystals, silicon and germanium, are even better, since their structure factors for the 222 reflection are actually zero.

result that the reflected beam is of
very low intensity although it is itself
perfectly parallel, at least in the plane
of the drawing. In a plane at right
angles, the reflected beam may contain both convergent and divergent
radiation.

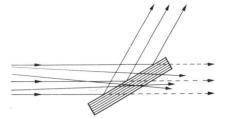

A large gain in intensity may be
obtained by using a bent and cut crystal, which operates on the focusing
principle illustrated in Fig. 6–15. A

Fig. 6–14. Monochromatic reflection when the incident beam is nonparallel.

line source of x-rays, the focal line on the tube target, is located at S perpendicular to the plane of the drawing. The crystal AB is in the form of a
rectangular plate and has a set of reflecting planes parallel to its surface.
It is elastically bent into a circular form so that the radius of curvature of
the plane through C is $2R = CM$; in this way, all the plane normals are
made to pass through M, which is located on the same circle, of radius R,
as the source S. If the face of the crystal is then cut away behind the
dotted line to a radius of R, then all rays diverging from the source S will
encounter the lattice planes at the same Bragg angle, since the angles
SDM, SCM, and SEM are all equal to one another, being inscribed on the
same arc SM, and have the value $(\pi/2 - \theta)$.

When the Bragg angle is adjusted to that required for reflection of the
$K\alpha$ component of the incident beam, then a strong monochromatic beam

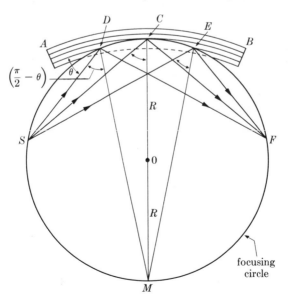

Fig. 6–15. Focusing monochromator (reflection type).

will be reflected by the crystal. Moreover, since the diffracted rays all originate on a circle passing through the source S, they will converge to a focus at F, located on the same circle as S and at the same distance from C, in much the same way as in the focusing cameras previously discussed.

In practice the crystal is not bent and then cut as described above, but the unbent crystal, usually of quartz, is first cut to a radius of $2R$ and then bent against a circular form of radius R. This procedure will produce the same net result. The value of θ required for the diffraction of a particular wavelength λ from planes of spacing d is given by the Bragg law:

$$\lambda = 2d \sin \theta. \tag{6-12}$$

The source-to-crystal distance SC, which equals the crystal-to-focus distance CF, is given by

$$SC = 2R \cos \left(\frac{\pi}{2} - \theta \right). \tag{6-13}$$

By combining Eqs. (6–12) and (6–13), we obtain

$$SC = R \frac{\lambda}{d}. \tag{6-14}$$

For reflection of Cu $K\alpha$ radiation from the (10·1) planes of quartz, the distance SC is 14.2 cm for a value of R of 30 cm.

The chief value of the focusing monochromator lies in the fact that all the monochromatic rays in the incident beam are utilized and the diffracted rays from a considerable area of the crystal surface are all brought to a focus. This leads to a large concentration of energy and a considerable reduction in exposure time compared to the unbent-crystal monochromator first described. However, the latter does produce a semiparallel beam of radiation, and, even though it is of very low intensity, such a beam is required in some experiments.

If the monochromating crystal is bent but not cut, some concentration of energy will be achieved inasmuch as the reflected beam will be convergent, but it will not converge to a perfect focus.

The focusing monochromator is best used with powder cameras especially made to take advantage of the particular property of the reflected beam, namely its focusing action. Figure 6–16(a) shows the best arrangement. A cylindrical camera is used with the specimen and film arranged on the surface of the cylinder. Low-angle reflections are registered with the camera placed in position C, in which case the specimen D must be thin enough to be examined in transmission. High-angle reflections are obtained by back reflection with the camera in position C', shown dotted, and the specimen at D'. In the latter case, the geometry of the camera is exactly similar to that of the Seemann-Bohlin camera, the focal point F of the

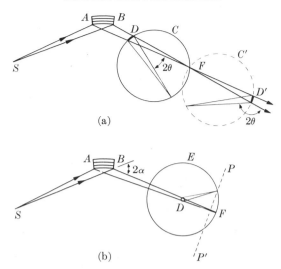

FIG. 6–16. Cameras used with focusing monochromators: (a) focusing cameras; (b) Debye-Scherrer and flat-film cameras. Only one diffracted beam is shown in each case. (After A. Guinier, *X-ray Crystallographic Technology*, Hilger and Watts, Ltd., London, 1952.)

monochromatic beam acting as a virtual source of divergent radiation. In either case, the diffracted rays from the specimen are focused on the film for all *hkl* reflections; the only requirement is that the film be located on a circle passing through the specimen and the point F.

A Debye-Scherrer or flat-film camera may also be used with a focusing monochromator, if the incident-beam collimator is removed. Figure 6–16(b) shows such an arrangement, where D is the specimen, E is a Debye camera, and PP' is the position where a flat film may be placed. In neither case, however, is the above-mentioned focusing requirement satisfied, with the result that no more than one diffracted beam, corresponding to one particular *hkl* reflection, can be focused on the film at the same time.

A bent crystal may also be used in transmission as a focusing mono-chromator. It must be thin enough to transmit a large fraction of the incident radiation and have a set of reflecting planes at right angles to its surface; mica is often used. In Fig. 6–17, the line ACB represents the crystal, bent to a radius $2R$, its center of curvature located at M. Three of its transverse reflecting planes are shown. If radiation converging to K were incident on these planes and reflected at the points H, C, and G, the reflected radiation would converge to a perfect focus at F, all the points mentioned being on a focusing circle of radius R centered at O. But the reflecting planes do not actually extend out of the crystal surface in the way shown in the drawing and reflection must occur at the points

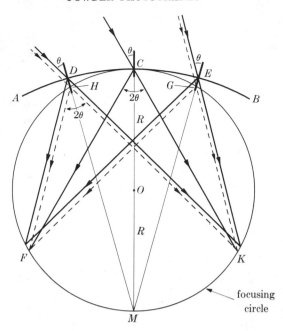

Fig. 6–17. Focusing monochromator (transmission type).

D, C, and E. Under these conditions the reflected rays from all parts of the crystal do not converge to a perfect focus at F. Nevertheless there is sufficient concentration of diffracted energy in a very narrow region near F to make this device a quite efficient and usable monochromator. The crystal-to-focus distance CF is given by

$$CF = 2R \cos \theta. \tag{6–15}$$

Combination of this equation with the Bragg law will give the bending radius required for specific applications.

The use of a monochromator produces a change in the relative intensities of the beams diffracted by the specimen. Equation (4–12), for example, was derived for the completely unpolarized incident beam obtained from the x-ray tube. Any beam diffracted by a crystal, however, becomes partially polarized by the diffraction process itself, which means that the beam from a crystal monochromator is partially polarized before it reaches the specimen. Under these circumstances, the usual polarization factor $(1 + \cos^2 2\theta)/2$, which is included in Eq. (4–12), must be replaced by the factor $(1 + \cos^2 2\alpha \cos^2 2\theta)/(1 + \cos^2 2\alpha)$, where 2α is the diffraction angle in the monochromator [Fig. 6–16(b)]. Since the denominator in this expression is independent of θ, it may be omitted; the combined Lorentz-polarization factor for a Debye-Scherrer camera and crystal-monochromated radiation is therefore $(1 + \cos^2 2\alpha \cos^2 2\theta)/\sin^2 \theta \cos \theta$.

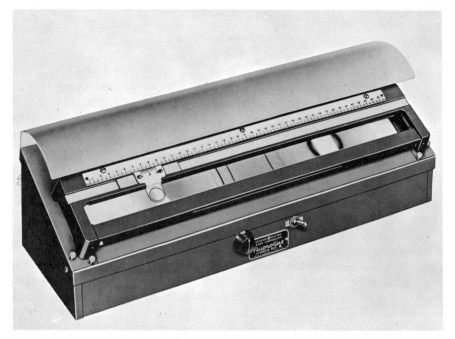

Fig. 6–18.   Film-measuring device.   (Courtesy of General Electric Co., X-Ray Department.)

6–13 Measurement of line position.   The solution of any powder photograph begins with the measurement of the positions of the diffraction lines on the film. A device of the kind shown in Fig. 6–18 is commonly used for this purpose. It is essentially a box with an opal-glass plate on top, illuminated from below, on which the film to be measured is placed. On top of the glass plate is a graduated scale carrying a slider equipped with a vernier and cross-hair; the cross-hair is moved over the illuminated film from one diffraction line to another and their positions noted. The film is usually measured without magnification. A low-power hand lens may be of occasional use, but magnification greater than 2 or 3 diameters usually causes the line to merge into the background and become invisible, because of the extreme graininess of x-ray film.

6–14 Measurement of line intensity.   Many diffraction problems require an accurate measurement of the integrated intensity, or the breadth at half maximum intensity, of a diffraction line on a powder photograph. For this purpose it is necessary to obtain a curve of intensity *vs.* 2θ for the line in question.

The intensity of an x-ray beam may be measured by the amount of blackening it causes on a photographic film. The photographic density D, or blackening, of a film is in turn measured by the amount of visible light it will transmit and is defined by the relation

$$D = \log_{10} \frac{I_0}{I},$$

where I_0 = intensity of a beam of light incident on the film and I = intensity of the transmitted beam. For most x-ray films, the density is directly proportional to the exposure up to a density of about 1.0 (which corresponds to 10 percent transmission of the incident light). Here, "exposure" is defined by the relation

Exposure = (intensity of x-ray beam)(time).

Since the time is constant for all the diffraction lines on one film, this means that the photographic density is directly proportional to the x-ray intensity.

Density is measured by means of a microphotometer. There are several forms of such instruments, the simplest consisting of a light source and an arrangement of lenses and slits which allows a narrow beam of light to pass through the x-ray film and strike a photocell or thermopile connected to a recording galvanometer. Since the current through the galvanometer is proportional to the intensity of the light striking the photocell, the galvanometer deflection S is proportional to the transmitted light intensity I.

The light beam is rectangular in cross section, normally about 3 mm high and 0.1 mm wide. With movement of the film, this beam is made to traverse the film laterally, crossing one diffraction line after another [Fig. 6–19(a)]. The resulting galvanometer record [Fig. 6–19(b)] shows galvanometer deflection as ordinate and distance along the film as abscissa, the latter being increased by a factor of about 5 in order to spread the lines out. The line A at the top of the record marks zero deflection of the galvanometer; the line B at the bottom marks the maximum galvanometer deflection S_0 when the light beam passes through an unexposed portion of the film, a portion which has been shielded from all scattered x-rays. S_0 is therefore constant and proportional to the incident light intensity I_0. In this way the readings are corrected for the normal background fog of unexposed film. The density of any exposed part of the film is then obtained from the relation

$$D = \log_{10} \frac{I_0}{I} = \log_{10} \frac{S_0}{S}.$$

Finally, a curve is constructed of x-ray intensity as a function of 2θ [Fig. 6–19(c)]. Such a plot is seen to consist of a number of diffraction peaks superimposed on a curve of slowly varying background intensity, due to fluorescent radiation, diffraction of the continuous spectrum, Compton

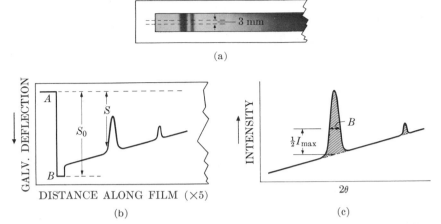

FIG. 6–19. Measurement of line intensity with a microphotometer (schematic): (a) film; (b) galvanometer record; (c) x-ray intensity curve.

scattering, etc., as previously discussed. A continuous background line is drawn in below each peak, after which measurements of the integrated intensity and the breadth B at half maximum intensity can be made. Note that the integrated intensity is given by the shaded area, measured *above* the background. A microphotometer record of an actual pattern is shown in Fig. 6–20.

In very precise work, or when the line density exceeds a value of 1.0, it is no longer safe to assume that the density is proportional to the x-ray exposure. Instead, each film should be calibrated by exposing a strip near its edge to a constant-intensity x-ray beam for increasing amounts of time so that a series of stepwise increasing exposures is obtained. The exact relation between density and x-ray exposure can then be determined experimentally.

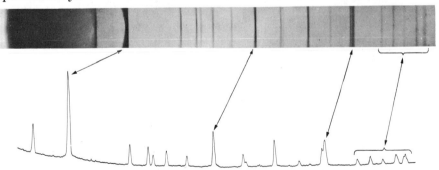

FIG. 6–20. Powder pattern of quartz (above) and corresponding microphotometer trace (below). (J. W. Ballard, H. I. Oshry, and H. H. Schrenk, *U. S. Bur. Mines R. I.* 3520. Courtesy of U. S. Bureau of Mines.)

PROBLEMS

6–1. Plot a curve similar to that of Fig. 6–3 showing the absorption of Fe $K\alpha$ radiation by air. Take the composition of air as 80 percent nitrogen and 20 percent oxygen, by weight. If a 1-hr exposure in air is required to produce a certain diffraction line intensity in a 19-cm-diameter camera with Fe $K\alpha$ radiation, what exposure is required to obtain the same line intensity with the camera evacuated, other conditions being equal?

6–2. Derive an equation for the resolving power of a Debye-Scherrer camera for two wavelengths of nearly the same value, in terms of ΔS, where S is defined by Fig. 6–2.

6–3. For a Debye pattern made in a 5.73-cm-diameter camera with Cu $K\alpha$ radiation, calculate the separation of the components of the $K\alpha$ doublet in degrees and in centimeters for $\theta = 10$, 35, 60, and 85°.

6–4. What is the smallest value of θ at which the Cr $K\alpha$ doublet will be resolved in a 5.73-cm-diameter Debye camera? Assume that the line width is 0.03 cm and that the separation must be twice the width for resolution.

6–5. A powder pattern of zinc is made in a Debye-Scherrer camera 5.73 cm in diameter with Cu $K\alpha$ radiation.

(a) Calculate the resolving power necessary to separate the 11.0 and 10.3 diffraction lines. Assume that the line width is 0.03 cm.

(b) Calculate the resolving power of the camera used, for these lines.

(c) What minimum camera diameter is required to produce resolution of these lines?

(See Fig. 3–13(c), which shows these lines unresolved from one another. They form the fifth line from the low-angle end.)

6–6. A transmission pinhole photograph is made of copper with Cu $K\alpha$ radiation. The film measures 4 by 5 in. What is the maximum specimen-to-film distance which can be used and still have the first two Debye rings completely recorded on the film?

6–7. A powder pattern of iron is made with Cu $K\alpha$ radiation. Assume that the background is due entirely to fluorescent radiation from the specimen. The maximum intensity (measured above the background) of the weakest line on the pattern is found to be equal to the background intensity itself at that angle. If the film is covered with aluminum foil 0.0015 in. thick, what will be the ratio of I_{max} for this line to the background intensity?

6–8. A microphotometer record of a diffraction line shows the following galvanometer deflections:

Position of Light Beam	Deflection
On unexposed film	5.0 cm
On background, just to left of line	3.0
On background, just to right of line	3.2
On center of diffraction line	1.2

Assume that x-ray intensity is proportional to photographic density. Calculate the ratio of I_{max} for the diffraction line (measured above the background) to the intensity of the background at the same Bragg angle.

CHAPTER 7

DIFFRACTOMETER MEASUREMENTS

7–1 Introduction. The x-ray spectrometer, briefly mentioned in Sec. 3–4, has had a long and uneven history in the field of x-ray diffraction. It was first used by W. H. and W. L. Bragg in their early work on x-ray spectra and crystal structure, but it then passed into a long period of relative disuse during which photographic recording in cameras was the most popular method of observing diffraction effects. The few spectrometers in use were all home made and confined largely to the laboratories of research physicists. In recent years, however, commercially made instruments (based mainly on a design developed by Friedman about 1943) have become available, and their use is growing rapidly because of certain particular advantages which they offer over film techniques. Initially a research tool, the x-ray spectrometer has now become an instrument for control and analysis in a wide variety of industrial laboratories.

Depending solely on the way it is used, the x-ray spectrometer is really two instruments:

(1) An instrument for measuring x-ray spectra by means of a crystal of known structure.

(2) An instrument for studying crystalline (and noncrystalline) materials by measurements of the way in which they diffract x-rays of known wavelength.

The term *spectrometer* has been, and still is, used to describe both instruments, but, properly, it should be applied only to the first instrument. The second instrument has been aptly called a *diffractometer:* this is a term of quite recent coinage but one which serves well to emphasize the particular use to which the instrument is being put, namely, diffraction analysis rather than spectrometry. In this chapter, the design and operation of diffractometers will be described with particular reference to the commercial models available.

7–2 General features. In a diffraction camera, the intensity of a diffracted beam is measured through the amount of blackening it produces on a photographic film, a microphotometer measurement of the film being required to convert "amount of blackening" into x-ray intensity. In the diffractometer, the intensity of a diffracted beam is measured directly, either by means of the ionization it produces in a gas or the fluorescence it produces in a solid. As we saw in Sec. 1–5, incident x-ray quanta can eject electrons from atoms and thus convert them into positive ions. If an x-ray beam is passed into a chamber containing a gas and two electrodes, one charged positively and the other negatively, then the ejected electrons will be drawn to the positive electrode (the anode) and the positive ions to the negative electrode (the cathode). A current therefore exists in the external circuit connecting anode to cathode. Under special conditions, which are described later in detail, this current can be caused to surge or pulse rather than be continuous; each pulse results from the ionization caused by a single entering x-ray quantum. By use of the proper external circuit, the number of current pulses produced per unit of time can be counted, and this number is directly proportional to the intensity of the x-ray beam entering the gas chamber. Appropriately, this device is called a *counter*, and two varieties are in common use, the proportional counter and the Geiger counter. In another type, the scintillation counter, incident x-ray quanta produce flashes or scintillations of fluorescent blue light in a crystal and these light flashes are converted into current pulses in a phototube.

Basically, a diffractometer is designed somewhat like a Debye-Scherrer camera, except that a movable counter replaces the strip of film. In both instruments, essentially monochromatic radiation is used and the x-ray detector (film or counter) is placed on the circumference of a circle centered on the powder specimen. The essential features of a diffractometer are shown in Fig. 7–1. A powder specimen C, in the form of a flat plate, is supported on a table H, which can be rotated about an axis O perpendicular to the plane of the drawing. The x-ray source is S, the line focal spot on the target T of the x-ray tube; S is also normal to the plane of the drawing and therefore parallel to the diffractometer axis O. X-rays diverge from this source and are diffracted by the specimen to form a convergent diffracted beam which comes to a focus at the slit F and then enters the counter G. A and B are special slits which define and collimate the incident and diffracted beams.

The receiving slits and counter are supported on the carriage E, which may be rotated about the axis O and whose angular position 2θ may be read on the graduated scale K. The supports E and H are mechanically coupled so that a rotation of the counter through $2x$ degrees is automatically accompanied by rotation of the specimen through x degrees. This coupling ensures that the angles of incidence on, and reflection from, the flat specimen will always be equal to one another and equal to half the total angle of diffraction, an arrangement necessary to preserve focusing conditions. The counter may be power-driven at a constant angular velocity about the diffractometer axis or moved by hand to any desired angular position.

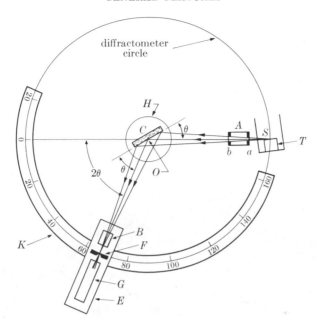

FIG. 7–1.　X-ray diffractometer (schematic).

Figures 7–2 and 7–3 illustrate two commercial instruments.　Basically, both adhere to the design principles described above, but they differ in detail and in positioning: in the General Electric unit, the diffractometer axis is vertical and the counter moves in a horizontal plane, whereas the axis of the Norelco unit is horizontal and the counter moves in a vertical plane.

The way in which a diffractometer is used to measure a diffraction pattern depends on the kind of circuit used to measure the rate of production of pulses in the counter.　The pulse rate may be measured in two different ways:

(1) The succession of current pulses is converted into a steady current, which is measured on a meter called a *counting-rate meter*, calibrated in such units as counts (pulses) per second.　Such a circuit gives a continuous indication of x-ray intensity.

(2) The pulses of current are counted electronically in a circuit called a *scaler*, and the average counting rate is obtained simply by dividing the number of pulses counted by the time spent in counting.　This operation is essentially discontinuous because of the time spent in counting, and a scaling circuit cannot be used to follow continuous changes in x-ray intensity.

Corresponding to these two kinds of measuring circuits, there are two ways in which the diffraction pattern of an unknown substance may be obtained with a diffractometer:

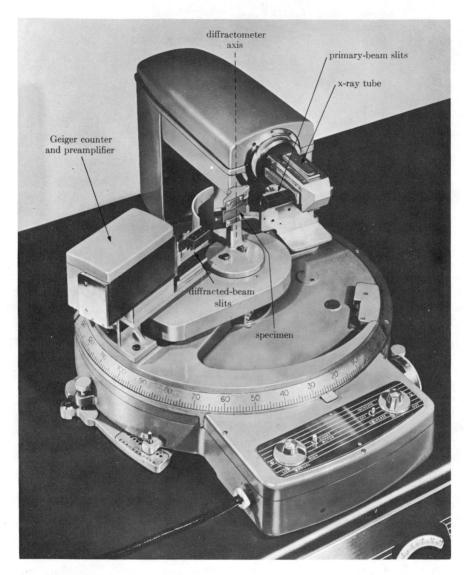

Fig. 7–2. General Electric diffractometer. (Courtesy of General Electric Co., X-Ray Department.)

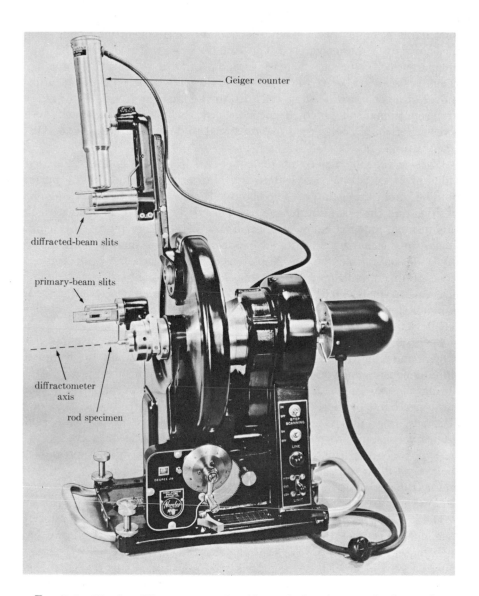

FIG. 7–3. Norelco diffractometer. In this particular photograph, the specimen holder for a thin rod specimen is shown instead of the usual holder for a flat plate specimen. X-ray tube not shown. (Courtesy of North American Philips Co., Inc.)

(1) *Continuous.* The counter is set near $2\theta = 0°$ and connected to a counting-rate meter. The output of this circuit is fed into a fast-acting automatic recorder of the kind used to record temperature changes as measured by a thermocouple. The counter is then driven at a constant angular velocity through increasing values of 2θ until the whole angular range is "scanned." At the same time, the paper chart on the recorder moves at a constant speed, so that distances along the length of the chart are proportional to 2θ. The result is a chart, such as Fig. 7–4, which gives a record of counts per second (proportional to diffracted intensity) *vs.* diffraction angle 2θ.

(2) *Intermittent.* The counter is connected to a scaler and set at a fixed value of 2θ for a time sufficient to make an accurate count of the pulses obtained from the counter. The counter is then moved to a new angular position and the operation repeated. The whole range of 2θ is covered in this fashion, and the curve of intensity *vs.* 2θ is finally plotted by hand. When the continuous background between diffraction lines is being measured, the counter may be moved in steps of several degrees, but determinations of line profile may require measurements of intensity at angular intervals as small as $0.01°$. This method of obtaining a diffraction pattern is much slower than that involving a rate meter and automatic recorder but it yields more precise measurements of intensity.

There is a fundamental difference between the operation of a powder camera and a diffractometer. In a camera, all diffraction lines are recorded simultaneously, and variations in the intensity of the incident x-ray beam during the exposure can have no effect on relative line intensities. On the other hand, with a diffractometer, diffraction lines are recorded one after the other, and it is therefore imperative to keep the incident-beam intensity constant when relative line intensities must be measured accurately. Since the usual variations in line voltage are quite appreciable, the x-ray tube circuit of a diffractometer must include a voltage stabilizer and a tube-current stabilizer, unless a monitoring system is used (see Sec. 7–8).

The kind of specimen used depends on the form and amount of material available. Flat metal sheet or plate may be examined directly; however, such materials almost always exhibit preferred orientation and this fact must be kept in mind in assessing relative intensities. This is also true of wires, which are best examined by cementing a number of lengths side by side to a glass plate. This plate is then inserted in the specimen holder so that the wire axes are at right angles to the diffractometer axis. Powder specimens are best prepared by placing the powder in a recess in a glass or plastic plate, compacting it under just sufficient pressure to cause cohesion without use of a binder, and smoothing off the surface. Too much pressure causes preferred orientation of the powder particles. Alternately, the powder may be mixed with a binder and smeared on the

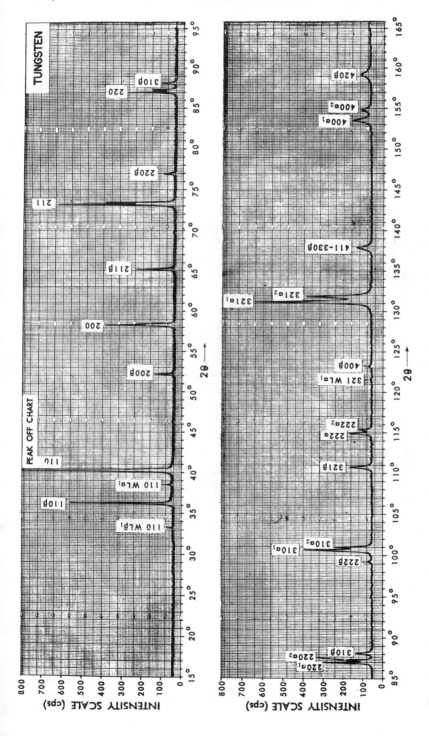

Fig. 7–4.　Automatically recorded diffraction pattern of tungsten powder.　Unfiltered copper radiation, 25 kv, 20 ma.　Different slits used for the front-reflection region (above) and the back-reflection region (below).　The weak tungsten $L\alpha_1$ lines are due to a small amount of tungsten contamination in the x-ray tube, after 3750 hours of use.　(Courtesy of North American Philips Co., Inc.)

surface of a glass slide. The powder should be ground extremely fine, to a size of 10 microns or less, if relative line intensities are to be accurately reproducible; since the flat specimen is not rotated as a Debye-Scherrer specimen is, the only way of obtaining an adequate number of particles having the correct orientation for reflection is to reduce their average size. Surface roughness also has a marked effect on relative line intensities. If the surface is rough, as in the case of a coarse powder compact, and the linear absorption coefficient high, the intensities of low-angle reflections will be abnormally low, because of the absorption of the diffracted rays in each projecting portion of the surface. The only way to avoid this effect is to use a flat-surfaced compact of very fine powders or a specimen with a polished surface.

If not enough powder is available for a flat specimen, a thin-rod specimen of the kind used in Debye-Scherrer cameras may be used; it is mounted on the diffractometer axis and continuously rotated by a small motor (see Fig. 7–3). However, the use of such a small specimen should be avoided if possible, since it leads to intensities very much lower than those obtainable with a flat specimen.

Single-crystal specimens may also be examined in a diffractometer by mounting the crystal on a three-circle goniometer, such as that shown in Fig. 5–7, which will allow independent rotation of the specimen and counter about the diffractometer axis.

A diffractometer may be used for measurements at high or low temperatures by surrounding the specimen with the appropriate heating or cooling unit. Such an adaptation of the instrument is much easier with the diffractometer than with a camera because of the generally larger amount of free working space around the specimen in the former.

In the succeeding sections, the various parts of the diffractometer will be described in greater detail. This summary of the general features of the instrument is enough to show its principal advantage over the powder camera: the quantitative measurement of line position and intensity is made in one operation with a diffractometer, whereas the same measurement with film technique requires three steps (recording the pattern on film, making a microphotometer record of the film, and conversion of galvanometer deflections to intensities) and leads to an over-all result which is generally of lower accuracy. This superiority of the diffractometer is reflected in the much higher cost of the instrument, a cost due not only to the precision machining necessary in its mechanical parts but also to the expensive circuits needed to stabilize the power supply and measure the intensity of diffracted beams.

7–3 X-ray optics. The chief reason for using a flat specimen is to take advantage of the focusing action described in Sec. 6–6 and so increase the

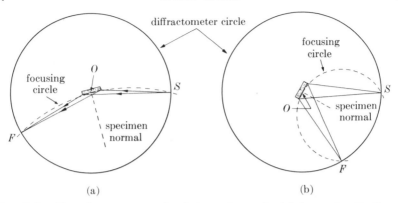

Fig. 7–5. Focusing geometry for flat specimens in (a) forward reflection and (b) back reflection.

intensity of weak diffracted beams to a point where they can be accurately measured. Figure 7–5 shows how this is done. For any position of the counter, the receiving slit F and the x-ray source S are always located on the diffractometer circle, which means that the face of the specimen, because of its mechanical coupling with the counter, is always tangent to a focusing circle centered on the normal to the specimen and passing through F and S. The focusing circle is not of constant size but increases in radius as the angle 2θ decreases, as indicated in Fig. 7–5. Perfect focusing at F requires that the specimen be curved to fit the focusing circle, but that is not practical because of the changing radius of curvature of the circle. This inevitably causes some broadening of the diffracted beam at F but not to any objectionable degree, so long as the divergence of the incident beam is not too large.

The line source S extends considerably above and below the plane of the drawing of Fig. 7–5 and emits radiation in all directions, but the focusing described above requires that all rays in the incident beam be parallel to the plane of the drawing. This condition is realized as closely as possible experimentally by passing the incident beam through a Soller slit (Fig. 7–6), slit A in Fig. 7–1, which contains a set of closely spaced, thin metal plates parallel to the plane of the diffractometer circle. These plates remove a large proportion of rays inclined to the plane of the diffractometer circle and still allow the use of a line source of considerable length. Typical dimensions of a Soller slit are: length of plates 32 mm, thickness of plates 0.05 mm, clear distance between plates 0.43 mm. At either end of the slit assembly are rectangular slits a and b, the entrance slit a next to the source being narrower than the exit slit b. The combination of slits and plates breaks up the incident beam into a set of triangular wedges of radiation, as indicated in Fig. 7–6. There are, of course, some rays, not shown in the drawing, which diverge in planes perpendicular to the plane

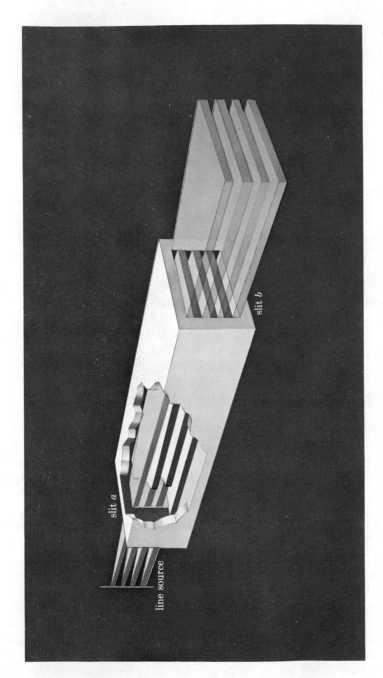

Fig. 7–6. Soller slit (schematic). For simplicity, only three metal plates are shown; actual Soller slits contain about a dozen.

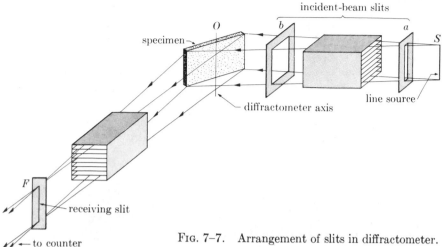

FIG. 7–7.   Arrangement of slits in diffractometer.

of the plates, and these rays cause the wedges of radiation to merge into one another a short distance away from the exit slit. However, the long, closely spaced plates do restrict this unwanted divergence to an angle of about 1.5°. Slits a and b define the divergence of the incident beam in the plane of the diffractometer circle. The slits commonly available have divergence angles ranging from very small values up to about 4°. In the forward-reflection region, a divergence angle of 1° is sufficient because of the low inclination of the specimen surface to the incident beam, but in back reflection an increase in divergence angle to 3 or 4° will increase the diffracted intensity. But if line intensities are to be compared over the whole range of 2θ, the same divergence must be used throughout and the specimen must be wider than the beam at all angles.

The beam diffracted by the specimen passes through another Soller-slit assembly and the receiving slit F before entering the counter. Since the receiving slit defines the width of the beam admitted to the counter, an increase in its width will increase the maximum intensity of any diffraction line being measured but at the expense of some loss of resolution. On the other hand, the relative *integrated intensity* of a diffraction line is independent of slit width, which is one reason for its greater fundamental importance.* Figure 7–7 illustrates the relative arrangement of the various

---

* A number of things besides slit width (e.g., x-ray tube current) will change the integrated intensity of a single diffraction line. The important thing to note, however, is that a change in any one of the operating variables changes the integrated intensities of all diffraction lines in the same ratio but can produce very unequal effects on maximum intensities. Thus, if I_1/I_2 is the ratio of the integrated intensities of two lines measured with a certain slit width and M_1/M_2 the ratio of their maximum intensities, then another measurement with a different slit width will result in the same ratio I_1/I_2 for the integrated intensities, but the ratio of the maximum intensities will now, in general, differ from M_1/M_2.

slits in a typical diffractometer and shows the passage of a few selected rays from source to counter.

Because of the focusing of the diffracted rays and the relatively large radius of the diffractometer circle, about 15 cm in commercial instruments, a diffractometer can resolve very closely spaced diffraction lines. Indicative of this is the fact that resolution of the Cu $K\alpha$ doublet can be obtained at 2θ angles as low as about 40°. Such resolution can only be achieved with a correctly adjusted instrument, and it is necessary to so align the component parts that the following conditions are satisfied for all diffraction angles:

(1) line source, specimen surface, and receiving-slit axis are all parallel,

(2) the specimen surface coincides with the diffractometer axis, and

(3) the line source and receiving slit both lie on the diffractometer circle.

7–4 Intensity calculations. The calculation of the relative integrated intensities of beams diffracted by a powder specimen in a diffractometer follows the general principles described in Chap. 4, but the details of the calculation depend on the form of the specimen.

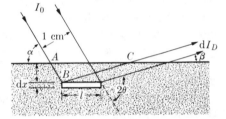

The use of a **flat-plate specimen,** making equal angles with the incident and diffracted beams, not only produces focusing as described above but makes the absorption factor independent of the angle θ. We can prove this by calculating the effect of absorption in the specimen on the intensity

FIG. 7–8. Diffraction from a flat plate: incident and diffracted beams have a thickness of 1 cm in a direction normal to the plane of the drawing.

of the diffracted beam, and, since this effect will come up again in later parts of this book, we will make our calculation quite general. In Fig. 7–8, the incident beam has intensity I_0 (ergs/cm²/sec), is 1 cm square in cross section, and is incident on the powder plate at an angle α. We consider the energy diffracted from this beam by a layer of the powder of length l and thickness dx, located at a depth x below the surface. Since the incident beam undergoes absorption by the specimen over the path length AB, the energy incident per second on the layer considered is $I_0 e^{-\mu(AB)}$ (ergs/sec), where μ is the linear absorption coefficient of the powder compact. Let a be the volume fraction of the specimen containing particles having the correct orientation for reflection of the incident beam, and b the fraction of the incident energy which is diffracted by unit volume. Then the energy diffracted by the layer considered, which has a volume $l\,dx$, is given by $abl I_0 e^{-\mu(AB)}\,dx$. But this diffracted energy is also decreased by absorption, by a factor of $e^{-\mu(BC)}$, since the diffracted rays have a path length of BC in the specimen. The energy flux per second in the diffracted beam outside the specimen, i.e., the integrated intensity, is therefore given by

$$dI_D = ablI_0 e^{-\mu(AB+BC)} \, dx \quad \text{(ergs/sec)}. \tag{7–1}$$

But

$$l = \frac{1}{\sin \alpha}, \quad AB = \frac{x}{\sin \alpha}, \quad BC = \frac{x}{\sin \beta}.$$

Therefore,

$$dI_D = \frac{I_0 ab}{\sin \alpha} e^{-\mu x(1/\sin \alpha + 1/\sin \beta)} \, dx. \tag{7–2}$$

For the particular specimen arrangement used in the diffractometer, $\alpha = \beta = \theta$, and the above equation becomes

$$dI_D = \frac{I_0 ab}{\sin \theta} e^{-2\mu x/\sin \theta} \, dx. \tag{7–3}$$

The total diffracted intensity is obtained by integrating over an infinitely thick specimen:

$$I_D = \int_{x=0}^{x=\infty} dI_D = \frac{I_0 ab}{2\mu}. \tag{7–4}$$

Here I_0, b, and μ are constant for all reflections (independent of θ) and we may also regard a as constant. Actually, a varies with θ, but this variation is already taken care of by the $\cos \theta$ portion of the Lorentz factor (see Sec. 4–9) and need not concern us here. We conclude that the absorption factor, $1/2\mu$, is independent of θ for a flat specimen making equal angles with the incident and diffracted beams, provided the specimen fills the incident beam at all angles and is effectively of infinite thickness.* This

---

* The criterion adopted for "infinite thickness" depends on the sensitivity of our intensity measurements or on what we regard as negligible diffracted intensity. For example, we might arbitrarily but quite reasonably define infinite thickness as that thickness t which a specimen must have in order that the intensity diffracted by a thin layer on the back side be $\frac{1}{1000}$ of the intensity diffracted by a thin layer on the front side. Then, from Eq. (7–3) we have

$$\frac{dI_D \text{ (at } x = 0)}{dI_D \text{ (at } x = t)} = e^{2\mu t/\sin \theta} = 1000,$$

from which

$$t = \frac{3.45 \sin \theta}{\mu}.$$

This expression shows that "infinite thickness," for a metal specimen, is very small indeed. For example, suppose a specimen of nickel powder is being examined with Cu $K\alpha$ radiation at θ values approaching 90°. The density of the powder compact may be taken as about 0.6 the density of bulk nickel, which is 8.9 gm/cm³, leading to a value of μ for the compact of 263 cm⁻¹. The value of t is therefore 1.31×10^{-2} cm, or about five thousandths of an inch.

independence of θ is due to the exact balancing of two opposing effects. When θ is small, the specimen area irradiated by an incident beam of fixed cross section is large, but the effective depth of x-ray penetration is small; when θ is large, the irradiated area is small, but the penetration depth is relatively large.   The net effect is that the effective irradiated volume is constant and independent of θ.   Absorption occurs in any case, however, and the larger the absorption coefficient of the specimen, the lower the intensity of the diffracted beams, other things being equal.   The important fact to note is that absorption decreases the intensities of all diffracted beams by the same factor and therefore does not enter into the calculation of *relative* intensities.   This means that Eq. (4–12) for the relative integrated intensity of a diffraction line from a powder specimen, namely,

$$I = |F|^2 p \left(\frac{1 + \cos^2 2\theta}{\sin^2 \theta \cos \theta} \right), \tag{4–12}$$

needs only the insertion of a temperature factor to make it precise, for the case of a flat specimen examined in a diffractometer.   As it stands, it may still be used to calculate the approximate relative intensities of two adjacent lines on the pattern, but the calculated intensity of the higher-angle line, relative to that of the lower-angle one, will always be somewhat too large because of the omission of the temperature factor.

When the specimen used in the diffractometer has the form of a **thin rod,** no focusing occurs and the incident-beam slits are chosen to produce a thin, essentially parallel beam.   The x-ray geometry is then entirely equivalent to that of a Debye-Scherrer camera equipped with slits, and Eq. (4–12) applies, with exactly the same limitations as mentioned in Sec. 4–12.

7–5 Proportional counters. Proportional, Geiger, and scintillation counters may be used to detect, not only x- and γ-radiation, but also charged particles such as electrons or α-particles, and the design of the counter and associated circuits depends to some extent on what is to be detected.   Here we are concerned only with counters for the detection of x-rays of the wavelengths commonly employed in diffraction.

Consider the device shown in Fig. 7–9, consisting of a cylindrical metal shell (the cathode) filled with a gas and containing a fine metal wire (the anode) running along its axis.   Suppose there is a constant potential difference of about 200 volts between anode and cathode.   One end of the cylinder is covered with a window material, such as mica or beryllium, of high transparency to x-rays.   Of the x-rays which enter the cylinder, a small fraction passes right through, but the larger part is absorbed by the gas, and this absorption is accompanied by the ejection of photoelectrons

and Compton recoil electrons from
the atoms of the gas. The net result
is ionization of the gas, producing
electrons, which move under the influence of the electric field toward
the wire anode, and positive gas ions,
which move toward the cathode shell.
At a potential difference of about
200 volts, all these electrons and ions
will be collected on the electrodes,
and, if the x-ray intensity is constant,
there will be a small constant current
of the order of 10^{-12} amp or less

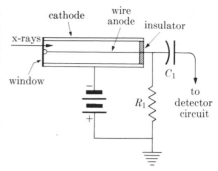

FIG. 7–9. Gas counter (proportional or Geiger) and basic circuit connections.

through the resistance R_1. This current is a measure of the x-ray intensity. When operated in this manner, this device is called an *ionization
chamber*. It was used in the original Bragg spectrometer but is now
obsolete for the measurement of x-ray intensities because of its low sensitivity.

The same instrument, however, can be made to act as a *proportional
counter* if the voltage is raised to the neighborhood of 600 to 900 volts.
A new phenomenon now occurs, namely, multiple ionization or "gas amplification." The electric-field intensity is now so high that the electrons
produced by the primary ionization are rapidly accelerated toward the
wire anode and at an ever increasing rate of acceleration, since the field
intensity increases as the wire is approached. The electrons thus acquire
enough energy to knock electrons out of other gas atoms, and these in turn
cause further ionization and so on, until the number of atoms ionized by
the absorption of a single x-ray quantum is some 10^3 to 10^5 times as large
as the number ionized in an ionization chamber. As a result of this amplification a veritable avalanche of electrons hits the wire and causes an easily
detectible pulse of current in the external circuit. This pulse leaks away
through the large resistance R_1 but not before the charge momentarily
added to the capacitor C_1 has been detected by the ratemeter or scaling
circuit connected to C_1. At the same time the positive gas ions move to
the cathode but at a much lower rate because of their larger mass. This
whole process, which is extremely fast, is triggered by the absorption of
one x-ray quantum.

We can define a gas amplification factor A as follows: if n is the number
of atoms ionized by one x-ray quantum, then An is the total number
ionized by the cumulative process described above. Figure 7–10 shows
schematically how the gas amplification factor varies with the applied
voltage. At the voltages used in ionization chambers, $A = 1$; i.e., there
is no gas amplification, since the electrons produced by the primary ioniza-

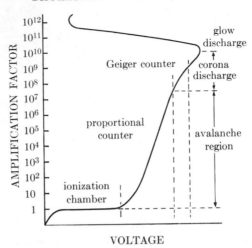

VOLTAGE

FIG. 7–10. Effect of voltage on the gas amplification factor. (H. Friedman, *Proc. I.R.E.* **37**, 791, 1949.)

tion do not acquire enough energy to ionize other atoms. But when the voltage is raised into the proportional counter region, A becomes of the order of 10^3 to 10^5.

The current pulse in the anode wire is normally expressed in terms of the momentary change of voltage in the wire, and this change is of the order of a few millivolts. The proportional counter receives its name from the fact that the size of this pulse, for a given applied voltage, is directly proportional to n, the number of ions formed by the primary ionization process, and this number is in turn proportional to the energy of the x-ray quantum absorbed. Thus, if absorption of a Cu $K\alpha$ quantum ($h\nu = 9,000$ ev) produces a voltage pulse of 1.0 mv, then absorption of a Mo $K\alpha$ quantum ($h\nu = 20,000$ ev) will produce a pulse of $(20,000/9,000)(1.0) = 2.2$ mv.

The proportional counter is essentially a very fast counter; i.e., it can resolve separate pulses arriving at a rate as high as 10^6 per second. It can do this because each avalanche is confined to an extremely narrow region of the wire, 0.1 mm or less, and does not spread longitudinally along the counter tube. This is an important feature of the process and one to which we will return in the next section.

By inserting special circuits between a proportional counter and the measuring instrument (scaler or ratemeter), it is possible to take advantage of the fact that the sizes of the pulses produced are inversely proportional to the wavelengths of the x-rays producing them. For example, one such circuit allows only pulses larger than a certain selected size to pass and discriminates against smaller ones; it is called a *pulse-height discriminator*. If two such circuits are used together, one set to pass only those pulses larger than V_1 volts and the other only those larger than V_2 volts, then the difference between their two outputs is due only to pulses having sizes in the V_1- to V_2-volt range. This subtraction may be done electronically, in which case the composite circuit is called a *single-channel pulse-height analyzer*.

Such a device allows a proportional counter to be operated under essentially monochromatic conditions. For example, if a diffraction pattern is being obtained with copper radiation, the analyzer can be set to pass only pulses due to Cu $K\alpha$ radiation and reject those due to other wavelengths, such as Cu $K\beta$, fluorescent radiation from the specimen, white radiation, etc.

7–6 Geiger counters. If the voltage on a proportional counter is increased some hundreds of volts, it will act as a Geiger counter. The exact operating voltage is determined in the following way. The counter is exposed to a beam of x-rays of constant intensity and connected to an appropriate circuit which will measure its counting rate, i.e., the rate of production of current pulses in the external circuit. The applied voltage is then gradually increased from zero, and the counting rate is found to vary with voltage in the manner shown in Fig. 7–11. No counts are obtained below a certain minimum voltage called the starting voltage,* but above this value the counting rate increases rapidly with voltage until the threshold of the Geiger region is reached. In this region, called the plateau, the counting rate is almost independent of voltage. At voltages beyond the plateau, the counter goes into a state of continuous discharge. A Geiger counter is operated on the plateau, normally at an overvoltage of about 100 volts, i.e., at 100 volts higher than threshold. The plateau has a finite slope, about 0.05 per-cent/volt, which means that the operating voltage must be stabilized if the counting rate is to be accurately pro-

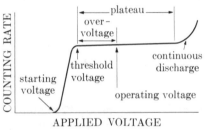

FIG. 7–11. Effect of voltage on counting rate for constant x-ray intensity.

portional to x-ray intensity. (The same is true of proportional counters.) No exact figures can be given for the starting voltage, threshold voltage, and length of plateau of Geiger counters, as these depend on such variables as counter dimensions and nature of the gas mixture, but the operating

---

* Pulses *are* produced below this voltage, but they are too small to be counted by the measuring circuit (scaler or ratemeter). Below the starting voltage, the counter is acting as a proportional counter and the pulses are much smaller than those produced in the Geiger region. Since the measuring circuit used with a Geiger counter is designed to operate only on pulses larger than a certain size, usually 0.25 volt, no pulses are counted at voltages less than the starting voltage.

voltage of most counters is commonly found to lie in the range of 1000 to 1500 volts. It should be noted that some counters can be permanently damaged if subjected, even for brief periods, to voltages high enough to cause a continuous discharge.

There are several important differences between the action of a Geiger counter and that of a proportional counter:

(1) The absorption of an x-ray quantum anywhere within the volume of a Geiger counter triggers an avalanche that extends over the whole length of the counter.

(2) The gas amplification factor of a Geiger counter is therefore much larger, about 10^8 to 10^9 (see Fig. 7–10), and so is the voltage pulse in the wire, now about 1 to 10 volts. This means that less amplification is needed in the external circuit. (Pulses from either kind of counter are always amplified before being fed to a scaler or ratemeter.)

(3) At a constant applied voltage, all Geiger pulses are of the same size, independent of the energy of the x-ray quantum that caused the primary ionization.

These differences are illustrated schematically in Fig. 7–12. The absorption of an x-ray quantum in a proportional counter produces a very localized radial column of ions and electrons. In a Geiger counter, on the other hand, the applied voltage is so high that not only are some atoms ionized but others are raised to excited states and caused to emit ultraviolet radiation. These ultraviolet photons then travel throughout the counter at the speed of light, knocking electrons out of other gas atoms and out of the cathode shell. All the

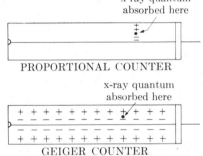

FIG. 7–12. Differences in the extent of ionization between proportional and Geiger counters. Each plus (or minus) symbol represents a large number of positive ions (or electrons).

electrons so produced trigger other avalanches, and the net result is that one tremendous avalanche of electrons hits the whole length of the anode wire whenever an x-ray quantum is absorbed anywhere in the tube.

All these electrons hit the wire in less than a microsecond, but the slowly moving positive ions require about 200 microseconds to reach the cathode. This means that the electron avalanche in a Geiger counter leaves behind it a cylindrical sheath of positive ions around the anode wire. The presence of this ion sheath reduces the electric field between it and the wire below the threshold value necessary to produce a Geiger pulse. Until this ion sheath has moved far enough away from the wire, the counter is insensitive to entering x-ray quanta. If these quanta are arriving at a very rapid

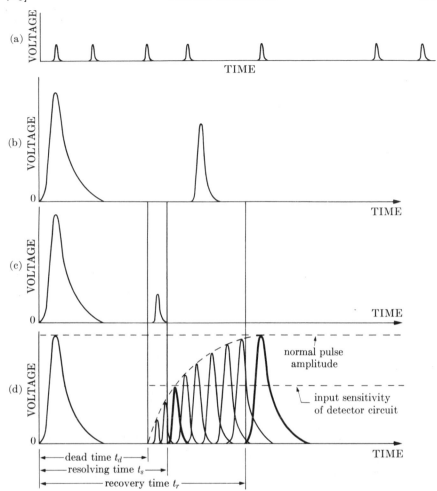

FIG. 7–13.   Dependence of pulse amplitude on pulse spacing.

rate, it follows that not every one will cause a separate pulse and the counter will become "choked." This places an upper limit on the rate at which entering quanta can be accurately counted without losses. This limit is much lower than that of a proportional counter, since the positive ions produced by a discharge are very localized in the proportional counter and do not render the rest of the counter volume insensitive.

The way in which pulses occur in a Geiger counter is worth examining in some detail. It must be remembered that the arrival of x-ray quanta in the counter is random in time. Therefore pulse production in the counter is also random in time, and a curve showing the change in voltage of the anode wire with time would have the appearance of Fig. 7–13(a). During each pulse, the voltage rises very rapidly to a maximum and then decreases more slowly to its normal value. All pulses have the same amplitude and are spaced at random time intervals.

But if the rate of pulse production is so high that two successive pulses occur too closely together, it is found that the second one has less than normal amplitude, as indicated in Fig. 7–13(b) on enlarged voltage-time scales. If the interval between pulses becomes smaller than that shown in (b), then the amplitude of the second pulse becomes still smaller, as shown in (c). Figure 7–13(d) sums up a number of curves of this kind; i.e., it is a superposition of a number of curves like (b) and (c), and it shows the amplitude which any given pulse will have when it follows the initial pulse at the time interval indicated by its position on the time axis. This decrease in pulse height with decrease in pulse spacing has been correlated with the phenomena occurring in the counter as follows. When the avalanche of electrons hits the anode wire to form the initial pulse, the voltage rapidly builds up to its maximum value and then decays more slowly to zero as the charge on the wire leaks away. But, as stated above, the positive ion sheath left behind reduces the field strength between it and the wire. The field strength increases as the ions move away from the wire, and the time at which the field reaches the threshold value marks the end of the *dead time* t_d, during which the counter is absolutely insensitive to entering quanta. The arrival of the ion sheath at the cathode restores the field to its normal strength and marks the end of the *recovery time* t_r. Between t_d and t_r the field is above threshold but not yet back to normal; during this interval entering quanta can cause pulses, but they will not have the full amplitude characteristic of the applied voltage. The recovery time, at which the pulses regain their full amplitude, is fixed by the counter design and generally is of the order of 2×10^{-4} sec. However, the detecting circuit can usually detect pulses smaller than maximum amplitude, and we can therefore speak of the *resolving time* t_s of the counter-circuit combination, defined by the time after the initial pulse at which a following pulse can first be detected.

If the arrival, and absorption, of entering quanta were absolutely periodic in time, the maximum counting rate without losses would be given simply by $1/t_s$. But even if their average rate of arrival is no greater than $1/t_s$, some successive quanta may be spaced less than t_s apart because of their randomness in time. It follows that counting losses will occur at rates less than $1/t_s$ and that the losses will increase as the rate increases, as shown in Fig. 7–14. Here "quanta absorbed per second" are directly proportional to the x-ray intensity, so that this curve has an important bearing on diffractometer measurements, since it shows the point at which the observed counting rate is no longer proportional to the x-ray intensity. The straight line shows the ideal response which can be obtained with a proportional counter at the rates shown.

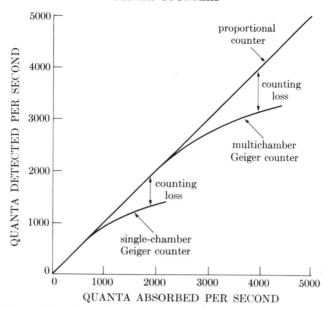

Fɪɢ. 7–14.   The effect of counting rate on counting losses (schematic).

Since the resolving time of the ordinary Geiger counter is of the order of 10^{-4} sec, counting-rate curves should be linear up to about 10,000 cps (counts per second) if the arrival of quanta were periodic in time. However, counting losses are observed to begin at much lower rates, namely, at a few hundred counts per second, as shown in Fig. 7–14. In the multichamber counter the counting rate is linear up to more than 1000 cps; such a counter has a number of chambers side by side, each with its own anode wire, and one chamber can therefore register a count while another one is in its insensitive period. (The proportional counter, much faster than either of these, has a linear counting curve up to about 10,000 cps. Its resolving time is less than a microsecond; this is the time required for an electron avalanche to hit the wire, immediately after which the proportional counter is ready to register another pulse, since the positive ions formed produce no interference.)

The particular counting rate where losses begin with a particular Geiger-counter–scaler combination must be determined experimentally, and this can be done as follows. Position the counter to receive a strong diffracted beam, and insert in this beam a sufficient number of metal foils of uniform thickness to reduce the counting rate almost to the cosmic background. (Cosmic rays, because of their high penetrating power, pass right through the walls of the counter and continually produce a few counts per second.) Measure the counting rate, remove one foil, measure the counting rate, and continue in this manner until all the foils have been removed. Since each

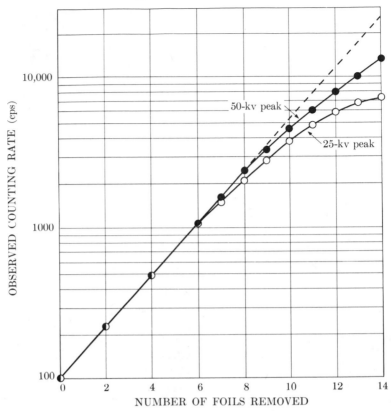

Fig. 7–15. Calibration curves of a multichamber Geiger counter for two values of the x-ray tube peak voltage. Cu $K\alpha$ radiation. Nickel foils, each 0.01 mm thick, used as absorbers.

foil produces the same fractional absorption of the energy incident on it, a plot of observed counting rate (on a logarithmic scale) *vs.* number of foils removed from the beam (on a linear scale) will be linear up to the point where losses begin and will in fact resemble Fig. 7–14. A curve of this kind is shown in Fig. 7–15. Once the length of the linear portion of the calibration curve has been determined, it is best to make all further measurements in this region. Of course, the losses attendant on very high counting rates can be determined from the calibration curve and used to correct the observed rate, but it is usually safer to reduce the intensity of a very strong beam, by means of foils of known absorption, to a point where the observed counting rate is on the linear portion of the curve.

Figure 7–15 also shows that the range of linearity of a counting rate curve is dependent on the *x-ray tube voltage* and is shorter for lower voltages. The reason for this dependence is the fact that the x-ray tube emits characteristic x-rays not continuously but only in bursts during those times when the tube voltage exceeds the critical excitation voltage of the target material. Suppose, for example, that a copper target (excitation voltage = 9 kv) is operated at a peak voltage of 50 kv. Then, if the wave form is like that shown in Fig. 7–16, Cu $K\alpha$ radiation will be emitted during the time intervals t_1t_2 and t_3t_4 but not during t_2t_3. But if the peak voltage is decreased to 25 kv, Cu $K\alpha$ emission is limited to the shorter time intervals t_5t_6 and t_7t_8. If the x-ray intensity is made the same at both voltages by adjusting the tube current, then it follows that the same number of Cu $K\alpha$

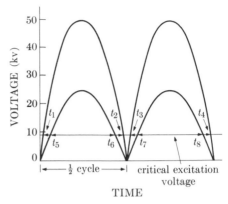

FIG. 7–16. Variation of tube voltage with time for a full-wave rectified x-ray tube (schematic).

quanta are bunched into shorter times at the lower tube voltage than at the higher. Lowering the tube voltage therefore decreases the average time interval between quanta entering the Geiger counter during each half-cycle and may cause counting losses to occur at rates at which no losses are produced at higher tube voltages. It follows that a counter calibration curve applies only to measurements made at voltages not less than the voltage at which the calibration was performed.

One other aspect of Geiger-counter operation deserves mention, and that is the method used to prevent the discharge actuated by the absorption of one quantum from continuing indefinitely. If the counter is filled with a single gas such as argon, the positive argon ions on reaching the cathode are able to eject electrons from the cathode material. These electrons are accelerated to the anode and initiate another chain of ionization, with the result that a continuous discharge is set up in the counter, rendering it incapable of counting any entering quanta after the first one. This discharge may be prevented or "quenched" if an external circuit is used which abruptly lowers the voltage on the counter after each pulse to a value below that necessary to maintain a discharge but high enough to clear all ions from the gas. As soon as the ions are neutralized at the cathode, the high voltage is reapplied and the counter is again sensitive. To avoid the necessity for a quenching circuit, counters have been designed which are self-quenching by virtue of the gas mixture they contain. To the main gas in the counter, usually argon or krypton, is added a small proportion of "quench gas," which is either a polyatomic organic vapor, such as alcohol, or a halogen, such as chlorine or bromine. As its name implies, the quench gas plays the role of the quenching circuit used with single-gas counters and prevents the initial avalanche of ionization from becoming a continuous discharge. In an argon-chlorine counter, for example, ionized argon atoms acquire electrons from chlorine molecules by collision, forming neutral argon atoms and ionized chlorine molecules. The latter are merely neutralized on reaching the cathode and do not release electrons as argon ions do. Most counters used today are of the self-quenching variety.

The *efficiency* of a Geiger or proportional counter and its associated circuits is given by the product of two efficiencies, that of quantum absorption and that of quantum detection. The absorption efficiency depends on the absorption coefficient and thickness of the counter window, both of which should be as small as possible, and on the absorption coefficient of the counter gas and the length of the counter, both of which should be as large as possible. The detection efficiency of a Geiger counter, as we have seen, depends on the counting rate and is effectively 100 percent at low rates; with a proportional counter this efficiency is near 100 percent at any rate likely to be encountered in diffraction experiments. The overall efficiency of either counter at low rates is therefore determined by the absorption efficiency, which is commonly about 60 to 80 percent.

The absorption efficiency, however, is very much dependent on the x-ray wavelength, the kind of gas used, and its pressure, since these factors determine the amount of radiation absorbed in a counter of given length. Figure 7–17 shows how the amount absorbed depends on wavelength for the two gases most often used in x-ray counters. Note that a krypton-filled counter has high sensitivity for all the characteristic radiations normally used in diffraction but that an argon-filled counter is sensitive only to the longer wavelengths. This latter characteristic may be advantageous in some circumstances. For example, if a diffraction pattern is made with filtered radiation from a copper target, use of an argon-filled counter will produce semimonochromatic conditions, in that the counter will be highly sensitive to Cu $K\alpha$ radiation and relatively insensitive to the short wavelength radiation which forms the most intense part of the continuous spectrum. The diffraction background will therefore be lower than if a krypton-filled counter had been used.

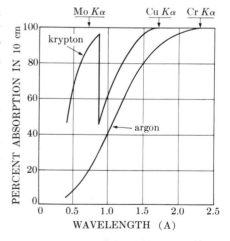

FIG. 7–17. Absorption of x-rays in a 10-cm path length of krypton and argon, each at a pressure of 65 cm Hg.

7–7 Scintillation counters.   This type of counter utilizes the ability of x-rays to cause certain substances to fluoresce visible light. The amount of light emitted is proportional to the x-ray intensity and can be measured by means of a phototube. Since the amount of light emitted is small, a special kind of phototube called a *photomultiplier* has to be employed in order to obtain a measurable current output.

The substance generally used to detect x-rays is a sodium iodide crystal activated with a small amount of thallium. It emits blue light under x-ray bombardment. The crystal is cemented to the face of a photo-multiplier tube, as indicated in Fig. 7–18, and shielded from external light by means of aluminum foil. A flash of light is produced in the crystal for every x-ray quantum absorbed, and this light passes into the photomulti-plier tube and ejects a number of electrons from the photocathode, which is a photosensitive material generally made of a caesium-antimony inter-metallic compound. (For simplicity, only one of these electrons is shown in Fig. 7–18.) The emitted electrons are then drawn to the first of several metal *dynodes*, each maintained at a potential about 100 volts more posi-tive than the preceding one, the last one being connected to the measuring circuit. On reaching the first dynode, each electron from the photocathode knocks two electrons, say, out of the metal surface, as indicated in the drawing. These are drawn to the second dynode where each knocks out two more electrons and so on. Actually, the gain at each dynode may be 4 or 5 and there are usually at least 10 dynodes. If the gain per dynode is 5 and there are 10 dynodes, then the multiplication factor is $5^{10} = 10^7$. Thus the absorption of one x-ray quantum in the crystal results in the collection of a very large number of electrons at the final dynode, producing a pulse about as large as a Geiger pulse, i.e., of the order of volts. Further-more, the whole process requires less than a microsecond, so that a scintil-lation counter can operate at rates as high as 10^5 counts per second without losses.

As in the proportional counter, the pulses produced in a scintillation counter have sizes proportional to the energy of the quanta absorbed.

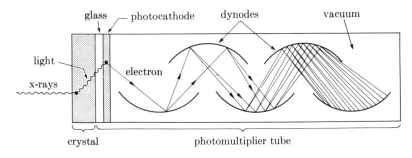

FIG. 7–18. Scintillation counter (schematic). Electrical connections not shown.

But the pulse size corresponding to a certain quantum energy is much less sharply defined than in a proportional counter; i.e., scintillation-counter pulses produced by x-ray quanta of a given energy have a mean size characteristic of that energy, but there is also a fairly wide distribution of pulse size about this mean. As a result, it is difficult to discriminate between x-ray quanta of different energies on the basis of pulse size.

The efficiency of a scintillation counter approaches 100 percent over the whole range of x-ray wavelengths, short and long, because all incident x-ray quanta are absorbed in the crystal. Its chief disadvantage is its rather high background count; a so-called "dark current" of pulses is produced even when no x-ray quanta are incident on the counter. The main source of this dark current is thermionic emission of electrons from the photocathode.

7–8 Scalers. A scaler is an electronic device which counts each pulse produced by the counter. Once the number of pulses over a measured period of time is known, the average counting rate is obtained by simple division. If the rate of pulse production were always low, say a few counts per second, the pulses could be counted satisfactorily by a fast mechanical counter, but such devices cannot handle high counting rates. It is therefore necessary to divide, or scale down, the pulses by a known factor before feeding them to the mechanical counter. As its name implies, the scaler fulfills this latter function. There are two main kinds, the *binary scaler*, in which the scaling factor is some power of 2, and the *decade scaler*, in which it is a power of 10.

We will consider scaler operation only in terms of binary scalers but the principles involved are applicable to either type. A typical binary scaler has several scaling factors available at the turn of a switch, ranging from 2^0 ($= 1$) to about 2^{14} ($= 16384$). The scaling circuit is made up of a number of identical "stages" connected in series, the number of stages being equal to n where 2^n is the desired scaling factor. Each stage is composed of a number of vacuum tubes, capacitors, and resistors so connected that only one pulse of current is transmitted for every two pulses received. Since the output of one stage is connected to the input of another, this division by two is repeated as many times as there are stages. The output of the last stage may be connected to a mechanical counter which will register one count for every pulse transmitted to it by the last stage. Thus, if N pulses from a counter are passed through a circuit of n stages, only $N/2^n$ will register on the mechanical counter.

There are two ways of using a scaler to obtain an average counting rate: counting for a fixed time and counting a fixed number of pulses. In the first method, the scaler is turned on for a time t and then shut off. If the mechanical counter then shows N_0 counts, the number of input pulses must have been

$$N = N_0(2^n) + a, \qquad (7\text{–}5)$$

where a is an integer ranging from 0 up to $(2^n - 1)$. The integer a gives the number of pulses still "in the circuit" when the input pulses were shut off, and its value is found by noting which of several neon interpolation lamps connected to the several stages are still on. As indicated in Fig. 7–19 for a scale-of-16 circuit, there is a neon lamp connected to each stage and the number opposite each lamp is 2^{n-1} where n is the number of the stage. The initial pulse entering a stage turns the lamp on and the second pulse turns it off. Since the second entering pulse causes a pulse to be transmitted to the next stage, the lamp on that stage goes on at the same time that the lamp on the preceding stage goes out. The integer a is therefore given by the sum of the numbers opposite lighted neon lamps. The total count shown in Fig. 7–19, for example, is $N = 18(16) + (2 + 4) = 294$. Once the total number of counts is known, the average counting rate is given simply by N/t.

In the second method of scaling (counting a fixed number of pulses), the mechanical counter is replaced by an electric timer. The timer is connected to the circuit in such a way that it starts when the scaler is started and stops at the instant a pulse is transmitted from the last stage. For example, if the timer is connected to a 10-stage scaler, it will stop when exactly 1024 $(= 2^{10})$ pulses have entered the first stage, because at that instant the tenth stage will transmit its first pulse; the average counting rate is then given by the quotient of 1024 and the time shown on the timer. Such a circuit requires no interpolation since no counts remain in the circuit at the instant the final stage transmits its pulse to the timer; i.e., all the neon lights are off. The total number of counts, which must be a power of 2 in a binary scaler, is selected by a switch which connects the timer to any desired stage, thus making that stage the final stage and short-circuiting the remainder.

Because the arrival of x-ray quanta in the counter is random in time, the accuracy of a counting rate measurement is governed by the laws of probability. Two counts of the same x-ray beam for identical periods of time will not be precisely the same because of the random spacing between

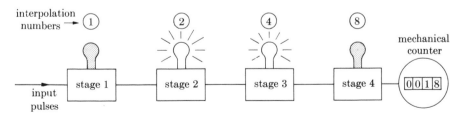

Fig. 7–19. Determination of scaler counts.

pulses, even though the counter and scaler are functioning perfectly. Clearly, the accuracy of a rate measurement of this kind improves as the time of counting is prolonged, and it is therefore important to know how long to count in order to attain a specified degree of accuracy. The probable error* in a single count of N pulses, relative to an average value obtained by a great many repetitions of the same counting operation, is given by

$$E_N = \frac{67}{\sqrt{N}} \text{ percent,} \qquad (7\text{–}6)$$

so long as N is fairly large. For some of the total counts obtainable from a binary scaler, this expression gives the following errors:

Total number of pulses counted	Percent probable error
256 ($= 2^8$)	4.2
512 ($= 2^9$)	3.0
1024 ($= 2^{10}$)	2.1
2048 ($= 2^{11}$)	1.5
4096 ($= 2^{12}$)	1.0
8192 ($= 2^{13}$)	0.7
16384 ($= 2^{14}$)	0.5

Note that the error depends only on the number of pulses counted and not on their rate, which means that high rates and low rates can be measured with the same accuracy, if the counting times are chosen to produce the same total number of counts in each measurement. It also follows that the second scaling method outlined above, in which the time is measured for a fixed number of counts, is generally preferable to the first, since it permits intensity measurements of the same precision of both high- and low-intensity beams.

Equation (7–6) is valid only when the counting rate due to the radiation being measured is large relative to the background. (Here "background" means the unavoidable background counting rate measured with the x-ray tube shut off, and not the "diffraction background" at non-Bragg angles due to any of the several causes listed in Sec. 6–11 and of which fluorescent radiation is usually the most important. The unavoidable background is due to cosmic rays and may be augmented, in some laboratories, by stray

---

* The probable error is that which is just as likely to be exceeded as not. Three times the probable error is a somewhat more useful figure, as the probability that this will be exceeded is only 0.04. Thus, if a single measurement gives 1000 counts, then the probable error is $67/\sqrt{1000} = 2.1$ percent or 21 counts. Then the probability is 0.5 that this count lies in the range $N_t \pm 21$, where N_t is the true number of counts, while the probability is 0.96 that the measured value lies in the range $N_t \pm 63$.

radiation from nearby radioactive material; it may be rather high, if a scintillation counter is used, because of the dark current of this counter.) Suppose a measurement is required of the diffraction background, always rather low, in the presence of a fairly large unavoidable background. In these circumstances, Eq. (7–6) does not apply. Let N be the number of pulses counted in a given time with the x-ray tube on, and N_b the number counted in the same time with the tube off. Then N_b counts are due to the unavoidable background and $(N - N_b)$ to the diffraction background being measured, and the relative probable error in $(N - N_b)$ is

$$E_{N-N_b} = \frac{67\sqrt{N + N_b}}{(N - N_b)} \text{ percent.} \qquad (7\text{–}7)$$

Comparison of Eqs. (7–6) and (7–7) shows that longer counts must be made when the unavoidable background is of comparable intensity to the radiation being measured than when the unavoidable background is completely negligible by comparison, if the same accuracy is to be obtained in both measurements.

As indicated in Sec. 7–2, the integrated intensity of a diffraction line may be measured with a scaler by determining the average counting rate at several angular positions of the counter. The line profile, the curve of intensity *vs.* 2θ, is then plotted on graph paper, and the area under the curve, and above the continuous background, is measured with a planimeter. To obtain the same relative accuracy of both the line profile and the adjacent background, all measurements should be made by counting a fixed number of pulses. Three other methods of measuring integrated intensities have been used, all of which utilize the integrating properties of the scaling circuit to replace the curve plotting and planimeter measurement:

(1) The line is scanned from one side to the other at a constant angular rate, the scaler being started at the beginning of the scan and stopped at its end. The total number of counts registered by the scaler, minus the number of counts due to the background, is then proportional to the integrated intensity of the line. All lines on the pattern must be measured with the same receiving slit and the same scanning rate. The background adjacent to, and on either side of, the line may be measured by the same procedure, i.e., by scanning at the same rate over the same angular range, or by counting at a fixed position for the same time required to scan the line.

(2) The counter is moved stepwise across the line and maintained in each position for the same length of time, the scaler being operated continuously except when changing counter positions. The total count accumulated by the scaler, minus the background correction, is again proportional to the integrated intensity. A wide receiving slit is used, and the

angular interval between counter positions is so chosen that the overlap between adjacent settings of the slit is negligibly small and constant and never coincides with the maximum intensity of the line being measured.

(3) A receiving slit is used which is wider than the line being measured. The slit is centered on the line and a count made for a given time. The background is measured by counting at a position adjacent to the line with the same slit for the same length of time.

Because all these methods involve counting for a fixed time, the background and low-intensity portions of the diffraction line are measured with less accuracy than the high-intensity portions. The counting time should be chosen so that the low intensities are measured to the accuracy required by the particular problem involved; it will then follow that the high intensities are measured with unnecessarily high accuracy, but that is unavoidable in fixed-time methods such as these.

The integrating ability of a scaler is also put to use in x-ray tube *monitors*. In Sec. 7–2 it was mentioned that the incident-beam intensity had to be maintained absolutely constant in a diffractometer and that this constancy required tube current and voltage stabilizers. These stabilizing circuits are not needed if an extra counter and scaler are available to "watch," or monitor, the tube output. The monitor counter may be positioned to receive the direct beam, suitably filtered to reduce its intensity, from another window of the x-ray tube, or an auxiliary crystal may be set to diffract a portion of the beam used in the diffractometer into the monitor counter. In either case, every intensity measurement with the diffractometer is made by starting the diffractometer scaler and monitor scaler simultaneously and stopping both when the monitor scaler has registered a constant number of counts N. In this way, every intensity measurement is made in terms of the same amount of energy incident on the specimen, and variations in tube output have no effect.

7–9 Ratemeters. The counting-rate meter, as its name implies, is a device which indicates the average counting rate directly without requiring, as in the scaler-timer combination, separate measurements of the number of counts and the time. It does this by a circuit which, in effect, smooths out the succession of randomly spaced pulses from the counter into a steady current, whose magnitude is proportional to the average rate of pulse production in the counter.

The heart of a ratemeter circuit is a series arrangement of a capacitor and resistor. To understand the action of a ratemeter, we must review some of the properties of such a circuit, notably the way in which the current and voltage vary with time. Consider the circuit shown in Fig. 7–20(a), in which the switch S can be used either to connect a to c and thus apply a voltage to the capacitor, or to connect b to c and thus short-circuit

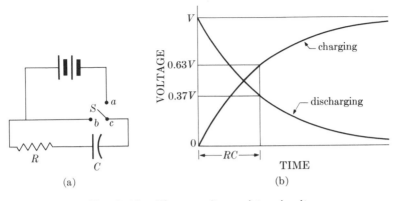

FIG. 7–20. The capacitor-resistor circuit.

the capacitor and resistor. When a is suddenly connected to c, the voltage across the capacitor reaches its final value V not instantaneously but only over a period of time, and at a rate which depends on the resistance R and the capacitance C, as shown in Fig. 7–20(b). The product of R and C has the dimensions of time (seconds, in fact, if R is in megohms and C in microfarads), and it may be shown that the voltage across the capacitor reaches 63 percent of its final value in a time given by RC, known as the *time constant* of the circuit. The time required to reach 99 percent of its final value is $4.6RC$. Conversely, if the fully charged capacitor, bearing a charge $Q = CV$, is suddenly shorted through the resistor by connecting b to c, the charge does not immediately disappear but leaks away at a rate dependent on the time constant. The charge drops to 37 percent of its initial value in a time equal to RC and to 1 percent in a time equal to $4.6RC$.

A complete ratemeter circuit consists of two parts. The first is a pulse-amplifying and pulse-shaping portion which electronically converts the counter pulses, which vary in amplitude and shape from counter to counter, into rectangular pulses of fixed dimensions in voltage and time. These pulses are then fed into the second portion, which is the measuring circuit shown in Fig. 7–21, a circuit basically similar to that of Fig. 7–20(a) and having a time constant R_2C_2. S, shown as a simple switch, is actually an electronic circuit which connects a to c each time a pulse arrives and then connects b to c immediately afterwards. A constant charge is thus added to the capacitor for each pulse received and this charge leaks away

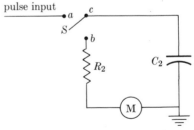

FIG. 7–21. Measuring portion of ratemeter circuit.

through the resistor until, at equilibrium, the rate of addition of charge is just balanced by the rate of leakage. The rate of charge leakage is simply the current through the microammeter M, which therefore indicates the rate of pulse production in the counter and, in turn, the x-ray intensity. The circuit usually contains, in addition to the indicating meter, a chart recorder which produces a continuous record of the intensity.

Even when the x-ray intensity is constant (constant average counting rate), the spacing of the counter pulses is random in time, which means that the counting rate actually varies with time over short periods. The ratemeter responds to these statistical fluctuations in the counting rate, and its response speed is greater the smaller the time constant. This follows from the discussion of the capacitor-resistor circuit: any change in the pulse rate causes a change in the current through the circuit, but the latter change always lags behind the former; the amount of lag is less for a small time constant than for a large one. Random fluctuations in the counting rate are therefore more evident with a small time constant, because the current in the circuit then follows the changes in counting rate more closely. This feature is illustrated in Fig. 7–22, which shows the automatically recorded output of a ratemeter when the counter is receiving a constant-intensity x-ray beam. The large fluctuations at the left have been reduced in magnitude by successive increases in the time constant, effected by changing the value of C_2. Evidently, a *single* reading of the position of the indicating meter needle or the recorder pen of a ratemeter may be seriously in error, and more so at low time constants than at high. In Sec. 7–8 we saw that the error in a counting-rate measurement decreased as the number of counts increased. Now it may be shown that a ratemeter acts as if it counted for a time $2R_2C_2$, in the sense that the accuracy of any single reading is equivalent to a count made with a scaler for a time $2R_2C_2$. Therefore, the relative probable error in any single ratemeter reading is given by the counterpart of Eq. (7–6), namely by

$$E = \frac{67}{\sqrt{2nR_2C_2}} \text{ percent,} \qquad (7\text{–}8)$$

where n is the average counting rate. This equation also shows that the probable error is less for high counting rates than for low, when the time constant remains the same. This is illustrated graphically in Fig. 7–23, which shows how the recorded fluctuations in the counting rate decrease as the rate itself is increased.

The most useful feature of a ratemeter is its ability to follow *changes* in the average counting rate, a function which the scaler is totally unable to perform, since a change in the average counting rate occurring during the time a count is being made with a scaler will go entirely undetected. It is this feature of a ratemeter which is so useful in diffractometry. A diffrac-

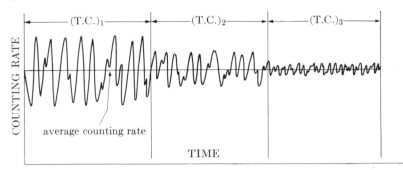

FIG. 7–22. Effect of time constant (T.C.) on recorded fluctuations in counting rate at constant x-ray intensity (schematic). Time constants changed abruptly at times shown. $(T.C.)_1 < (T.C.)_2 < (T.C.)_3$.

tion pattern can be scanned from one end to the other, and the moving counter automatically transmits, through the ratemeter, a continuous record of the intensity it observes as the diffraction angle is changed. On the other hand, the ratemeter is less accurate than the scaler, both because of the unavoidable statistical fluctuations in its output and because of the errors inherent in its indicating or recording instruments.

As mentioned earlier, a large time constant smooths out fluctuations in the average counting rate by increasing the response time to changes in rate. But when a sharp diffraction line is being scanned, the average counting rate is changing rapidly and we would like the ratemeter to indicate this change as accurately as possible. From this point of view a short response time, produced by a small time constant, is required. A ratemeter must therefore be designed with these two conflicting factors in

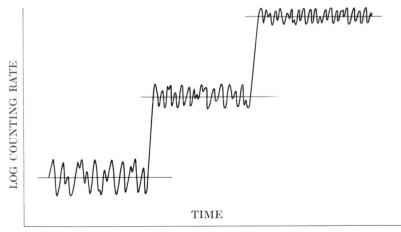

FIG. 7–23. Effect of average counting rate on recorded fluctuations in counting rate, for a fixed time constant (schematic). X-ray intensity changed abruptly at times shown.

mind, and the time constant should be chosen large enough to smooth out most of the statistical fluctuations and yet small enough to give a reasonably short response time.

Most commercial ratemeters have several scales available to cover various ranges of x-ray intensity (100, 1000, and 10,000 cps for full-scale deflection of the recorder pen, for example). Smaller time constants are used with the higher scales, just as short counting times are used with a scaler when the counting rate is high. In some instruments, the time constant appropriate to each scale is fixed by the manufacturer, and in others the operator can select any one of several time constants, ranging from about 0.5 to 15 sec, by switches which insert the proper capacitance in the circuit. The proper time constant to use is, of course, not unrelated to the scanning speed, for a fast scan demands a fast response from the ratemeter and therefore a short time constant. A time constant which is too large for the scanning speed used will slightly shift the peaks of diffraction lines in the direction of the scan and lower their maximum intensity and, because of its excessive smoothing action, may actually obliterate weak diffraction lines and cause them to go unnoticed. In choosing a time constant, it is therefore better to err on the short side. A good rule to follow is to make the time constant less than half the *time width* of the receiving slit, where the time width is defined as the time required for the slit to travel its own width. For example, if a 0.2° slit is used at a scanning speed of 2°/min, then the time width of the slit is $(0.2/2)(60) = 6$ sec, and the time constant should therefore be less than 3 sec. The same rule can be used to find the proper slit width for a given scanning speed when the time constant is fixed.

The relation between the x-ray intensity, i.e., the average counting rate, and the deflection of the indicating meter needle or recorder pen is linear for some ratemeters and logarithmic for others. The exact relation may be found by a calibration procedure similar to that used for the Geiger counter and scaler, as outlined in Sec. 7–6. A number of identical metal foils are placed in a strong diffracted beam entering the counter and these are withdrawn one by one, with the counter in a fixed position. After each withdrawal, the counting rate is measured accurately with a scaler, and the ratemeter operated for a time at least equal to the scaling time, the recording chart speed being selected to give a trace of reasonable length. An average straight line is then drawn through each trace, in such a way as to make the positive and negative fluctuations as nearly equal as possible. (Figure 7–23 shows a portion of a calibration run made in this way.) Finally, the distances of these straight lines from the chart zero are plotted against the corresponding average counting rates as determined by the scaler, and the calibration curve so obtained is used as a basis for future intensity measurements with the ratemeter-recorder combination.

7–10 Use of monochromators. Some research problems, notably the measurement of diffuse scattering at non-Bragg angles, require a strictly monochromatic incident beam if the effects to be measured are not to be blotted out by the continuous spectrum. In such a case, the focusing **crystal monochromator** described in Sec. 6–12 may be used in conjunction with a diffractometer in the manner shown in Fig. 7–24. Rays from the physical line source S on the x-ray tube target T are diffracted by the bent and cut crystal M to a line focus at S', located on the diffractometer circle, and then diverge to the specimen C. After diffraction from the specimen, they are again focused at F, the counter receiving slit. The diffractometer geometry is therefore identical with that shown in Fig. 7–1 but with the important difference that the rays incident on the specimen are monochromatic and issue from the virtual source S', the focal line of the monochromating crystal.

There is another method of operating under essentially monochromatic conditions, a method peculiar to the diffractometer, and that is by the use of **Ross filters,** also called balanced filters. This method depends on the fact that the absorption coefficients of all substances vary in the same way with wavelength; i.e., they are proportional to λ^3, as shown by Eq. (1–13). If filters are made of two substances differing in atomic number by one, and their thicknesses adjusted so that they produce the same absorption for a particular wavelength, then they will have the same absorption for all wavelengths *except* those lying in the narrow wavelength region between the K absorption edges of the two substances. This region is called the pass band of the filter combination. If these filters are placed alternately in a heterochromatic x-ray beam, i.e., a beam containing rays of different wavelengths, then the difference between the intensities transmitted in each case is due only to wavelengths lying in the pass band.

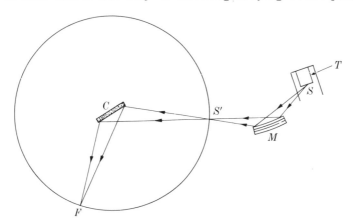

Fɪɢ. 7–24.   Use of crystal monochromator with diffractometer.

When the pass band is chosen to include a strong characteristic component of the spectrum, then the net effect is that of a strong monochromatic beam.

The isolation of Cu $K\alpha$ radiation may be taken as an example. Its wavelength is 1.542A, which means that cobalt and nickel can be used as filter materials since their K absorption edges (1.608 and 1.488A, respectively) effectively bracket the Cu $K\alpha$ line. Their linear absorption coefficients μ are plotted in Fig. 7–25(a), which shows that balancing can be obtained by making the nickel filter somewhat thinner than the cobalt one. When their thicknesses x are adjusted to the correct ratio, then $\mu_{Ni}x_{Ni} = \mu_{Co}x_{Co}$ except in the pass band, and a plot of μx vs. λ has the appearance of Fig. 7–25(b). Since $\mu x = -\ln I_x/I_0$, the transmission factors I_x/I_0 (ratio of transmitted to incident intensity) of the two filters are now equal for all wavelengths except those in the pass band, which is only 0.12A wide. At each angle 2θ at which the intensity is to be measured with the diffractometer, first one filter and then the other is placed in the diffracted beam before it enters the counter. The intensity of the diffracted beam passing through each filter is then measured, and the difference in the measurements gives the diffracted intensity of only the Cu $K\alpha$ line and the relatively weak wavelengths immediately adjacent to it in the pass band.

It should be emphasized that the beam entering the counter is never physically monochromatic, as it is when a crystal monochromator is used. Radiation with a great many wavelengths enters the counter when either filter is in place, but every wavelength transmitted by one filter has the same intensity as that transmitted by the other filter, except those wavelengths lying in the pass band, and these are transmitted quite unequally by the two filters. Therefore, when the intensity measured with one filter is subtracted from that measured with the other filter, the difference is zero for every wavelength except those in the pass band.

In practice, balancing of the filters is carried out by inserting two foils of approximately the same thickness into suitable holders which can be slipped into place in the beam entering the counter. One foil is always perpendicular to the x-ray beam, while the other may be rotated about an axis at right angles to the beam; in this way the second foil may be inclined to the beam at such an angle that its effective thickness x equals the thickness required for balancing. Perfect balancing at all wavelengths outside the pass band is not possible, although it may be approached quite closely, because μ does not vary exactly as λ^3 and because the magnitude of the K absorption jump (ratio of absorption coefficients for wavelengths just shorter and just longer than the K edge) is not exactly the same for all elements.

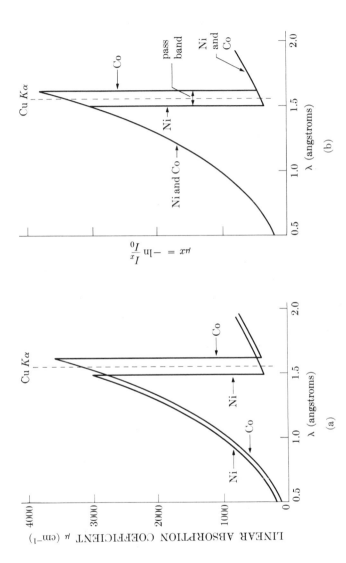

FIG. 7-25.   Ross filters for Cu $K\alpha$ radiation: (a) absorption coefficients of filter materials; (b) μx values after balancing.

PROBLEMS

7-1. A powder specimen in the form of a rectangular plate has a width of 0.5 in., measured in the plane of the diffractometer circle, which has a radius of 5.73 in. If it is required that the specimen entirely fill the incident beam at all angles and that measurements must be made to angles as low as $2\theta = 10°$, what is the maximum divergence angle (measured in the plane of the diffractometer circle) that the incident beam may have?

7-2. Prove the statement made in Sec. 7–4 that the effective irradiated volume of a flat plate specimen in a diffractometer is constant and independent of θ.

7-3. In measuring the maximum intensity of a certain diffraction line with a scaler, 2048 pulses were counted in 1.9 sec. When the "diffraction background" a few degrees away from the line was measured, 2048 pulses were counted in 182 seconds. The average counting rate determined over a long period of time with the x-ray tube shut off was 2.2 cps.

(a) What is the ratio of the maximum intensity of the line to that of the "diffraction background"?

(b) What is the probable error in each of these intensities?

(c) How long must the "diffraction background" be counted in order to obtain its intensity with the same accuracy as that of the diffraction line?

7-4. (a) Calculate the ratio of the effective thicknesses of cobalt and nickel filters when they are balanced for all wavelengths except Cu $K\alpha$. (Obtain an average value applicable to a wavelength range extending from about 0.5A to about 2A.)

(b) When the filters are balanced, calculate the ratio of the intensity of Cu $K\alpha$ radiation transmitted by the nickel filter to that transmitted by the cobalt filter, assuming the same incident intensity in each case. The effective thickness of the nickel filter is 0.00035 in.

CHAPTER 8

ORIENTATION OF SINGLE CRYSTALS

8–1 Introduction. Much of our understanding of the properties of poly-crystalline materials has been gained by studies of isolated single crystals, since such studies permit measurement of the properties of the individual building blocks in the composite mass. Because single crystals are usually anisotropic, research of this kind always requires accurate knowledge of the orientation of the single crystal test specimen in order that measurements may be made along known crystallographic directions or planes. By varying the crystal orientation, we can obtain data on the property measured (e.g., yield strength, electrical resistivity, corrosion rate) as a function of crystal orientation.

In this chapter the three main x-ray methods of determining crystal orientation will be described: the back-reflection Laue method, the transmission Laue method, and the diffractometer method. It is also convenient to treat here the question of crystal deformation and the measurement of this deformation by x-ray methods. Finally, the subject of relative crystal orientation is discussed, and methods are given for determining the relative orientation of two naturally associated crystals, such as the two parts of a twin or a precipitated crystal and its parent phase.

8–2 The back-reflection Laue method. As mentioned in Sec. 3–6, the Laue pattern of a single crystal consists of a set of diffraction spots on the film and the positions of these spots depend on the orientation of the crystal. This is true of either Laue method, transmission or back-reflection, so either can be used to determine crystal orientation. However, the back-reflection method is the more widely used of the two because it requires no special preparation of the specimen, which may be of any thickness, whereas the transmission method requires relatively thin specimens of low absorption.

In either case, since the orientation of the specimen is to be determined from the location of the Laue spots on the film, it is necessary to orient the specimen relative to the film in some known manner. The single crystal specimens encountered in metallurgical work are usually in the form of wire, rod, sheet, or plate, but crystals of irregular shape must occasionally be dealt with. Wire or rod specimens are best mounted with their axis parallel to one edge of the square or rectangular film; a fiducial mark on the specimen surface, for example on the side nearest the film, then fixes the orientation of the specimen completely. It is convenient to

215

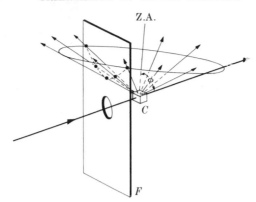

FIG. 8–1. Intersection of a conical array of diffracted beams with a film placed in the back-reflection position. C = crystal, F = film, Z.A. = zone axis.

mount sheet or plate specimens with their plane parallel to the plane of the film and one edge of the sheet or plate parallel to an edge of the film. Irregularly shaped crystals must have fiducial marks on their surface which will definitely fix their orientation relative to that of the film.

The problem now is to determine the orientation of the crystal from the position of the back-reflection Laue spots on the film. If we wished, we could determine the Bragg angle θ corresponding to each Laue spot from Eq. (5–2), but that would be no help in identifying the planes producing that spot, since the wavelength of the diffracted beam is unknown. We can, however, determine the orientation of the normal to the planes causing each spot, because the plane normal always bisects the angle between incident and diffracted beams. The directions of the plane normals can then be plotted on a stereographic projection, the angles between them measured, and the planes identified by comparison with a list of known interplanar angles for the crystal involved.

Our first problem, therefore, is to derive, from the measured position of each diffraction spot on the film, the position on a stereographic projection of the pole of the plane causing that spot. In doing this it is helpful to recall that all of the planes of one zone reflect beams which lie on the surface of a cone whose axis is the zone axis and whose semi-apex angle is equal to the angle ϕ at which the zone axis is inclined to the transmitted beam (Fig. 8–1). If ϕ does not exceed 45°, the cone will not intersect a film placed in the back-reflection region; if ϕ lies between 45° and 90°, the cone intersects the film in a hyperbola; and, if ϕ equals 90°, the intersection is a straight line passing through the incident beam. (If ϕ exceeds 90°, the cone shifts to a position below the transmitted beam and intersects the lower half of the film, as may be seen by viewing Fig. 8–1 upside down.) Diffraction spots on a back-reflection Laue film therefore lie on hyper-

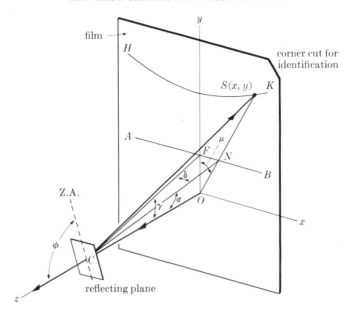

FIG. 8–2.   Location of back-reflection Laue spot.   Note that $\gamma = 90° - \phi$.

bolas or straight lines, and the distance of any hyperbola from the center of the film is a measure of the inclination of the zone axis.

In Fig. 8–2 the film is viewed from the crystal. Coordinate axes are set up such that the incident beam proceeds along the z-axis in the direction Oz and the x- and y-axes lie in the plane of the film. The beam reflected by the plane shown strikes the film at S. The normal to this reflecting plane is CN and the plane itself is assumed to belong to a zone whose axis lies in the yz-plane. If we imagine this plane to rotate about the zone axis, it will pass through all the positions at which planes of this zone in an actual crystal might lie. During this rotation, the plane normal would cut the film in the straight line AB and the reflected beam in the hyperbola HK. AB is therefore the locus of plane normal intersections with the film and HK the locus of diffracted beam intersections. The plane which reflects a beam to S, for example, has a normal which intersects the film at N, since the incident beam, plane normal, and diffracted beam are coplanar. Since the orientation of the plane normal in space can be described by its angular coordinates γ and δ, the problem is to determine γ and δ from the measured coordinates x and y of the diffraction spot S on the film.

A graphical method of doing this was devised by Greninger who developed a chart which, when placed on the film, gives directly the γ and δ coordinates corresponding to any diffraction spot. To plot such a chart, we note from Fig. 8–2 that

$$x = OS \sin \mu, \quad y = OS \cos \mu, \quad \text{and} \quad OS = OC \tan 2\sigma,$$

where $OC = D$ = specimen-film distance. The angles μ and σ are obtained from γ and δ as follows:

$$\tan \mu = \frac{FN}{FO} = \frac{CF \tan \delta}{CF \sin \gamma} = \frac{\tan \delta}{\sin \gamma},$$

$$\tan \sigma = \frac{ON}{OC} = \left(\frac{FN}{\sin \mu}\right)\left(\frac{1}{CF \cos \gamma}\right) = \left(\frac{CF \tan \delta}{\sin \mu}\right)\left(\frac{1}{CF \cos \gamma}\right)$$

$$= \frac{\tan \delta}{\sin \mu \cos \gamma}.$$

With these equations, the position (in terms of x and y) of any diffraction spot can be plotted for given values of γ and δ and any desired specimen-film distance D. The result is the Greninger chart, graduated at 2° intervals shown in Fig. 8–3. The hyperbolas running from left to right are curves of constant γ, and any one of these curves is the locus of diffraction spots from planes of a zone whose axis is tilted away from the plane of the film by the indicated angle γ. If points having the same value of δ are joined together, another set of hyperbolas running from top to bottom is obtained. The lower half of the chart contains a protractor whose use will be referred to later. Greninger charts should have dark lines on a transparent background and are best prepared as positive prints on photographic film.

In use, the chart is placed over the film with its center coinciding with the film center and with the edges of chart and film parallel. The γ and δ coordinates corresponding to any diffraction spot are then read directly. Note that use of the chart avoids any measurement of the actual coordinate distances x and y of the spot. The chart gives directly, not the x and y coordinates of the spot, but *the angular coordinates γ and δ of the normal to the plane causing the spot.*

Knowing the γ and δ coordinates of any plane normal, for example CN in Fig. 8–2, we can plot the pole of the plane on a stereographic projection. Imagine a reference sphere centered on the crystal in Fig. 8–2 and tangent to the film, and let the projection plane coincide with the film. The point of projection is taken as the intersection of the transmitted beam and the reference sphere. Since the plane normal CN intersects the side of the sphere nearest the x-ray source, the projection must be viewed from that side and the film "read" from that side. In order to know, after processing, the orientation the film had during the x-ray exposure, the upper right-hand corner of the film (viewed from the crystal) is cut away before it is placed in the cassette, as shown in Fig. 8–2. When the film is read, this

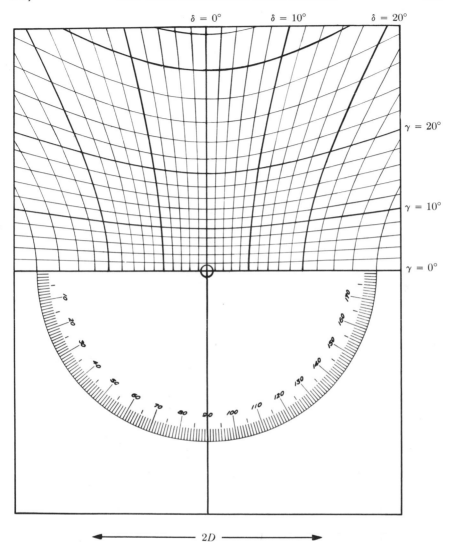

FIG. 8–3. Greninger chart for the solution of back-reflection Laue patterns, reproduced in the correct size for a specimen-to-film distance D of 3 cm.

cut corner must therefore be at the upper left, as shown in Fig. 8–4(a). The angles γ and δ, read from the chart, are then laid out on the projection as indicated in Fig. 8–4(b). Note that the underlying Wulff net must be oriented so that its meridians run from side to side, not top to bottom. The reason for this is the fact that diffraction spots which lie on curves of constant γ come from planes of a zone, and the poles of these planes must

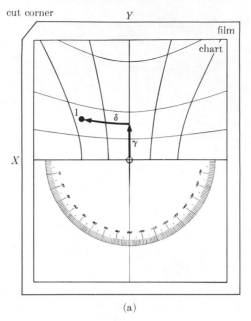

(a)

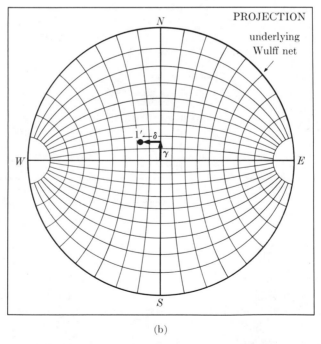

(b)

FIG. 8–4. Use of the Greninger chart to plot the pole of a reflecting plane on a stereographic projection. Pole 1′ in (b) is the pole of the plane causing diffraction spot 1 in (a).

therefore lie on a great circle on the projection. The γ, δ coordinates corresponding to diffraction spots on the lower half of the film are obtained simply by reversing the Greninger chart end for end.

This procedure may be illustrated by determining the orientation of the aluminum crystal whose back-reflection Laue pattern is shown in Fig. 3–6(b). Fig. 8–5 is a tracing of this photograph, showing the more important spots numbered for reference. The poles of the planes causing these numbered spots are plotted stereographically in Fig. 8–6 by the method of Fig. 8–4 and are shown as solid circles.

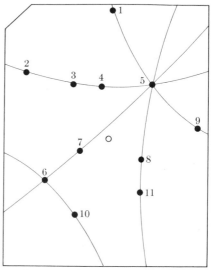

Fig. 8–5. Selected diffraction spots of back-reflection Laue pattern of an aluminum crystal, traced from Fig. 3–6(b).

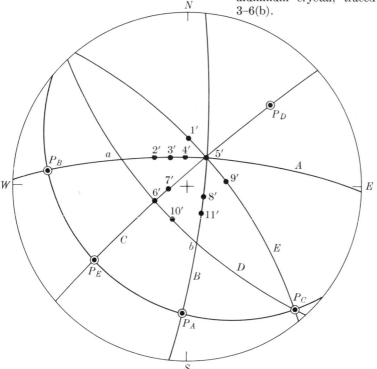

Fig. 8–6. Stereographic projection corresponding to back-reflection pattern of Fig. 8–5.

The problem now is to "index" these planes, i.e., to find their Miller indices, and so disclose the orientation of the crystal. With the aid of a Wulff net, great circles are drawn through the various sets of poles corresponding to the various hyperbolas of spots on the film. These great circles connect planes of a zone, and planes lying at their intersections are generally of low indices, such as $\{100\}$, $\{110\}$, $\{111\}$, and $\{112\}$. The axes of the zones themselves are also of low indices, so it is helpful to locate these axes on the projection. They are shown as open circles in Fig. 8–6, P_A being the axis of zone A, P_B the axis of zone B, etc. We then measure the angles between important poles (zone intersections and zone axes) and try to identify the poles by comparison of these measured angles with those calculated for cubic crystals (Table 2–3). The method is essentially one of trial and error. We note, for example, that the angles $P_A - P_B$, $P_A - 5'$, and $P_B - 5'$ are all 90°. This suggests that one or more of these poles might be $\{100\}$ or $\{110\}$, since the angle between two $\{100\}$ poles or between two $\{110\}$ poles is 90°. Suppose we tentatively assume that P_A, P_B, and $5'$ are all $\{100\}$ poles.* Then P_E, which lies on the great circle between P_A and P_B and at an angular distance of 45° from each, must be a $\{110\}$ pole. We then turn our attention to zone C and find that the distance between pole $6'$ and either pole $5'$ or P_E is also 45°. But reference to a standard projection, such as Fig. 2–37, shows that there is no important pole located midway on the great circle between $\{100\}$, which we have identified with $5'$, and $\{110\}$, which we have identified with P_E. Our original assumption is therefore wrong. We therefore make a second assumption, which is consistent with the angles measured so far, namely that $5'$ is a $\{100\}$ pole, as before, but that P_A and P_B are $\{110\}$ poles. P_E must then be a $\{100\}$ pole and $6'$ a $\{110\}$ pole. We can check this assumption by measuring the angles in the triangle $a - b - 5'$. Both a and b are found to be 55° from $5'$, and 71° from each other, which conclusively identifies a and b as $\{111\}$ poles. We note also, from a standard projection, that a $\{111\}$ pole must lie on a great circle between $\{100\}$ and $\{110\}$, which agrees with the fact that a, for example, lies on the great circle between $5'$, assumed to be $\{100\}$, and P_B, assumed to be $\{110\}$. Our second assumption is therefore shown to be correct.

---

* The reader may detect an apparent error in nomenclature here. Pole $5'$ for example, is assumed to be a $\{100\}$ pole and spot 5 on the diffraction pattern is assumed, tacitly, to be due to a 100 reflection. But aluminum is face-centered cubic and we know that there is no 100 reflection from such a lattice, since hkl must be unmixed for diffraction to occur. Actually, spot 5, if our assumption is correct, is due to overlapping reflections from the $\{200\}$, $\{400\}$, $\{600\}$, etc., planes. But these planes are all parallel and are represented on the stereographic projection by one pole, which is conventionally referred to as $\{100\}$. The corresponding diffraction spot is also called, conventionally but loosely, the 100 spot.

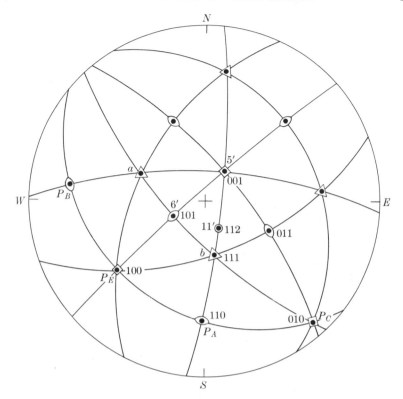

Fig. 8–7. Stereographic projection of Fig. 8–6 with poles identified.

Figure 8–7 shows the stereographic projection in a more complete form, with all poles of the type {100}, {110}, and {111} located and identified. Note that it was not necessary to index all the observed diffraction spots in order to determine the crystal orientation, which is specified completely, in fact, by the locations of any two {100} poles on the projection. The information given in Fig. 8–7 is therefore all that is commonly required. Occasionally, however, we may wish to know the Miller indices of a particular diffraction spot on the film, spot 11 for example. To find these indices, we note that pole 11′ is located 35° from (001) on the great circle passing through (001) and (111). Reference to a standard projection and a table of interplanar angles shows that its indices are (112).

As mentioned above, the stereographic projection of Fig. 8–7 is a complete description of the orientation of the crystal. Other methods of description are also possible. The crystal to which Fig. 8–7 refers had the form of a square plate and was mounted with its plane parallel to the plane of the film (and the projection) and its edges parallel to the film edges, which are in turn parallel to the *NS* and *EW* axes of the projection. Since the (001) pole is near the center of the projection, which corresponds to the specimen normal, and the (010) pole near the edge of the projection and approximately midway between the E and S poles, we may very roughly describe the crystal orientation as follows: one set of cube planes is approximately parallel to the surface of the plate while another set passes diagonally through the plate and approximately at right angles to its surface.

Another method of description may be used when only one direction in the crystal is of physical significance, such as the plate normal in the present case. For example, we may wish to make a compression test of this crystal, with the axis of compression normal to the plate surface. We are then interested in the orientation of the crystal relative to the compression axis (plate normal) or, stated inversely, in the orientation of the compression axis relative to certain directions of low indices in the crystal. Now inspection of a standard projection such as Fig. 2–36(a) shows that each half of the reference sphere is covered by 24 similar and equivalent spherical triangles, each having {100}, {110}, and {111} as its vertices. The plate normal will fall in one of these triangles and it is necessary to draw only one of them in order to describe the precise location of the normal. In Fig. 8–7, the plate normal lies in the (001)-(101)-(111) triangle which is redrawn in Fig. 8–8 in the conventional orientation, as though it formed part of a (001) standard projection. To locate the plate normal on this new drawing, we measure the angles between the center of the projection in Fig. 8–7 and the three adjacent poles. Let these angles be ρ_{001}, ρ_{101}, and ρ_{111}. These angles are then used to determine the three arcs shown

in Fig. 8–8. These are circle arcs, but they are *not* centered on the corresponding poles; rather, each one is the locus of points located at an equal *angular* distance from the pole involved and their intersection therefore locates the desired point. An alternate method of arriving at Fig. 8–8 from Fig. 8–7 consists simply in rotating the whole projection, poles and plate normal together, from the orientation shown in Fig. 8–7 to that of a standard (001) projection.

Similarly, the orientation of a single-crystal wire or rod may be described in terms of the location of its axis in the unit stereographic triangle. Note that this method does not completely describe the orientation

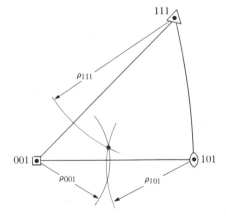

FIG. 8–8. Use of the unit stereographic triangle to describe crystal orientation. The point inside the triangle is the normal to the single crystal plate whose orientation is shown in Fig. 8–7.

of the crystal, since it allows one rotational degree of freedom about the specimen axis. This is of no consequence, however, when we are only interested in the value of some measured physical or mechanical property along a particular direction in the crystal.

There are alternate ways of manipulating both the Greninger chart and the stereographic projection, and the particular method used is purely a matter of personal preference. For example, we may ignore the individual spots on the film and focus our attention instead on the various hyperbolas on which they lie. The spots on one hyperbola are due to reflections from planes of one zone and, by means of the Greninger chart, we can plot directly the axis of this zone without plotting the poles of any of the planes belonging to it. The procedure is illustrated in Fig. 8–9. Keeping the centers of film and chart coincident, we rotate the film about this center until a particular hyperbola of spots coincides with a curve of constant γ on the chart, as in (a). The amount of rotation required is read from the intersection of a vertical pencil line, previously ruled through the center of the film and parallel to one edge, with the protractor of the Greninger chart. Suppose this angle is ϵ. Then the projection is rotated by the same angle ϵ with respect to the underlying Wulff net and the zone axis is plotted on the vertical axis of the projection at an angle γ from the *circumference,* as in (b). (Note that zone A itself is represented by a great circle located at an angle γ above the *center* of the projection. However, the plotting of the zone circle is not ordinarily necessary since the zone axis adequately represents the whole zone.)* Proceeding in this way, we plot the poles of all the important zones and, by the method of Fig. 8–4, the pole of the plane causing the most important spot or spots on the pattern. (The latter are, like spot 5 of Fig. 8–5, of high intensity, at the intersection of a number of hyperbolas, and well separated from their neighbors.) The points so obtained are always of low indices and can usually be indexed without difficulty.

An alternate method of indexing plotted poles depends on having available a set of detailed standard projections in a number of orientations, such as {100}, {110}, and {111} for cubic crystals. It is also a trial and error method and may be illustrated with reference to Fig. 8–6. First, a prominent zone is selected and an assumption is made as to its indices: for example, we might assume that zone B is a $\langle 100 \rangle$ zone. This assumption is then tested by (a) rotating the projection about its center until P_B lies on the equator of the Wulff net and the ends of the zone circle coincide with the N and S poles of the net, and (b) rotating all the important points on the projection about the NS-axis of the net until P_B lies at the center and the zone circle at the circumference. The new projection is then superimposed on a {100} standard projection and rotated about the center until all points on the projection coincide with those on the standard. If no such coincidence is obtained, another standard projection is tried. For the particular case

---

* Note that, when a hyperbola of spots is lined up with a horizontal hyperbola on the chart as in Fig. 8–9(a), the vertical hyperbolas can be used to measure the difference in angle δ for any two spots and that this angle is equal to the angle between the planes causing those spots, just as the angle between two poles lying on a meridian of a Wulff net is given by their difference in latitude.

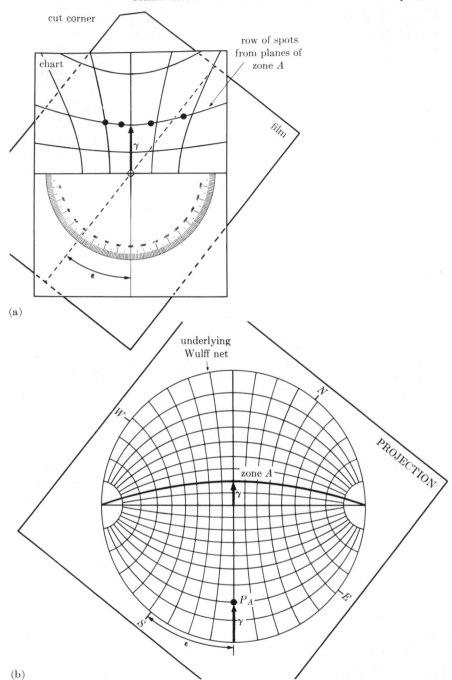

FIG. 8–9. Use of the Greninger chart to plot the axis of a zone of planes on the stereographic projection. P_A is the axis of zone A.

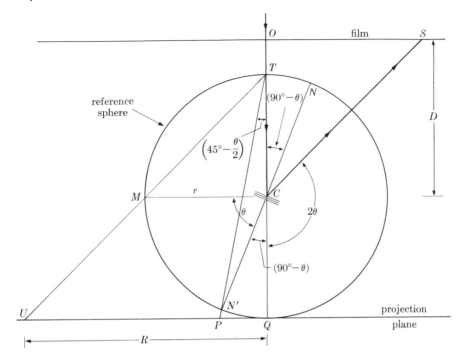

FIG. 8–10. Relation between diffraction spot S and stereographic projection P of the plane causing the spot, for back reflection.

of Fig. 8–6, a coincidence would be obtained only on a {110} standard, since P_B is actually a {110} pole. Once a match has been found, the indices of the unknown poles are given simply by the indices of the poles on the standard with which they coincide.

In the absence of a Greninger chart, the pole corresponding to any observed Laue spot may be plotted by means of an easily constructed "stereographic ruler." The construction of the ruler is based on the relations shown in Fig. 8–10. This drawing is a section through the incident beam OC and any diffracted beam CS. Here it is convenient to use the plane normal CN' rather than CN and to make the projection from T, the intersection of the reference sphere with the incident beam. The projection of the pole N' is therefore at P. From the measured distance OS of the diffraction spot from the center of the film, we can find the distance PQ of the projected pole from the center of the projection, since

$$OS = OC \tan (180° - 2\theta) = D \tan (180° - 2\theta) \qquad (8\text{–}1)$$

and

$$PQ = TQ \tan \left(45° - \frac{\theta}{2}\right) = 2r \tan \left(45° - \frac{\theta}{2}\right), \qquad (8\text{–}2)$$

where D is the specimen-film distance and r the radius of the reference sphere. The value of r is fixed by the radius R of the Wulff net used, since the latter equals the radius of the basic circle of the projection. We note that, if the pole of the

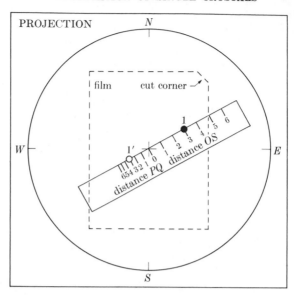

FIG. 8–11. Use of a stereographic ruler to plot the pole of a reflecting plane on a stereographic projection in the back-reflection Laue method. Pole 1′ is the pole of the plane causing diffraction spot 1.

plane were in its extreme position at M, then its projection would be at U. The point U therefore lies on the basic circle of the projection, and UQ is the radius R of the basic circle. Because the triangles TUQ and TMC are similar, $R = 2r$ and

$$PQ = R \tan \left(45° - \frac{\theta}{2} \right). \qquad (8\text{–}3)$$

The ruler is constructed by marking off, from a central point, a scale of centimeters by which the distance OS may be measured. The distance PQ corresponding to each distance OS is then calculated from Eqs. (8–1) and (8–3), and marked off from the center of the ruler in the opposite direction. Corresponding graduations are given the same number and the result is the ruler shown in Fig. 8–11, which also illustrates the method of using it. [Calculation of the various distances PQ can be avoided by use of the Wulff net itself. Fig. 8–10 shows that the pole of the reflecting plane is located at an angle θ from the edge of the projection, and θ is given for each distance OS by Eq. (8–1). The ruler is laid along the equator of the Wulff net, its center coinciding with the net center, and the distance PQ corresponding to each angle θ is marked off with the help of the angular scale on the equator.]

From the choice of plane normal made in Fig. 8–10, it is apparent that the projection must be viewed from the side opposite the x-ray source. This requires that the film be read from that side also, i.e., with its cut corner in the upper right-hand position. The projection is then placed over the film, illuminated from below, as shown in Fig. 8–11. With the center of the ruler coinciding with the center of the projection, the ruler is rotated until its edge passes through a particular diffraction spot. The distance OS is noted and the corresponding pole plotted as shown, on the other side of center and at the corresponding distance PQ. This procedure is repeated for each important diffraction spot, after which the projection is transferred to a Wulff net and the poles indexed by either of the methods previously described. Note that this procedure gives a projection of the crystal from the side opposite the x-ray source, whereas the Greninger chart gives a projection of the crystal as seen from the x-ray source. A crystal orientation can, of course, be described just as well from one side as the other, and either projection can be made to coincide with the other by a 180° rotation of the projection about its EW-axis. Although simple to use and construct, the stereographic ruler is not as accurate as the Greninger chart in the solution of back-reflection patterns.

The methods of determining and describing crystal orientation have been presented here exclusively in terms of cubic crystals, because these are the simplest kind to consider and the most frequently encountered. These methods are quite general, however, and can be applied to a crystal of any system as long as its interplanar angles are known.

8–3 Transmission Laue method. Given a specimen of sufficiently low absorption, a transmission Laue pattern can be obtained and used, in much the same way as a back-reflection Laue pattern, to reveal the orientation of the crystal.

In either Laue method, the diffraction spots on the film, due to the planes of a single zone in the crystal, always lie on a curve which is some kind of conic section. When the film is in the transmission position, this curve is a complete ellipse for sufficiently small values of ϕ, the angle between the zone axis and the transmitted beam (Fig. 8–12). For somewhat larger values of ϕ, the ellipse is incomplete because of the finite size of the film. When $\phi = 45°$, the curve becomes a parabola, when ϕ exceeds 45°, a

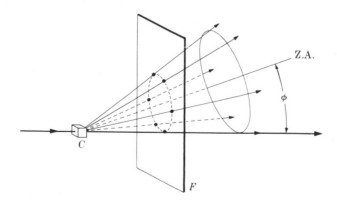

FIG. 8–12.   Intersection of a conical array of diffracted beams with a film placed in the transmission position. C = crystal, F = film, Z.A. = zone axis.

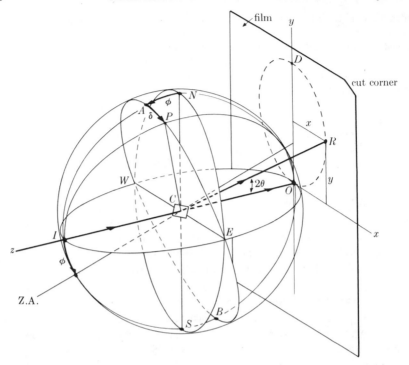

Fig. 8–13. Relation between plane normal orientation and diffraction spot position in the transmission Laue method.

hyperbola, and when $\phi = 90°$, a straight line. In all cases, the curve passes through the central spot formed by the transmitted beam.

The angular relationships involved in the transmission Laue method are illustrated in Fig. 8–13. Here a reference sphere is described about the crystal at C, the incident beam entering the sphere at I and the transmitted beam leaving at O. The film is placed tangent to the sphere at O, and its upper right-hand corner, viewed from the crystal, is cut off for identification of its position during the x-ray exposure. The beam reflected by the lattice plane shown strikes the film at R, and the normal to this plane intersects the sphere at P.

Suppose we consider diffraction from a zone of planes whose axis lies in the yz-plane at an angle ϕ to the transmitted (or incident) beam. If a single plane of this zone is rotated so that its pole, initially at A, travels along the great circle $APEBWA$, then it will pass through all the orientations in which planes of this zone might occur in an actual crystal. During this rotation, the diffraction spot on the film, initially at D, would travel along the elliptical path $DROD$ shown by the dashed line.

Any particular orientation of the plane, such as the one shown in the drawing, is characterized by particular values of ϕ and δ, the angular co-

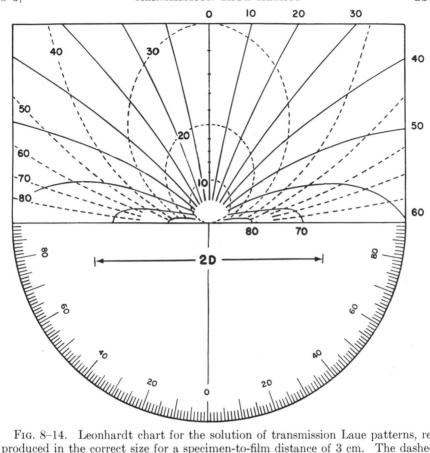

FIG. 8–14. Leonhardt chart for the solution of transmission Laue patterns, re-produced in the correct size for a specimen-to-film distance of 3 cm. The dashed lines are lines of constant ϕ, and the solid lines are lines of constant δ. (Courtesy of C. G. Dunn.)

ordinates of its pole. These coordinates in turn, for a given crystal-film distance D ($= CO$), determine the x,y coordinates of the diffraction spot R on the film. From the spot position we can therefore determine the plane orientation, and one way of doing this is by means of the Leonhardt chart shown in Fig. 8–14.

This chart is exactly analogous to the Greninger chart for solving back-reflection patterns and is used in precisely the same way. It consists of a grid composed of two sets of lines: the lines of one set are lines of constant ϕ and correspond to the meridians on a Wulff net, and the lines of the other are lines of constant δ and correspond to latitude lines. By means of this chart, the pole of a plane causing any particular diffraction spot may be plotted stereographically. The projection plane is tangent to the sphere at the point I of Fig. 8–13 and the projection is made from the point O. This requires that the film be read from the side facing the crystal, i.e.,

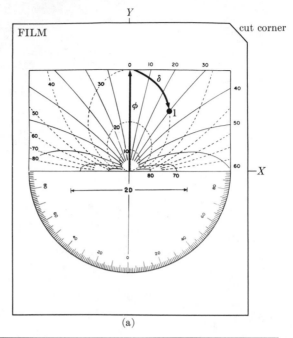

(a)

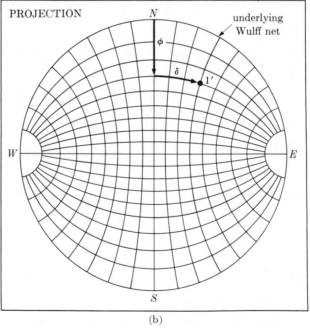

(b)

FIG. 8–15. Use of the Leonhardt chart to plot the pole of a plane on a stereographic projection.   Pole 1′ in (b) is the pole of the plane causing diffraction spot 1 in (a).

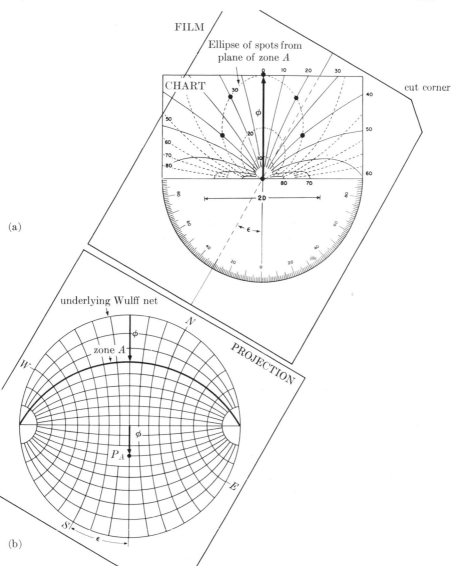

FIG. 8–16. Use of the Leonhardt chart to plot the axis of a zone of planes on the projection. P_A is the axis of zone A.

with the cut corner at the upper right. Figure 8–15 shows how the pole corresponding to a particular spot is plotted when the film and chart are in the parallel position. An alternate way of using the chart is to rotate it about its center until a line of constant ϕ coincides with a row of spots from planes of a single zone, as shown in Fig. 8–16; knowing ϕ and the rotation angle ϵ, we can then plot the axis of the zone directly.

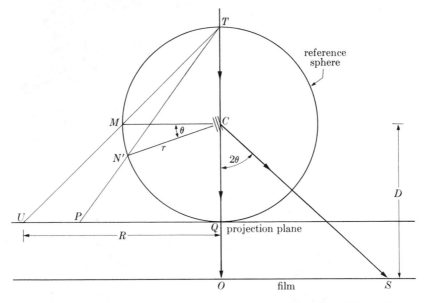

FIG. 8–17. Relation between diffraction spot S and stereographic projection P of the plane causing the spot, in transmission.

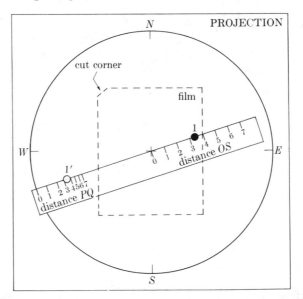

FIG. 8–18. Use of a stereographic ruler to plot the pole of a reflecting plane on a stereographic projection in the transmission Laue method. Pole $1'$ is the pole of the plane causing diffraction spot 1.

A stereographic ruler may be constructed for the transmission method and it will give greater accuracy of plotting than the Leonhardt chart, particularly when the angle ϕ approaches 90°. Figure 8–17, which is a section through the incident beam and any diffracted beam, shows that the distance of the diffraction spot from the center of the film is given by

$$OS = D \tan 2\theta.$$

The distance of the pole of the reflecting plane from the center of the projection is given by

$$PQ = R \tan \left(45° - \frac{\theta}{2} \right).$$

Figure 8–18 illustrates the use of a ruler constructed according to these equations. In this case, the projection is made on a plane located on the same side of the crystal as the film and, accordingly, the film must be read with its cut corner in the upper left-hand position.

Whether the chart or the ruler is employed to plot the poles of reflecting planes, they are indexed in the same way as back-reflection patterns. For example, the transmission Laue pattern shown in Fig. 8–19 in the form of a tracing yields the stereographic projection shown in Fig. 8–20. The solid symbols in the latter are the poles of planes responsible for spots on the film and are numbered accordingly; the open symbols are poles derived by construction. (The reader will note that the poles of planes responsible for observed spots on a transmission film are all located near the edge of the projection, since such planes must necessarily be inclined at small angles to the incident beam. The reverse is true of back-reflection patterns, as inspection of Fig. 8–6 will show.) The solution of Fig. 8–20 hinged on the identification of the zone axes P_A, P_B, and P_C. Measurement showed that the stereographic triangle formed by these axes had sides equal to 35° $(P_A - P_B)$, 45° $(P_B - P_C)$, and 30° $(P_C - P_A)$, which identified P_A, P_B, and P_C as $\{211\}$, $\{100\}$, and $\{110\}$ poles, respectively. Now the transmission pattern shown in Fig. 8–19 and the back-reflection pattern shown in Fig. 8–5 were both obtained from the same crystal in the same orientation relative to the incident beam. The corresponding projections, Figs. 8–20 and 8–7, therefore refer to a crystal of the same orientation. But these were made from opposite sides of the crystal and so appear completely dissimilar. However, a rotation of either projection by 180° about its EW-axis will make it coincide with the other, although no attempt has been made to make the indexing of one projection consistent with that of the other.

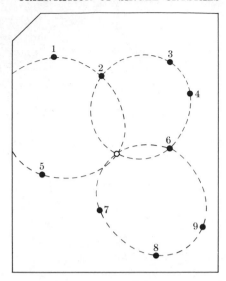

FIG. 8–19. Transmission Laue pattern of an aluminum crystal, traced from Fig. 3–6(a). Only selected diffraction spots are shown.

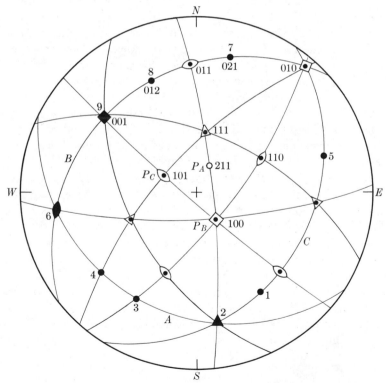

FIG. 8–20. Stereographic projection corresponding to transmission pattern of Fig. 8–19.

8–4 Diffractometer method. Still another method of determining crystal orientation involves the use of the diffractometer and a procedure radically different from that of either Laue method. With the essentially monochromatic radiation used in the diffractometer, a single crystal will produce a reflection only when its orientation is such that a certain set of reflecting planes is inclined to the incident beam at an angle θ which satisfies the Bragg law for that set of planes and the characteristic radiation employed. But when the counter, fixed in position at the corresponding angle 2θ, discloses that a reflection *is* produced, then the inclination of the reflecting planes to any chosen line or plane on the crystal surface is known from the position of the crystal. Two kinds of operation are required:

(1) rotation of the crystal about various axes until a position is found for which reflection occurs,

(2) location of the pole of the reflecting plane on a stereographic projection from the known angles of rotation.

The diffractometer method has many variations, depending on the particular kind of goniometer used to hold and rotate the specimen. Only one of these variations will be described here, that involving the goniometer used in the reflection method of determining preferred orientation, since that is the kind most generally available in metallurgical laboratories. This specimen holder, to be described in detail in Sec. 9–9, needs very little modification for use with single crystals, the chief one being an increase in the width of the primary beam slits in a direction parallel to the diffractometer axis in order to increase the diffracted intensity. This type of holder provides the three possible rotation axes shown in Fig. 8–21: one coincides with the diffractometer axis, the second (AA') lies in the plane of the incident beam I and diffracted beam D and tangent to the specimen surface, shown here as a flat plate, while the third (BB') is normal to the specimen surface.

Suppose the orientation of a cubic crystal is to be determined. For such crystals it is convenient to use the $\{111\}$ planes as reflectors; there are four sets of these and their reflecting power is usually high. First, the 2θ value for the 111 reflection (or, if desired, the 222 reflection) is computed from the known spacing of the $\{111\}$ planes and the known wavelength of the radiation used. The counter is then fixed in this 2θ position. The specimen holder is now rotated about the diffractometer axis until its surface, and the rotation axis AA', is equally inclined to the incident beam and the diffracted beam, or rather, to the line from crystal to counter with which the diffracted beam, when formed, will coincide. The specimen holder is then fixed in this position, no further rotation about the diffractometer axis being required. Then, by rotation about the axis BB', one edge of the specimen or a line drawn on it is made parallel to the diffractometer axis. This is the initial position illustrated in Fig. 8–21.

The crystal is then slowly rotated about the axes AA' and BB' until an indication of a reflection is observed on the counting-rate meter. Once a reflecting position of the crystal has been found, we know that the normal to one set of {111} planes coincides with the line CN, that is, lies in the plane of the diffractometer circle and bisects the angle between incident and diffracted beams. The pole of these diffracting planes may now be plotted stereographically, as shown in Fig. 8–22. The projection is made on a plane parallel to the specimen surface, and with the NS-axis of the projection parallel to the reference edge or line mentioned above. When

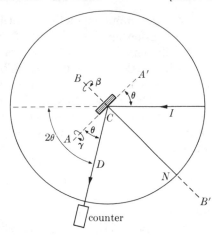

FIG. 8–21. Crystal rotation axes for the diffractometer method of determining orientation.

the crystal is rotated β degrees about BB' from its initial position, the projection is also rotated β degrees about its center. The direction CN, which might be called the normal to "potential" reflecting planes, is repre-

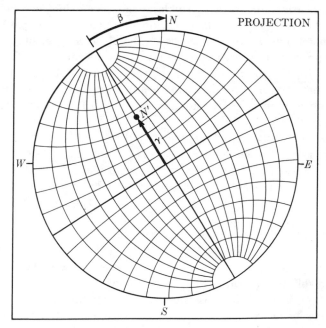

FIG. 8–22. Plotting method used when determining crystal orientation with the diffractometer. (The directions of the rotations shown here correspond to the directions of the arrows in Fig. 8–21.)

sented by the pole N', which is initially at the center of the projection but which moves γ degrees along a radius when the crystal is rotated γ degrees about AA'.

What we are trying to do, essentially, is to make N' coincide with a {111} pole and so disclose the location of the latter on the projection. The search may be made by varying γ continuously for fixed values of β 4 or 5° apart; the projection is then covered point by point along a series of radii. It is enough to examine one quadrant in this way since there will always be at least one {111} pole in any one quadrant. Once one pole has been located, the search for the second is aided by the knowledge that it must be 70.5° from the first. Although two {111} poles are enough to fix the orientation of the crystal, a third should be located as a check.

Parenthetically, it should be noted that the positioning of the crystal surface and the axis AA' at equal angles to the incident and diffracted beams is done only for convenience in plotting the stereographic projection. There is no question of focusing when monochromatic radiation is reflected from an undeformed single crystal, and the ideal incident beam for the determination of crystal orientation is a parallel beam, not a divergent one.

In the hands of an experienced operator, the diffractometer method is faster than either Laue method. Furthermore, it can yield results of greater accuracy if narrow slits are used to reduce the divergence of the incident beam, although the use of extremely narrow slits will make it more difficult to locate the reflecting positions of the crystal. On the other hand, the diffractometer method furnishes no permanent record of the orientation determination, whereas Laue patterns may be filed away for future reference. But what is more important, the diffractometer method does not readily disclose the state of perfection of the crystal, whereas a Laue pattern yields this kind of information at a glance, as we will see in Sec. 8–6, and in many investigations the metallurgist is just as much interested in the relative perfection of a single crystal as he is in its orientation.

All things considered, the Laue methods are preferable when only occasional orientation determinations are required, or when there is any doubt as to the perfection of the crystal. When the orientations of large numbers of crystals have to be determined in a routine manner, the diffractometer method is superior. In fact, this method was developed largely for just such an application during World War II, when the orientation of large numbers of quartz crystals had to be determined. These crystals were used in radio transmitters to control, through their natural frequency of vibration, the frequency of the transmitted signal. For this purpose quartz wafers had to be cut with faces accurately parallel to certain crystallographic planes, and the diffractometer was used to determine the orientations of these planes in the crystal.

8–5 Setting a crystal in a required orientation. Some x-ray investigations require that a diffraction pattern be obtained of a single crystal having a specified orientation relative to the incident beam. To obtain this orientation, the crystal is mounted in a three-circle goniometer like that shown in Fig. 5–7, whose arcs have been set at zero, and its orientation is determined by, for example, the back-reflection Laue method. A projection of the crystal is then made, and from this projection the goniometer rotations which will bring the crystal into the required orientation are determined.

For example, suppose it is required to rotate the crystal whose orientation is given by Fig. 8–7 into a position where [011] points along the incident beam and [100] points horizontally to the left, i.e., into the standard (011) orientation shown by Fig. 2–36(b) if the latter were rotated 90° about the center. The initial orientation (Position 1) is shown in Fig. 8–23 by the open symbols, referred to *NSEW*-axes. Since (011) is to be brought to the center of the projection and (100) to the left side, (010) will lie on the vertical axis of the projection when the crystal is in its final position. The first step therefore is to locate a point 90° away from (011) on the great circle joining (010) to (011), because this point must coincide with the north pole of the final projection. This is simply a construction point;

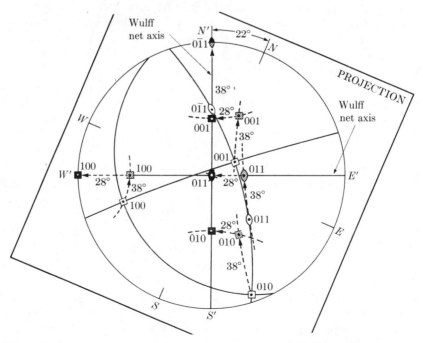

Fig. 8–23. Crystal rotation to produce specified orientation. Positions 1 and 2 are indicated by open symbols, position 3 by shaded symbols, and position 4 by solid symbols.

in the present case it happens to coincide with the (0$\bar{1}$1) pole, but generally it is of no crystallographic significance. The projection is then rotated 22° clockwise about the incident-beam axis to bring this point onto the vertical axis of the underlying Wulff net. (In Fig. 8–23, the latitude and longitude lines of this net have been omitted for clarity.) The crystal is now in Position 2, shown by open symbols referred to $N'S'E'W'$-axes. The next rotation is performed about the $E'W'$-axis, which requires that the underlying Wulff net be arranged with its equator vertical so that the latitude lines will run from top to bottom. This rotation, of 38°, moves all poles along latitude lines, shown as dashed small circles, and brings (0$\bar{1}$1) to the N'-pole, and (100) and (011) to the $E'W'$-axis of the projection, as indicated by the shaded symbols (Position 3). The final orientation is obtained by a 28° rotation about the $N'S'$-axis, with the equator of the underlying Wulff net now horizontal; the poles move to the positions shown by solid symbols (Position 4).

The necessity for selecting a construction point 90° from (011) should now be evident. If this point, which here happens to be (0$\bar{1}$1), is brought to the N'-pole, then (011) and (100) must of necessity lie on the $E'W'$-axis; the final rotation about $N'S'$ will then move the latter to their required positions without disturbing the position of the (0$\bar{1}$1) pole, since [0$\bar{1}$1] coincides with the $N'S'$-axis.

The order of these three rotations is not arbitrary. The stereographic rotations correspond to physical rotations on the goniometer and must be made in such a way that one rotation does not physically alter the position of any axis about which a subsequent rotation is to be made. The goniometer used here was initially set with the axis of its uppermost arc horizontal and coincident with the primary beam, and with the axis of the next arc horizontal and at right angles to the incident beam. The first rotation about the beam axis therefore did not disturb the position of the second axis (the $E'W'$-axis), and neither of the first two rotations dis-

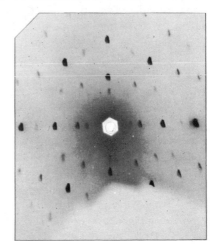

FIG. 8–24. Back-reflection Laue pattern of an aluminum crystal. The incident beam is parallel to [011], [0$\bar{1}$1] points vertically upward, and [100] points horizontally to the left. Tungsten radiation, 30 kv, 19 ma, 40 min exposure, 5 cm specimen-to-film distance. (The shadow at the bottom is that of the goniometer which holds the specimen.)

turbed the position of the third axis (the vertical $N'S'$-axis). Whether or not the stereographic orientations are performed in the correct order makes a great difference in the rotation angles found, but once the right angles are determined by the correct stereographic procedure, the actual physical rotations on the goniometer may be performed in any sequence.

The back-reflection Laue pattern of an aluminum crystal rotated into the orientation described above is shown in Fig. 8–24. Note that the arrangement of spots has 2-fold rotational symmetry about the primary beam, corresponding to the 2-fold rotational symmetry of cubic crystals about their $\langle 110 \rangle$ axes. (Conversely, the observed symmetry of the Laue pattern of a crystal of unknown structure is an indication of the kind of symmetry possessed by that crystal. Thus the Laue method can be used as an aid in the determination of crystal structure.)

There is another method of setting a crystal in a standard orientation, which does not require either photographic registration of the diffraction pattern or stereographic manipulation of the data. It depends on the fact that the diffracted beams formed in the transmission Laue method are so intense, for a crystal of the proper thickness, that the spots they form on a fluorescent screen are visible in a dark room. The observer merely rotates the crystal about the various arcs of the goniometer until the pattern corresponding to the required orientation appears on the screen. Obviously, he must be able to recognize this pattern when it appears, but a little study of a few Laue photographs made of crystals in standard orientations will enable him to do this. The necessity for working in a darkened room may be avoided by use of a light-tight viewing box, if the job of crystal setting occurs sufficiently often to justify its construction. This box encloses the fluorescent screen which the observer views through a binocular eyepiece set in the wall of the box, either directly along the direction of the transmitted beam, or indirectly in a direction at right angles by means of a mirror or a right-angle prism. For x-ray protection, the optical system should include lead glass, and the observer's hands should be shielded during manipulation of the crystal.

8–6 The effect of plastic deformation. Nowhere have x-ray methods been more fruitful than in the study of plastic deformation. The way in which a single crystal deforms plastically is markedly anisotropic, and almost all of our knowledge of this phenomenon has been gained by x-ray diffraction examination of crystals at various stages during plastic deformation. At the outset we can distinguish between two kinds of deformation, that of the crystal lattice itself and that of the crystal as a whole. This distinction is worth while because crystal deformation, defined as a change in the shape of the crystal due to lattice rotation, can occur with or without lattice deformation, defined as the bending and/or twisting of originally flat lattice planes. On the other hand, lattice deformation cannot occur without some deformation of the crystal as a whole.

A crystal lattice can therefore behave in two quite different ways during plastic deformation: it can simply rotate without undergoing deformation itself, or it can become bent and/or twisted. Laue photographs can easily decide between these two possibilities. In the Laue method, any change in the orientation of the reflecting planes is accompanied by a corresponding change in the direction (and wavelength) of the reflected beam. In fact, Laue reflection of x-rays is often compared to the reflection of visible light by a mirror. If the lattice simply rotates during deformation, then Laue patterns made before and after will merely show a change in the position of the diffraction spots, corresponding to the change in orientation of the lattice, but the spots themselves will remain sharp. On the other hand, if the lattice is bent or twisted, the Laue spots will become smeared out into streaks because of the continuous change in orientation of the reflecting planes, just as a spot of light reflected by a flat mirror becomes elongated when the mirror is curved.

A classic example of simple **lattice rotation** during crystal deformation is afforded by the tensile elongation of long cylindrical single metal crystals. When such a crystal is extended plastically, Laue photographs of the center section made before and after the extension show that the lattice has been rotated but not deformed. Yet the crystal itself has undergone considerable deformation as evidence by its change in shape—it has become longer and thinner. How this occurs is suggested by Fig. 8–25. The initial form of the crystal is shown in (a), with the potential slip planes seen in profile. The applied tensile forces can be resolved into

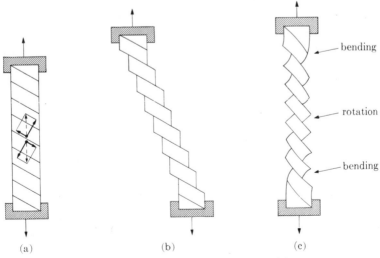

(a)   (b)   (c)

Fig. 8–25.   Slip in tension (schematic).

shearing forces parallel to these slip planes and tensile forces normal to them. The normal forces have no effect, but the shearing forces cause slip to occur, and the crystal would, as a result, assume the shape shown in (b) if the ends were not constrained laterally. However, the grips of the tensile machine keep the ends of the crystal aligned, causing bending of the crystal lattice near each grip, as indicated in (c), which illustrates the appearance of the crystal after considerable extension. Note that the lattice of the central portion has undergone reorientation but not distortion. This reorientation clearly consists in a rotation which makes the active slip plane more nearly parallel to the tension axis.

Analysis of the Laue patterns yields further information about the deformation process. The changes in orientation which occur in the central section can be followed stereographically, either by plotting the before and after orientations of the crystal on a fixed projection plane, or by plotting the before and after orientations of the specimen axis in the unit stereographic triangle. The latter method is the more common one and is illustrated by Fig. 8–26, which applies to a face-centered cubic crystal. The initial position of the tension axis is represented by point 1. After successive extensions, the position of this axis is found to be at points 2, 3, 4, ... ; i.e., the axis moves along a great circle passing through the initial position and the direction $[\bar{1}01]$, which is the direction of slip. During this extension the active slip plane is (111). We can conclude that the lattice reorientation occurs in such a way that both the slip plane and the slip direction in that plane rotate toward the axis of tension. This process becomes more complicated at later stages of the deformation, and the interested reader is referred to books on crystal plasticity for further details. Enough has been said here to indicate the way in which x-ray diffraction may be applied to this particular problem.

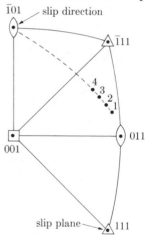

FIG. 8–26. Lattice rotation during slip in elongation of FCC metal crystal.

One other example of lattice reorientation during slip may be given in order to illustrate the alternate method of plotting the data. In Fig. 8–27, the successive orientations which a cylindrical magnesium crystal assumes during plastic torsion are plotted on a fixed projection plane parallel to the specimen axis (the axis of torsion). Since the poles of reflecting planes are found to move along latitude circles on the projection, it follows that

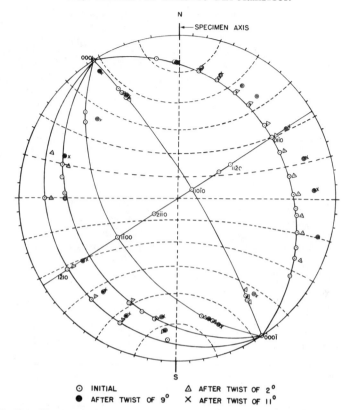

FIG. 8–27. Change in lattice orientation during plastic torsion of a magnesium crystal. The active slip plane is (0001), the basal plane of the hexagonal lattice. (S. S. Hsu and B. D. Cullity, *Trans. A.I.M.E.* **200**, 305, 1954.)

the lattice reorientation is mainly one of rotation about the specimen axis. Some lattice distortion also occurs, since special x-ray methods reveal that twisting of the lattice planes takes place, but the main feature of the deformation is the lattice rotation described above. Similarly, in the plastic elongation of single crystals, it should not be supposed that absolutely no lattice deformation occurs. Here again the main feature is lattice rotation, but sensitive x-ray methods will always show some bending or twisting of lattice planes, and in some cases this lattice distortion may be so severe that ordinary Laue patterns will reveal it.

A good example of severe **lattice distortion** is afforded by those parts of a single-crystal tension specimen immediately adjacent to the grips. As mentioned earlier, these portions of the crystal lattice are forced to bend during elongation of the specimen, and Laue photographs made of these sections will accordingly show elongated spots. If the bending is about a single axis, the Miller indices of the bending axis can usually be determined

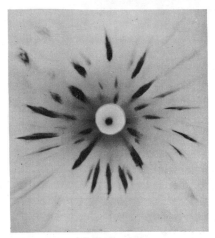
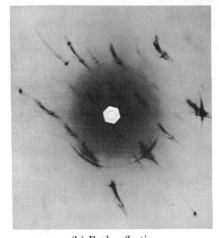

(a) Transmission   (b) Back reflection

FIG. 8–28. Laue photographs of a deformed aluminum crystal. Specimen-to-film distance 3 cm, tungsten radiation, 30 kv.

stereographically; each Laue streak is plotted as an arc representing the range of orientation of the corresponding lattice plane, and a rotation axis which will account for the directions of these arcs on the projection is found. The angular lengths of the arcs are a measure of the amount of bending which has occurred. In measuring the amount of bending by this method, it must be remembered that the wavelengths present in the incident beam do not cover an infinite range. There is no radiation of wavelength shorter than the short-wavelength limit, and on the long-wavelength side the intensity decreases continuously as the wavelength increases. This means that, for a given degree of lattice bending, some Laue streaks may not be as long as they might be if a full range of wavelengths were available. The amount of bending estimated from the lengths of these streaks would therefore be smaller than that actually present.

Transmission and back-reflection Laue patterns made from the same deformed region usually differ markedly in appearance. The photographs in Fig. 8–28 were made, under identical conditions, of the same region of a deformed aluminum crystal having the same orientation relative to the incident beam for each photograph. Both show elongated spots, which are evidence of lattice bending, but the spots are elongated primarily in a radial direction on the transmission pattern while on the back-reflection pattern they tend to follow zone lines. The term *asterism* (from the Greek *aster* = star) was used initially to describe the starlike appearance of a transmission pattern such as Fig. 8–28(a), but it is now used to describe any form of streaking, radial or nonradial, on either kind of Laue photograph.

The striking difference between these two photographs is best understood by considering a very general case. Suppose a crystal is so deformed

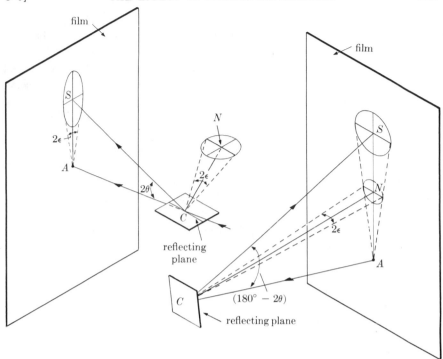

FIG. 8–29. Effect of lattice distortion on the shape of a transmission Laue spot. CN is the normal to the reflecting plane.

FIG. 8–30. Effect of lattice distortion on the shape of a back-reflection Laue spot. CN is the normal to the reflecting plane.

that the normal to a particular set of reflecting lattice planes describes a small cone of apex angle 2ϵ; i.e., in various parts of the crystal the normal deviates by an angle ϵ in all directions from its mean position. This is equivalent to rocking a flat mirror through the same angular range and, as Fig. 8–29 shows, the reflected spot S is roughly elliptical on a film placed in the transmission position. When the plane normal rocks through the angle 2ϵ in the plane ACN, the reflected beam moves through an angle 4ϵ, and the major axis of the ellipse is given approximately by $4\epsilon(AC)$ when 2θ is small. On the other hand, when the plane normal rocks through the angle 2ϵ in a direction normal to the plane of reflection ACN, the only effect is to rock the plane of reflection through the same angle 2ϵ about the incident beam. The minor axis of the elliptical spot is therefore given by $2\epsilon(AS) \approx 2\epsilon(AC)\tan 2\theta \approx 2\epsilon(AC)2\theta$. The shape of the spot is characterized by the ratio

$$\frac{\text{Major axis}}{\text{Minor axis}} = \frac{4\epsilon(AC)}{2\epsilon(AC)2\theta} = \frac{1}{\theta}.$$

For $2\theta = 10°$, the major axis is some 12 times the length of the minor axis.

In the back-reflection region, the situation is entirely different and the spot S is roughly circular, as shown in Fig. 8–30. Both axes of the spot subtend an angle of approximately 4ϵ at the crystal. We may therefore conclude that the shape of a back-reflection spot is more directly related to the nature of the lattice distortion than is the shape of a transmission spot since, in the general case, circular motion of the end of the reflecting plane normal causes circular motion of the backward-reflected beam but elliptical motion of the forward-reflected beam. For this reason, the back-reflection method is generally preferable for studies of lattice distortion. It must not be supposed, however, that only radial streaking is possible on transmission patterns. The direction of streaking depends on the orientation of the axis about which the reflecting planes are bent and if, for example, they are bent only about an axis lying in the plane ACN of Fig. 8–29, then the spot will be elongated in a direction at right angles to the radius AS.

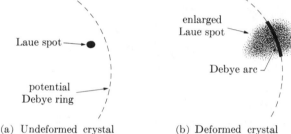

(a) Undeformed crystal   (b) Deformed crystal

FIG. 8–31.   Formation of Debye arcs on Laue patterns of deformed crystals.

One feature of the back-reflection pattern of Fig. 8–28 deserves some comment, namely, the short arcs, concentric with the film center, which pass through many of the elongated Laue spots. These are portions of Debye rings, such as one might expect on a pinhole photograph made of a polycrystalline specimen with characteristic radiation (Sec. 6–9). With a polycrystalline specimen of random orientation a complete Debye ring is formed, because the normals to any particular set of planes (hkl) have all possible orientations in space; in a deformed single crystal, the same normals are restricted to a finite range of orientations with the result that only fragments of Debye rings appear. We may imagine a circle on the film along which a Debye ring would form if a polycrystalline specimen were used, as indicated in Fig. 8–31. If a Laue spot then becomes enlarged as a result of lattice deformation and spreads over the potential Debye ring, then a short portion of a Debye ring will form. It will be much darker than the Laue spot, since the characteristic radiation* which

---

* In Fig. 8–28(b), the characteristic radiation involved is tungsten L radiation. The voltage used (30 kv) is too low to excite the K lines of tungsten (excitation voltage = 70 kv) but high enough to excite the L lines (excitation voltage = 12 kv).

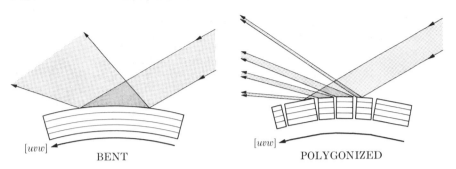

FIG. 8–32.   Reflection of white radiation by bent and polygonized lattices (schematic).

forms it is much more intense than the wavelengths immediately adjacent to it in the continuous spectrum.   In fact, if the x-ray exposure is not sufficiently long, only the Debye arcs may be visible on the film, and the observer may be led to erroneous conclusions regarding the nature and extent of the lattice deformation.

With these facts in mind, re-examination of the patterns shown in Fig. 8–28 leads to the following conclusions:

(1) Since the asterism on the transmission pattern is predominantly radial, lattice planes inclined at small angles to the incident beam are bent about a number of axes, in such a manner that their plane normals are confined to a small cone in space.

(2) Since the asterism on the back-reflection pattern chiefly follows zone lines, the major portion of planes inclined at large angles to the incident beam are bent about a single axis.   However, the existence of Debye arcs shows that there are latent Laue spots of considerable area superimposed on the visible elongated spots, and that a small portion of the planes referred to are therefore bent about a number of axes.

On annealing a deformed crystal at a sufficiently high temperature, one of the following effects is usually produced:

(1) *Polygonization.*   If the deformation is not too severe, plastically bent portions of the crystal break up into smaller blocks, which are strain-free and disoriented by approximately the same total amount (never more than a few degrees) as the bent fragment from which they originate, as suggested by Fig. 8–32.   (The term "polygonization" describes the fact that a certain crystallographic direction [uvw] forms part of an arc before annealing and part of a polygon afterwards.)   Moreover, the mean orientation of the blocks is the same as that of the parent fragment.   The effect of polygonization on a Laue pattern is therefore to replace an elongated Laue streak (from the bent lattice) with a row of small sharp spots (from the individual blocks) occupying the same position on the film, provided each block is sufficiently disoriented from its neighbor so that the beams

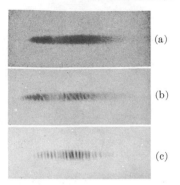

FIG. 8–33. Enlarged transmission Laue spots from a thin crystal of silicon ferrite (α-iron containing 3.3 percent silicon in solid solution): (a) as bent to a radius of $\frac{3}{8}$ in., (b) after annealing 10 min at 950°C, (c) after annealing 4 hr at 1300°C. (C. G. Dunn and F. W. Daniels, *Trans. A.I.M.E.* **191**, 147, 1951.)

reflected by adjoining blocks are resolved one from another. Figure 8–33 shows an example of polygonization in a crystal of silicon ferrite.

(2) *Recrystallization.* If the deformation is severe enough, the crystal may recrystallize into a new set of strain-free grains differing completely in orientation from the original crystal. The appearance of the diffraction pattern then depends on the size of the new grains relative to the cross-sectional area of the incident x-ray beam. The appearance of such patterns is discussed and illustrated in Sec. 9–2.

8–7 Relative orientation of twinned crystals. In this and the next section we shall consider, not single crystals, but pairs of crystals which are naturally associated one with another in certain particular ways. Twinned crystals are obvious examples of such pairs: the two parts of the twin have different orientations, but there is a definite orientation relationship between the two. Furthermore, the two parts are united on a plane, the composition plane, which is also fixed and invariable, not merely a random surface of contact such as that between two adjacent grains in a polycrystalline mass. Twinned crystals therefore present a twofold problem, that of determining the orientation relationship and that of determining the indices of the composition plane.

The orientation relationship is established by finding the orientation of each part of the twin and plotting the two together on the same stereographic projection. Determination of the composition-plane indices requires a knowledge of how to plot the trace, or line of intersection, of one plane in another, and we must digress at this point to consider that problem. Suppose that, on the polished surface of a twinned grain, the trace of the composition plane makes an angle α with some reference line NS, as shown in Fig. 8–34(a). Then, if we make the projection plane parallel to the plane of polish, the latter will be represented by the basic circle of the projection and any directions in the plane of polish by diametrically opposite *points* on the basic circle. Thus, in Fig. 8–34(b), the N- and S-poles represent the reference line NS and the points A and B, located at an angle α

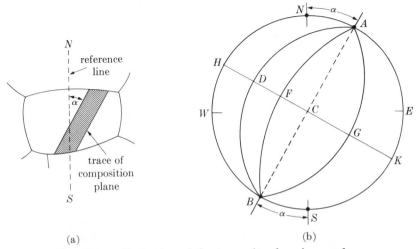

(a)

(b)

FIG. 8–34.   Projection of the trace of a plane in a surface.

from N and S, represent the trace.   Note that the diameter ACB does *not* represent the trace; ACB represents a plane perpendicular to the plane of polish which could have caused the observed trace, but so could the inclined planes ADB, AFB, and AGB.   Evidently any number of planes could have caused the observed trace, and all we can say with certainty is that the pole of the composition plane lies somewhere on the diameter HK, where H and K are 90° from the trace direction A,B. HK is called a trace normal.

To fix the orientation of the composition plane requires additional information which can be obtained by sectioning the twinned grain by another

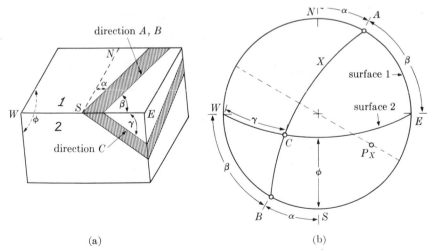

(a)

(b)

FIG. 8–35.   Projection of the trace of a plane in two surfaces.

plane and determining the trace direction in this new plane. Suppose the section is made through a line WE, chosen for convenience to be at right angles to NS, and that the new plane of polish (Plane 2) makes an angle ϕ with the original one (Plane 1), as shown in Fig. 8–35(a). It is now convenient to use the edge WE as a reference direction. Let the traces of the composition plane in surfaces 1 and 2 make angles of β (equal to $90° - \alpha$) and γ with the edge WE. Then, if the stereographic projection plane is again made parallel to surface 1, surface 2 is represented by a great circle through W and E and at an angle ϕ from the circumference [Fig. 8–35(b)]. The trace of the composition plane in surface 1 is then represented by A,B as before and the same trace in surface 2 by the direction C, both angles β

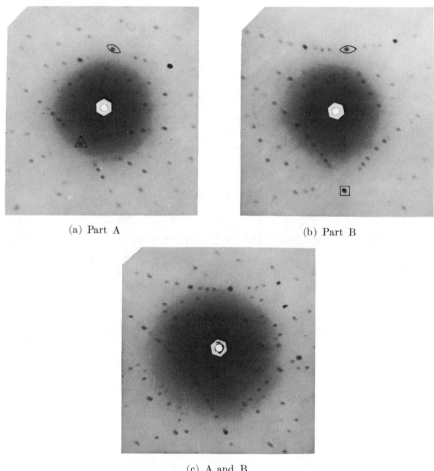

(a) Part A   (b) Part B

(c) A and B

FIG. 8–36. Back-reflection Laue photographs of two parts, A and B, of a twinned crystal of copper. Tungsten radiation, 30 kv, 20 ma. Film covered with 0.01-in.-thick aluminum to reduce the intensity of K fluorescent radiation from specimen.

and γ being measured from the edge W,E. Two nonparallel lines in the unknown composition plane X are now known, namely the direction A,B and the direction C. A great circle drawn through B, C, and A therefore describes the orientation of plane X, and P_X is its pole.

An application of this method is afforded by annealing twins in copper. The back-reflection Laue photographs of Fig. 8–36 were obtained from a large grain containing a twin band; by shifting the specimen in its own plane between exposures, the incident beam was made to fall first on one part of the twin [pattern (a)], then on the other part [pattern (b)], and finally on each side of the trace of the composition plane [pattern (c)]. The latter photograph is therefore a double pattern of both parts of the twin together.

The orientations derived from patterns (a) and (b) are shown in Fig. 8–37, and certain poles of each part of the twin are seen to coincide, particularly the (111) pole in the lower right quadrant. These coincidences are also evident in Fig. 8–36(c) in the form of coincident Laue spots. By measuring the directions of the trace of the composition plane X in two surfaces, the orientation of X was determined, as shown in the projection. P_X is found to coincide with the (111) pole common to each part of the

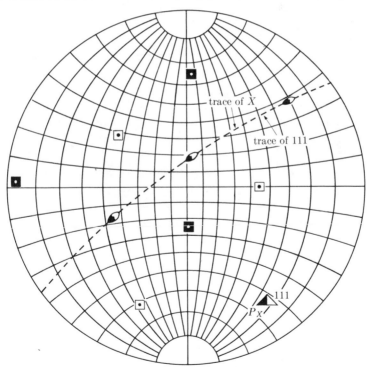

Fig. 8–37.   Projection of part A (open symbols) and part B (solid symbols) of a twin in copper, made from Figs. 8–36(a) and (b).

twin, thus disclosing the indices of the composition plane. By the methods
described in Sec. 2–11, it may also be shown that the two parts of the twin
are related by reflection in this same (111) plane. The twinning plane
(the plane of reflection) in copper is therefore shown to be identical with
the composition plane.

Similar problems arise in studies of plastic deformation. For example,
we may wish to find the indices of slip planes responsible for the observable
slip lines on a polished surface. Or we may wish to identify the composition plane of a deformation twin. The simplest procedure, if it can be
used, is to convert the test specimen into grains large enough so that the
orientation of any selected grain can be directly determined by one of the
Laue methods. The polished specimen is then strained plastically to produce visible slip lines or deformation twins. The orientation of a grain
showing such traces is determined and the directions of these traces are
measured. If traces are measured on two surfaces, the method of solution
is identical with that described above for twinned copper. If traces are
measured only on one plane, then the trace normals are plotted on a stereographic projection of the grain; the crystal orientation and the trace normals are rotated into some standard orientation and superimposed on a
detailed standard projection. Intersection of the normals with certain
poles of the standard will then disclose the indices of the planes causing the
observed traces.

But it may happen that the grain size is too small to permit a determination of grain orientation. The problem is now much more difficult,
even when trace directions are measured on two surfaces. The first step
is to plot the trace normals corresponding to the traces on both surfaces;
these normals will be straight lines for the traces on the surface on which
the projection is being made and great circles for the traces on the other
surface. A standard $(h_1 k_1 l_1)$ projection is then superimposed on the projection of the trace normals, and a rotation is sought which will bring
$\{h_1 k_1 l_1\}$ poles into coincidence with the intersections of straight and curved
trace normals. If such coincidence cannot be found, an $(h_2 k_2 l_2)$ standard
projection is tried, and so on. If the traces in either plane have more than
one direction, it will be helpful to note how many different directions are
involved. For example, if there are more than three different directions in
one grain of a cubic metal, the traces cannot be caused by $\{100\}$ planes;
if more than four directions are observed, both $\{100\}$ and $\{111\}$ planes
are ruled out; and so on.

Up to this point we have been concerned with the problem of finding
the indices of planes causing certain observed traces, generally in a grain
of known orientation. The same problem may be solved in reverse: given
traces in two surfaces of a plane of known indices (hkl), the orientation of
the crystal may be found without using x-rays. The trace normals are

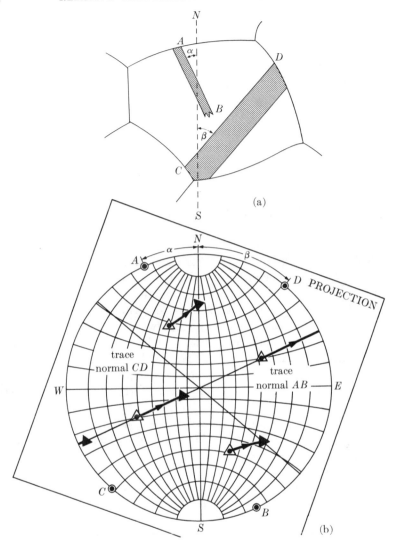

FIG. 8-38. Determination of crystal orientation of copper from traces of two known twin planes in one surface.

plotted on one sheet of paper and on this is superposed a standard projection showing only $\{hkl\}$ planes. By trial and error, a rotation is found which will make the $\{hkl\}$ poles fall on the observed trace normals.

By the same method, crystal orientation can also be determined from two nonparallel traces of planes of known indices in one surface. In this way, it is sometimes possible to determine the orientation of a single grain in a polycrystalline mass when the grain size is too small to permit direct x-ray determination. For example, we may use the fact that annealing

twins in copper have {111} composition planes to determine the orientation of the grain shown in Fig. 8–38(a), where twin bands have formed on
two different {111} planes of the parent grain. The trace normals are
plotted in Fig. 8–38(b), and on this is placed a standard (001) projection
containing only {111} poles. If the standard is rotated about its center
to the position shown, then it is possible by a further rotation about the
axis AB to bring the {111} poles of the standard, shown by open symbols,
to positions lying on trace normals, shown by solid symbols. The solid
symbols therefore show an orientation of the crystal which will account
for the observed traces. Unfortunately, it is not the only one: the orientation found by reflecting the one shown in the plane of projection is also a
possible solution. A choice between these two possibilities can be made
only by sectioning the crystal so as to expose trace directions in a second
surface.

8–8 Relative orientation of precipitate and matrix. When a supersaturated solid solution precipitates a second phase, the latter frequently
takes the form of thin plates which lie parallel to certain planes of low
indices in the matrix. The matrix plane on which the precipitate plate
lies is called the *habit plane* and its indices always refer to the lattice of the
matrix. There is also a definite orientation relationship between the lattice
of the precipitate and that of the matrix. Both of these effects result from
a tendency of the atomic arrangement in the precipitate to conform as
closely as possible to the atomic arrangement in the matrix at the interface
between the two. For example, precipitation of an HCP phase from an
FCC solid solution often occurs in such a way that the basal (0001) plane
of the precipitate is parallel to a (111) plane of the matrix, since on both
of these planes the atoms have a
hexagonal arrangement.

Relations of this kind are illustrated
on an atomic scale in Fig. 8–39. In
this hypothetical case the habit plane
is $(1\bar{1}0)$ and the lattice relationship is
such that the plane (010) of the precipitate is parallel to the plane $(1\bar{1}0)$
of the matrix; the direction [100] in
the former plane is parallel to the
direction [110] in the latter, or, in the
usual shorthand notation,

$$(010)_p \| (1\bar{1}0)_m, \qquad [100]_p \| [110]_m,$$

where the subscripts p and m refer to
precipitate and matrix, respectively.

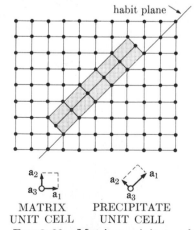

Fig. 8–39. Matrix-precipitate relationship.

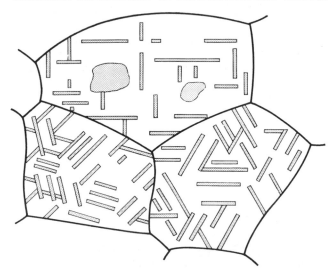

Fig. 8–40. Widmanstätten structure (schematic). Cubic matrix has {100} habit. Top grain is intersected parallel to {100}.

If a certain solid solution has an {hkl} habit plane, then precipitation can of course take place on all planes of the form {hkl}. Thus one grain may contain sets of precipitate plates having quite different orientations. When such a grain is sectioned, the thin precipitate plates appear as needles on the plane of polish resulting in a structure such as that shown in Fig. 8–40 in a highly idealized form. This is called a *Widmanstätten structure*. It is very often the product of nucleation and growth reactions, such as precipitation and eutectoid decomposition. Somewhat similar structures are also observed as the result of the martensitic reaction and other diffusionless transformations. (There are some secondary differences, however: martensite often takes the form of needles as well as plates and the indices of its habit plane are often irrational, e.g., (259), and may even, as in the case of Fe-C martensite, change with composition.)

The crystallographic problems presented by such structures are very much the same as those described in Sec. 8–7, except that the plates of the second phase almost always differ in crystal structure from the matrix, unlike the two parts of a twin or the material on either side of a slip plane. The habit plane is identified by the methods previously described for the identification of slip or twinning planes. The orientation relationship is easily determined if a single precipitate plate can be found which is large enough to permit determination of its orientation by one of the Laue methods. Ordinarily, however, the precipitate is so fine that this method cannot be applied and some variant of the rotating-crystal method must be used.

PROBLEMS

8–1. A back-reflection Laue photograph is made of an aluminum crystal with a crystal-to-film distance of 3 cm. When viewed from the x-ray source, the Laue spots have the following x,y-coordinates, measured (in inches) from the center of the film:

x	y	x	y
$+0.26$	$+0.09$	-0.44	$+1.24$
$+0.45$	$+0.70$	-1.10	$+1.80$
$+1.25$	$+1.80$	-1.21	$+0.40$
$+1.32$	$+0.40$	-1.70	$+1.19$
$+0.13$	-1.61	-0.76	-1.41
$+0.28$	-1.21	-0.79	-0.95
$+0.51$	-0.69	-0.92	-0.26
$+0.74$	-0.31		

Plot these spots on a sheet of graph paper graduated in inches. By means of a Greninger chart, determine the orientation of the crystal, plot all poles of the form $\{100\}$, $\{110\}$, and $\{111\}$, and give the coordinates of the $\{100\}$ poles in terms of latitude and longitude measured from the center of the projection.

8–2. A transmission Laue photograph is made of an aluminum crystal with a crystal-to-film distance of 5 cm. To an observer looking through the film toward the x-ray source, the spots have the following x,y-coordinates (in inches):

x	y	x	y
$+0.66$	$+0.88$	-0.10	$+0.79$
$+0.94$	$+2.44$	-0.45	$+2.35$
$+1.24$	$+0.64$	-0.77	$+1.89$
$+1.36$	$+0.05$	-0.90	$+1.00$
$+1.39$	$+1.10$	-1.27	$+0.50$
$+0.89$	-1.62	-1.75	$+1.55$
$+1.02$	-0.95	-1.95	$+0.80$
$+1.66$	-1.10	-0.21	-0.58
		-0.59	-0.28
		-0.85	-1.31
		-1.40	-1.03
		-1.55	-0.36

Proceed as in Prob. 8–1, but use a stereographic ruler to plot the poles of reflecting planes.

8–3. Determine the necessary angular rotations about (*a*) the incident beam axis, (*b*) the east-west axis, and (*c*) the north-south axis to bring the crystal of Prob. 8–2 into the "cube orientation," i.e., that shown by Fig. 2–36(a).

8–4. With reference to Fig. 8–35(a), if $\beta = 120°$, $\gamma = 135°$, and $\phi = 100°$, what are the coordinates (in terms of latitude and longitude) of the pole of the composition plane?

8–5. Precipitate plates in a cubic matrix form a Widmanstätten structure. The traces of the plates in the plane of polish lie in three directions in one particular grain, making azimuthal angles of 15°, 64°, and 113°, measured clockwise from a "vertical" *NS* reference line. Determine the indices of the habit plane and the orientation of the matrix grain (in terms of the coordinates of its $\{100\}$ poles).

CHAPTER 9

THE STRUCTURE OF POLYCRYSTALLINE AGGREGATES

9–1 Introduction. In the previous chapter we were concerned with the orientation and relative perfection of single crystals. But the single metal crystal is, after all, somewhat of a laboratory curiosity; the normal way in which metals and alloys are used is in the form of polycrystalline aggregates, composed of a great many individual crystals usually of microscopic size. Since the properties of such aggregates are of great technological importance, they have been intensively studied in many ways. In such studies the two most useful techniques are microscopic examination and x-ray diffraction, and the wise investigator will use them both; one complements the other, and both together can provide a great deal of information about the structure of an aggregate.

The properties (mechanical, electrical, chemical, etc.) of a single-phase aggregate are determined by two factors:

(1) the properties of a single crystal of the material, and

(2) the way in which the single crystals are put together to form the composite mass.

In this chapter we will be concerned with the second factor, namely, the *structure* of the aggregate, using this term in its broadest sense to mean the relative size, perfection, and orientation of the grains making up the aggregate. Whether these grains are large or small, strained or unstrained, oriented at random or in some preferred direction, frequently has very important effects on the properties of the material.

If the aggregate contains more than one phase, its properties naturally depend on the properties of each phase considered separately and on the way these phases occur in the aggregate. Such a material offers wide structural possibilities since, in general, the size, perfection, and orientation of the grains of one phase may differ from those of the other phase or phases.

CRYSTAL SIZE

9–2 Grain size. The size of the grains in a polycrystalline metal or alloy has pronounced effects on many of its properties, the best known being the increase in strength and hardness which accompanies a decrease in grain size. This dependence of properties on grain size makes the measurement of grain size a matter of some importance in the control of most metal forming operations.

The grain sizes encountered in commercial metals and alloys range from about 10^{-1} to 10^{-4} cm. These limits are, of course, arbitrary and represent rather extreme values; typical values fall into a much narrower range, namely, about 10^{-2} to 10^{-3} cm   The most accurate method of measuring grain size in this range is by microscopic examination; the usual procedure is to determine the average number of grains per unit area of the polished section and report this in terms of an "index number" established by the American Society for Testing Materials.   The equation

$$n = 2^{N-1}$$

relates n, the number of grains per square inch when viewed at a magnification of $100\times$, and N, the ASTM "index number" or "grain-size number."

Although x-ray diffraction is decidedly inferior to microscopic examination in the accurate measurement of grain size, one diffraction photograph can yield semiquantitative information about grain size, *together with* information about crystal perfection and orientation. A transmission or back-reflection pinhole photograph made with filtered radiation is best. If the back-reflection method is used, the surface of the specimen (which need not be polished) should be etched to remove any disturbed surface layer which might be present, because most of the diffracted radiation originates in a thin surface layer (see Secs. 9–4 and 9–5).

The nature of the changes produced in pinhole photographs by progressive reductions in specimen grain size is illustrated in Fig. 9–1. The governing effect here is the number of grains which take part in diffraction. This number is in turn related to the cross-sectional area of the incident beam, and its depth of penetration (in back reflection) or the specimen thickness (in transmission). When the grain size is quite coarse, as in Fig. 9–1(a), only a few crystals diffract and the photograph consists of a set of superimposed Laue patterns, one from each crystal, due to the white radiation present. A somewhat finer grain size increases the number of Laue spots, and those which lie on potential Debye rings generally are more intense than the remainder, because they are formed by the strong characteristic component of the incident radiation. Thus, the suggestion of a Debye ring begins to appear, as in (b). When the grain size is further reduced, the Laue spots merge into a general background and only Debye rings are visible, as in (c). These rings are spotty, however, since not enough crystals are present in the irradiated volume of the specimen to reflect to all parts of the ring. A still finer grain size produces the smooth, continuous Debye rings shown in (d).

Several methods have been proposed for the estimation of grain size purely in terms of various geometrical factors. For example, an equation may be derived which relates the observed number of spots on a Debye ring to the grain size and other such variables as incident-beam diameter, multiplicity of the reflection, and specimen-film distance. However, many approximations are involved and the resulting equation is not very accu-

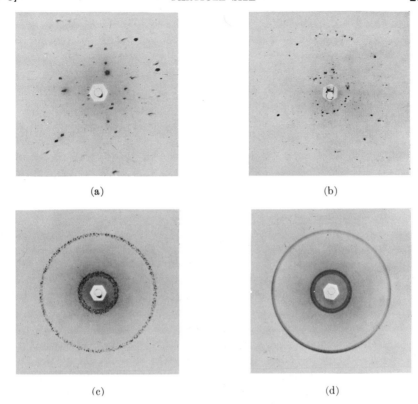

(a)   (b)

(c)   (d)

FIG. 9–1. Back-reflection pinhole patterns of recrystallized aluminum specimens; grain size decreases in the order (a), (b), (c), (d). Filtered copper radiation.

rate. The best way to estimate grain size by diffraction is to obtain a set of specimens having known ASTM grain-size numbers, and to prepare from these a standard set of photographs of the kind shown in Fig. 9–1. The grain-size number of an unknown specimen of the same material is then obtained simply by matching its diffraction pattern with one of the standard photographs, *provided both are made under identical conditions.*

When the grain size reaches a value somewhere in the range 10^{-3} to 10^{-4} cm, the exact value depending on experimental conditions, the Debye rings lose their spotty character and become continuous. Between this value and 10^{-5} cm (1000A), no change occurs in the diffraction pattern. At about 10^{-5} cm the first signs of line broadening, due to small crystal size, begin to be detectable. There is therefore a size range, from 10^{-3} (or 10^{-4}) to 10^{-5} cm, where x-ray diffraction is quite insensitive to variations in grain size.

9–3 Particle size. When the size of the individual crystals is less than about 10^{-5} cm (1000A), the term "particle size" is usually used. As we saw in Sec. 3–7, crystals in this size range cause broadening of the Debye rings, the extent of the broadening being given by Eq. (3–13):

$$B = \frac{0.9\lambda}{t \cos \theta},$$ (3–13)

where B = broadening of diffraction line measured at half its maximum intensity (radians) and t = diameter of crystal particle. All diffraction lines have a measurable breadth, even when the crystal size exceeds 1000A, due to such causes as divergence of the incident beam and size of the sample (in Debye cameras) and width of the x-ray source (in diffractometers). The breadth B in Eq. (3–13) refers, however, to the *extra* breadth, or broadening, due to the particle-size effect alone. In other words, B is essentially zero when the particle size exceeds about 1000A.

The chief problem in determining particle size from line breadths is to determine B from the measured breadth B_M of the diffraction line. Of the many methods proposed, Warren's is the simplest. The unknown is mixed with a standard which has a particle size greater than 1000A, and which produces a diffraction line near that line from the unknown which is to be used in the determination. A diffraction pattern is then made of the mixture in either a Debye camera or, preferably, a diffractometer. This pattern will contain sharp lines from the standard and broad lines from the unknown, assumed to consist of very fine particles. Let B_S be the measured breadth, at half maximum intensity, of the line from the standard. Then B is given, not simply by the difference between B_M and B_S, but by the equation

$$B^2 = B_M{}^2 - B_S{}^2.$$ (9–1)

(This equation results from the assumption that the diffraction line has the shape of an error curve.) Once B has been obtained from Eq. (9–1), it can be inserted into Eq. (3–13) to yield the particle size t. There are several other methods of finding B from B_M; compared with Warren's method, they are somewhat more accurate and considerably more intricate.

The experimental difficulties involved in measuring particle size from line broadening increase with the size of the particle measured. Roughly speaking, relatively crude measurements suffice in the range 0–500A, but very good experimental technique is needed in the range 500–1000A. The maximum size measurable by line broadening has usually been placed at 1000A, chiefly as a result of the use of camera techniques. Recently, however, the diffractometer has been applied to this problem and the upper limit has been pushed to almost 2000A. Very careful work was required and back-reflection lines were employed, since such lines exhibit the largest particle-size broadening, as shown by Eq. (3–13).

From the above discussion it might be inferred that line broadening is chiefly used to measure the particle size of loose powders rather than the size of the individual crystals in a solid aggregate. That is correct. Attempts have been made to apply Eq. (3–13) to the broadened diffraction lines from very fine-grained metal specimens and so determine the size of the individual grains. Such determinations are never very reliable, however, because the individual grains of such a material are often nonuniformly strained, and this condition, as we shall see in the next section, can also broaden the diffraction lines; an uncertainty therefore exists as to the exact cause of the observed broadening. On the other hand, the individual crystals which make up a loose powder of fine particle size can often be assumed to be strain-free, provided the material involved is a brittle (nonplastic) one, and all the observed broadening can confidently be ascribed to the particle-size effect. (But note that loose, unannealed *metal* powders, produced by filing, grinding, ball milling, etc., almost always contain nonuniform strain.) The chief applications of the line-broadening method have been in the measurement of the particle size of such materials as carbon blacks, catalysts, and industrial dusts.

Another x-ray method of measuring the size of small particles deserves some mention, although a complete description is beyond the scope of this book. This is the method of *small-angle scattering*. It is a form of diffuse scattering very near the undeviated transmitted beam, i.e., at angles 2θ ranging from 0° up to roughly 2 or 3°. From the observed variation of the scattered intensity *vs.* angle 2θ, the size, and to some extent the shape, of small particles can be determined, whether they are amorphous or crystalline. Small-angle scattering has also been used to study precipitation effects in metallic solid solutions.

CRYSTAL PERFECTION

9–4 Crystal perfection. Of the many kinds of crystal imperfection, the one we are concerned with here is nonuniform strain because it is so characteristic of the *cold-worked state* of metals and alloys. When a polycrystalline piece of metal is plastically deformed, for example by rolling, slip occurs in each grain and the grain changes its shape, becoming flattened and elongated in the direction of rolling. The change in shape of any one grain is determined not only by the forces applied to the piece as a whole, but also by the fact that each grain retains contact on its boundary surfaces with all its neighbors. Because of this interaction between grains, a single grain in a polycrystalline mass is not free to deform in the same way as an isolated single crystal would, if subjected to the same deformation by rolling. As a result of this restraint by its neighbors, a plastically deformed grain in a solid aggregate usually has regions of its lattice left in an elastically bent or twisted condition or, more rarely, in a state of uniform tension or compression. The metal is then said to contain *residual* *stress.* (Such stress is often called "internal stress" but the term is not very informative since all stresses, residual or externally imposed, are internal. The term "residual stress" emphasizes the fact that the stress remains after all external forces are removed.) Stresses of this kind are also called *microstresses* since they vary from one grain to another, or from one part of a grain to another part, on a microscopic scale. On the other hand, the stress may be quite uniform over large distances; it is then referred to as *macrostress*.

The effect of strain, both uniform and nonuniform, on the direction of x-ray reflection is illustrated in Fig. 9–2. A portion of an unstrained grain appears in (a) on the left, and the set of transverse reflecting planes shown has everywhere its equilibrium spacing d_0. The diffraction line from these planes appears on the right. If the grain is then given a uniform tensile strain at right angles to the reflecting planes, their spacing becomes larger than d_0, and the corresponding diffraction line shifts to lower angles but does not otherwise change, as shown in (b). This line shift is the basis of the x-ray method for the measurement of macrostress, as will be described in Chap. 17. In (c) the grain is bent and the strain is nonuniform; on the top (tension) side the plane spacing exceeds d_0, on the bottom (compression) side it is less than d_0, and somewhere in between it equals d_0. We may imagine this grain to be composed of a number of small regions in

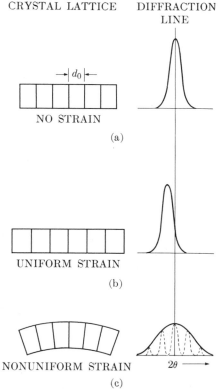

FIG. 9–2. Effect of lattice strain on Debye-line width and position.

each of which the plane spacing is substantially constant but different from the spacing in adjoining regions. These regions cause the various sharp diffraction lines indicated on the right of (c) by the dotted curves. The sum of these sharp lines, each slightly displaced from the other, is the broadened diffraction line shown by the full curve and, of course, the broadened line is the only one experimentally observable. We can find a relation between the broadening produced and the nonuniformity of the strain by differentiating the Bragg law. We obtain

$$b = \Delta 2\theta = -2\frac{\Delta d}{d}\tan\theta, \qquad (9\text{–}2)$$

where b is the broadening due to a fractional variation in plane spacing $\Delta d/d$. This equation allows the variation in strain, $\Delta d/d$, to be calculated from the observed broadening. This value of $\Delta d/d$, however, includes both tensile and compressive strain and must be divided by two to obtain the maximum tensile strain alone, or maximum compressive strain alone, if these two are assumed equal. The maximum strain so found can then be multiplied by the elastic modulus E to give the maximum stress present. For example,

$$(\text{Max. tens. stress}) = E \cdot (\text{max. tens. strain}) = (E)(\tfrac{1}{2})\left(\frac{\Delta d}{d}\right) = \frac{Eb}{4\tan\theta}.$$

When an annealed metal or alloy is cold worked, its diffraction lines become broader. This is a well-established, easily verified experimental fact, but its explanation has been a matter of controversy. Some investigators have felt that the chief effect of cold work is to fragment the grains to a point where their small size alone is sufficient to account for all the observed broadening. Others have concluded that the nonuniformity of strain produced by cold work is the major cause of broadening, with grain fragmentation possibly a minor contributing cause. Actually, it is impossible to generalize, inasmuch as different metals and alloys may behave quite differently. By advanced methods of mathematical analysis, it is possible to divide the observed change in line shape produced by cold work into two parts, one due to fine particle size and the other due to nonuniform strain. When this is done, it is found, for example, that in alpha brass containing 30 percent zinc the observed broadening is due almost entirely to nonuniform strain, while in thoriated tungsten (tungsten containing 0.75 percent thorium oxide) it is due both to nonuniform strain and fine particle size. But no example is known where all the observed broadening can be ascribed to fine particle size. In fact, it is difficult to imagine how cold work could fragment the grains to the degree necessary to cause particle-size broadening without at the same time introducing nonuniform strains, in view of the very complex forces that must act on any one grain of an aggregate no matter how simple the forces applied to the aggregate as a whole.

The broadening of a diffraction line by cold work cannot always be observed by simple inspection of a photograph unless some standard is available for comparison. However, the separation of the $K\alpha$ doublet furnishes a very good "internal standard." In the back-reflection region, an annealed metal produces a well-resolved doublet, one component due to $K\alpha_1$ radiation and the other to $K\alpha_2$. For a given set of experimental conditions, the separation of this doublet on the film is constant and independent of the amount of cold work. But as the amount of cold work is increased, the broadening increases, until finally the two components of the doublet overlap to such an extent that they appear as one unresolved line. An unresolved $K\alpha$ doublet can therefore be taken as evidence of cold work, if the same doublet is resolved when the metal is in the annealed condition.

We are now in a position to consider some of the diffraction effects associated with the processes of *recovery, recrystallization,* and *grain growth.* When a cold-worked metal or alloy is annealed at a low temperature, recovery takes place; at a somewhat higher temperature, recrystallization; and at a still higher temperature, grain growth. Or at a sufficiently high constant temperature, these processes may be regarded as occurring consecutively in time. Recovery is usually defined as a process involving changes in certain properties without any observable change in microstructure, while recrystallization produces an easily visible structure of new grains, which then grow at the expense of one another during the grain-growth stage.

The above is a highly oversimplified description of some very complex processes which are not yet completely understood. In particular, the exact nature of recovery is still rather obscure. It seems clear, however, that some form of polygonization takes place during recovery and may, in fact, constitute the most important part of that process. (Polygonization can occur in the individual grains of an aggregate just as in a single crystal. The structure so produced is called a substructure, and the smaller units into which a grain breaks up are called subgrains. Subgrain boundaries can be made visible under the microscope if the proper etching technique is used.) In some metals and alloys, recovery appears to overlap recrystallization (in temperature or time), while in others it is quite separate. It is usually associated with a partial relief of residual stress, on both a microscopic and a macroscopic scale, without any marked change in hardness. Since microstress is the major cause of line broadening, we usually find that the broad diffraction lines characteristic of cold-worked metal partially sharpen during recovery. When recrystallization occurs, the lines attain their maximum sharpness and the hardness decreases rather abruptly. During grain growth, the lines become increasingly spotty as the grain size increases.

The nature of these changes is illustrated for alpha brass containing 30 weight percent zinc by the hardness curve and diffraction patterns of Fig. 9–3. The hardness remains practically constant, for an annealing period of one hour, until a temperature of 200°C is exceeded, and then decreases rapidly with increasing temperature, as shown in (a). The diffraction pattern in (b) exhibits the broad diffuse Debye lines produced by the cold-rolled, unannealed alloy. These lines become somewhat narrower for specimens annealed at 100° and 200°C, and the $K\alpha$ doublet becomes partially resolved at 250°C. At 250°, therefore, the recovery process

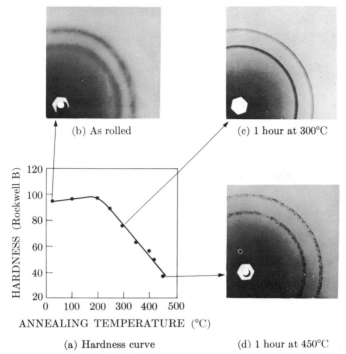

(b) As rolled   (c) 1 hour at 300°C

(a) Hardness curve   (d) 1 hour at 450°C

FIG. 9–3. Changes in hardness and diffraction lines of 70–30 brass specimens, reduced in thickness by 90 percent by cold rolling, and annealed for 1 hour at the temperatures indicated in (a). (b), (c), and (d) are portions of back-reflection pinhole patterns of specimens annealed at the temperatures stated (filtered copper radiation).

appears to be substantially complete in one hour and recrystallization is just beginning, as evidenced by the drop in Rockwell B hardness from 98 to 90. At 300°C the diffraction lines are quite sharp and the doublets completely resolved, as shown in (c). Annealing at temperatures above 300°C causes the lines to become increasingly spotty, indicating that the newly recrystallized grains are increasing in size. The pattern of a specimen annealed at 450°C, when the hardness had dropped to 37 Rockwell B, appears in (d).

Diffractometer measurements made on the same specimens disclose both more, and less, information. Some automatically recorded profiles of the 331 line, the outer ring of the patterns shown in Fig. 9–3, are reproduced in Fig. 9–4. It is much easier to follow changes in line shape by means of these curves than by inspection of pinhole photographs. Thus the slight sharpening of the line at 200°C is clearly evident in the diffractometer record, and so is the doublet resolution which occurs at 250°C. But note that the diffractometer cannot "see" the spotty diffraction lines caused by coarse grains. There is nothing in the diffractometer records

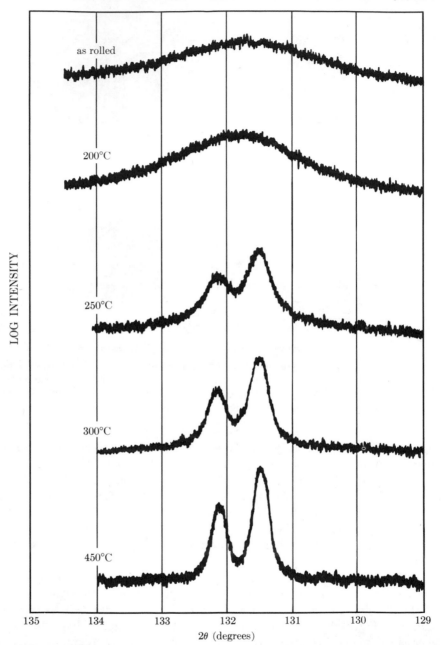

FIG. 9–4. Diffractometer traces of the 331 line of the cold-rolled and annealed 70–30 brass specimens referred to in Fig. 9–3. Filtered copper radiation. Logarithmic intensity scale. All curves displaced vertically by arbitrary amounts.

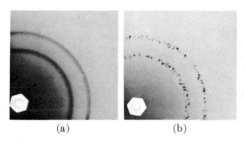

(a)   (b)

FIG. 9–5. Back-reflection pinhole patterns of coarse-grained recrystallized copper. Unfiltered copper radiation: (a) from surface ground on a belt sander; (b) after removal of 0.003 in. from this surface by etching.

made at 300° and 450°C which would immediately suggest that the specimen annealed at 450°C had the coarser grain size, but this fact is quite evident in the pinhole patterns shown in Figs. 9–3(c) and (d).

It must always be remembered that a back-reflection photograph is representative of only a thin surface layer of the specimen. For example, Fig. 9–5(a) was obtained from a piece of copper and exhibits unresolved doublets in the high-angle region. The unexperienced observer might conclude that this material was highly cold worked. What the x-ray "sees" *is* cold worked, but it sees only to a limited depth. Actually, the bulk of this specimen is in the annealed condition, but the surface from which the x-ray pattern was made had had 0.002 in. removed by grinding on a belt sander after annealing. This treatment cold worked the surface to a considerable depth. By successive etching treatments and diffraction patterns made after each etch, the change in structure of the cold-worked layer could be followed as a function of depth below the surface. Not until a total of 0.003 in. had been removed did the diffraction pattern become characteristic of the bulk of the material; see Fig. 9–5(b), where the spotty lines indicate a coarse-grained, recrystallized structure.

9–5 Depth of x-ray penetration. Observations of this kind suggest that it might be well to consider in some detail the general problem of x-ray penetration. Most metallurgical specimens strongly absorb x-rays, and the intensity of the incident beam is reduced almost to zero in a very short distance below the surface. The diffracted beams therefore originate chiefly in a thin surface layer whenever a reflection technique, as opposed to a transmission technique,* is used, i.e., whenever a diffraction pattern

---

* Not even in transmission methods, however, is the information on a diffraction pattern truly representative of the entire cross section of the specimen. Calculations such as those given in this section show that a greater proportion of the total diffracted energy originates in a layer of given thickness on the back side of the specimen (the side from which the transmitted beam leaves) than in a layer of equal thickness on the front side. If the specimen is highly absorbing, a transmission method can be just as non-representative of the entire specimen as a back-reflection method, in that most of the diffracted energy will originate in a thin surface layer. See Prob. 9–5.

is obtained in a back-reflection camera of any kind, a Seemann-Bohlin camera or a diffractometer as normally used. We have just seen how a back-reflection pinhole photograph of a ground surface discloses the cold-worked condition of a thin surface layer and gives no information whatever about the bulk of the material below that layer.

These circumstances naturally pose the following question: what is the effective depth of x-ray penetration? Or, stated in a more useful manner, to what depth of the specimen does the information in such a diffraction pattern apply? This question has no precise answer because the intensity of the incident beam does not suddenly become zero at any one depth but rather decreases exponentially with distance below the surface. However, we can obtain an answer which, although not precise, is at least useful, in the following way. Equation (7–2) gives the integrated intensity diffracted by an infinitesimally thin layer located at a depth x below the surface as

$$dI_D = \frac{I_0 ab}{\sin \alpha} e^{-\mu x(1/\sin \alpha + 1/\sin \beta)} \, dx, \tag{7–2}$$

where the various symbols are defined in Sec. 7–4. This expression, integrated over any chosen depth of material, gives the total integrated intensity diffracted by that layer, but only in terms of the unknown constants I_0, a, and b. However, these constants will cancel out if we express the intensity diffracted by the layer considered as a fraction of the total integrated intensity diffracted by a specimen of infinite thickness. (As we saw in Sec. 7–4, "infinite thickness" amounts to only a few thousandths of an inch for most metals.) Call this fraction G_x. Then

$$G_x = \frac{\int_{x=0}^{x=x} dI_D}{\int_{x=0}^{x=\infty} dI_D} = \left[1 - e^{-\mu x(1/\sin \alpha + 1/\sin \beta)} \right]. \tag{9–3}$$

This expression permits us to calculate the fraction G_x of the total diffracted intensity which is contributed by a surface layer of depth x. If we arbitrarily decide that a contribution from this surface layer of 95 percent (or 99 or 99.9 percent) of the total is enough so that we can ignore the contribution from the material below that layer, then x is the effective depth of penetration. We then know that the information recorded on the diffraction pattern (or, more precisely, 95 percent of the information) refers to the layer of depth x and not to the material below it.

In the case of the diffractometer, $\alpha = \beta = \theta$, and Eq. (9–3) reduces to

$$G_x = (1 - e^{-2\mu x/\sin \theta}), \tag{9–4}$$

which shows that the effective depth of penetration decreases as θ decreases and therefore varies from one diffraction line to another. In back-reflection cameras, $\alpha = 90°$, and

$$G_x = [1 - e^{-\mu x(1 + 1/\sin \beta)}], \quad (9\text{–}5)$$

where $\beta = 2\theta - 90°$.

For example, the conditions applicable to the outer diffraction ring of Fig. 9–5 are $\mu = 473 \text{ cm}^{-1}$ and $2\theta = 136.7°$. By using Eq. (9–5), we can construct the plot of G_x as function of x which is shown in Fig. 9–6. We note that 95 percent of the information on the diffraction pattern refers to a depth of only about 0.001 in. It is therefore not surprising that the pattern of Fig. 9–5(a) discloses only the presence of cold-worked metal,

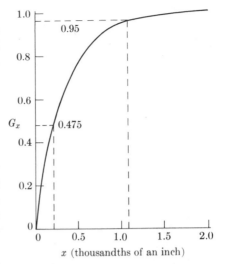

FIG. 9–6. The fraction G_x of the total diffracted intensity contributed by a surface layer of depth x, for $\mu = 473 \text{ cm}^{-1}$, $2\theta = 136.7°$, and normal incidence.

since we found by repeated etching treatments that the depth of the cold-worked layer was about 0.003 in. Of course, the information recorded on the pattern is heavily weighted in terms of material just below the surface; thus 95 percent of the recorded information applies to a depth of 0.001 in., but 50 percent of *that* information originates in the first 0.0002 in. (Note that an effective penetration of 0.001 in. means that a surface layer only one grain thick is effectively contributing to the diffraction pattern if the specimen has an ASTM grain-size number of 8.)

Equation (9–4) can be put into the following form, which is more suitable for calculation:

$$\frac{2\mu x}{\sin \theta} = \ln \left(\frac{1}{1 - G_x} \right) = K_x,$$

$$x = \frac{K_x \sin \theta}{2\mu}.$$

Similarly, we can rewrite Eq. (9–5) in the form

$$\mu x \left(1 + \frac{1}{\sin \beta} \right) = \ln \left(\frac{1}{1 - G_x} \right) = K_x,$$

$$x = \frac{K_x \sin \beta}{\mu(1 + \sin \beta)}.$$

TABLE 9–1

G_x	0.50	0.75	0.90	0.95	0.99	0.999
K_x	0.69	1.39	2.30	3.00	4.61	6.91

Values of K_x corresponding to various assumed values of G_x are given in Table 9–1.

Calculations of the effective depth of penetration can be valuable in many applications of x-ray diffraction. We may wish to make the effective depth of penetration as large as possible in some applications. Then α and β in Eq. (9–3) must be as large as possible, indicating the use of high-angle lines, and μ as small as possible, indicating short-wavelength radiation. Other applications may demand very little penetration, as when we wish information, e.g., chemical composition or lattice parameter, from a very thin surface layer. Then we must make μ large, by using radiation which is highly absorbed, and α and β small, by using a diffractometer at low values of 2θ.* By these means the depth of penetration can often be made surprisingly small. For instance, if a steel specimen is examined in a diffractometer with Cu $K\alpha$ radiation, 95 percent of the information afforded by the lowest angle line of ferrite (the 110 line at $2\theta = 45°$) applies to a depth of only 9×10^{-5} in. There are limits, of course, to reducing the depth of x-ray penetration, and when information is required from very thin surface films, electron diffraction is a far more suitable tool (see Appendix 14).

CRYSTAL ORIENTATION

9–6 General. Each grain in a polycrystalline aggregate normally has a crystallographic orientation different from that of its neighbors. Considered as a whole, the orientations of all the grains may be randomly distributed in relation to some selected frame of reference, or they may tend to cluster, to a greater or lesser degree, about some particular orientation or orientations. Any aggregate characterized by the latter condition is said to have a *preferred orientation*, or *texture*, which may be defined simply as a condition in which the distribution of crystal orientations is nonrandom.

There are many examples of preferred orientation. The individual crystals in a cold-drawn wire, for instance, are so oriented that the same crystallographic direction [uvw] in most of the grains is parallel or nearly parallel

* Some of these requirements may be contradictory. For example, in measuring the lattice parameter of a thin surface layer with a diffractometer, we must compromise between the low value of θ required for shallow penetration and the high value of θ required for precise parameter measurements.

to the wire axis. In cold-rolled sheet, most of the grains are oriented with a certain plane (hkl) roughly parallel to the sheet surface, and a certain direction [uvw] in that plane roughly parallel to the direction in which the sheet was rolled. These are called *deformation textures*. Basically, they are due to the tendency, already noted in Sec. 8–6, for a grain to rotate during plastic deformation. There we considered the rotation of a single crystal subjected to tensile forces, but similar rotations occur for each grain of an aggregate as a result of the complex forces involved, with the result that a preferred orientation of the individual grains is produced by the deformation imposed on the aggregate as a whole.

When a cold-worked metal or alloy, possessed of a deformation texture, is recrystallized by annealing, the new grain structure usually has a preferred orientation too, often different from that of the cold-worked material. This is called an *annealing texture* or *recrystallization texture*, and two kinds are usually distinguished, primary and secondary, depending on the recrystallization process involved. Such textures are due to the influence which the texture of the matrix has on the nucleation and/or growth of the new grains in that matrix.

Preferred orientation can also exist in castings, hot-dipped coatings, evaporated films, electrodeposited layers, etc. Nor is it confined to metallurgical products: rocks, natural and artificial fibers and sheets, and similar organic or inorganic aggregates usually exhibit preferred orientation. In fact, preferred orientation is generally the rule, not the exception, and the preparation of an aggregate with a completely random crystal orientation is a difficult matter. To a certain extent, however, preferred orientation in metallurgical products can be controlled by the proper operating conditions. For example, some control of the texture of rolled sheet is possible by the correct choice of degree of deformation, annealing temperature, and annealing time.

The industrial importance of preferred orientation lies in the effect, often very marked, which it has on the over-all, macroscopic properties of materials. Given the fact that most single crystals are anisotropic, i.e., have different properties in different directions, it follows that an aggregate having preferred orientation must also have directional properties to a greater or lesser degree. Such properties are usually objectionable. For example, in the deep drawing of sheet the metal should flow evenly in all directions, but this will not occur if the metal has a high degree of preferred orientation, since the yield point, and in fact the whole flow stress curve of the material, will then differ in different directions in the sheet. More rarely, the intended use of the material requires directional properties, and then preferred orientation is desirable. For example, the steel sheet used for transformer cores must undergo repeated cycles of magnetization and demagnetization in use, requiring a high permeability in the direction of the applied field. Since single crystals of iron are more easily magnetized in the [100] direction than in any other, the rolling and annealing treatments given the steel sheet are deliberately chosen to produce a high degree of preferred orientation, in which as many grains as possible have their [100] directions parallel to a single direction in the sheet, in this case the rolling direction.

It should be noted that preferred orientation is solely a crystallographic condition and has nothing to do with grain shape as disclosed by the microscope. Therefore, the presence or absence of preferred orientation cannot be disclosed by microscopic examination. It is true that grain ·shape is affected by the same forces which produce preferred orientation; thus grains become flattened by rolling, and rolling is usually accompanied by preferred orientation, but a flattened shape is not in itself direct evidence of preferred orientation. Only x-ray diffraction can give such evidence. This fact is most apparent in recrystallized metals, which may have an equiaxed microstructure and, at the same time, a high degree of preferred orientation.

At various places in this book, we have already noted that a pinhole photograph made of a polycrystalline specimen with characteristic radiation consists of concentric Debye rings. We have more or less tacitly assumed that these rings are always continuous and of constant intensity around their circumference, but actually such rings are not formed unless the individual crystals in the specimen have completely random orientations.* If the specimen exhibits preferred orientation, the Debye rings are of nonuniform intensity around their circumference (if the preferred orientation is slight), or actually discontinuous (if there is a high degree of preferred orientation). In the latter case, certain portions of the Debye ring are missing because the orientations which would reflect to those parts of the ring are simply not present in the specimen. Nonuniform Debye rings can therefore be taken as conclusive evidence for preferred orientation, and by analyzing the nonuniformity we can determine the kind and degree of preferred orientation present.

Preferred orientation is best described by means of a *pole figure*. This is a stereographic projection which shows the variation in pole density with pole orientation for a selected set of crystal planes. This method of describing textures was first used by the German metallurgist Wever in 1924, and its meaning can best be illustrated by the following simple example. Suppose we have a very coarse-grained sheet of a cubic metal containing only 10 grains, and that we determine the orientation of each of these 10 grains by one of the Laue methods. We decide to represent the orientations of all of these grains together by plotting the positions of

---

* See the next section for one exception to this statement.

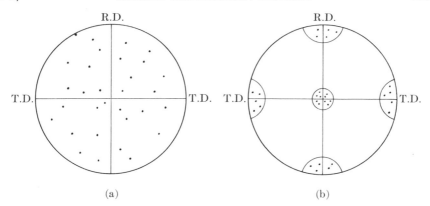

FIG. 9–7. (100) pole figures for sheet material, illustrating (a) random orientation and (b) preferred orientation. R.D. (rolling direction) and T.D. (transverse direction) are reference directions in the plane of the sheet.

their {100} poles on a single stereographic projection, with the projection plane parallel to the sheet surface. Since each grain has three {100} poles, there will be a total of $3 \times 10 = 30$ poles plotted on the projection. If the grains have a completely random orientation, these poles will be distributed uniformly* over the projection, as indicated in Fig. 9–7(a). But if preferred orientation is present, the poles will tend to cluster together into certain areas of the projection, leaving other areas virtually unoccupied. For example, this clustering might take the particular form shown in Fig. 9–7(b). This is called the "cube texture," because each grain is oriented with its (100) planes nearly parallel to the sheet surface and the [001] direction in these planes nearly parallel to the rolling direction. (This simple texture, which may be described by the shorthand notation (100) [001], actually forms as a recrystallization texture in many face-centered cubic metals and alloys under suitable conditions.) If we had chosen to construct a (111) pole figure, by plotting only {111} poles, the resulting pole figure would look entirely different from Fig. 9–7(b) for the same preferred orientation; in fact, it would consist of four "high-intensity" areas, one near the center of each quadrant. This illustrates the fact that the appearance of a pole figure depends on the indices of the poles plotted, and that the choice of indices depends on which aspect of the texture one wishes to show most clearly.

---

* If the orientation is random, there will be equal numbers of poles in equal areas on the surface of a reference sphere centered on the specimen. There will not be equal numbers, however, on equal areas of the pole figure, since the stereographic projection is not area-true. This results, for randomly oriented grains, in an apparent clustering of poles at the center of the pole figure, since distances representing equal angles are much smaller in this central region than in other parts of the pole figure.

Naturally, when the grain size is small, as it normally is, separate determination of the orientations of a representative number of grains is out of the question, so x-ray methods are used in which the diffraction effects from thousands of grains are automatically averaged. The (hkl) pole figure of a fine-grained material is constructed by analyzing the distribution of intensity around the circumference of the corresponding hkl Debye ring. There are two methods of doing this, the photographic and the diffractometer method. The photographic method is qualitative and, although affording sufficient accuracy for many purposes, it is rapidly being made obsolete by the more accurate diffractometer method. Both methods are described in the following sections.

Although only a pole figure can provide a complete description of preferred orientation, some information can be obtained simply by a comparison of calculated diffraction line intensities with those observed with a Debye-Scherrer camera or a diffractometer. As stated in Sec. 4–12, relative line intensities are given accurately by Eq. (4–12) only when the crystals of the specimen have completely random orientations. Therefore any radical disagreement between observed and calculated intensities is immediate evidence of preferred orientation in the specimen, and, from the nature of the disagreement, certain limited conclusions can usually be drawn concerning the nature of the texture. For example, if a sheet specimen is examined in the diffractometer in the usual way (the specimen making equal angles with the incident and diffracted beams), then the only grains which can contribute to the hkl reflection are those whose (hkl) planes are parallel to the sheet surface. If the texture is such that there are very few such grains, the intensity of the hkl reflection will be abnormally low. Or a given reflection may be of abnormally high intensity, which would indicate that the corresponding planes were preferentially oriented parallel or nearly parallel to the sheet surface. As an illustration, the 200 diffractometer reflection from a specimen having the cube texture is abnormally high, and from this fact alone it is possible to conclude that there is a preferred orientation of (100) planes parallel to the sheet surface. However, no conclusion is possible as to whether or not there is a preferred direction in the (100) plane parallel to some reference direction on the sheet surface. Such information can be obtained only by making a pole figure.

9–7 The texture of wire and rod (photographic method). As mentioned in the previous section, cold-drawn wire normally has a texture in which a certain crystallographic direction $[uvw]$ in most of the grains is parallel, or nearly parallel, to the wire axis. Since a similar texture is found in natural and artificial fibers, it is called a *fiber texture* and the axis of the wire is called the *fiber axis*. Materials having a fiber texture have rota-

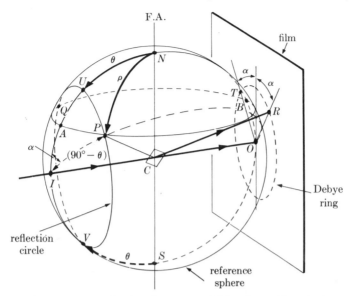

FIG. 9–8. Geometry of reflection from material having a fiber texture. F.A. = fiber axis.

tional symmetry about an axis in the sense that all orientations about this axis are equally probable. A fiber texture is therefore to be expected in any material formed by forces which have rotational symmetry about a line, for example, in wire and rod, formed by drawing, swaging, or extrusion. Less common examples of fiber texture are sometimes found in sheet formed by simple compression, in coatings formed by hot-dipping, electro-deposition, and evaporation, and in castings among the columnar crystals next to the mold wall. The fiber axis in these is perpendicular to the plane of the sheet or coating, and parallel to the axis of the columnar crystals.

Fiber textures vary in perfection, i.e., in the scatter of the direction [uvw] about the fiber axis, and both single and double fiber textures have been observed. Thus, cold-drawn aluminum wire has a single [111] texture, but copper, also face-centered cubic, has a double [111] + [100] texture; i.e., in drawn copper wire there are two sets of grains, the fiber axis of one set being [111] and that of the other set [100].

The only crystallographic problem presented by fiber textures is that of determining the indices [uvw] of the fiber axis, and that problem is best approached by considering the diffraction effects associated with an ideal case, for example, that of a wire of a cubic material having a perfect [100] fiber texture. Suppose we consider only the 111 reflection. In Fig. 9–8, the wire specimen is at C with its axis along NS, normal to the incident beam IC. CP is the normal to a set of (111) planes. Diffraction from these planes can occur only when they are inclined to the incident beam

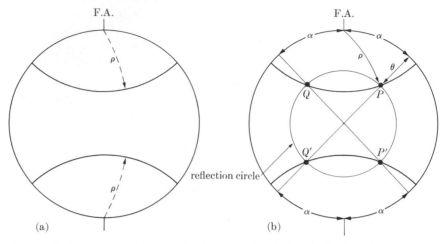

FIG. 9–9. Perfect [100] fiber texture: (a) (111) pole figure; (b) location of reflecting plane normals.

at an angle θ which satisfies the Bragg law, and this requires that the (111) pole lie somewhere on the circle $PUQV$, since then the angle between the plane normal and the incident beam will always be $90° - \theta$. For this reason, $PUQV$ is called the *reflection circle*. If the grains of the wire had completely random orientations, then (111) poles would lie at all positions on the reflection circle, and the 111 reflection would consist of the complete Debye ring indicated in the drawing. But if the wire has a perfect [100] fiber texture, then the diffraction pattern produced by a stationary specimen is identical with that obtained from a single crystal rotated about the axis [100], because of the rotational symmetry of the wire. During this rotation, the (111) pole is confined to the small circle $PAQB$, all points of which make a constant angle $\rho = 54.7°$ with the [100] direction N. Diffraction can now occur only when the (111) pole lies at the intersections of the reflection circle and the circle $PAQB$. These intersections are located at P and Q, and the corresponding diffraction spots at R and T, at an azimuthal angle α from a vertical line through the center of the film. Two other spots, not shown, are located in symmetrical positions on the lower half of the film. If the texture is not perfect, each of these spots will broaden peripherally into an arc whose length is a function of the degree of scatter in the texture.

By solving the spherical triangle IPN, we can find the following general relation between the angles ρ, θ, and α:

$$\cos \rho = \cos \theta \cos \alpha. \tag{9–6}$$

These angles are shown stereographically in Fig. 9–9, projected on a plane normal to the incident beam. The (111) pole figure in (a) consists simply of two arcs which are the paths traced out by {111} poles during rotation of a single crystal about [100]. In (b), this pole figure has been superposed on a projection of the reflection circle in order to find the locations of the reflecting plane normals. Radii drawn through these points (P, Q, P', and Q') then enable the angle α to be measured and the appearance of the diffraction pattern to be predicted.

An unknown fiber axis is identified by measuring the angle α on the film and obtaining ρ from Eq. (9–6). When this is done for a number of different hkl reflections, a set of ρ values is obtained from which the indices [uvw] of the fiber axis can be determined. The procedure will be illustrated with reference to the diffraction pattern of drawn aluminum wire shown in Fig. 9–10. The first step is to index the incomplete Debye rings. Values of θ for each ring are calculated from measurements of ring diameter, and hkl indices are assigned by the use of Eq. (3–10) and Appendix 6. In this way the inner ring is identified as a 111 reflection and the outer one as 200. The angle α is then measured from a vertical line through the center

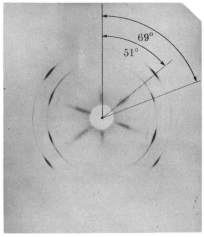

Fig. 9–10. Transmission pinhole pattern of cold-drawn aluminum wire, wire axis vertical. Filtered copper radiation. (The radial streaks near the center are formed by the white radiation in the incident beam.)

of the film to the center of each strong Debye arc. The average values of these angles are given below, together with the calculated values of ρ:

Line	hkl	α	θ	ρ
Inner	111	69°	19.3°	70°
Outer	200	52	22.3	55

The normals to the (111) and (200) planes therefore make angles of 70° and 55°, respectively, with the fiber axis. We can determine the indices [uvw] of this axis either by the graphical construction shown in Fig. 8–8 or by inspection of a table of interplanar angles. In this case, inspection of Table 2–3 shows that [uvw] must be [111], since the angle between ⟨111⟩ and ⟨111⟩ is 70.5° and that between ⟨111⟩ and ⟨100⟩ is 54.7°, and these values agree with the values of ρ given above within experimental error. The fiber axis of drawn aluminum wire is therefore [111]. There is some scatter of the [111] direction about the wire axis, however, inasmuch as the reflections on the film are short arcs rather than sharp spots. If we wish, this can be taken into account by measuring the angular range of α for each arc and calculating the corresponding angular range of ρ. A (111) pole figure of the wire would then resemble Fig. 9–9(a) except that the two curved lines would be replaced by two curved bands, each equal in width to the calculated range of ρ for the (111) poles.

One other aspect of fiber textures should be noted. In materials having a fiber texture, the individual grains have a common crystallographic direction parallel to the fiber axis but they can have any rotational position about that axis. It follows that the diffraction pattern of such materials will have continuous Debye rings if the incident x-ray beam is *parallel* to the fiber axis. However, the relative intensities of these rings will not be the same as those calculated for a specimen containing randomly oriented grains. Therefore, continuous Debye rings are not, in themselves, evidence for a lack of preferred orientation.

9–8 The texture of sheet (photographic method). The texture of rolled sheet, either as rolled or after recrystallization, differs from that of drawn wire in having less symmetry. There is no longer a common crystallographic direction about which the grains can have any rotational position. Sheet textures can therefore be described adequately only by means of a pole figure, since only this gives a complete map of the distribution of crystal orientation.

The photographic method of determining the pole figure of sheet is quite similar to the method just described for determining wire textures. A transmission pinhole camera is used, together with general radiation containing a characteristic component. The sheet specimen, reduced in thickness by etching to a few thousandths of an inch, is initially mounted perpendicular to the incident beam with the rolling direction vertical. The resulting photograph resembles that of a drawn wire: it contains Debye rings of nonuniform intensity and the pattern is symmetrical about a vertical line through the center of the film. However, if the sheet is now rotated by, say, 10° about the rolling direction and another photograph made, the resulting pattern will differ from the first, because the texture of sheet does not have rotational symmetry about the rolling direction. This new pattern will not be symmetrical about a vertical line, and the regions of high intensity on the Debye rings will not have the same azimuthal positions as they had in the first photograph. Figure 9–11 illustrates this effect for cold-rolled aluminum. To determine the complete texture of sheet, it is therefore necessary to measure the distribution of orientations about the rolling direction by making several photographs with the sheet normal at various angles to the incident beam.

Figure 9–12 shows the experimental arrangement and defines the angle β between the sheet normal and the incident beam. The intensity of the

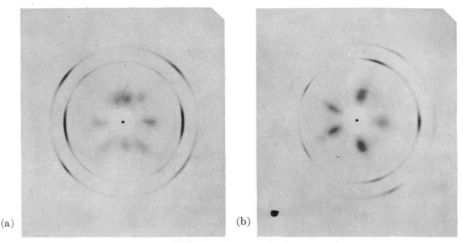

(a)   (b)

FIG. 9–11. Transmission pinhole patterns of cold-rolled aluminum sheet, rolling direction vertical: (a) sheet normal parallel to incident beam; (b) sheet normal at 30° to incident beam (the specimen has been rotated clockwise about the rolling direction, as in Fig. 9–12).   Filtered copper radiation.

diffracted rays in any one Debye cone is decreased by absorption in the specimen by an amount which depends on the angle β, and when β is not zero the rays going to the left side of the film undergo more absorption than those going to the right. For this reason it is often advisable to make measurements only on the right side of the film, particularly when β is large.

The usual practice is to make photographs at about 10° intervals from $\beta = 0$ to $\beta = 80°$, and to measure the intensity distribution around a par-

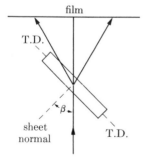

FIG. 9–12. Section through sheet specimen and incident beam (specimen thickness exaggerated). Rolling direction normal to plane of drawing. T.D. = transverse direction.

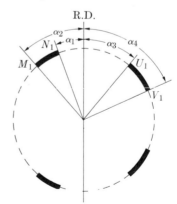

FIG. 9–13. Measurement of azimuthal position of high-intensity arcs on a Debye ring. $\beta = 40°$, R.D. = rolling direction.

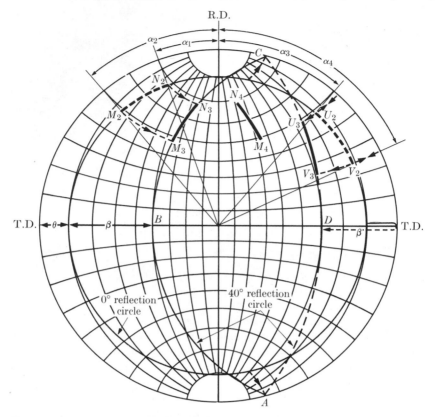

FIG. 9–14. Method of plotting reflecting pole positions for nonzero values of β. Drawn for $\theta = 10°$ and $\beta = 40°$.

ticular Debye ring on each photograph. The procedure for plotting the pole figure from these measurements will be illustrated here for an idealized case like that shown in Fig. 9–13, where the intensity of the Debye ring is constant over certain angular ranges and zero between them. The range of blackening of the Debye arcs is plotted stereographically as a range of reflecting pole positions along the reflection circle, the azimuthal angle α on the film equal to the azimuthal angle α on the projection. Although the reflection circle is fixed in space (see Fig. 9–8 where SCN is now the rolling direction of the sheet specimen), its position on the projection varies with the rotational position β of the specimen, since the projection plane is parallel to the surface of the sheet and rotates with it.

When $\beta = 0°$, the reflection circle is concentric with the basic circle of the projection and θ degrees inside it, as shown in Fig. 9–14, which is drawn for $\theta = 10°$. When the specimen is then rotated, for example by 40° in the sense shown in Fig. 9–12, the new position of the reflection circle is found by rotating two or three points on the 0°.reflection circle by 40°

to the right along latitude lines and drawing circle arcs, centered on the equator or its extension, through these points. This new position of the reflection circle is indicated by the arcs $ABCDA$ in Fig. 9–14; since in this example β exceeds θ, part of the reflection circle, namely CDA, lies in the back hemisphere. The arcs in Fig. 9–13 are first plotted on the 0° reflection circle, as though the projection plane were still perpendicular to the incident beam, and then rotated to the right along latitude circles onto the 40° reflection circle. Thus, arc M_1N_1 in Fig. 9–13 becomes M_2N_2 and then, finally, M_3N_3 in Fig. 9–14. Similarly, Debye arc U_1V_1 is plotted as U_3V_3, lying on the back hemisphere.

The texture of sheet is normally such that two planes of symmetry exist, one normal to the rolling direction (R.D.) and one normal to the transverse direction (T.D.). For this reason, arc M_3N_3 may be reflected in the latter plane to give the arc M_4N_4, thus helping to fill out the pole figure. These symmetry elements are also the justification for plotting the arc U_3V_3 as though it were situated on the front hemisphere, since reflection in the center of the projection (to bring it to the front hemisphere) and successive reflections in the two symmetry planes will bring it to this position anyway. If the diffraction patterns indicate that these symmetry planes are not present, then these short cuts in plotting may not be used.

By successive changes in β, the reflection circle can be made to move across the projection and so disclose the positions of reflecting poles. With the procedure described, however, the regions near the N and S poles of the projection will never be cut by a reflection circle. To explore these regions, we must rotate the specimen 90° in its own plane, so that the transverse direction is vertical, and take a photograph with $\beta \approx 5°$.

Figure 9–15 shows what might result from a pole figure determination involving measurements at $\beta = 0, 20, 40, 60,$ and 80° (R.D. vertical) and

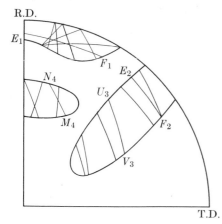

Fig. 9–15.   Plotting a pole figure.

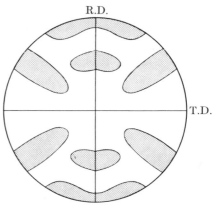

Fig. 9–16.   Hypothetical pole figure derived from Fig. 9–15.

$\beta = 5°$ (T.D. vertical). The arcs in Fig. 9–14 are replotted here with the same symbols, and the arcs E_1F_1 and E_2F_2 lie on the 5° reflection circle with the transverse direction vertical. The complete set of arcs defines areas of high pole density and, by reflecting these areas in the symmetry planes mentioned above, we arrive at the complete pole figure shown in Fig. 9–16.

In practice, the variation of intensity around a Debye ring is not abrupt but gradual, as Fig. 9–11 demonstrates. This is taken into account by plotting ranges in which the intensity is substantially constant, and no more than four such ranges are usually required, namely, zero, weak, medium, and strong. The result is a pole figure in which various areas, distinguished by different kinds of cross-hatching, represent various degrees of pole density from zero to a maximum. Figure 9–17 is a photographically determined pole figure in which this has been done. It repre-

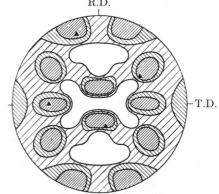

FIG. 9–17.   (111) pole figure of recrystallized 70–30 brass, determined by the photographic method. (R. M. Brick, *Trans. A.I.M.E.* **137**, 193, 1940.)

sents the primary recrystallization texture of 70–30 brass which has been cold-rolled to a 99 percent reduction in thickness and then annealed at 400°C for 30 minutes.

The texture of sheet is often described in terms of an "ideal orientation," i.e., the orientation of a single crystal whose poles would lie in the high-density regions of the pole figure. For example, in Fig. 9–17 the solid triangular symbols mark the positions of the {111} poles of a single crystal which has its (113) plane parallel to the plane of the sheet and the [2̄11] direction in this plane parallel to the rolling direction. This orientation, when reflected in the two symmetry planes normal to the rolling and transverse directions, will approximately account for all the high-density regions on the pole figure. Accordingly, this texture has been called a (113) [2̄11] texture. The actual pole figure, however, is a far better description of the texture than any statement of an ideal orientation, since the latter is frequently not very exact and gives no information about the degree of scatter of the actual texture about the ideal orientation.

The inaccuracies of photographically determined pole figures are due to two factors:

(1) intensity "measurements" made on the film are usually only visual estimates, and

(2) no allowance is made for the change in the absorption factor with changes in β and α. This variation in the absorption factor makes it very difficult to relate intensities observed on one film to those observed on another, even when the exposure time is varied for different films in an attempt to allow for changes in absorption.

9–9 The texture of sheet (diffractometer method). In recent years methods have been developed for the determination of pole figures with the diffractometer. These methods are capable of quite high precision because

(1) the intensity of the diffracted rays is measured quantitatively with a counter, and

(2) either the intensity measurements are corrected for changes in absorption, or the x-ray optics are so designed that the absorption is constant and no correction is required.

For reasons given later, two different methods must be used to cover the whole pole figure.

The first of these, called the **transmission method,** is due to Decker, Asp, and Harker, and Fig. 9–18 illustrates its principal features. To determine an (hkl) pole figure, the counter is fixed in position at the correct angle 2θ to receive the hkl reflection. The sheet specimen, in a special holder, is positioned initially with the rolling direction vertical and coincident with the diffractometer axis,* and with the plane of the specimen bisecting the angle between the incident and diffracted beams. The specimen holder allows rotation of the specimen about the diffractometer axis and about a horizontal axis normal to the specimen surface. Although it is impossible to move the counter around the Debye ring and so explore the variation in diffracted intensity around this ring, we can accomplish essentially the same thing by keeping the counter fixed and rotating the specimen in its own plane. This rotation, combined with the other rotation about the diffractometer axis, moves the pole of the (hkl)

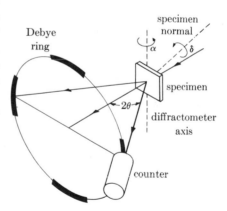

FIG. 9–18. Transmission method for pole-figure determination. (After A. H. Geisler, "Crystal Orientation and Pole Figure Determination" in *Modern Research Techniques in Physical Metallurgy*, American Society for Metals, Cleveland, 1953.)

* For simplicity, the method is described here only in terms of a vertical-axis diffractometer.

specimen

FIG. 9–19. Specimen holder used in the transmission method, viewed from trans-mitted-beam side.   (Courtesy of Paul A. Beck.)

reflecting plane over the surface of the pole figure, which is plotted on a projection plane parallel to the specimen plane, as in the photographic method.   At each position of the specimen, the measured intensity of the diffracted beam, after correction for absorption, gives a figure which is pro-portional to the pole density at the corresponding point on the pole figure. Figure 9–19 shows the kind of specimen holder used for this method.

The method of plotting the data is indicated in Fig. 9–20.   The angle α measures the amount of rotation about the diffractometer axis;* it is zero when the sheet bisects the angle between incident and diffracted beams.   The positive direction of α is conventionally taken as counter-clockwise.   The angle δ measures the amount by which the transverse direction is rotated about the sheet normal out of the horizontal plane and

---

* α is the conventional symbol for this angle, which is measured in a horizontal plane.   It should not be confused with the angle α used in Sec. 9–8 to measure azimuthal positions in a vertical plane.

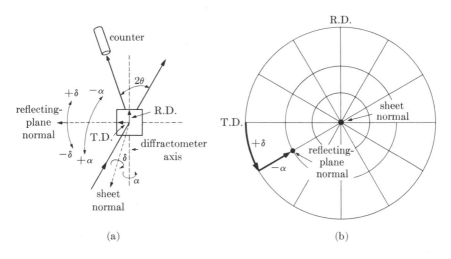

(a)   (b)

Fig. 9–20. Angular relationships in the transmission pole-figure method (a) in space and (b) on the stereographic projection. (On the projection, the position of the reflecting plane normal is shown for $\delta = 30°$ and $\alpha = -30°$.)

is zero when the transverse direction is horizontal. The reflecting plane normal bisects the angle between incident and diffracted beams, and remains fixed in position whatever the orientation of the specimen. To plot the pole of the reflecting plane on the pole figure, we note that it coincides initially, when α and δ are both zero, with the left transverse direction. A rotation of the specimen by δ degrees in its own plane then moves the pole of the reflecting plane δ degrees around the circumference of the pole figure, and a rotation of $-\alpha$ degrees about the diffractometer axis then moves it α degrees from the circumference along a radius. To explore the pole figure, it is convenient to make intensity readings at intervals of 5° or 10° of $-\alpha$ for a fixed value of δ: the pole figure is thus mapped out along a series of radii.* By this procedure the entire pole figure can be determined except for a region at the center extending from about $\alpha = -50°$ to $\alpha = -90°$; in this region not only does the absorption correction become inaccurate but the frame of the specimen holder obstructs the diffracted x-ray beam.

An absorption correction is necessary in this method because variations in α cause variations in both the volume of diffracting material and the path length of the x-rays within the specimen. Variations in δ have no effect. We can determine the angular dependence of the absorption factor

---

* The chart shown in skeleton form in Fig. 9–20(b) is useful for this purpose. It is called a polar stereographic net, because it shows the latitude lines (circles) and longitude lines (radii) of a ruled globe projected on a plane normal to the polar NS-axis. In the absence of such a net, the equator or central meridian of a Wulff net can be used to measure the angle α.

by a method similar to that used for the reflection case considered in Sec. 7–4. The incident beam in Fig. 9–21 has intensity I_0 (ergs/cm^2/sec) and is 1 cm square in cross section. It is incident on a sheet specimen of thickness t and linear absorption coefficient μ, and the individual grains of this specimen are assumed to have a completely random orientation. Let a be the volume fraction of the specimen containing grains correctly oriented for reflection of the incident beam, and b the fraction of the incident energy diffracted by unit volume. Then the total energy per second in the diffracted beam outside the specimen, originating in a layer of thickness dx located at a depth x, is given by

$$dI_D = ab(DB)I_0 e^{-\mu(AB+BC)} \, dx \quad \text{(ergs/sec)},$$

where

$$DB = \frac{1}{\cos(\theta - \alpha)}, \quad AB = \frac{x}{\cos(\theta - \alpha)}, \quad \text{and} \quad BC = \frac{t - x}{\cos(\theta + \alpha)}.$$

By substitution, we obtain

$$dI_D = \frac{abI_0}{\cos(\theta - \alpha)} e^{-\mu t/\cos(\theta+\alpha)} e^{-\mu x[1/\cos(\theta-\alpha) - 1/\cos(\theta+\alpha)]} \, dx. \quad (9\text{–}7)$$

(Only clockwise rotation of the specimen about the diffractometer axis, i.e., rotation in the sense usually designated by $-\alpha$, is considered here. However, in these equations and in Fig. 9–21, the proper sign has already been inserted, and the symbol α stands for the absolute value of this angle.) If we put $\alpha = 0$ in Eq. (9–7) and integrate from $x = 0$ to $x = t$, we obtain the total diffracted energy per second, the integrated intensity, for this position of the specimen:*

$$I_D(\alpha = 0) = \frac{abtI_0}{\cos \theta} e^{-\mu t/\cos \theta}. \quad (9\text{–}8)$$

When α is not zero, the same integration gives

$$I_D(\alpha = \alpha) = \frac{abI_0[e^{-\mu t/\cos(\theta-\alpha)} - e^{-\mu t/\cos(\theta+\alpha)}]}{\mu[\cos(\theta - \alpha)/\cos(\theta + \alpha) - 1]}. \quad (9\text{–}9)$$

---

* In Sec. 6–9 mention was made of the fact that the diffracted beams in any transmission method were of maximum intensity when the thickness of the specimen was made equal to $1/\mu$. This result follows from Eq. (9–8). If we put $\theta = \alpha = 0$, then the primary beam will be incident on the specimen at right angles (see Fig. 9–21), as in the usual transmission pinhole method, and our result will apply approximately to diffracted beams formed at small angles 2θ. The intensity of such a beam is given by

$$I_D = abtI_0 e^{-\mu t}.$$

By differentiating this expression with respect to t and setting the result equal to zero, we can find that I_D is a maximum when $t = 1/\mu$.

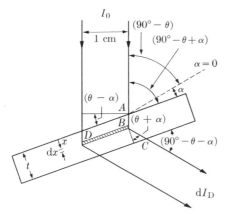

FIG. 9–21. Path length and irradiated volume in the transmission method.

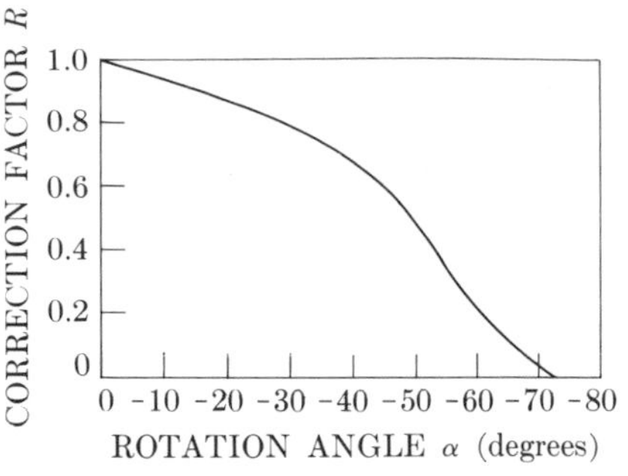

FIG. 9–22. Variation of the correction factor R with α for clockwise rotation from the zero position. $\mu t = 1.0$, $\theta = 19.25°$.

We are interested only in the ratio of these two integrated intensities, namely,

$$R = \frac{I_D(\alpha = \alpha)}{I_D(\alpha = 0)} = \frac{\cos \theta [e^{-\mu t/\cos (\theta-\alpha)} - e^{-\mu t/\cos (\theta+\alpha)}]}{\mu t e^{-\mu t/\cos \theta}[\cos (\theta - \alpha)/\cos (\theta + \alpha) - 1]}. \quad (9\text{–}10)$$

A plot of R vs. α is given in Fig. 9–22 for typical values involved in the 111 reflection from aluminum with Cu $K\alpha$ radiation, namely, $\mu t = 1.0$ and $\theta = 19.25°$. This plot shows that the integrated intensity of the reflection decreases as α increases in the clockwise direction from zero, even for a specimen containing randomly oriented grains. In the measurement of preferred orientation, it is therefore necessary to *divide* each measured intensity by the appropriate value of the correction factor R in order to arrive at a figure proportional to the pole density. From the way in which the correction factor R was derived, it follows that we must measure the *integrated intensity* of the diffracted beam. To do this with a fixed counter, the counter slits must be as wide as the diffracted beam for all values of α so that the whole width of the beam can enter the counter. The ideal incident beam for this method is a parallel one. However, a divergent beam may be used without too much error, provided the divergence is not too great. There is no question of focusing here: if the incident beam is divergent, the diffracted beam will diverge also and very wide counter slits will be required to admit its entire width.

The value of μt used in Eq. (9–10) must be obtained by direct measurement, since it is not sufficiently accurate to use a tabulated value of μ together with the measured thickness t of the specimen. To determine μt we use a strong diffracted beam from any convenient material and measure its intensity when the sheet specimen is inserted in the diffracted beam

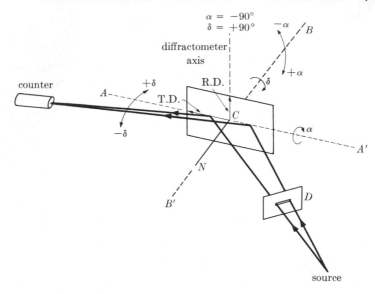

FIG. 9–23.   Reflection method for pole-figure determination.

and again when it is not.   The value of μt is then obtained from the general absorption equation, $I_t = I_0 e^{-\mu t}$, where I_0 and I_t are the intensities incident on and transmitted by the sheet specimen, respectively.

As already mentioned, the central part of the pole figure cannot be covered by the transmission method.   To explore this region we must use a **reflection method,** one in which the measured diffracted beam issues from that side of the sheet on which the primary beam is incident.   The reflection method here described was developed by Schulz.   It requires a special holder which allows rotation of the specimen in its own plane about an axis normal to its surface and about a horizontal axis; these axes are shown as BB' and AA' in Fig. 9–23.   The horizontal axis AA' lies in the specimen surface and is initially adjusted, by rotation about the diffractometer axis, to make equal angles with the incident and diffracted beams.   After this is done, no further rotation about the diffractometer axis is made.   Since the axis AA' remains in a fixed position during the other rotations of the specimen, the irradiated surface of the specimen is always tangent to a focusing circle passing through the x-ray source and counter slits.   A divergent beam may therefore be used since the diffracted beam will converge to a focus at the counter slits.   Figure 9–24 shows a specimen holder for the reflection method.

When the specimen is rotated about the axis AA', the axis BB' normal to the specimen surface rotates in a vertical plane, but CN, the reflecting plane normal, remains fixed in a horizontal position normal to AA'.   The rotation angles α and δ are defined in Fig. 9–23.   The angle α is zero when

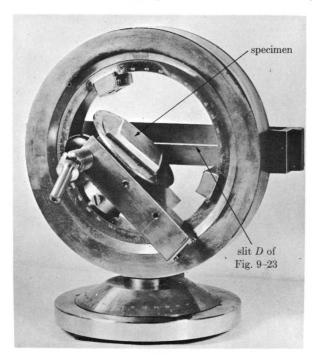

FIG. 9–24. Specimen holder used in the reflection method, viewed from re-flected-beam side. (Courtesy of Paul A. Beck.)

the sheet is horizontal and has a value of $-90°$ when the sheet is in the vertical position shown in the drawing. In this position of the specimen, the reflecting plane normal is at the center of the projection. The angle δ measures the amount by which the rolling direction is rotated away from the left end of the axis AA' and has a value of $+90°$ for the position illus-trated. With these conventions the angles α and δ may be plotted on the pole figure in the same way as in the transmission method [Fig. 9–20(b)].

The great virtue of the reflection method is that no absorption correc-tion is required for values of α between $-90°$ and about $-40°$, i.e., up to about 50° from the center of the pole figure. In other words, a specimen whose grains have a completely random orientation can be rotated over this range of α values without any change in the measured intensity of the diffracted beam. Under these circumstances, the intensity of the dif-fracted beam is directly proportional to the pole density in the specimen, without any correction. The constancy of the absorption factor is due essentially to the narrow horizontal slit placed in the primary beam at D (Fig. 9–23). The vertical opening in this slit is only about 0.020 in. in height, which means that the specimen is irradiated only over a long nar-row rectangle centered on the fixed axis AA'. It can be shown that a

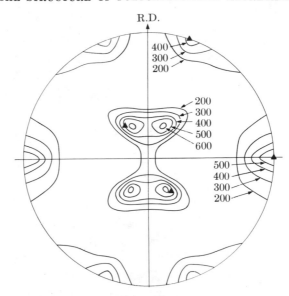

FIG. 9–25. (111) pole figure of cold-rolled 70–30 brass, determined by the diffractometer method. (H. Hu, P. R. Sperry, and P. A. Beck, *Trans. A.I.M.E.* **194,** 76, 1952.)

change in absorption does occur, as the specimen is rotated about AA', but it is exactly canceled by a change in the volume of diffracting material, the net result being a constant diffracted intensity for a random specimen when α lies between $-90°$ and about $-40°$. To achieve this condition, the reflecting surface of the specimen must be adjusted to accurately coincide with the axis AA' for all values of α and δ. This adjustment is extremely important.

It is evident that the transmission and reflection methods complement one another in their coverage of the pole figure. The usual practice is to use the transmission method to cover the range of α from $0°$ to $-50°$ and the reflection method from $-40°$ to $-90°$. This produces an overlap of $10°$ which is useful in checking the accuracy of one method against the other, and necessary in order to find a normalizing factor for one set of readings which will make them agree with the other set in the region of overlap.

When this is done, the numbers which are proportional to pole density can then be plotted on the pole figure at each point at which a measurement was made. Contour lines are then drawn at selected levels connecting points of the same pole density, and the result is a pole figure such as that shown in Fig. 9–25, which represents the deformation texture of 70–30 brass cold-rolled to a reduction in thickness of 95 percent. The numbers attached to each contour line give the pole density in arbitrary units. A pole figure such as this is far more accurate than any photo-graphically determined one, and represents the best description available today of the kind and extent of preferred orientation. The accuracy obtainable with the diffractometer method is sufficient to allow investigation, with some confidence, of possible asymmetry in sheet textures. In most sheet, no asymmetry of texture is found (see Fig. 9–25), but it does occur when sheet is carefully rolled in the same direction, i.e., without any reversal end for end between passes. In such sheet, the texture has only one reflection plane of symmetry, normal to the transverse direction; the plane normal to the rolling direction is no longer a symmetry plane.

In Fig. 9–25, the solid triangular symbols representing the ideal orientation (110) [$1\bar{1}2$] lie approximately in the high-density regions of the pole figure. But here again the pole figure itself must be regarded as a far better description of the texture than any bare statement of an ideal orientation. A quantitative pole figure of this kind has about the same relation to an ideal orientation as an accurate contour map of a hill has to a statement of the height, width, and length of the hill.

Geisler has recently pointed out two sources of error in the diffractometer method, both of which can lead to spurious intensity maxima on the pole figure if the investigator is not aware of them:

(1) When an ($h_1k_1l_1$) pole figure is being determined, the counter is set at the appropriate angle 2θ to receive $K\alpha$ radiation reflected from the ($h_1k_1l_1$) planes. But at some position of the specimen, there may be another set of planes, ($h_2k_2l_2$), so oriented that they can reflect a component of the continuous spectrum at the same angle 2θ. If the ($h_2k_2l_2$) planes have a high reflecting power, this reflection may be so strong that it may be taken for an $h_1k_1l_1$ reflection of the $K\alpha$ wavelength. Apparently the only sure way of eliminating this possibility is to use balanced filters.

(2) The crystal structure of the material being investigated may be such that a set of planes, ($h_3k_3l_3$), has very nearly the same spacing as the ($h_1k_1l_1$) planes. The $K\alpha$ reflections of these two sets will therefore occur at very nearly the same angle 2θ. If the counter is set to receive the $h_1k_1l_1$ reflection, then there is a possibility that some of the $h_3k_3l_3$ reflection may also be received, especially in the transmission method for which a wide receiving slit is used. The best way out of this difficulty is to select another reflection, $h_4k_4l_4$, well separated from its neighbors, and construct an $h_4k_4l_4$ pole figure instead of an $h_1k_1l_1$. [It is not advisable to attempt to exclude the unwanted $h_3k_3l_3$ reflection by narrowing the slits. If this is done, then the counter may not receive the entire $h_1k_1l_1$ diffracted beam, and if all of this beam is not received, Eq. (9–10) will no longer give the correct value of R. If a narrow receiving slit must be used, then the variation of R with α must be determined experimentally. This determination requires a specimen of the same material as that under investigation, with

the same value of μt and a perfectly random orientation of its constituent grains.]

One other point about pole-figure determinations should be mentioned, and that is the necessity for integrating devices when the grain size of the specimen is large, as in recrystallized metals and alloys. With such specimens, the incident x-ray beam will not strike enough grains to give a good statistical average of the orientations present. This is true of both methods, the photographic and the diffractometer. With coarse-grained specimens it is therefore necessary to use some kind of integrating device, which will move the specimen back and forth, or in a spiral, in its own plane and so expose a larger number of grains to the incident beam.

Pole-figure determination is by no means a closed subject, and variations and improvements are constantly being described in the technical literature. The most interesting among these are devices for the automatic plotting of pole figures by the diffractometer method. In these devices, the specimen is slowly rotated about the various axes by a mechanical drive, and the output of the counter-ratemeter circuit is fed to a recorder whose chart is driven in synchronism with the rotation of the specimen. The chart may be either of the simple strip variety, or even a circular pole-figure chart on which the recorder prints selected levels of pole density at the proper positions. The time is probably not far off when most pole figures will be determined in an automatic or semi-automatic manner, at least in the larger laboratories.

TABLE 9–2

Appearance of diffraction lines	Condition of specimen
Continuous	Fine-grained (or coarse-grained and cold-worked)
Spotty	Coarse-grained
Narrow (1)	Strain-free
Broad (1)	Residual stress and possibly small particle size (if specimen is a solid aggregate) Small particle size (if specimen is a brittle powder)
Uniform intensity	Random orientation (2)
Nonuniform intensity	Preferred orientation

Notes:
(1) Best judged by noting whether or not the $K\alpha$ doublet is resolved in back reflection.
(2) Or possibly presence of a fiber texture, if the incident beam is parallel to the fiber axis.

9–10 Summary. In this chapter we have considered various aspects of the structure of polycrystalline aggregates and the quantitative effects of variations in crystal size, perfection, and orientation on the diffraction pattern. Although a complete investigation of the structure of an aggregate requires a considerable amount of time and rather complex apparatus, the very great utility of the simple pinhole photograph should not be overlooked. It is surprising how much information an experienced observer can obtain simply by inspection of a pinhole photograph, without any knowledge of the specimen, i.e., without knowing its chemical identity, crystal structure, or even whether it is amorphous or crystalline. The latter point can be settled at a glance, since diffraction lines indicate crystallinity and broad haloes an amorphous condition. If the specimen is crystalline, the conclusions that can be drawn from the appearance of the lines are summarized in Table 9–2.

PROBLEMS

9–1. A cold-worked polycrystalline piece of metal, having a Young's modulus of 30,000,000 psi, is examined with Cu $K\alpha$ radiation. A diffraction line occurring at $2\theta = 150°$ is observed to be 1.28 degrees 2θ broader than the same line from a recrystallized specimen. If this broadening is assumed to be due to residual microstresses varying from zero to the yield point both in tension and compression, what is the yield point of the material?

9–2. If the observed broadening given in Prob. 9–1 is ascribed entirely to a fragmentation of the grains into small crystal particles, what is the size of these particles?

9–3. For given values of θ and μ, which results in a greater effective depth of x-ray penetration, a back-reflection pinhole camera or a diffractometer?

9–4. Assume that the effective depth of penetration of an x-ray beam is that thickness of material which contributes 99 percent of the total energy diffracted by an infinitely thick specimen. Calculate the penetration depth in inches for a low-carbon steel specimen under the following conditions:

(a) Diffractometer; lowest-angle reflection; Cu $K\alpha$ radiation.
(b) Diffractometer; highest-angle reflection; Cu $K\alpha$ radiation.
(c) Diffractometer; highest-angle reflection; Cr $K\alpha$ radiation.
(d) Back-reflection pinhole camera; highest-angle reflection; Cr $K\alpha$ radiation.

9–5. (a) A transmission pinhole photograph is made of a sheet specimen of thickness t and linear absorption coefficient μ. Show that the fraction of the total diffracted energy in any one reflection contributed by a layer of thickness w is given by

$$W = \frac{e^{-\mu[x + (t-x)/\cos 2\theta]}[e^{-\mu w(1 - 1/\cos 2\theta)} - 1]}{e^{-\mu t} - e^{-\mu t/\cos 2\theta}},$$

where x is the distance to the side of the layer involved, measured from the side of the specimen on which the primary beam is incident.

(b) A transmission pinhole photograph is made of a sheet of aluminum 0.5 mm thick with Cu $K\alpha$ radiation. Consider only the 111 reflection which occurs at $2\theta = 38.4°$. Imagine the sheet to be divided into four layers, the thickness of each being equal to one-fourth of the total thickness. Calculate W for each layer.

9-6. A transmission pinhole pattern is made with Co $K\alpha$ radiation of an iron wire having an almost perfect [110] fiber texture. The wire axis is vertical. How many high-intensity maxima will appear on the lowest-angle 110 Debye ring and what are their azimuthal angles on the film?

CHAPTER 10

THE DETERMINATION OF CRYSTAL STRUCTURE

10–1 Introduction. Since 1913, when W. L. Bragg solved the structure of NaCl, the structures of some five thousand crystals, organic and inorganic, have been determined. This vast body of knowledge is of fundamental importance in such fields as crystal chemistry, solid-state physics, and the biological sciences because, to a large extent, structure determines properties and the properties of a substance are never fully understood until its structure is known. In metallurgy, a knowledge of crystal structure is a necessary prerequisite to any understanding of such phenomena as plastic deformation, alloy formation, or phase transformations.

The work of structure determination goes on continuously since there is no dearth of unsolved structures. New substances are constantly being synthesized, and the structures of many old ones are still unknown. In themselves crystal structures vary widely in complexity: the simplest can be solved in a few hours, while the more complex may require months or even years for their complete solution. (Proteins form a notable example of the latter kind; despite intensive efforts of many investigators, their structure has not yet been completely determined.) Complex structures require complex methods of solution, and structure determination in its entirety is more properly the subject of a book than of a single chapter. All we can do here is to consider some of the principles involved and how they can be applied to the solution of fairly simple structures. Moreover, we will confine our attention to the methods of determining structure from powder patterns alone, because such patterns are the kind most often encountered by the metallurgist.

The basic principles involved in structure determination have already been introduced in Chaps. 3 and 4. We saw there that the crystal structure of a substance determines the diffraction pattern of that substance or, more specifically, that the shape and size of the unit cell determines the angular positions of the diffraction lines, and the arrangement of the atoms within the unit cell determines the relative intensities of the lines. It may be worthwhile to state this again in tabular form:

Crystal structure		Diffraction pattern
Unit cell	$\leftrightarrow$	Line positions
Atom positions	$\leftrightarrow$	Line intensities

Since structure determines the diffraction pattern, it should be possible to go in the other direction and deduce the structure from the pattern. It is possible, *but not in any direct manner*. Given a structure, we can calculate its diffraction pattern in a very straightforward fashion, and examples of such calculations were given in Sec. 4–13; but the reverse problem, that of directly calculating the structure from the observed pattern, has never been solved, for reasons to be discussed in Sec. 10–8. The procedure adopted is essentially one of trial and error. On the basis of an educated guess, a structure is assumed, its diffraction pattern calculated, and the calculated pattern compared with the observed one. If the two agree in all detail, the assumed structure is correct; if not, the process is repeated as often as is necessary to find the correct solution. The problem is not unlike that of deciphering a code, and requires of the crystallographer the same qualities possessed by a good cryptanalyst, namely, knowledge, perseverance, and not a little intuition.

The determination of an unknown structure proceeds in three major steps:

(1) The shape and size of the unit cell are deduced from the angular positions of the diffraction lines. An assumption is first made as to which of the seven crystal systems the unknown structure belongs to, and then, on the basis of this assumption, the correct Miller indices are assigned to each reflection. This step is called "indexing the pattern" and is only possible when the correct choice of crystal system has been made. Once this is done, the shape of the unit cell is known (from the crystal system), and its size is calculable from the positions and Miller indices of the diffraction lines.

(2) The number of atoms per unit cell is then computed from the shape and size of the unit cell, the chemical composition of the specimen, and its measured density.

(3) Finally, the positions of the atoms within the unit cell are deduced from the relative intensities of the diffraction lines.

Only when these three steps have been accomplished is the structure determination complete. The third step is generally the most difficult, and there are many structures which are known only incompletely, in the sense that this final step has not yet been made. Nevertheless, a knowledge of the shape and size of the unit cell, without any knowledge of atom positions, is in itself of very great value in many applications.

The average metallurgist is rarely, if ever, called upon to determine an unknown crystal structure. If the structure is at all complex, its determination is a job for a specialist in x-ray crystallography, who can bring special techniques, both experimental and mathematical, to bear on the problem. The metallurgist should, however, know enough about structure determination to unravel any simple structures he may encounter and, what is more important, he must be able to index the powder patterns of substances of *known* structure, as this is a routine problem in almost all diffraction work. The procedures given below for indexing patterns are applicable whether the structure is known or not, but they are of course very much easier to apply if the structure is known beforehand.

10–2 Preliminary treatment of data. The powder pattern of the unknown is obtained with a Debye-Scherrer camera or a diffractometer, the object being to cover as wide an angular range of 2θ as possible. A camera such as the Seemann-Bohlin, which records diffraction lines over only a limited angular range, is of very little use in structure analysis. The specimen preparation must ensure random orientation of the individual particles of powder, if the observed relative intensities of the diffraction lines are to have any meaning in terms of crystal structure. After the pattern is obtained, the value of $\sin^2 \theta$ is calculated for each diffraction line; this set of $\sin^2 \theta$ values is the raw material for the determination of cell size and shape.

Since the problem of structure determination is one of finding a structure which will account for all the lines on the pattern, in both position and intensity, the investigator must make sure at the outset that the observed pattern does not contain any extraneous lines. The ideal pattern contains lines formed by x-rays of a single wavelength, diffracted only by the substance whose structure is to be determined. There are therefore two sources of extraneous lines:

(1) *Diffraction of x-rays having wavelengths different from that of the principal component of the radiation.* If filtered radiation is used, then $K\alpha$ radiation is the principal component, and characteristic x-rays of any other wavelength may produce extraneous lines. The chief offender is $K\beta$ radiation, which is never entirely removed by a filter and may be a source of extraneous lines when diffracted by lattice planes of high reflecting power. The presence of $K\beta$ lines on a pattern can usually be revealed by calculation, since if a certain set of planes reflect $K\beta$ radiation at an angle θ_β, they must also reflect $K\alpha$ radiation at an angle θ_α (unless θ_α exceeds 90°), and one angle may be calculated from the other. It follows from the Bragg law that

$$\left(\frac{\lambda_{K\alpha}^2}{\lambda_{K\beta}^2}\right) \sin^2 \theta_\beta = \sin^2 \theta_\alpha, \tag{10–1}$$

where $\lambda_{K\alpha}^2/\lambda_{K\beta}^2$ has a value near 1.2 for most radiations. If it is suspected that a particular line is due to $K\beta$ radiation, multiplication of its $\sin^2 \theta$ value by $\lambda_{K\alpha}^2/\lambda_{K\beta}^2$ will give a value equal, or nearly equal, to the value of $\sin^2 \theta$ for some $K\alpha$ line on the pattern, unless the product exceeds unity. The $K\beta$ line corresponding to a given $K\alpha$ line is always located at a smaller angle 2θ and has lower intensity. However, since $K\alpha$ and $K\beta$ lines (from different planes) may overlap on the pattern, Eq. (10–1) alone can only establish the possibility that a given line is due to $K\beta$ radiation, but it can never prove that it is. Another possible source of extraneous lines is L characteristic radiation from tungsten contamination on the target of the x-ray tube, particularly if the tube is old. If such contamination is suspected, equations such as (10–1) can be set up to test the possibility that certain lines are due to tungsten radiation.

(2) *Diffraction by substances other than the unknown.* Such substances are usually impurities in the specimen but may also include the specimen mount or badly aligned slits. Careful specimen preparation and good experimental technique will eliminate extraneous lines due to these causes.

For reasons to be discussed in Chap. 11, the observed values of $\sin^2 \theta$ always contain small systematic errors. These errors are not large enough to cause any difficulty in indexing patterns of cubic crystals, but they can seriously interfere with the determination of some noncubic structures. The best method of removing such errors from the data is to calibrate the camera or diffractometer with a substance of known lattice parameter, mixed with the unknown. The difference between the observed and calcu-

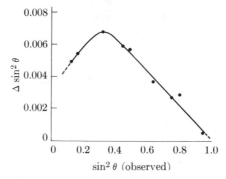

FIG. 10–1. An example of a correction curve for $\sin^2 \theta$ values.

lated values of $\sin^2 \theta$ for the standard substance gives the error in $\sin^2 \theta$, and this error can be plotted as a function of the observed values of $\sin^2 \theta$. Figure 10–1 shows a correction curve of this kind, obtained with a particular specimen and a particular Debye-Scherrer camera.* The errors represented by the ordinates of such a curve can then be applied to each of the observed values of $\sin^2 \theta$ for the diffraction lines of the unknown substance. For the particular determination represented by Fig. 10–1, the errors shown are to be subtracted from the observed values.

---

* For the shape of this curve, see Prob. 11–5.

10–3 Indexing patterns of cubic crystals. A cubic crystal gives diffraction lines whose $\sin^2 \theta$ values satisfy the following equation, obtained by combining the Bragg law with the plane-spacing equation for the cubic system:

$$\frac{\sin^2 \theta}{(h^2 + k^2 + l^2)} = \frac{\sin^2 \theta}{s} = \frac{\lambda^2}{4a^2}. \qquad (10\text{–}2)$$

Since the sum $s = (h^2 + k^2 + l^2)$ is always integral and $\lambda^2/4a^2$ is a constant for any one pattern, the problem of indexing the pattern of a cubic substance is one of finding a set of integers s which will yield a constant quotient when divided one by one into the observed $\sin^2 \theta$ values. (Certain integers, such as 7, 15, 23, 28, 31, etc., are impossible because they cannot be formed by the sum of three squared integers.) Once the proper integers s are found, the indices hkl of each line can be written down by inspection or from the tabulation in Appendix 6.

The proper integers s can be determined by means of the C and D scales of an ordinary slide rule, which permit simultaneous division of one set of numbers by another, if the quotient is constant. Pencil marks corresponding to the $\sin^2 \theta$ values of the first five or six lines on the pattern are placed on the D scale. A single setting of the C scale is then sought which will bring a set of integers on the C scale into coincidence with all the pencil marks on the D scale. Because of the systematic errors mentioned earlier, these coincidences are never exact, but they are usually close enough to permit selection of the proper integer, particularly if the C scale is shifted slightly from line to line to compensate for the systematic errors in $\sin^2 \theta$. If a set of integers satisfying Eq. (10–2) cannot be found, then the substance involved does not belong to the cubic system, and other possibilities (tetragonal, hexagonal, etc.) must be explored.

The following example will illustrate the steps involved in indexing the pattern of a cubic substance and finding its lattice parameter. In this particular example, Cu $K\alpha$ radiation was used and eight diffraction lines were observed. Their $\sin^2 \theta$ values are listed in the second column of Table 10–1. By means of a slide rule, the integers s listed in the third column were found to produce the reasonably constant quotients listed in the fourth column, when divided into the observed $\sin^2 \theta$ values. The fifth column lists the lattice parameter calculated from each line position, and the sixth column gives the Miller indices of each line. The systematic error in $\sin^2 \theta$ shows up as a gradual decrease in the value of $\lambda^2/4a^2$, and a gradual increase in the value of a, as θ increases. We shall find in Chap. 11 that the systematic error decreases as θ increases; therefore we can select the value of a for the highest-angle line, namely, 3.62A, as being the most accurate of those listed. Our analysis of line positions therefore leads to

TABLE 10–1

1	2	3	4	5	6
Line	$\sin^2\theta$	$s = (h^2 + k^2 + l^2)$	$\dfrac{\lambda^2}{4a^2}$	$a(\text{A})$	hkl
1	0.140	3	0.0466	3.57	111
2	0.185	4	0.0463	3.58	200
3	0.369	8	0.0462	3.59	220
4	0.503	11	0.0457	3.61	311
5	0.548	12	0.0456	3.61	222
6	0.726	16	0.0454	3.62	400
7	0.861	19	0.0453	3.62	331
8	0.905	20	0.0453	3.62	420

the conclusion that the substance involved, copper in this case, is cubic in structure with a lattice parameter of 3.62A.

We can also determine the Bravais lattice of the specimen by observing which lines are present and which absent. Examination of the sixth column of Table 10–1 shows that all lines which have mixed odd and even indices, such as 100, 110, etc., are absent from the pattern. Reference to the rules relating Bravais lattices to observed and absent reflections, given in Table 4–1, shows that the Bravais lattice of this specimen is face-centered. We now have certain information about the arrangement of atoms within the unit cell, and it should be noted that we have had to make use of observed line intensities in order to obtain this information. In this particular case, the observation consisted simply in noting which lines had zero intensity.

Each of the four common cubic lattice types is recognizable by a characteristic sequence of diffraction lines, and these in turn may be described by their sequential s values:

Simple cubic: 1, 2, 3, 4, 5, 6, 8, 9, 10, 11, 12, 13, 14, 16, ...
Body-centered cubic: 2, 4, 6, 8, 10, 12, 14, 16, ...
Face-centered cubic: 3, 4, 8, 11, 12, 16, ...
Diamond cubic: 3, 8, 11, 16, ...

The same information is tabulated in Appendix 6 and shown graphically in Fig. 10–2, in the form of calculated diffraction patterns. The calculations are made for Cu $K\alpha$ radiation and a lattice parameter a of 3.50A. The positions of all the diffraction lines which would be formed under these conditions are indicated as they would appear on a film or chart of the length shown. (For comparative purposes, the pattern of a hexagonal close-packed structure is also illustrated, since this structure is frequently

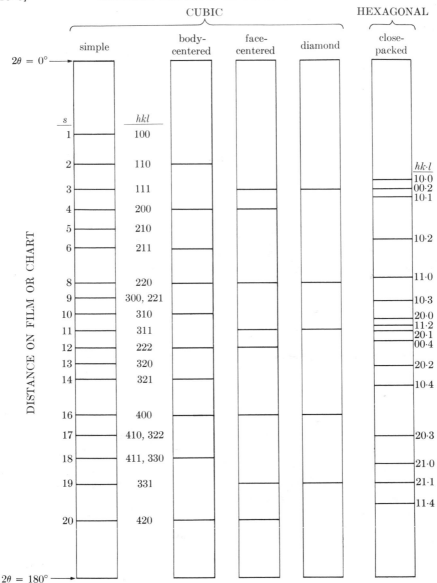

FIG. 10–2. Calculated diffraction patterns for various lattices. $s = h^2 + k^2 + l^2$.

encountered among metals and alloys. The line positions are calculated for Cu $K\alpha$ radiation, $a = 2.50$A, and $c/a = 1.633$, which corresponds to the close packing of spheres.)

Powder patterns of cubic substances can usually be distinguished at a glance from those of noncubic substances, since the latter patterns normally contain many more lines. In addition, the Bravais lattice can usually be identified by inspection: there is an almost regular sequence of lines in simple cubic and body-centered cubic patterns, but the former contains almost twice as many lines, while a face-centered cubic pattern is characterized by a pair of lines, followed by a single line, followed by a pair, another single line, etc.

The problem of indexing a cubic pattern is of course very much simplified if the substance involved is *known* to be cubic and if the lattice parameter is also known. The simplest procedure then is to calculate the value of $\lambda^2/4a^2$ and divide this value into the observed $\sin^2 \theta$ values to obtain the value of s for each line.

There is one difficulty that may arise in the interpretation of cubic powder patterns, and that is due to a possible ambiguity between simple cubic and body-centered cubic patterns. There is a regular sequence of lines in both patterns up to the sixth line; the sequence then continues regularly in body-centered cubic patterns, but is interrupted in simple cubic patterns since $s = 7$ is impossible. Therefore, if λ is so large, or a so small, that six lines or less appear on the pattern, the two Bravais lattices are indistinguishable. For example, suppose that the substance involved is actually body-centered cubic but the investigator mistakenly indexes it as simple cubic, assigning the value $s = 1$ to the first line, $s = 2$ to the second line, etc. He thus obtains a value of $\lambda^2/4a^2$ twice as large as the true one, and a value of a which is $1/\sqrt{2}$ times the true one. This sort of difficulty can be avoided simply by choosing a wavelength short enough to produce at least seven lines on the pattern.

10–4 Indexing patterns of noncubic crystals (graphical methods). The problem of indexing powder patterns becomes more difficult as the number of unknown parameters increases. There is only one unknown parameter for cubic crystals, the cell edge a, but noncubic crystals have two or more, and special graphical and analytical techniques have had to be devised in order to index the patterns of such crystals.

The **tetragonal** system will be considered first. The plane-spacing equation for this system involves two unknown parameters, a and c:

$$\frac{1}{d^2} = \frac{h^2 + k^2}{a^2} + \frac{l^2}{c^2}. \tag{10–3}$$

This may be rewritten in the form

$$\frac{1}{d^2} = \frac{1}{a^2}\left[(h^2 + k^2) + \frac{l^2}{(c/a)^2} \right],$$

or

$$2 \log d = 2 \log a - \log \left[(h^2 + k^2) + \frac{l^2}{(c/a)^2} \right]. \tag{10-4}$$

Suppose we now write Eq. (10–4) for any two planes of a tetragonal crystal, distinguishing the two planes by subscripts 1 and 2, and then subtract the two equations. We obtain

$$2 \log d_1 - 2 \log d_2 = - \log \left[(h_1^2 + k_1^2) + \frac{l_1^2}{(c/a)^2} \right]$$

$$+ \log \left[(h_2^2 + k_2^2) + \frac{l_2^2}{(c/a)^2} \right]. \tag{10-5}$$

This equation shows that the difference between the 2 log d values for any two planes is independent of a and depends only on the axial ratio c/a and the indices hkl of each plane. This fact was used by Hull and Davey as the basis for a graphical method of indexing the powder patterns of tetragonal crystals.

The construction of a Hull-Davey chart is illustrated in Fig. 10–3. First, the variation of the quantity $[(h^2 + k^2) + l^2/(c/a)^2]$ with c/a is plotted on two-range semilog paper for particular values of hkl. Each set of indices hkl, as long as they correspond to planes of different spacing, produces a different curve, and when l = 0 the curve is a straight line parallel to the c/a axis. Planes of different indices but the same spacing, such as (100) and (010), are represented by the same curve on the chart, which is then marked with the indices of either one of them, in this case (100). [The chart shown is for a simple tetragonal lattice; one for a body-centered tetragonal lattice is made simply by omitting all curves for which (h + k + l) is an odd number.] A single-range logarithmic d scale is then constructed; it extends over two ranges of the $[(h^2 + k^2) + l^2/(c/a)^2]$ scale and runs in the opposite direction, since the coefficient of log d in Eq. (10–4) is −2 times the coefficient of log $[(h^2 + k^2) + l^2/(c/a)^2]$. This means that the d values of two planes, for a given c/a ratio, are separated by the same distance on the scale as the horizontal separation, at the same c/a ratio, of the two corresponding curves on the chart.

The chart and scale are used for indexing in the following manner. The spacing d of the reflecting planes corresponding to each line on the diffraction pattern is calculated. Suppose that the first seven of these values for a particular pattern are 6.00, 4.00, 3.33, 3.00, 2.83, 2.55, and 2.40A. A strip of paper is then laid alongside the d scale in position I of Fig. 10–3, and the observed d values are marked off on its edge with a pencil. The

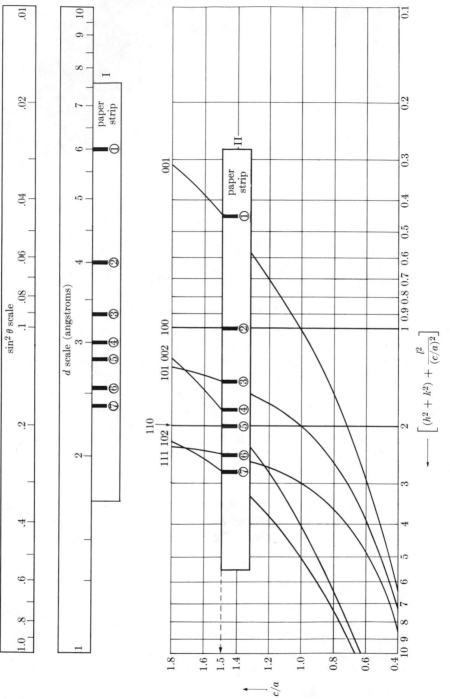

FIG. 10-3.   Partial Hull-Davey chart for simple tetragonal lattices.

paper strip is then placed on the chart and moved about, both vertically and horizontally, until a position is found where each mark on the strip coincides with a line on the chart. Vertical and horizontal movements correspond to trying various c/a and a values, respectively, and the only restriction on these movements is that the edge of the strip must always be horizontal. When a correct fit has been obtained, as shown by position II of Fig. 10–3, the indices of each line are simply read from the corresponding curves, and the approximate value of c/a from the vertical position of the paper strip. In the present example, the c/a ratio is 1.5 and the first line on the pattern (formed by planes of spacing 6.00A) is a 001 line, the second a 100 line, the third a 101 line, etc. After all the lines have been indexed in this way, the d values of the two highest-angle lines are used to set up two equations of the form of Eq. (10–3), and these are solved simultaneously to yield the values of a and c. From these values, the axial ratio c/a may then be calculated with more precision than it can be found graphically.

Figure 10–3 is only a partial Hull-Davey chart. A complete one, showing curves of higher indices, is reproduced on a small scale in Fig. 10–4, which applies to body-centered tetragonal lattices. Note that the curves of high indices are often so crowded that it is difficult to assign the proper indices to the observed lines. It then becomes necessary to calculate the indices of these high-angle lines on the basis of a and c values derived from the already indexed low-angle lines.

Some Hull-Davey charts, like the one shown in Fig. 10–4, are designed for use with $\sin^2 \theta$ values rather than d values. No change in the chart itself is involved, only a change in the accompanying scale. This is possible because an equation similar to Eq. (10–4) can be set up in terms of $\sin^2 \theta$ rather than d, by combining Eq. (10–3) with the Bragg law. This equation is

$$\log \sin^2 \theta = \log \frac{\lambda^2}{4a^2} + \log \left[(h^2 + k^2) + \frac{l^2}{(c/a)^2} \right]. \qquad (10\text{–}6)$$

The $\sin^2 \theta$ scale is therefore a two-range logarithmic one (from 0.01 to 1.0), equal in length to the two-range $[(h^2 + k^2) + l^2/(c/a)^2]$ scale on the chart and running in the same direction. A scale of this kind appears at the top of Fig. 10–3.

When the c/a ratio becomes equal to unity, a tetragonal cell becomes cubic. It follows that a cubic pattern can be indexed on a tetragonal Hull-Davey chart by keeping the paper strip always on the horizontal line corresponding to $c/a = 1$. This is seldom necessary because a slide rule will serve just as well. However, it is instructive to consider a tetragonal cell as a departure from a cubic one and to examine a Hull-Davey chart in

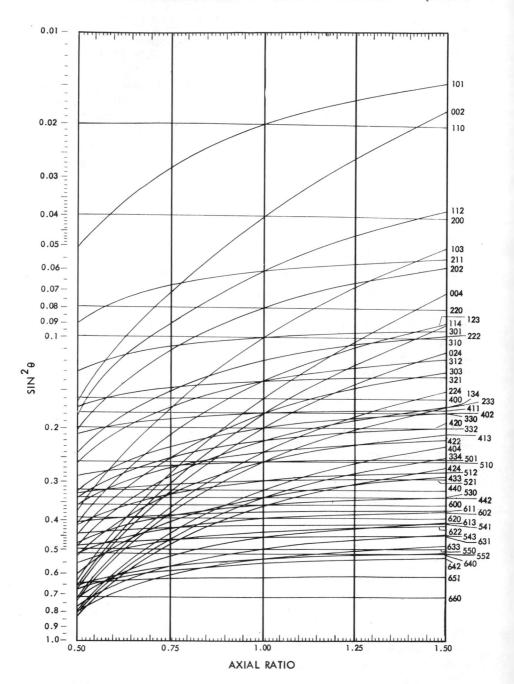

FIG. 10–4.   Complete Hull-Davey chart for body-centered tetragonal lattices.

that light, since the chart shows at a glance how the powder pattern changes for any given change in the c/a ratio. It shows, for example, how certain lines split into two as soon as the c/a ratio departs from unity, and how even the order of the lines on the pattern can change with changes in c/a.

Another graphical method of indexing tetragonal patterns has been devised by Bunn. Like the Hull-Davey chart, a Bunn chart consists of a network of curves, one for each value of hkl, but the curves are based on somewhat different functions of hkl and c/a than those used by Hull and Davey, with the result that the curves are less crowded in certain regions of the chart. The Bunn chart is accompanied by a logarithmic scale of d values, and the combination of chart and scale is used in exactly the same way as a Hull-Davey chart and scale.

Patterns of **hexagonal** crystals can also be indexed by graphical methods, since the hexagonal unit cell, like the tetragonal, is characterized by two variable parameters, a and c. The plane-spacing equation is

$$\frac{1}{d^2} = \frac{4}{3} \cdot \frac{h^2 + hk + k^2}{a^2} + \frac{l^2}{c^2}.$$

After some manipulation, this becomes

$$2 \log d = 2 \log a - \log \left[\frac{4}{3} (h^2 + hk + k^2) + \frac{l^2}{(c/a)^2} \right],$$

which is of exactly the same form as Eq. (10–4) for the tetragonal system. A Hull-Davey chart for the hexagonal system can therefore be constructed by plotting the variation of $\log \left[\frac{4}{3}(h^2 + hk + k^2) + l^2/(c/a)^2 \right]$ with c/a. A Bunn chart may also be constructed for this system. Special charts for hexagonal close-packed lattices may also be prepared by omitting all curves for which $(h + 2k)$ is an integral multiple of 3 and l is odd.

Figure 3–13(c), the powder pattern of zinc made with Cu $K\alpha$ radiation, will serve to illustrate how the pattern of a hexagonal substance is indexed. Thirteen lines were observed on this pattern; their $\sin^2 \theta$ values and relative intensities are listed in Table 10–2. A fit was obtained on a Hull-Davey chart for hexagonal close-packed lattices at an approximate c/a ratio of 1.87. The chart lines disclosed the indices listed in the fourth column of the table. In the case of line 5, two chart lines $(10 \cdot 3$ and $11 \cdot 0)$ almost intersect at $c/a = 1.87$, so the observed line is evidently the sum of two lines, almost overlapping, one from the $(10 \cdot 3)$ planes and the other from $(11 \cdot 0)$ planes. The same is true of line 11. Four lines on the chart, namely, $20 \cdot 0$, $10 \cdot 4$, $21 \cdot 0$, and $20 \cdot 4$, do not appear on the pattern, and it must be inferred that these are too weak to be observed. On the other hand, all the observed lines are accounted for, so we may conclude that

TABLE 10–2

Line	Intensity	$\sin^2 \theta$	$hk \cdot l$
1	s	0.097	00·2
2	s	0.112	10·0
3	vs	0.136	10·1
4	m	0.209	10·2
5	s	0.332	10·3, 11·0
6	vw	0.390	00·4
7	m	0.434	11·2
8	m	0.472	20·1
9	vw	0.547	20·2
10	w	0.668	20·3
11	m	0.722	11·4, 10·5
12	m	0.806	21·1
13	w	0.879	21·2

the lattice of zinc is actually hexagonal close-packed. The next step is to calculate the lattice parameters. Combination of the Bragg law and the plane-spacing equation gives

$$\sin^2 \theta = \frac{\lambda^2}{4} \left[\frac{4}{3} \cdot \frac{(h^2 + hk + k^2)}{a^2} + \frac{l^2}{c^2} \right],$$

where $\lambda^2/4$ has a value of $0.595A^2$ for Cu $K\alpha$ radiation. Writing this equation out for the two highest-angle lines, namely, 12 and 13, we obtain:

$$0.806 = 0.595 \left(\frac{4}{3} \cdot \frac{7}{a^2} + \frac{1}{c^2} \right),$$

$$0.879 = 0.595 \left(\frac{4}{3} \cdot \frac{7}{a^2} + \frac{4}{c^2} \right).$$

Simultaneous solution of these two equations gives $a = 2.66A$, $c = 4.95A$, and $c/a = 1.86$.

Rhombohedral crystals are also characterized by unit cells having two parameters, in this case a and α. No new chart is needed, however, to index the patterns of rhombohedral substances, since, as mentioned in Sec. 2–4, any rhombohedral crystal may be referred to hexagonal axes. A hexagonal Hull-Davey or Bunn chart may therefore be used to index the pattern of a rhombohedral crystal. The indices so found will, of course, refer to a hexagonal cell, and the method of converting them to rhombohedral indices is described in Appendix 2.

We can conclude that the pattern of any two-parameter crystal (tetragonal, hexagonal, or rhombohedral) can be indexed on the appropriate Hull-Davey or Bunn chart. If the structure is known, the procedure is quite straightforward. The best method is to calculate the c/a ratio from the known parameters, lay a straightedge on the chart to discover the proper line sequence for this value of c/a, calculate the value of $\sin^2 \theta$ for each line from the indices found on the chart, and then determine the indices of the observed lines by a comparison of calculated and observed $\sin^2 \theta$ values.

If the structure is unknown, the problem of indexing is not always so easy as it seems in theory. The most common source of trouble is the presence of extraneous lines, as defined in Sec. 10–2, in the observed pattern. Such lines can be very confusing and, if any difficulty in indexing is encountered, every effort should be made to eliminate them from the pattern, either experimentally or by calculation. In addition, the observed $\sin^2 \theta$ values usually contain systematic errors which make a simultaneous fit of all the pencil marks on the paper strip to curves on the chart impossible, even when the paper strip is at the correct c/a position. Because of these errors, the strip has to be shifted slightly from line to line in order to make successive pencil marks coincide with curves on the chart. Two important rules must always be kept in mind when using Hull-Davey or Bunn charts:

(1) Every mark on the paper strip must coincide with a curve on the chart, except for extraneous lines. A structure which accounts for only a portion of the observed lines is not correct: *all* the lines in the pattern must be accounted for, either as due to the structure of the substance involved or as extraneous lines.

(2) There need not be a mark on the paper strip for every curve on the chart, because some lines may have zero intensity or be too weak to be observed.

Orthorhombic, monoclinic, and **triclinic** substances yield powder patterns which are almost impossible to index by graphical methods, although the patterns of some orthorhombic crystals have been indexed by a combination of graphical and analytical methods. The essential difficulty is the large number of variable parameters involved. In the orthorhombic system there are three such parameters (a, b, c), in the monoclinic four (a, b, c, β), and in the triclinic six $(a, b, c, \alpha, \beta, \gamma)$. If the structure is known, patterns of substances in these crystal systems can be indexed by comparison of the observed $\sin^2 \theta$ values with those calculated for all possible values of hkl.

10–5 Indexing patterns of noncubic crystals (analytical methods). Analytical methods of indexing involve arithmetical manipulation of the observed $\sin^2 \theta$ values in an attempt to find certain relationships between them. Since each crystal system is characterized by particular relationships between $\sin^2 \theta$ values, recognition of these relationships identifies the crystal system and leads to a solution of the line indices.

For example, the $\sin^2 \theta$ values in the **tetragonal** system must obey the relation:

$$\sin^2 \theta = A(h^2 + k^2) + Cl^2, \qquad (10\text{-}7)$$

where A $(= \lambda^2/4a^2)$ and C $(= \lambda^2/4c^2)$ are constants for any one pattern. The problem is to find these constants, since, once found, they will disclose the cell parameters a and c and enable the line indices to be calculated. The value of A is obtained from the $hk0$ lines. When $l = 0$, Eq. (10-7) becomes

$$\sin^2 \theta = A(h^2 + k^2).$$

The permissible values of $(h^2 + k^2)$ are 1, 2, 4, 5, 8, etc. Therefore the $hk0$ lines must have $\sin^2 \theta$ values in the ratio of these integers, and A will be some number which is 1, $\frac{1}{2}$, $\frac{1}{4}$, $\frac{1}{5}$, $\frac{1}{8}$, etc., times the $\sin^2 \theta$ values of these lines. C is obtained from the other lines on the pattern and the use of Eq. (10-7) in the form

$$\sin^2 \theta - A(h^2 + k^2) = Cl^2.$$

Differences represented by the left-hand side of the equation are set up, for various assumed values of h and k, in an attempt to find a consistent set of Cl^2 values, which must be in the ratio 1, 4, 9, 16, etc. Once these values are found, C can be calculated.

For **hexagonal** crystals, an exactly similar procedure is used. In this case, $\sin^2 \theta$ values are given by

$$\sin^2 \theta = A(h^2 + hk + k^2) + Cl^2,$$

where $A = \lambda^2/3a^2$ and $C = \lambda^2/4c^2$. Permissible values of $(h^2 + hk + k^2)$ are tabulated in Appendix 6; they are 1, 3, 4, 7, 9, etc. The indexing procedure is best illustrated by means of a specific example, namely, the powder pattern of zinc, whose observed $\sin^2 \theta$ values are listed in Table 10-2. We first divide the $\sin^2 \theta$ values by the integers 1, 3, 4, etc., and tabulate the results, as shown by Table 10-3, which applies to the first six lines of the pattern. We then examine these numbers, looking for quotients which are equal to one another or equal to one of the observed $\sin^2 \theta$ values. In

TABLE 10-3

Line	$\sin^2 \theta$	$\dfrac{\sin^2 \theta}{3}$	$\dfrac{\sin^2 \theta}{4}$	$\dfrac{\sin^2 \theta}{7}$	hkl
1	0.097	0.032	0.024	0.014	
2	0.112*	0.037	0.028	0.016	100
3	0.136	0.045	0.034	0.019	
4	0.209	0.070	0.052	0.030	
5	0.332	0.111*	0.083	0.047	110
6	0.390	0.130	0.098	0.056	

TABLE 10–4

Line	$\sin^2 \theta$	$\sin^2 \theta - A$	$\sin^2 \theta - 3A$	hkl
1	0.097*			002
2	0.112	0.000*		100
3	0.136	0.024*		101
4	0.209	0.097*		102
5	0.332	0.221*		110, 103
6	0.390*	0.278	0.054	004

this case, the two starred entries, 0.112 and 0.111, are the most nearly equal, so we assume that lines 2 and 5 are $hk0$ lines. We then tentatively put $A = 0.112$ which is equivalent to saying that line 2 is 100. Since the $\sin^2 \theta$ value of line 5 is very nearly 3 times that of line 2, line 5 should be 110. To find the value of C, we must use the equation

$$\sin^2 \theta - A(h^2 + hk + k^2) = Cl^2.$$

We now subtract from each $\sin^2 \theta$ value the values of A $(= 0.112)$, $3A$ $(= 0.336)$, $4A$ $(= 0.448)$, etc., and look for remainders (Cl^2) which are in the ratio of 1, 4, 9, 16, etc. These figures are given in Table 10–4. Here the five starred entries are of interest, because these numbers (0.024, 0.097, 0.221, and 0.390) are very nearly in the ratio 1, 4, 9, and 16. We therefore put $0.024 = C(1)^2$, $0.097 = C(2)^2$, $0.221 = C(3)^2$, and $0.390 = C(4)^2$. This gives $C = 0.024$ and immediately identifies line 1 as 002 and line 6 as 004. Since line 3 has a $\sin^2 \theta$ value equal to the sum of A and C, its indices must be 101. Similarly, the indices of lines 4 and 5 are found to be 102 and 103, respectively. In this way, indices are assigned to all the lines on the pattern, and a final check on their correctness is made in the usual manner, by a comparison of observed and calculated $\sin^2 \theta$ values.

In the **orthorhombic** system, the basic equation governing the $\sin^2 \theta$ values is

$$\sin^2 \theta = Ah^2 + Bk^2 + Cl^2.$$

The indexing problem is considerably more difficult here, in that three unknown constants, A, B, and C, have to be determined. The general procedure, which is too lengthy to illustrate here, is to search for significant differences between various pairs of $\sin^2 \theta$ values. For example, consider any two lines having indices $hk0$ and $hk1$, with hk the same for each, such as 120 and 121; the difference between their $\sin^2 \theta$ values is C. Similarly, the difference between the $\sin^2 \theta$ values of two lines such as 310 and 312 is $4C$, and so on. If the structure is such that there are many lines missing from the pattern, because of a zero structure factor for the corresponding planes, then the difficulties of indexing are considerably increased, inasmuch as the missing lines may be the very ones which would supply the most easily recognized clues if they were present. Despite such difficulties, this analytical method has been applied successfully to a number of orthorhombic patterns. One requisite for its success is fairly high accuracy in the $\sin^2 \theta$ values (at least ± 0.0005), and the investigator should therefore correct his observations for systematic errors before attempting to index the pattern.

Monoclinic and **triclinic** substances yield powder patterns of great complexity because the number of independent constants involved is now four and six, respectively. No generally successful method, either analytical or graphical, of indexing such patterns has yet been devised.

We can therefore conclude that the powder pattern of a substance having more than two independently variable cell parameters is extremely difficult, if not impossible, to solve. The structures of such materials are almost always determined by the examination of a single crystal, by either the rotating-crystal method or one of its variations. With these methods it is a relatively easy matter to determine the shape and size of an unknown unit cell, no matter how low its symmetry. Many substances, of course, are very difficult to prepare in single-crystal form, but, on the other hand, if the substance involved is one of low symmetry, the time spent in trying to obtain a single crystal is usually more fruitful than the time spent in trying to solve the powder pattern. The single-crystal specimen need not be large: a crystal as small as 0.1 mm in any dimension can be successfully handled and will give a satisfactory diffraction pattern. Readers interested in these single-crystal methods will find them described in some of the books listed in Chap. 18.

10–6 The effect of cell distortion on the powder pattern. At this point we might digress slightly from the main subject of this chapter, and examine some of the changes produced in a powder pattern when the unit cell of the substance involved is distorted in various ways. As we have already seen, there are many more lines on the pattern of a substance of low symmetry, such as triclinic, than on the pattern of a substance of high symmetry, such as cubic, and we may take it as a general rule that any distortion of the unit cell which decreases its symmetry, in the sense of introducing additional variable parameters, will increase the number of lines on the powder pattern.

Figure 10–5 graphically illustrates this point. On the left is the calculated diffraction pattern of the body-centered cubic substance whose unit cell is shown at the top. The line positions are computed for $a = 4.00\text{A}$ and Cr $K\alpha$ radiation. If this cell is expanded or contracted uniformly but still remains cubic, the diffraction lines merely shift their positions but do not increase in number, since no change in cell symmetry is involved. However, if the cubic cell is distorted along only one axis, then it becomes

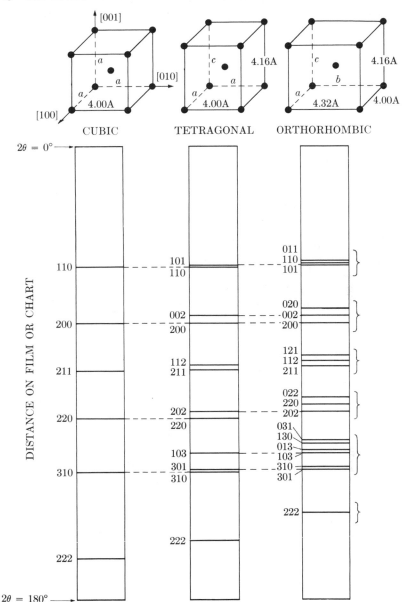

Fig. 10–5.   Effects of cell distortion on powder patterns.   Lines unchanged in position are connected by dashed lines.

tetragonal, its symmetry decreases, and more diffraction lines are formed. The center pattern shows the effect of stretching the cubic cell by 4 percent along its [001] axis, so that c is now 4.16A.   Some lines are unchanged in position, some are shifted, and new lines have appeared.   If the tetragonal cell is now stretched by 8 percent along its [010] axis, it becomes ortho-rhombic, with $a = 4.00A$, $b = 4.32A$, and $c = 4.16A$, as shown on the right. The result of this last distortion is to add still more lines to the pattern. The increase in the number of lines is due essentially to the introduction of new plane spacings, caused by nonuniform distortion. Thus, in the cubic cell, the (200), (020), and (002) planes all have the same spacing and only one line is formed, called the 200 line, but this line splits into two when the cell becomes tetragonal, since now the (002) plane spacing differs from the other two. When the cell becomes orthorhombic, all three spacings are different and three lines are formed.

Changes of this nature are not uncommon among phase transformations and ordering reactions. For example, the powder pattern of slowly cooled plain carbon steel shows lines due to ferrite (body-centered cubic) and cementite (Fe_3C, orthorhombic). When the same steel is quenched from the austenite region, the phases present are martensite (body-centered tetragonal) and, possibly, some untransformed austenite (face-centered cubic). The a and c parameters of the martensite cell do not differ greatly from the a parameter of the ferrite cell (see Fig. 12–5). The result is that the diffraction pattern of a quenched steel shows pairs of martensite lines occurring at about the same 2θ positions as the individual lines of ferrite in the previous pattern. If the quenched steel is now tempered, the martensite will ultimately decompose into ferrite and cementite, and each pair of martensite lines will coalesce into a single ferrite line. Somewhat similar effects can be produced in a copper-gold alloy having the composition represented by the formula AuCu. This alloy is cubic in the disordered state but becomes either tetragonal or orthorhombic when ordered, depending on the ordering temperature (see Sec. 13–3).

The changes produced in a powder pattern by cell distortion depend, in degree, on the amount of distortion. If the latter is small, the pattern retains the main features of the pattern of the original undistorted cell. Thus, in Fig. 10–5, the nineteen lines of the orthorhombic pattern fall into the six bracketed groups shown, each group corresponding to one of the single lines on the cubic pattern. In fact, an experienced crystallographer, if confronted with this orthorhombic pattern, might recognize this grouping and guess that the unit cell of the substance involved was not far from cubic in shape, and that the Bravais lattice was either simple or body-centered, since the groups of lines are spaced in a fairly regular manner. But if the distortion of the cubic cell had been much larger, each line of the original pattern would split into such widely separated lines that no features of the original pattern would remain.

10–7 Determination of the number of atoms in a unit cell. To return to the subject of structure determination, the next step after establishing the shape and size of the unit cell is to find the number of atoms in that cell, because the number of atoms must be known before their positions can be determined. To find this number we use the fact that the volume of the unit cell, calculated from the lattice parameters by means of the equations given in Appendix 1, multiplied by the measured density of the substance equals the weight of all the atoms in the cell. From Eq. (3–9), we have

$$\Sigma A = \frac{\rho V}{1.66020},$$

where ΣA is the sum of the atomic weights of the atoms in the unit cell, ρ is the density (gm/cm^3), and V is the volume of the unit cell (A^3). If the substance is an element of atomic weight A, then

$$\Sigma A = n_1 A,$$

where n_1 is the number of atoms per unit cell. If the substance is a chemical compound, or an intermediate phase whose composition can be represented by a simple chemical formula, then

$$\Sigma A = n_2 M,$$

where n_2 is the number of "molecules" per unit cell and M the molecular weight. The number of atoms per cell can then be calculated from n_2 and the composition of the phase.

When determined in this way, the number of atoms per cell is always an integer, within experimental error, except for a very few substances which have "defect structures." In these substances, atoms are simply missing from a certain fraction of those lattice sites which they would be expected to occupy, and the result is a nonintegral number of atoms per cell. FeO and the β phase in the Ni-Al system are well-known examples.

10–8 Determination of atom positions. We now have to find the positions of a known number of atoms in a unit cell of known shape and size. To solve this problem, we must make use of the observed relative *intensities* of the diffracted beams, since these intensities are determined by atom positions. In finding the atom positions, however, we must again proceed by trial and error, because there is no known method of directly calculating atom positions from observed intensities.

To see why this is so, we must consider the two basic equations involved, namely,

$$I = |F|^2 p \left(\frac{1 + \cos^2 2\theta}{\sin^2 \theta \cos \theta} \right), \tag{4–12}$$

which gives the relative intensities of the reflected beams, and

$$F = \sum_{1}^{N} f_n e^{2\pi i(hu_n + kv_n + lw_n)}, \tag{4-11}$$

which gives the value of the structure factor F for the hkl reflection in terms of the atom positions uvw. Since the relative intensity I, the multiplicity factor p, and the Bragg angle θ are known for each line on the pattern, we can find the value of $|F|$ for each reflection from Eq. (4–12). But $|F|$ measures only the relative amplitude of each reflection, whereas in order to use Eq. (4–11) for calculating atom positions, we must know the value of F, which measures both the amplitude *and* phase of one reflection relative to another. This is the crux of the problem. The intensities of two reflected beams are proportional to the squares of their amplitudes but independent of their relative phase. Since all we can measure is intensity, we can determine amplitude but not phase, which means that we cannot compute the structure factor but only its absolute value. Any method of avoiding this basic difficulty would constitute the much-sought-after *direct method* of structure determination. This difficulty appears to be insurmountable, however, since no direct method, generally applicable to all structures, has yet been devised, despite the large amount of effort devoted to the problem.

Atom positions, therefore, can be determined only by trial and error. A set of atom positions is assumed, the intensities corresponding to these positions are calculated, and the calculated intensities are compared with the observed ones, the process being repeated until satisfactory agreement is reached. The problem of selecting a structure for trial is not as hopelessly broad as it sounds, since the investigator has many aids to guide him. Foremost among these is the accumulated knowledge of previously solved structures. From these known structures he may be able to select a few likely candidates, and then proceed on the assumption that his unknown structure is the same as, or very similar to, one of these known ones. A great many known structures may be classified into groups according to the kind of bonding (ionic, covalent, metallic, or mixtures of these) which holds the atoms together, and a selection among these groups is aided by a knowledge of the probable kind of atomic bonding in the unknown phase, as judged from the positions of its constituent elements in the periodic table. For example, suppose the phase of unknown structure has the chemical formula AB, where A is strongly electropositive and B strongly electronegative, and that its powder pattern is characteristic of a simple cubic lattice. Then the bonding is likely to be ionic, and the CsCl structure is strongly suggested. But the FeSi structure shown in Fig. 2–19 is also a possibility. In this particular case, one or other can be excluded by a density measurement, since the CsCl cell contains one "molecule" and the FeSi cell four. If this were not possible, diffracted intensities would have to be calculated on the basis of each cell and compared with the observed ones. It is this simple kind of structure determination, illustrated by an example in the next section, which the metallurgist should be able to carry out unaided.

Needless to say, many structures are too complex to be solved by this simple approach and the crystallographer must turn to more powerful methods. Chief among these are space-group theory and Fourier series. Although any complete description of these subjects is beyond the scope of this book, a few general remarks may serve to show their utility in structure determination. The *theory of space groups*, one of the triumphs of mathematical crystallography, relates crystal symmetry, on the atomic scale, to the possible atomic arrangements which possess that symmetry. For example, if a given substance is known to be hexagonal and to have n atoms in its unit cell, then space-group theory lists all possible arrangements of n atoms which will have hexagonal symmetry. This listing of possible arrangements aids tremendously in the selection of trial structures. A further reduction in the number of possibilities can then be made by noting the indices of the reflections absent from the diffraction pattern. By such means alone, i.e., before any detailed consideration is given to relative diffracted intensities, space-group theory can often exclude all but two or three possible atomic arrangements.

A *Fourier series* is a type of infinite trigonometric series by which any kind of periodic function may be expressed. Now the one essential property of a crystal is that its atoms are arranged in space in a periodic fashion. But this means that the density of electrons is also a periodic function of position in the crystal, rising to a maximum at the point where an atom is located and dropping to a low value in the region between atoms. To regard a crystal in this manner, as a positional variation of electron density rather than as an arrangement of atoms, is particularly appropriate where diffraction is involved, in that x-rays are scattered by electrons and not by atoms as such. Since the electron density is a periodic function of position, a crystal may be described analytically by means of Fourier series. This method of description is very useful in structure determination because it can be shown that the coefficients of the various terms in the series are related to the F values of the various x-ray reflections. But such a series is not of immediate use, since the structure factors are not usually known both in magnitude and phase. However, another kind of series has been devised whose coefficients are related to the experimentally observable $|F|$ values and which gives, not electron density, but information regarding the various interatomic vectors in the unit cell. This information is frequently enough to determine the phase of the various structure factors; then the first kind of series can be used to map out the actual electron density throughout the cell and thus disclose the atom positions.

10–9 Example of structure determination. As a simple example, we will consider an intermediate phase which occurs in the cadmium-tellurium system. Chemical analysis of the specimen, which appeared essentially one phase under the microscope, showed it to contain 46.6 weight percent Cd and 53.4 weight percent Te. This is equivalent to 49.8 atomic percent Cd and can be represented by the formula CdTe. The specimen was reduced to powder and a diffraction pattern obtained with a Debye-Scherrer camera and Cu $K\alpha$ radiation.

The observed values of $\sin^2 \theta$ for the first 16 lines are listed in Table 10–5, together with the visually estimated relative line intensities. This pattern can be indexed on the basis of a cubic unit cell, and the indices of the observed lines are given in the table. The lattice parameter, calculated from the $\sin^2 \theta$ value for the highest-angle line, is 6.46A.

The density of the specimen, as determined by weighing a quantity of the powder in a pyknometer bottle, was 5.82 gm/cm^3. We then find, from Eq. (3–9), that

$$\Sigma A = \frac{(5.82)(6.46)^3}{1.66020} = 948.$$

Since the molecular weight of CdTe is 240.02, the number of "molecules" per unit cell is 948/240.02 = 3.94, or 4, within experimental error.

At this point, we know that the unit cell of CdTe is cubic and that it contains 4 "molecules" of CdTe, i.e., 4 atoms of cadmium and 4 atoms of tellurium. We must now consider possible arrangements of these atoms in the unit cell. First we examine the indices listed in Table 10–5 for evidence of the Bravais lattice. Since the indices of the observed lines are all

TABLE 10–5

Line	Intensity	$\sin^2 \theta$	hkl
1	s	0.0462	111
2	vs	0.1198	220
3	vs	0.1615	311
4	vw	0.1790	222
5	m	0.234	400
6	m	0.275	331
7	s	0.346	422
8	m	0.391	511, 333
9	w	0.461	440
10	m	0.504	531
11	m	0.575	620
12	w	0.616	533
13	w	0.688	444
14	m	0.729	711, 551
15	vs	0.799	642
16	s	0.840	731, 553

unmixed, the Bravais lattice must be face-centered. (Not all possible sets of unmixed indices are present, however: 200, 420, 600, 442, 622, and 640 are missing from the pattern. But these reflections may be too weak to be observed, and the fact that they are missing does not invalidate our conclusion that the lattice is face-centered.) Now there are two common face-centered cubic structures of the AB type, i.e., containing two different atoms in equal proportions, and both contain four "molecules" per unit cell: these are the NaCl structure [Fig. 2–18(b)] and the zinc-blende form of ZnS [Fig. 2–19(b)]. Both of these are logical possibilities even though the bonding in NaCl is ionic and in ZnS covalent, since both kinds of bonding have been observed in telluride structures.

The next step is to calculate relative diffracted intensities for each structure and compare them with experiment, in order to determine whether or not one of these structures is the correct one. If CdTe has the NaCl structure, then its structure factor for unmixed indices [see Example (e) of Sec. 4–6] is given by

$$F^2 = 16(f_{Cd} + f_{Te})^2, \text{ if } (h + k + l) \text{ is even,}$$
$$F^2 = 16(f_{Cd} - f_{Te})^2, \text{ if } (h + k + l) \text{ is odd.}$$

$$(10\text{–}8)$$

On the other hand, if the ZnS structure is correct, then the structure factor for unmixed indices (see Sec. 4–13) is given by

$$|F|^2 = 16(f_{Cd}{}^2 + f_{Te}{}^2), \text{ if } (h + k + l) \text{ is odd,}$$
$$|F|^2 = 16(f_{Cd} - f_{Te})^2, \text{ if } (h + k + l) \text{ is an odd multiple of 2,} \quad (10\text{–}9)$$
$$|F|^2 = 16(f_{Cd} + f_{Te})^2, \text{ if } (h + k + l) \text{ is an even multiple of 2.}$$

Even before making a detailed calculation of relative diffracted intensities by means of Eq. (4–12), we can almost rule out the NaCl structure as a possibility simply by inspection of Eqs. (10–8). The atomic numbers of cadmium and tellurium are 48 and 52, respectively, so the value of $(f_{Cd} + f_{Te})^2$ is several hundred times greater than the value of $(f_{Cd} - f_{Te})^2$, for all values of $\sin \theta / \lambda$. Then, if CdTe has the NaCl structure, the 111 reflection should be very weak and the 200 reflection very strong. Actually, 111 is strong and 200 is not observed. Further evidence that the NaCl structure is incorrect is given in the fourth column of Table 10–6, where the calculated intensities of the first eight possible lines are listed: there is no agreement whatever between these values and the observed intensities.

On the other hand, if the ZnS structure is assumed, intensity calculations lead to the values listed in the fifth column. The agreement between these values and the observed intensities is excellent, except for a few minor inconsistencies among the low-angle reflections, and these are due to neglect of the absorption factor. In particular, we note that the ZnS

TABLE 10-6

1	2	3	4	5
Line	hkl	Observed intensity	Calculated intensity	
			NaCl structure	ZnS structure
1	111	s	0.05	12.4
	200	nil	13.2	0.03
2	220	vs	10.0 ◄————►	10.0
3	311	vs	0.02	6.2
4	222	vw	3.5	0.007
5	400	m	1.7	1.7
6	331	m	0.01	2.5
	420	nil	4.6	0.01
7	422	s	. . . . . .	3.4
8	511, 333	m	. . . . . .	1.8
9	440	w	. . . . . .	1.1
10	531	m	. . . . . .	2.0
	600, 442	nil	. . . . . .	0.005
11	620	m	. . . . . .	1.8
12	533	w	. . . . . .	0.9
	622	nil	. . . . . .	0.004
13	444	w	. . . . . .	0.6
14	711, 551	m	. . . . . .	1.8
	640	nil	. . . . . .	0.005
15	642	vs	. . . . . .	4.0
16	731, 553	s	. . . . . .	3.3

(N.B. Calculated intensities have been adjusted so that the 220 line has an intensity of 10.0 for both structures.)

structure satisfactorily accounts for all the missing reflections (200, 420, etc.), since the calculated intensities of these reflections are all extremely low. We can therefore conclude that CdTe has the structure of the zinc-blende form of ZnS.

After a given structure has been shown to be in accord with the diffraction data, it is advisable to calculate the interatomic distances involved in that structure. This calculation not only is of interest in itself, but serves to disclose any gross errors that may have been made, since there is obviously something wrong with a proposed structure if it brings certain atoms impossibly close together. In the present structure, the nearest neighbor to the Cd atom at $0\ 0\ 0$ is the Te atom at $\frac{1}{4}\ \frac{1}{4}\ \frac{1}{4}$. The Cd-Te interatomic distance is therefore $\sqrt{3}\ a/4 = 2.80$A. For comparison, we can calculate a "theoretical" Cd-Te interatomic distance simply by averaging the distances of closest approach in the pure elements. In doing this, we regard the atoms as rigid spheres in contact, and ignore the effects of coordination number and type of bonding on atom size. These distances of closest approach are 2.98A in pure cadmium and 2.87A in pure tellurium, the average being 2.93A. The observed Cd-Te interatomic distance is 2.80A, or some 4.5 percent smaller than the calculated value; this difference is not unreasonable and can be largely ascribed to the covalent bonding which characterizes this structure. In fact, it is a general rule that the A-B interatomic distance in an intermediate phase A_xB_y is always somewhat smaller than the average distance of closest approach in pure A and pure B, because the mere existence of the phase shows that the attractive forces between unlike atoms is greater than that between like atoms. If this were not true, the phase would not form.

PROBLEMS

10–1. The powder pattern of aluminum, made with Cu $K\alpha$ radiation, contains ten lines, whose $\sin^2 \theta$ values are 0.1118, 0.1487, 0.294, 0.403, 0.439, 0.583, 0.691, 0.727, 0.872, and 0.981. Index these lines and calculate the lattice parameter.

10–2. A pattern is made of a cubic substance with unfiltered chromium radiation. The observed $\sin^2 \theta$ values and intensities are 0.265(m), 0.321(vs), 0.528(w), 0.638(s), 0.793(s), and 0.958(vs). Index these lines and state which are due to $K\alpha$ and which to $K\beta$ radiation. Determine the Bravais lattice and lattice parameter. Identify the substance by reference to Appendix 13.

10–3. Construct a Hull-Davey chart, and accompanying $\sin^2 \theta$ scale, for hexagonal close-packed lattices. Use two-range semilog graph paper, $8\frac{1}{2} \times 11$ in. Cover a c/a range of 0.5 to 2.0, and plot only the curves $00\cdot2$, $10\cdot0$, $10\cdot1$, $10\cdot2$, and $11\cdot0$.

10–4. Use the chart constructed in Prob. 10–3 to index the first five lines on the powder pattern of α-titanium. With Cu $K\alpha$ radiation, these lines have the following $\sin^2 \theta$ values: 0.091, 0.106, 0.117, 0.200, and 0.268.

In each of the following problems the powder pattern of an element is represented by the observed $\sin^2 \theta$ values of the first seven or eight lines on the pattern, made with Cu $K\alpha$ radiation. In each case, index the lines, find the crystal system, Bravais lattice, and approximate lattice parameter (or parameters), and identify the element from the tabulation given in Appendix 13.

10–5	10–6	10–7	10–8
0.0806	0.0603	0.1202	0.0768
0.0975	0.1610	0.238	0.0876
0.1122	0.221	0.357	0.0913
0.210	0.322	0.475	0.1645
0.226	0.383	0.593	0.231
0.274	0.484	0.711	0.274
0.305	0.545	0.830	0.308
0.321	0.645		0.319

CHAPTER 11

PRECISE PARAMETER MEASUREMENTS

11–1 Introduction. Many applications of x-ray diffraction require precise knowledge of the lattice parameter (or parameters) of the material under study. In the main, these applications involve solid solutions; since the lattice parameter of a solid solution varies with the concentration of the solute, the composition of a given solution can be determined from a measurement of its lattice parameter. Thermal expansion coefficients can also be determined, without a dilatometer, by measurements of lattice parameter as a function of temperature in a high-temperature camera. Or the stress in a material may be determined by measuring the expansion or contraction of its lattice as a result of that stress. Since, in general, a change in solute concentration (or temperature, or stress) produces only a small change in lattice parameter, rather precise parameter measurements must be made in order to measure these quantities with any accuracy. In this chapter we shall consider the methods that are used to obtain high precision, leaving the various applications to be discussed at a later time. Cubic substances will be dealt with first, because they are the simplest, but our general conclusions will also be valid for noncubic materials, which will be discussed in detail later.

The process of measuring a lattice parameter is a very indirect one, and is fortunately of such a nature that high precision is fairly easily obtainable. The parameter a of a cubic substance is directly proportional to the spacing d of any particular set of lattice planes. If we measure the Bragg angle θ for this set of planes, we can use the Bragg law to determine d and, knowing d, we can calculate a. But it is $\sin \theta$, not θ, which appears in the Bragg law. Precision in d, or a, therefore depends on precision in $\sin \theta$, a derived quantity, and not on precision in θ, the measured quantity. This is fortunate because the value of $\sin \theta$ changes very slowly with θ in the neighborhood of 90°, as inspection of Fig. 11–1 or a table of sines will show. For this reason, a very accurate value

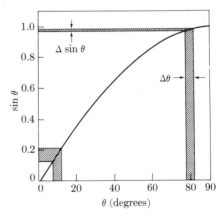

FIG. 11–1. The variation of $\sin \theta$ with θ. The error in $\sin \theta$ caused by a given error in θ decreases as θ increases ($\Delta\theta$ exaggerated).

324

of $\sin \theta$ can be obtained from a measurement of θ which is itself not particularly precise, *provided that θ is near 90°*. At $\theta = 85°$, for example, a 1 percent error in θ leads to an error in $\sin \theta$ of only 0.1 percent. Stated in another way, the angular position of a diffracted beam is much more sensitive to a given change in plane spacing when θ is large than when it is small.

We can obtain the same result directly by differentiating the Bragg law with respect to θ. We obtain

$$\frac{\Delta d}{d} = - \cot \theta \Delta \theta. \tag{11–1}$$

In the cubic system,

$$a = d\sqrt{h^2 + k^2 + l^2}.$$

Therefore

$$\frac{\Delta a}{a} = \frac{\Delta d}{d} = - \cot \theta \Delta \theta. \tag{11–2}$$

Since $\cot \theta$ approaches zero as θ approaches 90°, $\Delta a/a$, the fractional error in a caused by a given error in θ, also approaches zero as θ approaches 90°, or as 2θ approaches 180°. The key to precision in parameter measurements therefore lies in the use of backward-reflected beams having 2θ values as near to 180° as possible.

Although the parameter error disappears as 2θ approaches 180°, we cannot observe a reflected beam at this angle. But since the values of a calculated for the various lines on the pattern approach the true value more closely as 2θ increases, we should be able to find the true value of a simply by plotting the measured values against 2θ and extrapolating to $2\theta = 180°$. Unfortunately, this curve is not linear and the extrapolation of a nonlinear curve is not accurate. However, it may be shown that if the measured values of a are plotted against certain functions of θ, rather than against θ or 2θ directly, the resulting curve is a straight line which may be extrapolated with confidence. The bulk of this chapter is devoted to showing how these functions can be derived and used. Because the exact form of the function depends on the kind of camera employed, we shall have to consider successively the various cameras that are normally used for parameter measurements.

But first we might ask: what sort of precision is possible with such methods? Without any extrapolation or any particular attention to good experimental technique, simply by selection of the parameter calculated for the highest-angle line on the pattern, we can usually obtain an accuracy of 0.01A. Since the lattice parameters of most substances of metallurgical interest are in the neighborhood of 3 to 4A, this represents an accuracy of about 0.3 percent. With good experimental technique and the use of the proper extrapolation function, this accuracy can be increased to 0.001A, or 0.03 percent, without much difficulty. Finally, about the best accuracy that can be expected is 0.0001A, or 0.003 percent, but this can be obtained only by the expenditure of considerable effort, both experimental and computational.

In work of high precision it is imperative that the units in which the measured parameter is expressed, kX or A, be correctly stated. In order to avoid confusion on this point, the reader is advised to review the discussion of these units given in Sec. 3–4.

11–2 Debye-Scherrer cameras. The general approach in finding an extrapolation function is to consider the various effects which can lead to errors in the measured values of θ, and to find out how these errors in θ vary with the angle θ itself. For a Debye-Scherrer camera, the chief sources of error in θ are the following:

(1) Film shrinkage.
(2) Incorrect camera radius.
(3) Off-centering of specimen.
(4) Absorption in specimen.

Since only the back-reflection region is suitable for precise measurements, we shall consider these various errors in terms of the quantities S' and ϕ, defined in Fig. 11–2. S' is the distance on the film between two corresponding back-reflection lines; 2ϕ is the supplement of 2θ, i.e., $\phi = 90° - \theta$. These quantities are related to the camera radius R by the equation

$$\phi = \frac{S'}{4R}. \tag{11–3}$$

Shrinkage of the film, caused by processing and drying, causes an error $\Delta S'$ in the quantity S'. The camera *radius* may also be in error by an amount ΔR. The effects of these two errors on the value of ϕ may be found by writing Eq. (11–3) in logarithmic form:

$$\ln \phi = \ln S' - \ln 4 - \ln R.$$

Differentiation then gives

$$\frac{\Delta\phi}{\phi} = \frac{\Delta S'}{S'} - \frac{\Delta R}{R}. \tag{11–4}$$

The error in ϕ due to shrinkage and the radius error is therefore given by

$$\Delta\phi_{S',R} = \left(\frac{\Delta S'}{S'} - \frac{\Delta R}{R}\right)\phi. \tag{11–5}$$

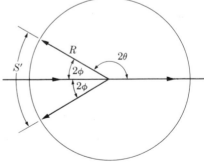

FIGURE 11–2

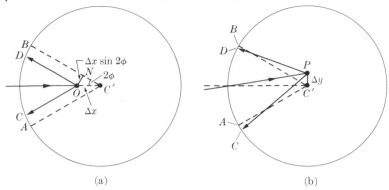

(a)   (b)

FIG. 11–3.   Effect of specimen displacement on line positions.

The shrinkage error can be minimized by loading the film so that the incident beam enters through a hole in the film, since corresponding back-reflection lines are then only a short distance apart on the film, and their separation S' is little affected by film shrinkage. The method of film loading shown in Fig. 6–5(a) is not at all suitable for precise measurements. Instead, methods (b) or (c) of Fig. 6–5 should be used. Method (c), the unsymmetrical or Straumanis method of film loading, is particularly recommended since no knowledge of the camera radius is required.

An *off-center specimen* also leads to an error in ϕ. Whatever the displacement of the specimen from the camera center, this displacement can always be broken up into two components, one (Δx) parallel to the incident beam and the other (Δy) at right angles to the incident beam. The effect of the parallel displacement is illustrated in Fig. 11–3(a). Instead of being at the camera center C', the specimen is displaced a distance Δx to the point O. The diffraction lines are registered at D and C instead of at A and B, the line positions for a properly centered specimen. The error in S' is then $(AC + DB) = 2DB$, which is approximately equal to $2ON$, or

$$\Delta S' = 2ON = 2\Delta x \sin 2\phi. \tag{11–6}$$

The effect of a specimen displacement at right angles to the incident beam [Fig. 11–3(b)] is to shift the lines from A to C and from B to D. When Δy is small, AC is very nearly equal to BD and so, to a good approximation, no error in S' is introduced by a right-angle displacement.

The total error in S' due to specimen displacement in some direction inclined to the incident beam is therefore given by Eq. (11–6). This error in S' causes an error in the computed value of ϕ. Inasmuch as we are considering the various errors one at a time, we can now put the radius error ΔR equal to zero, so that Eq. (11–4) becomes

$$\frac{\Delta\phi}{\phi} = \frac{\Delta S'}{S'}, \tag{11–7}$$

which shows how an error in S' alone affects the value of ϕ. By combining Eqs. (11–3), (11–6), and (11–7), we find that the error in ϕ due to the fact that the specimen is off center is given by

$$\Delta\phi_C = \frac{\phi\Delta S'}{S'} = \frac{\phi(2\Delta x \sin 2\phi)}{4R\phi} = \frac{\Delta x}{R} \sin \phi \cos \phi. \qquad (11\text{–}8)$$

It should not be assumed that the centering error is removed when the specimen is so adjusted, relative to the rotating shaft of the camera, that no perceptible wobble can be detected when the shaft is rotated. This sort of adjustment is taken for granted in this discussion. The off-center error refers to the possibility that the axis of rotation of the *shaft* is not located at the center of the camera, due to improper construction of the camera.

Absorption in the specimen also causes an error in ϕ. This effect, often the largest single cause of error in parameter measurements, is unfortunately very difficult to calculate with any accuracy. But we have seen, in Fig. 4–18(b), that back-reflected rays come almost entirely from that side of the specimen which faces the collimator. Therefore, to a rough approximation, the effect of a centered, highly absorbing specimen is the same as that of a nonabsorbing specimen displaced from the camera center in the manner shown in Fig. 11–3(a). Consequently we can assume that the error in ϕ due to absorption, $\Delta\phi_A$, is included in the centering error given by Eq. (11–8).

Thus, the over-all error in ϕ due to film shrinkage, radius error, centering error, and absorption, is given by the sum of Eqs. (11–5) and (11–8):

$$\Delta\phi_{S',R,C,A} = \left(\frac{\Delta S'}{S'} - \frac{\Delta R}{R}\right)\phi + \frac{\Delta x}{R} \sin \phi \cos \phi. \qquad (11\text{–}9)$$

But

$$\phi = 90° - \theta, \quad \Delta\phi = -\Delta\theta, \quad \sin \phi = \cos \theta, \quad \text{and} \quad \cos \phi = \sin \theta.$$

Therefore Eq. (11–2) becomes

$$\frac{\Delta d}{d} = -\frac{\cos \theta}{\sin \theta} \Delta\theta = \frac{\sin \phi}{\cos \phi} \Delta\phi$$

and

$$\frac{\Delta d}{d} = \frac{\sin \phi}{\cos \phi}\left[\left(\frac{\Delta S'}{S'} - \frac{\Delta R}{R}\right)\phi + \frac{\Delta x}{R} \sin \phi \cos \phi\right]. \qquad (11\text{–}10)$$

In the back-reflection region, ϕ is small and may be replaced, in the second term of Eq. (11–10), by $\sin \phi \cos \phi$, since $\sin \phi \approx \phi$ and $\cos \phi \approx 1$, for small values of ϕ. We then have

$$\frac{\Delta d}{d} = \left(\frac{\Delta S'}{S'} - \frac{\Delta R}{R} + \frac{\Delta x}{R}\right) \sin^2 \phi.$$

The bracketed terms are constant for any one film, so that

$$\frac{\Delta d}{d} = K \sin^2 \phi = K \cos^2 \theta, \qquad (11\text{–}11)$$

where K is a constant. Accordingly, we have the important result that the fractional errors in d are directly proportional to $\cos^2 \theta$, and therefore approach zero as $\cos^2 \theta$ approaches zero or as θ approaches 90°. In the cubic system,

$$\frac{\Delta d}{d} = \frac{\Delta a}{a} = K \cos^2 \theta. \qquad (11\text{–}12)$$

Hence, for cubic substances, if the value of a computed for each line on the pattern is plotted against $\cos^2 \theta$, a straight line should result, and a_0, the true value of a, can be found by extrapolating this line to $\cos^2 \theta = 0$. (Or, since $\sin^2 \theta = 1 - \cos^2 \theta$, the various values of a may be plotted against $\sin^2 \theta$, and the line extrapolated to $\sin^2 \theta = 1$.)

From the various approximations involved in the derivation of Eq. (11–12), it is clear that this equation is true only for large values of θ (small values of ϕ). Therefore, only lines having θ values greater than about 60° should be used in the extrapolation, and the more lines there are with θ greater than 80°, the more precise is the value of a_0 obtained. To increase the number of lines in the back-reflection region, it is common practice to employ unfiltered radiation so that $K\beta$ as well as $K\alpha$ can be reflected. If the x-ray tube is demountable, special alloy targets can also be used to increase the number of lines; or two exposures can be made on the same film with different characteristic radiations. In any case, it must never be assumed that the process of extrapolation can automatically produce a precise value of a_0 from careless measurements made on a film of poor quality. For high precision, the lines must be sharp and the $K\alpha$ doublets well resolved at high angles, which means in turn that the individual particles of the specimen must be strain-free and not too fine. The line positions must be determined carefully and it is best to measure each one two or three times and average the results. In computing a for each line, the proper wavelength must be assigned to each component of the $K\alpha$ doublet when that line is resolved and, when it is not resolved, the weighted mean wavelength should be used.

To illustrate this extrapolation method, we shall consider a powder pattern of tungsten made in a Debye-Scherrer camera 5.73 cm in diameter with unfiltered copper radiation. The data for all lines having θ values

TABLE 11–1

Line	hkl	Radiation	θ	$\sin^2\theta$	$a(\text{A})$
6	400	Kβ	61.71°	0.7754	3.162
5	321	Kα	65.91	0.8334	3.160
4	411, 330	Kβ	69.05	0.8722	3.162
3	400	Kα_1	76.73	0.9473	3.166
2	400	Kα_2	77.48	0.9530	3.164
1	420	Kβ	79.67	0.9678	3.164

greater than 60° are given in Table 11–1. The drift in the computed a values is obvious: in general they increase with θ and tend to approach the true value a_0 at high angles. In Fig. 11–4, these values of a are plotted against $\sin^2\theta$, and a_0 is found by extrapolation to be 3.165A.

Other functions of θ, besides $\sin^2\theta$ or $\cos^2\theta$, may be used as a basis for extrapolation. For example, if we replace $\sin\phi\cos\phi$ in Eq. (11–10) by ϕ, instead of replacing ϕ by $\sin\phi\cos\phi$, we obtain

$$\frac{\Delta d}{d} = K\phi\tan\phi.$$

Therefore, a plot of a against $\phi\tan\phi$ will also be linear and will extrapolate to a_0 at $\phi\tan\phi = 0$. In practice, there is not much difference between an extrapolation against $\phi\tan\phi$ and one against $\cos^2\theta$ (or $\sin^2\theta$), and either will give satisfactory results. If the various sources of error, particularly absorption, are analyzed more rigorously than we have done here, it can be shown that the relation

$$\frac{\Delta d}{d} = K\left(\frac{\cos^2\theta}{\sin\theta} + \frac{\cos^2\theta}{\theta}\right)$$

holds quite accurately down to very low values of θ and not just at high angles. The value of a_0 can be found by plotting a against $(\cos^2\theta/\sin\theta + \cos^2\theta/\theta)$, which approaches zero as θ approaches 90°. Although it is doubtful whether any advantage results from using $(\cos^2\theta/\sin\theta + \cos^2\theta/\theta)$

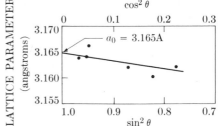

FIG. 11–4. Extrapolation of measured lattice parameters against $\sin^2\theta$ (or $\cos^2\theta$).

instead of $\cos^2\theta$ in the back-reflection region, the greater range of linearity of the former function is an advantage in certain cases.

Noncubic crystals present additional difficulties, regardless of the particular extrapolation function chosen. (In the following discussion, we shall confine our attention to hexagonal and tetragonal crystals, but the methods to be described can be generalized to apply to crystals of still lower symmetry.) The difficulty is simply this: the position of a line which has indices hkl is determined by two parameters, a and c, and it is impossible to calculate both of them from the observed $\sin^2 \theta$ value of that line alone. One way of avoiding this difficulty is to ignore the hkl lines and divide the remainder into two groups, those with indices $hk0$ and those with indices $00l$. A value of a is calculated for each $hk0$ line and a value of c from each $00l$ line; two separate extrapolations are then made to find a_0 and c_0. Since there are usually very few $hk0$ and $00l$ lines in the back-reflection region, some low-angle lines have to be included, which means that the extrapolations must be made against $(\cos^2 \theta/\sin \theta + \cos^2 \theta/\theta)$ and not against $\cos^2 \theta$. And if there are *no* lines of the type $hk0$ and $00l$ with θ greater than 80°, even the former function will not assure an accurate extrapolation.

A better but more laborious method, and one which utilizes all the data, is that of successive approximations. In the tetragonal system, for example, the value of a for any line is given by

$$a = \frac{\lambda}{2 \sin \theta} \left[(h^2 + k^2) + \frac{l^2}{(c/a)^2} \right]^{\frac{1}{2}}. \tag{11-13}$$

The first step is to calculate approximate values, a_1, and c_1, of the lattice parameters from the positions of the two highest-angle lines, as was done in Sec. 10–4. The approximate axial ratio c_1/a_1 is then calculated and used in Eq. (11–13) to determine an a value for each high-angle line on the pattern. These values of a are then extrapolated against $\cos^2 \theta$ to find a more accurate value of a, namely a_2. The value of c_2 is found in similar fashion by use of the relation

$$c = \frac{\lambda}{2 \sin \theta} \left[\left(\frac{c}{a}\right)^2 (h^2 + k^2) + l^2 \right]^{\frac{1}{2}} \tag{11-14}$$

and another extrapolation against $\cos^2 \theta$. The process is repeated with the new value of the axial ratio c_2/a_2 to yield still more accurate values of the parameters, namely c_3 and a_3. Three extrapolations are usually sufficient to fix the parameters with high accuracy. In addition, the accuracy of each extrapolation can be improved by a suitable choice of lines. For example, the value of a calculated from Eq. (11–13) is only slightly affected by inaccuracies in c/a when $(h^2 + k^2)$ is large compared to l^2, since the term involving c/a is itself small. Therefore, lines with large h and k indices and a small l index should be chosen for each determination of a. Just the reverse is true in the determination of c, as inspection of Eq. (11–14) will show.

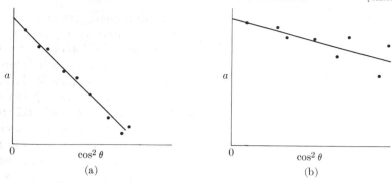

FIG. 11–5. Extreme forms of extrapolation curves (schematic): (a) large systematic errors, small random errors; (b) small systematic errors, large random errors.

To conclude this section, a few general remarks on the nature of errors may not be amiss. In the measurement of a lattice parameter, as in many other physical observations, two kinds of error are involved, *systematic* and *random*. A systematic error is one which varies in a regular manner with some particular parameter. Thus the fractional errors in a due to the various effects considered above (film shrinkage, incorrect radius, off-center specimen, absorption) are all systematic errors because they vary in a regular way with θ, decreasing as θ increases. Further, a systematic error is always of the same sign: for example, the effect of absorption in a Debye-Scherrer camera is always to make the computed value of a less than the true value. Random errors, on the other hand, are the ordinary chance errors involved in any direct observation. For example, the errors involved in measuring the positions of the various lines on a film are random errors; they may be positive or negative and do not vary in any regular manner with the position of the line on the film.

As we have already seen, the systematic errors in a approach zero as θ approaches 90°, and may be eliminated by use of the proper extrapolation function. The magnitude of these errors is proportional to the slope of the extrapolation line and, if these errors are small, the line will be quite flat. In fact, if we purposely increase the systematic errors, say, by using a slightly incorrect value of the camera radius in our calculations, the slope of the line will increase but the extrapolated value of a_0 will remain the same. The random errors involved in measuring line positions show up as random errors in a, and are responsible for the deviation of the various points from the extrapolation line. The random errors in a also decrease in magnitude as θ increases, due essentially to the slow variation of $\sin \theta$ with θ at large angles.

These various effects are summarized graphically in Fig. 11–5. In (a) the calculated points conform quite closely to the line, indicating small random errors, but the line itself is quite steep because of large systematic errors. The opposite situation is shown in (b): here the systematic error is small, but the wide scatter of the points shows that large random errors have been made. Inasmuch as the difficulty of drawing the line increases with the degree of scatter, it is obvious that every possible effort should be made to minimize random errors at the start.

11–3 Back-reflection focusing cameras. A camera of this kind is preferred for work of the highest precision, since the position of a diffraction line on the film is twice as sensitive to small changes in plane spacing with this camera as it is with a Debye-Scherrer camera of the same diameter. It is, of course, not free from sources of systematic error. The most important of these are the following:

(1) Film shrinkage.
(2) Incorrect camera radius.
(3) Displacement of specimen from camera circumference.
(4) Absorption in specimen. (If the specimen has very *low* absorption, many of the diffracted rays will originate at points outside the camera circumference even though the specimen surface coincides with the circumference.)

A detailed analysis of these various sources of error shows that they produce fractional errors in d which are very closely proportional to $\phi \tan \phi$, where ϕ is again equal to $(90° - \theta)$. This function is therefore the one to use in extrapolating lattice parameters measured with this camera.

11–4 Pinhole cameras. The pinhole camera, used in back reflection, is not really an instrument of high precision in the measurement of lattice parameters, but it is mentioned here because of its very great utility in metallurgical work. Since both the film and the specimen surface are flat, no focusing of the diffracted rays occurs, and the result is that the diffraction lines are much broader than is normally desirable for precise measurement of their positions. The chief sources of systematic error are the following:

(1) Film shrinkage.
(2) Incorrect specimen-to-film distance.
(3) Absorption in the specimen.

In this case it may be shown that the fractional error in d is proportional to $\sin 4\phi \tan \phi$, or to the equivalent expression $\cos^2 \theta (2 \cos^2 \theta - 1)$, where $\phi = (90° - \theta)$. With either of these extrapolation functions a fairly precise value of the lattice parameter can be obtained; in addition, the back-reflection pinhole camera has the particular advantage that mounted metallographic specimens may be examined directly. This means that a parameter determination can be made on the same part of a specimen as that examined under the microscope. A dual examination of this kind is quite valuable in many problems, especially in the determination of phase diagrams.

11–5 Diffractometers.   The commercial diffractometer is a rather new instrument and relatively little use has been made of it for the precise measurement of lattice parameters.   For that reason, no generally valid procedure for use in such measurements has yet been devised, and until this is done the back-reflection focusing camera must be recognized as the most accurate instrument for parameter measurements.

One reason for the inferiority of the diffractometer in this respect is the impossibility of observing the same back-reflected cone of radiation on both sides of the incident beam.   Thus, the experimenter has no automatic check on the accuracy of the angular scale of the instrument or the precision of its alignment.

When a diffractometer is used to measure plane spacings, the more important sources of systematic error in d are the following:

(1) Misalignment of the instrument.   In particular, the center of the incident beam must intersect the diffractometer axis and the 0° position of the receiving slit.

(2) Use of a flat specimen instead of a specimen curved to conform to the focusing circle.

(3) Absorption in the specimen.

(4) Displacement of the specimen from the diffractometer axis.   (This is usually the largest single source of error.)

(5) Vertical divergence of the incident beam.

These sources of error cause the fractional error in d to vary in a complicated way with θ, so that no simple extrapolation function can be used to obtain high accuracy.   Because some, but not all, of these sources of error cause $\Delta d/d$ to be approximately proportional to $\cos^2 \theta$, a fairly accurate value of the lattice parameter can be obtained by simple extrapolation against $\cos^2 \theta$, just as with the Debye-Scherrer camera.   Therefore, in the light of our present knowledge, the suggested procedure is:

(a) Carefully align the component parts of the instrument in accordance with the manufacturer's instructions.

(b) Adjust the specimen surface to coincide as closely as possible with the diffractometer axis.

(c) Extrapolate the calculated parameters against $\cos^2 \theta$.

This procedure will undoubtedly be improved as additional experience with this instrument is accumulated.   In fact, some investigators feel that lattice parameters will one day be measurable with the diffractometer with greater accuracy than with any kind of powder camera, but whether this is true or not remains to be seen.   There is, however, one circumstance in which the diffractometer is superior to a camera for parameter measurements and that is when the diffraction lines are abnormally broad; this particular application arises in stress measurement and will be described in Chap. 17.

11–6 Method of least squares. All the previously described methods of accurately measuring lattice parameters depend in part on graphical extrapolation. Their accuracy therefore depends on the accuracy with which a straight line can be drawn through a set of experimental points, each of which is subject to random errors. However, different persons will in general draw slightly different lines through the same set of points, so that it is desirable to have an objective, analytical method of finding the line which best fits the data. This can be done by the method of least squares. Since this method can be used in a variety of problems, it will be described here in a quite general way; in the next section, its application to parameter measurements will be taken up in detail.

If a number of measurements are made of the same physical quantity and if these measurements are subject only to random errors, then the theory of least squares states that the most probable value of the measured quantity is that which makes the sum of the squares of the errors a minimum. The proof of this theorem is too long to reproduce here but we can at least demonstrate its reasonableness by the following simple example. Suppose five separate measurements are made of the same physical quantity, say the time required for a falling body to drop a given distance, and that these measurements yield the following values: 1.70, 1.78, 1.74, 1.79, and 1.74 sec. Let x equal the most probable value of the time. Then the error in the first measurement is $e_1 = (x - 1.70)$, the error in the second is $e_2 = (x - 1.78)$, and so on. The sum of the squares of the errors is given by

$$\Sigma(e^2) = (x - 1.70)^2 + (x - 1.78)^2$$
$$+ (x - 1.74)^2 + (x - 1.79)^2 + (x - 1.74)^2.$$

We can minimize the sum of the squared errors by differentiating this expression with respect to x and equating the result to zero:

$$\frac{d\Sigma(e^2)}{dx} = 2(x - 1.70) + 2(x - 1.78) + 2(x - 1.74) + 2(x - 1.79)$$
$$+ 2(x - 1.74) = 0$$

whence

$$x = 1.75 \text{ sec.}$$

On the other hand, the arithmetic average of the measurements is also 1.75 sec. This should not surprise us as we know, almost intuitively, that the arithmetic average of a set of measurements gives the most probable value. This example may appear trivial, in that no one would take the trouble to use the method of least squares when the same result can be obtained by simple averaging, but at least it illustrates the basic principle involved in the least-squares method.

Naturally, there are many problems in which the method of simple averaging cannot be applied and then the method of least squares becomes particularly valuable. Consider, for example, the problem referred to above, that of finding the straight line which best fits a set of experimentally determined points. If there are only two points, there is no problem, because the two constants which define a straight line can be unequivocally determined from these two points. But, in general, there will be more points available than constants to be determined. Suppose that the various points have coordinates x_1y_1, x_2y_2, x_3y_3, ... and that it is known that x and y are related by an equation of the form

$$y = a + bx. \tag{11–15}$$

Our problem is to find the values of the constants a and b, since these define the straight line. In general, the line will not pass exactly through any of the points since each is subject to a random error. Therefore each point is in error by an amount given by its deviation from the straight line. For example, Eq. (11–15) states that the value of y corresponding to $x = x_1$ is $(a + bx_1)$. Yet the first experimental point has a value of $y = y_1$. Therefore e_1, the error in the first point, is given by

$$e_1 = (a + bx_1) - y_1.$$

We can calculate the errors in the other points in similar fashion, and then write down the expression for the sum of the squares of these errors:

$$\Sigma(e^2) = (a + bx_1 - y_1)^2 + (a + bx_2 - y_2)^2 + \cdots. \tag{11–16}$$

According to the theory of least squares, the "best" straight line is that which makes the sum of the squared errors a minimum. Therefore, the best value of a is found by differentiating Eq. (11–16) with respect to a and equating the result to zero:

$$\frac{d\Sigma(e^2)}{da} = 2(a + bx_1 - y_1) + 2(a + bx_2 - y_2) + \cdots = 0,$$

or

$$\Sigma a + b\Sigma x - \Sigma y = 0. \tag{11–17}$$

The best value of b is found in a similar way:

$$\frac{d\Sigma(e^2)}{db} = 2x_1(a + bx_1 - y_1) + 2x_2(a + bx_2 - y_2) + \cdots = 0,$$

or

$$a\Sigma x + b\Sigma x^2 - \Sigma xy = 0. \tag{11–18}$$

Equations (11–17) and (11–18) are the *normal equations*. Simultaneous solution of these two equations yields the best values of a and b, which can then be substituted into Eq. (11–15) to give the equation of the line.

The normal equations as written above can be rearranged as follows:

$$\Sigma y = \Sigma a + b\Sigma x$$

and　　　　　　　　　　　　　　　　　　　　　　　　　　　　　　(11–19)

$$\Sigma xy = a\Sigma x + b\Sigma x^2.$$

A comparison of these equations and Eq. (11–15) shows that the following rules can be laid down for the formation of the normal equations:

(a) Substitute the experimental values of x and y into Eq. (11–15). If there are n experimental points, n equations in a and b will result.

(b) To obtain the first normal equation, multiply each of these n equations by the coefficient of a in each equation, and add.

(c) To obtain the second normal equation, multiply each equation by the coefficient of b, and add.

As an illustration, suppose that we determine the best straight line through the following four points:

x	10	18	30	42
y	15	11	11	8

The normal equations are obtained in three steps:

(a) Substitution of the given values:

$$15 = a + 10b$$
$$11 = a + 18b$$
$$11 = a + 30b$$
$$8 = a + 42b$$

(b) Multiplication by the coefficient of a:

$$15 = a + 10b$$
$$11 = a + 18b$$
$$11 = a + 30b$$
$$8 = a + 42b$$

$$\overline{45 = 4a + 100b} \quad \text{(first normal equation)}$$

(c) Multiplication by the coefficient of b:

$$150 = 10a + 100b$$
$$198 = 18a + 324b$$
$$330 = 30a + 900b$$
$$336 = 42a + 1764b$$

$$\overline{1014 = 100a + 3088b} \quad \text{(second normal equation)}$$

Simultaneous solution of the two normal equations gives $a = 16.0$ and $b = -0.189$. The required straight line is therefore

$$y = 16.0 - 0.189x.$$

This line is shown in Fig. 11–6, together with the four given points.

The least-squares method is not confined to finding the constants of a straight line; it can be applied to any kind of curve. Suppose, for example, that x and y are known to be related by a parabolic equation

$$y = a + bx + cx^2.$$

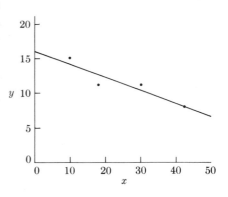

FIG. 11–6. Best straight line, determined by least-squares method.

Since there are three unknown constants here, we need three normal equations. These are

$$\Sigma y = \Sigma a + b\Sigma x + c\Sigma x^2,$$

$$\Sigma xy = a\Sigma x + b\Sigma x^2 + c\Sigma x^3, \qquad (11\text{--}20)$$

$$\Sigma x^2 y = a\Sigma x^2 + b\Sigma x^3 + c\Sigma x^4.$$

These normal equations can be found by the same methods as were used for the straight-line case, i.e., successive multiplication of the n observational equations by the coefficients of a, b, and c, followed by addition of the equations in each set.

It should be noted that the least-squares method is not a way of finding the best curve to fit a given set of observations. The investigator must know at the outset, from his understanding of the phenomenon involved, the kind of relation (linear, parabolic, exponential, etc.) the two quantities x and y are supposed to obey. All the least-squares method can do is give him the best values of the constants in the equation he selects, but it does this in a quite objective and unbiased manner.

11–7 Cohen's method. In preceding sections we have seen that the most accurate value of the lattice parameter of a cubic substance is found by plotting the value of a calculated for each reflection against a particular function, which depends on the kind of camera used, and extrapolating to a value a_0 at $\theta = 90°$. Two different things are accomplished by this procedure: (a) systematic errors are eliminated by selection of the proper extrapolation function, and (b) random errors are reduced in proportion to the skill of the investigator in drawing the best straight line through the experimental points. M. U. Cohen proposed, in effect, that the least-squares method be used to find the best straight line so that the random errors would be minimized in a reproducible and objective manner.

Suppose a **cubic** substance is being examined in a Debye-Scherrer camera. Then Eq. (11–12), namely,

$$\frac{\Delta d}{d} = \frac{\Delta a}{a} = K \cos^2 \theta, \qquad (11\text{–}12)$$

defines the extrapolation function. But instead of using the least-squares method to find the best straight line on a plot of a against $\cos^2 \theta$, Cohen applied the method to the observed $\sin^2 \theta$ values directly. By squaring the Bragg law and taking logarithms of each side, we obtain

$$\ln \sin^2 \theta = \ln \left(\frac{\lambda^2}{4}\right) - 2 \ln d.$$

Differentiation then gives

$$\frac{\Delta \sin^2 \theta}{\sin^2 \theta} = -\frac{2 \Delta d}{d}. \qquad (11\text{–}21)$$

By substituting this into Eq. (11–12) we find how the error in $\sin^2 \theta$ varies with θ:

$$\Delta \sin^2 \theta = -2K \sin^2 \theta \cos^2 \theta = D \sin^2 2\theta, \qquad (11\text{–}22)$$

where D is a new constant. [This equation is valid only when the $\cos^2 \theta$ extrapolation function is valid. If some other extrapolation function is used, Eq. (11–22) must be modified accordingly.] Now the true value of $\sin^2 \theta$ for any diffraction line is given by

$$\sin^2 \theta \text{ (true)} = \frac{\lambda^2}{4a_0{}^2} (h^2 + k^2 + l^2),$$

where a_0, the true value of the lattice parameter, is the quantity we are seeking. But

$$\sin^2 \theta \text{ (observed)} - \sin^2 \theta \text{ (true)} = \Delta \sin^2 \theta,$$

$$\sin^2 \theta - \frac{\lambda^2}{4a_0{}^2} (h^2 + k^2 + l^2) = D \sin^2 2\theta,$$

$$\sin^2 \theta = C\alpha + A\delta, \qquad (11\text{–}23)$$

where

$$C = \lambda^2/4a_0{}^2, \quad \alpha = (h^2 + k^2 + l^2), \quad A = D/10, \quad \text{and} \quad \delta = 10 \sin^2 2\theta.$$

(The factor 10 is introduced into the definitions of the quantities A and δ solely to make the coefficients of the various terms in the normal equations of the same order of magnitude.)

The experimental values of $\sin^2 \theta$, α, and δ are now substituted into Eq. (11–23) for each of the n back-reflection lines used in the determination. This gives n equations in the unknown constants C and A, and these equations can be solved for the most probable values of C and A by the method of least squares. Once C is found, a_0 can be calculated directly from the relation given above; the constant A is related to the amount of systematic error involved and is constant for any one film, but varies slightly from one film to another. The two normal equations we need to find C and A are found from Eq. (11–23) and the rules previously given. They are

$$\Sigma \alpha \sin^2 \theta = C \Sigma \alpha^2 + A \Sigma \alpha \delta,$$

$$\Sigma \delta \sin^2 \theta = C \Sigma \alpha \delta + A \Sigma \delta^2.$$

To illustrate the way in which such calculations are carried out, we will apply Cohen's method to a determination of the lattice parameter of tungsten from measurements made on the pattern shown in Fig. 6–10. Since this pattern was made with a symmetrical back-reflection focusing camera, the correct extrapolation function is

$$\frac{\Delta d}{d} = K \phi \tan \phi.$$

Substituting this into Eq. (11–21), we have

$$\Delta \sin^2 \theta = -2K\phi \sin^2 \theta \tan \phi$$

$$= -2K\phi \cos^2 \phi \tan \phi$$

$$= D\phi \sin 2\phi,$$

where D is a new constant. We can therefore write, for each line on the pattern,

$$\sin^2 \theta = \cos^2 \phi = \frac{\lambda^2}{4a_0^2} (h^2 + k^2 + l^2) + D\phi \sin 2\phi, \qquad (11\text{–}24)$$

$$\cos^2 \phi = C\alpha + A\delta, \qquad (11\text{–}25)$$

where

$$C = \lambda^2/4a_0^2, \quad \alpha = (h^2 + k^2 + l^2), \quad A = D/10, \quad \text{and} \quad \delta = 10\phi \sin 2\phi.$$

Equation 11–24 cannot be applied directly because lines due to three different wavelengths (Cu $K\alpha_1$, Cu $K\alpha_2$, and Cu $K\beta$) are present on the pattern, which means that λ varies from line to line, whereas in Eq. (11–24) it is treated as a constant. But the data can be "normalized" to any one wavelength by use of the proper multiplying factor. For example, suppose we decide to normalize all lines to the $K\beta$ wavelength. Then for a

TABLE 11–2

Line	hkl	λ	α	φ	Observed		Normalized to Kβ	
					$\cos^2 \phi$	δ	$\cos^2 \phi$	δ
1	321	$K\alpha_1$	14	24.518°	0.82779	3.2	0.67606	2.6
2	321	$K\alpha_2$	14	24.193	0.83205	3.2	0.67617	2.6
3	411, 330	Kβ	18	21.167	0.86961	2.5	0.86961	2.5
4	400	$K\alpha_1$	16	13.302	0.94706	1.0	0.77346	0.8
5	400	$K\alpha_2$	16	12.667	0.95191	1.0	0.77357	0.8
6	420	Kβ	20	10.454	0.96708	0.7	0.96708	0.7

particular line formed by $K\alpha_1$ radiation, for instance, we have

$$\cos^2 \phi_{K\alpha_1} = \frac{\lambda_{K\alpha_1}^2}{4a_0^2} \alpha + A \delta_{K\alpha_1},$$

$$\left(\frac{\lambda_{K\beta}^2}{\lambda_{K\alpha_1}^2}\right) \cos^2 \phi_{K\alpha_1} = \left(\frac{\lambda_{K\beta}^2}{\lambda_{K\alpha_1}^2}\right)\left(\frac{\lambda_{K\alpha_1}^2}{4a_0^2}\right) \alpha + \left(\frac{\lambda_{K\beta}^2}{\lambda_{K\alpha_1}^2}\right) A \delta_{K\alpha_1}.$$

From the Bragg law,

$$\left(\frac{\lambda_{K\beta}^2}{\lambda_{K\alpha_1}^2}\right) \cos^2 \phi_{K\alpha_1} = \cos^2 \phi_{K\beta},$$

$$\cos^2 \phi_{K\beta} = \left(\frac{\lambda_{K\beta}^2}{4a_0^2}\right) \alpha + A \left(\frac{\lambda_{K\beta}^2}{\lambda_{K\alpha_1}^2}\right) \delta_{K\alpha_1}, \qquad (11\text{--}26)$$

where $(\lambda_{K\beta}^2/\lambda_{K\alpha_1}^2)\delta_{K\alpha_1}$ is a normalized δ. Equation (11–26) now refers only to the Kβ wavelength. Lines due to $K\alpha_2$ radiation can be normalized in a similar manner. When this has been done for all lines, the quantity C in Eq. (11–25) is then a true constant, equal to $\lambda_{K\beta}^2/4a_0^2$. The values of the two normalizing factors, for copper radiation, are

$$\lambda_{K\beta}^2/\lambda_{K\alpha_1}^2 = 0.816699 \quad \text{and} \quad \lambda_{K\beta}^2/\lambda_{K\alpha_2}^2 = 0.812651.$$

Table 11–2 shows the observed and normalized values of $\cos^2 \phi$ and δ for each line on the tungsten pattern. The values of δ need not be calculated to more than two significant figures, since δ occurs in Eq. (11–25) only in the last term which is very small compared to the other two. From the data in Table 11–2, we obtain

$$\Sigma\alpha^2 = 1628, \quad \Sigma\delta^2 = 21.6, \quad \Sigma\alpha\delta = 157.4,$$

$$\Sigma\alpha \cos^2 \phi = 78.6783, \quad \Sigma\delta \cos^2 \phi = 7.6044.$$

The normal equations are

$$78.6783 = 1628C + 157.4A,$$

$$7.6044 = 157.4C + 21.6A.$$

Solving these, we find

$$C = \lambda_{K\beta}^2/4a_0^2 = 0.0483654 \quad \text{and} \quad a_0 = 3.1651\text{A},$$

$$A = -0.000384.$$

The constant A, called the drift constant, is a measure of the total systematic error involved in the determination.

Cohen's method of determining lattice parameters is even more valuable when applied to **noncubic** substances, since, as we saw in Sec. 11–2, straightforward graphical extrapolation cannot be used when there is more than one lattice parameter involved. Cohen's method, however, provides a direct means of determining these parameters, although the equations are naturally more complex than those needed for cubic substances. For example, suppose that the substance involved is hexagonal. Then

$$\sin^2 \theta \text{ (true)} = \frac{\lambda^2}{4} \cdot \frac{4}{3} \cdot \frac{h^2 + hk + k^2}{a_0^2} + \frac{\lambda^2}{4} \cdot \frac{l^2}{c_0^2}$$

and

$$\sin^2 \theta - \frac{\lambda^2}{3a_0^2}(h^2 + hk + k^2) - \frac{\lambda^2}{4c_0^2}(l^2) = D \sin^2 2\theta,$$

if the pattern is made in a Debye-Scherrer camera. By rearranging this equation and introducing new symbols, we obtain

$$\sin^2 \theta = C\alpha + B\gamma + A\delta, \tag{11–27}$$

where

$$C = \lambda^2/3a_0^2, \quad \alpha = (h^2 + hk + k^2), \quad B = \lambda^2/4c_0^2, \quad \gamma = l^2,$$

$$A = D/10, \quad \text{and} \quad \delta = 10 \sin^2 2\theta.$$

The values of C, B, and A, of which only the first two are really needed, are found from the three normal equations:

$$\Sigma\alpha \sin^2 \theta = C\Sigma\alpha^2 + B\Sigma\alpha\gamma + A\Sigma\alpha\delta,$$

$$\Sigma\gamma \sin^2 \theta = C\Sigma\alpha\gamma + B\Sigma\gamma^2 + A\Sigma\gamma\delta,$$

$$\Sigma\delta \sin^2 \theta = C\Sigma\alpha\delta + B\Sigma\delta\gamma + A\Sigma\delta^2.$$

11–8 Calibration method. One other procedure for obtaining accurate lattice parameters is worth mentioning, if only for its relative simplicity, and that is the calibration method already alluded to in Sec. 6–7. It is based on a calibration of the camera film (or diffractometer angular scale) by means of a substance of known lattice parameter.

If the specimen whose parameter is to be determined is in the form of a powder, it is simply mixed with the powdered standard substance and a pattern made of the composite powder. If the specimen is a polycrystalline piece of metal, the standard powder may be mixed with petroleum jelly and smeared over the surface of the specimen in a thin film. The amount of the standard substance used should be adjusted so that the intensities of the diffraction lines from the standard and those from the specimen are not too unequal. Inasmuch as the true angle θ can be calculated for any diffraction line from the standard substance, a calibration curve can be prepared relating the true angle θ to distance along the camera film (or angular position on the diffractometer scale). This curve is then used to find the true angle θ for any diffraction line from the specimen, since it may be assumed that any systematic errors involved in the determination will affect the diffraction lines of both substances in the same way.

This method works best when there is a diffraction line from the standard substance very close to a line from the specimen and both lines are in the back-reflection region. Practically all systematic errors are thus eliminated. To achieve this condition requires an intelligent choice of the standard substance and/or the incident wavelength. The most popular standard substances are probably quartz and sodium chloride, although pure metals such as gold and silver are also useful.

One disadvantage of the calibration method is that the accuracy of the parameter determination depends on the accuracy with which the parameter of the standard substance is known. If the absolute value of the parameter of the standard is known, then the calibration method gives the absolute value of the parameter of the specimen quite accurately. If not, then only a relative value of the parameter of the specimen can be obtained, but it is an accurate relative value. And frequently this is no disadvantage at all, since we are often interested only in the *differences* in the parameters of a number of specimens and not in the absolute values of these parameters.

If absolute values are required, the only safe procedure is to measure the absolute value of the parameter of the standard substance by one of the methods described in the preceding sections. It should not be assumed that a particular sample of quartz, for example, has the exact lattice parameters tabulated under "quartz" in some reference book, because this particular sample may contain enough impurities in solid solution to make its lattice parameters differ appreciably from the tabulated values.

PROBLEMS

11–1. The lattice parameter of copper is to be determined to an accuracy of ±0.0001A at 20°C. Within what limits must the temperature of the specimen be controlled if errors due to thermal expansion are to be avoided? The linear coefficient of thermal expansion of copper is 16.6×10^{-6} in./in./°C.

11-2. The following data were obtained from a Debye-Scherrer pattern of a simple cubic substance, made with copper radiation. The given $\sin^2 \theta$ values are for the $K\alpha_1$ lines only.

$h^2 + k^2 + l^2$	$\sin^2 \theta$
38	0.9114
40	0.9563
41	0.9761
42	0.9980

Determine the lattice parameter a, accurate to four significant figures, by graphical extrapolation of a against $\cos^2 \theta$.

11-3. From the data given in Prob. 11–2, determine the lattice parameter to four significant figures by Cohen's method.

11-4. From the data given in Table 11–2, determine the lattice parameter of tungsten to five significant figures by graphical extrapolation of a against $\phi \tan \phi$.

11-5. If the fractional error in the plane spacing d is accurately proportional to the function $(\cos^2 \theta / \sin \theta + \cos^2 \theta / \theta)$ over the whole range of θ, show that a plot of $\Delta \sin^2 \theta$ against $\sin^2 \theta$ has a maximum, as illustrated for a particular case by Fig. 10–1. At approximately what value of θ does the maximum occur?

CHAPTER 12

PHASE-DIAGRAM DETERMINATION

12-1 Introduction. An alloy is a combination of two or more metals, or of metals and nonmetals. It may consist of a single phase or of a mixture of phases, and these phases may be of different types, depending only on the composition of the alloy and the temperature,* provided the alloy is at equilibrium. The changes in the constitution of the alloy produced by given changes in composition or temperature may be conveniently shown by means of a *phase diagram*, also called an equilibrium diagram or constitution diagram. It is a plot of temperature *vs.* composition, divided into areas wherein a particular phase or mixture of phases is stable. As such it forms a sort of map of the alloy system involved. Phase diagrams are therefore of great importance in metallurgy, and much time and effort have been devoted to their determination. In this chapter we will consider how x-ray methods can be used in the study of phase diagrams, particularly of binary systems. Ternary systems will be discussed separately in Sec. 12-6.

X-ray methods are, of course, not the only ones which can be used in investigations of this kind. The two classical methods are thermal analysis and microscopic examination, and many diagrams have been determined by these means alone. X-ray diffraction, however, supplements these older techniques in many useful ways and provides, in addition, the only means of determining the crystal structures of the various phases involved. Most phase diagrams today are therefore determined by a combination of all three methods. In addition, measurements of other physical properties may be used to advantage in some alloy systems: the most important of these subsidiary techniques are measurements of the change in length and of the change in electric resistance as a function of temperature.

In general, the various experimental techniques differ in sensitivity, and therefore in usefulness, from one portion of the phase diagram to another. Thus, thermal analysis is the best method for determining the liquidus and solidus, including eutectic and peritectic horizontals, but it may fail to reveal the existence of eutectoid and peritectoid horizontals because of the sluggishness of some solid-state reactions or the small heat effects involved. Such features of the diagram are best determined by microscopic examination or x-ray diffraction, and the same applies to the determination of solvus (solid solubility) curves. It is a mistake to rely entirely on any one method, and the wise investigator will use whichever technique is most appropriate to the problem at hand.

---

* The pressure on the alloy is another effective variable, but it is usually held constant at that of the atmosphere and may be neglected.

12–2 General principles. The key to the interpretation of the powder patterns of alloys is the fact that each phase produces its own pattern independently of the presence or absence of any other phase. Thus a single-phase alloy produces a single pattern while the pattern of a two-phase alloy consists of two superimposed patterns, one due to each phase.

Assume, for example, that two metals A and B are *completely soluble* in the solid state, as illustrated by the phase diagram of Fig. 12–1. The solid phase α, called a *continuous solid solution*, is of the substitutional type; it varies in composition, but not in crystal structure, from pure A to pure B, which must necessarily have the same structure. The lattice parameter of α also varies continuously from that of pure A to that of pure B. Since all alloys in a system of this kind consist of the same single phase, their powder patterns appear quite similar, the only effect of a change in composition being to shift the diffraction-line positions in accordance with the change in lattice parameter.

More commonly, the two metals A and B are only *partially soluble* in the solid state. The first additions of B to A go into solid solution in the A lattice, which may expand or contract as a result, depending on the relative sizes of the A and B atoms and the type of solid solution formed (substitutional or interstitial). Ultimately the solubility limit of B in A is reached, and further additions of B cause the precipitation of a second phase. This second phase may be a B-rich solid solution with the same structure as B,

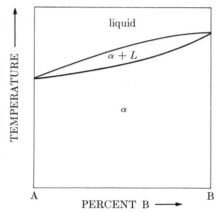

FIG. 12–1. Phase diagram of two metals, showing complete solid solubility.

as in the alloy system illustrated by Fig. 12-2(a). Here the solid solutions α and β are called *primary solid solutions* or *terminal solid solutions*. Or the second phase which appears may have no connection with the B-rich solid solution, as in the system shown in Fig. 12-2(b). Here the effect of supersaturating α with metal B is to precipitate the phase designated γ. This phase is called an *intermediate solid solution* or *intermediate phase*. It usually has a crystal structure entirely different from that of either α or β, and it is separated from each of these terminal solid solutions, on the phase diagram, by at least one two-phase region.

Phase diagrams much more complex than those just mentioned are often encountered in practice, but they are always reducible to a combination of fairly simple types. When an unknown phase diagram is being investigated, it is best to make a preliminary survey of the whole system by pre-

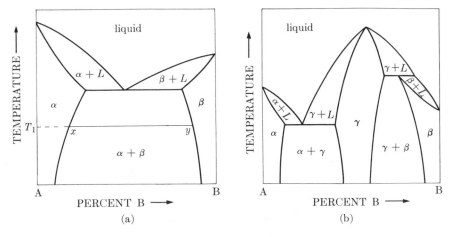

Fig. 12–2. Phase diagrams showing (a) partial solid solubility, and (b) partial solid solubility together with the formation of an intermediate phase.

paring a series of alloys at definite composition intervals, say 5 or 10 atomic percent, from pure A to pure B. The powder pattern of each alloy and each pure metal is then prepared. These patterns may appear quite complex but, no matter what the complexities, the patterns may be unraveled and the proper sequence of phases across the diagram may be established, if proper attention is paid to the following principles:

(1) *Equilibrium.* Each alloy must be at equilibrium at the temperature where the phase relations are being studied.

(2) *Phase sequence.* A horizontal (constant temperature) line drawn across the diagram must pass through single-phase and two-phase regions alternately.

(3) *Single-phase regions.* In a single-phase region, a change in composition generally produces a change in lattice parameter and therefore a shift in the positions of the diffraction lines of that phase.

(4) *Two-phase regions.* In a two-phase region, a change in composition of the alloy produces a change in the relative amounts of the two phases but no change in their compositions. These compositions are fixed at the intersections of a horizontal "tie line" with the boundaries of the two-phase field. Thus, in the system illustrated in Fig. 12–2(a), the tie line drawn at temperature T_1 shows that the compositions of α and β at equilibrium at this temperature are x and y respectively. The powder pattern of a two-phase alloy brought to equilibrium at temperature T_1 will therefore consist of the superimposed patterns of α of composition x and β of composition y. The patterns of a series of alloys in the xy range will all contain the same diffraction lines at the same positions, but the intensity of the lines of the α phase relative to the intensity of the lines of the β phase will decrease in

a regular manner as the concentration of B in the alloy changes from x to y, since this change in total composition decreases the amount of α relative to the amount of β.

These principles are illustrated with reference to the hypothetical alloy system shown in Fig. 12–3. This system contains two substitutional terminal solid solutions α and β, both assumed to be face-centered cubic, and an intermediate phase γ, which is body-centered cubic. The solubility of either A or B in γ is assumed to be negligibly small: the lattice parameter of γ is therefore constant in all alloys in which this phase appears. On the other hand, the parameters of α and β vary with composition in the manner shown by the lower part of Fig. 12–3. Since the B atom is assumed to be larger than the A atom, the addition of B expands the A lattice, and the parameter of α increases from a_1 for pure A to a_3 for a solution of composition x, which represents the limit of solubility of B in A at room temperature. In two-phase $(\alpha + \gamma)$ alloys containing more than x percent B, the parameter of α remains constant at its saturated value a_3. Similarly, the addition of A to B causes the parameter of β to decrease from a_2 to a_4 at the solubility limit, and then remain constant in the two-phase $(\gamma + \beta)$ field.

Calculated powder patterns are shown in Fig. 12–4 for the eight alloys designated by number in the phase diagram of Fig. 12–3. It is assumed that the alloys have been brought to equilibrium at room temperature by slow cooling. Examination of these patterns reveals the following:

(1) Pattern of pure A (face-centered cubic).

(2) Pattern of α almost saturated with B. The expansion of the lattice causes the lines to shift to smaller angles 2θ.

(3) Superimposed patterns of α and γ. The α phase is now saturated and has its maximum parameter a_3.

(4) Same as pattern 3, except for a change in the relative intensities of the two patterns which is not indicated on the drawing.

(5) Pattern of pure γ (body-centered cubic).

(6) Superimposed patterns of γ and of saturated β with a parameter of a_4.

(7) Pattern of pure β with a parameter somewhat greater than a_4.

(8) Pattern of pure B (face-centered cubic).

When an *unknown* phase diagram is being determined, the investigator must, of course, work in the reverse direction and deduce the sequence of phases across the diagram from the observed powder patterns. This is done by visual comparison of patterns prepared from alloys ranging in composition from pure A to pure B, and the previous example illustrates the nature of the changes which can be expected from one pattern to another. Corresponding lines in different patterns are identified by placing the films side by side as in Fig. 12–4 and noting which lines are common to

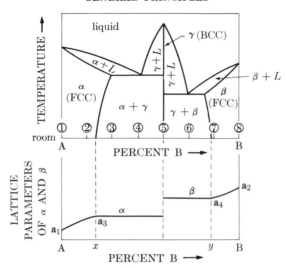

Fig. 12–3. Phase diagram and lattice constants of a hypothetical alloy system.

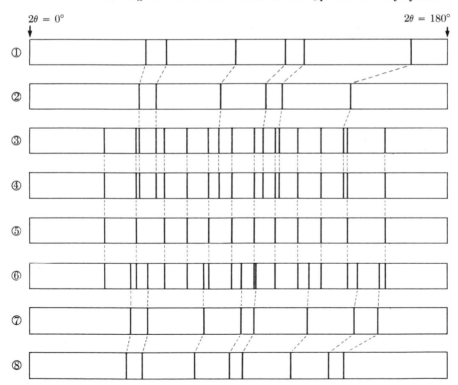

Fig. 12–4. Calculated powder patterns of alloys 1 to 8 in the alloy system shown in Fig. 12–3.

the two patterns.* This may be difficult in some alloy systems where the phases involved have complex diffraction patterns, or where it is suspected that lines due to $K\beta$ radiation may be present in some patterns and not in others. It is important to remember that a diffraction pattern of a given phase is characterized not only by line positions but also by line intensities. This means that the presence of phase X in a mixture of phases cannot be proved merely by coincidence of the lines of phase X with a set of lines in the pattern of the mixture; the lines in the pattern of the mixture which coincide with the lines of phase X must also have the *same relative intensities* as the lines of phase X. The addition of one or more phases to a particular phase weakens the diffraction lines of that phase, simply by dilution, but it cannot change the intensities of those lines relative to one another. Finally, it should be noted that the crystal structure of a phase need not be known for the presence of that phase to be detected in a mixture: it is enough to know the positions and intensities of the diffraction lines of that phase.

Phase diagram determination by x-ray methods usually begins with a determination of the room-temperature equilibria. The first step is to prepare a series of alloys by melting and casting, or by melting and solidification in the melting crucible. The resulting ingots are homogenized at a temperature just below the solidus to remove segregation, and very slowly cooled to room temperature.† Powder specimens are then prepared by grinding or filing, depending on whether the alloy is brittle or not. If the alloy is brittle enough to be ground into powder, the resulting powder is usually sufficiently stress-free to give sharp diffraction lines. Filed powders, however, must be re-annealed to remove the stresses produced by plastic deformation during filing before they are ready for x-ray examination. Only relatively low temperatures are needed to relieve stresses, but the filings should again be slowly cooled, after the stress-relief anneal, to ensure equilibrium at room temperature. Screening is usually necessary to obtain fine enough particles for x-ray examination, and when two-phase alloys are being screened, the precautions mentioned in Sec. 6–3 should be observed.

After the room-temperature equilibria are known, a determination of the phases present at high temperatures can be undertaken. Powder

---

* Superposition of the two films is generally confusing and may make some of the weaker lines almost invisible. A better method of comparison consists in slitting each Debye-Scherrer film lengthwise down its center and placing the center of one film adjacent to the center of another. The curvature of the diffraction lines then does not interfere with the comparison of line positions.

† Slow cooling alone may not suffice to produce room-temperature equilibrium, which is often very difficult to achieve. It may be promoted by cold working and recrystallizing the cast alloy, in order to decrease its grain size and thus accelerate diffusion, prior to homogenizing and slow cooling.

specimens are sealed in small evacuated silica tubes, heated to the desired temperature long enough for equilibrium to be attained, and rapidly quenched. Diffraction patterns of the quenched powders are then made at room temperature. This method works very well in many alloy systems, in that the quenched powder retains the structure it had at the elevated temperature. In some alloys, however, phases stable at high-temperature will decompose on cooling to room temperature, no matter how rapid the quench, and such phases can only be studied by means of a high-tempera- ture camera or diffractometer.

The latter instrument is of particular value in work of this kind because it allows continuous observation of a diffraction line. For example, the temperature below which a high-temperature phase is unstable, such as a eutectoid temperature, can be determined by setting the diffractometer counter to receive a prominent diffracted beam of the high-temperature phase, and then measuring the intensity of this beam as a function of tem- perature as the specimen is slowly cooled. The temperature at which the intensity falls to that of the general background is the temperature re- quired, and any hysteresis in the transformation can be detected by a simi- lar measurement on heating.

12–3 Solid solutions. Inasmuch as solid solubility, to a greater or lesser extent, is so common between metals, we might digress a little at this point to consider how the various kinds of solid solutions may be dis- tinguished experimentally. Irrespective of its extent or its position on the phase diagram, any solid solution may be classified as one of the following types, solely on the basis of its crystallography:

(1) Intersitial.
(2) Substitutional.
    (a) Random.
    (b) Ordered. (Because of its special interest, this type is described separately in Chap. 13.)
    (c) Defect. (A very rare type.)

An **interstitial solid solution** of B in A is to be expected only when the B atom is so small compared to the A atom that it can enter the interstices of the A lattice without causing much distortion. As a consequence, about the only interstitial solid solutions of any importance in metallurgy are those formed between a metal and one of the elements, carbon, nitrogen, hydrogen, and boron, all of which have atoms less than 2A in diameter. The interstitial addition of B to A is always accompanied by an increase in the volume of the unit cell. If A is cubic, then the single lattice parameter a must increase. If A is not cubic, then one parameter may increase and the other decrease, as long as these changes result in an increase in cell

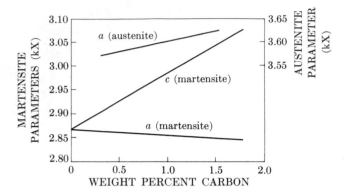

FIG. 12–5. Variation of martensite and austenite lattice parameters with carbon content. (After C. S. Roberts, *Trans. A.I.M.E.* **197,** 203, 1953.)

volume. Thus, in austenite, which is an interstitial solid solution of carbon in face-centered cubic γ-iron, the addition of carbon increases the cell edge a. But in martensite, a supersaturated interstitial solid solution of carbon in α-iron, the c parameter of the body-centered tetragonal cell increases while the a parameter decreases, when carbon is added. These effects are illustrated in Fig. 12–5.

The density of an interstitial solid solution is given by the basic density equation

$$\rho = \frac{1.66020 \Sigma A}{V}, \tag{3–9}$$

where

$$\Sigma A = n_s A_s + n_i A_i; \tag{12–1}$$

n_s and n_i are numbers of solvent and interstitial atoms, respectively, per unit cell; and A_s and A_i are atomic weights of solvent and interstitial atoms, respectively. Note that the value of n_s is constant and independent of the concentration of the interstitial element, and that n_i is normally a small fraction of unity.

The formation of a **random substitutional solid solution** of B and A may be accompanied either by an increase or decrease in cell volume, depending on whether the B atom is larger or smaller than the A atom. In continuous solid solutions of ionic salts, the lattice parameter of the solution is directly proportional to the atomic percent solute present. This relationship, known as Vegard's law, is not strictly obeyed by metallic solid solutions and, in fact, there is no reason why it should be. However, it is often used as a sort of yardstick by which one solution may be compared with another. Figure 12–6 shows examples of both positive and negative deviations from Vegard's law among solutions of face-centered cubic metals, and even larger deviations have been found in hexagonal close-

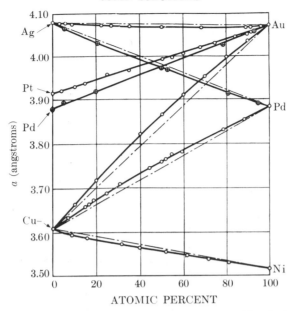

FIG. 12–6. Lattice parameters of some continuous solid solutions. Dot-dash lines indicate Vegard's law. (From *Structure of Metals*, by C. S. Barrett, 1952, McGraw-Hill Book Company, Inc.)

packed solutions. In terminal and intermediate solid solutions, the lattice parameter may or may not vary linearly with the atomic percent solute and, when the variation *is* linear, the parameter found by extrapolating to 100 percent solute does not usually correspond to the atom size deduced from the parameter of the pure solute, even when allowance is made for a possible change in coordination number.

The density of a random substitutional solid solution is found from Eq. (3–9) with the ΣA factor being given by

$$\Sigma A = n_{\text{solvent}}A_{\text{solvent}} + n_{\text{solute}}A_{\text{solute}}, \tag{12–2}$$

where n again refers to the number of atoms per cell and A to the atomic weight. Whether a given solution is interstitial or substitutional may be decided by determining whether the x-ray density calculated according to Eq. (12–1) or that calculated according to Eq. (12–2) agrees with the directly measured density.

Defect substitutional solid solutions are ones in which some lattice sites, normally occupied by atoms at certain compositions, are simply vacant at other compositions. Solutions of this type are rare among metals; the best-known example is the intermediate β solution in the nickel-aluminum system. A defect solution is disclosed by anomalies in the curves of density and lattice parameter *vs.* composition. Suppose, for example, that the solid solution of B and A is perfectly normal up to x percent B, but beyond that point a defect lattice is formed; i.e., further increases in B content are obtained, not by further substitution of B for A, but by dropping A atoms from the lattice to leave vacant sites. Under these circumstances, the density and parameter curves will show sudden changes in slope, or even maxima or minima, at the composition x. Furthermore, the x-ray density calculated according to Eq. (12–2) will no longer agree with the direct density simply because Eq. (12–2), as usually used, applies only to normal solutions where all lattice sites are occupied; i.e., it is tacitly assumed there that ($n_{\text{solvent}} + n_{\text{solute}}$) equals the total number of lattice sites in the structure involved. The actual structure of a defect solid solution, including the proportion of vacant lattice sites at any given composition, can be determined by a comparison of the direct density with the x-ray density, calculated according to Eq. (12–2), and an analysis of the diffracted intensities.

12–4 Determination of solvus curves (disappearing-phase method). To return to the main subject of this chapter, we might now consider the methods used for determining the position of a solvus curve on a phase diagram. Such a curve forms the boundary between a single-phase solid region and a two-phase solid region, and the single-phase solid may be a primary or intermediate solid solution.

One method of locating such curves is based on the "lever law." This law, with reference to Fig. 12–7 for example, states that the relative proportions of α and β in an alloy of composition z in equilibrium at temperature T_1 is given by the relative lengths of the lines zy and zx, or that

$$W_\alpha(z - x) = W_\beta(y - z), \qquad (12–3)$$

where W_α and W_β denote the relative weights of α and β if x, y, and z are expressed in weight percent. It follows from Eq. (12–3) that the weight fraction of β in the alloy varies linearly with composition from 0 at point x to 1 at point y. The intensity of any diffraction line from the β phase also varies from zero at x to a maximum at y, but the variation with weight percent B is not generally linear.* Nevertheless, this variation may be used to locate the point x. A series of alloys in the two-phase region

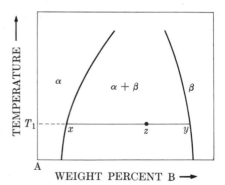

FIG. 12–7. Lever-law construction for finding the relative amounts of two phases in a two-phase field.

* The reasons for nonlinearity are discussed in Sec. 14–9.

is brought to equilibrium at temperature T_1 and quenched. From diffraction patterns made at room temperature, the ratio of the intensity I_β of a prominent line of the β phase to the intensity I_α of a prominent line of the α phase is plotted as a function of weight percent B. The composition at which the ratio I_β/I_α extrapolates to zero is taken as the point x. (Use of the ratio I_β/I_α rather than I_β alone eliminates the effect of any change which may occur in the intensity of the incident beam from one diffraction pattern to another. However, this ratio also varies nonlinearly with weight percent B.) Other points on the solvus curve are located by similar experiments on alloys quenched from other temperatures. This method is known, for obvious reasons, as the disappearing-phase method.

Since the curve of I_β/I_α vs. weight percent B is not linear, high accuracy in the extrapolation depends on having several experimental points close to the phase boundary which is being determined. The accuracy of the disappearing-phase method is therefore governed by the sensitivity of the x-ray method in detecting small amounts of a second phase in a mixture, and this sensitivity varies widely from one alloy system to another. The intensity of a diffraction line depends on, among other things, the atomic scattering factor f, which in turn is almost directly proportional to the atomic number Z. Therefore, if A and B have nearly the same atomic number, the α and β phases will consist of atoms having almost the same scattering powers, and the intensities of the α and β diffraction patterns will also be roughly equal when the two phases are present in equal amounts. Under favorable circumstances such as these, an x-ray pattern can reveal the presence of less than 1 percent of a second phase. On the other hand, if the atomic number of B is considerably less than that of A, the intensity of the β pattern may be so much lower than that of the α pattern that a relatively large amount of β in a two-phase mixture will go completely undetected. This amount may exceed 50 percent in extreme cases, where the atomic numbers of A and B differ by some 70 or 80 units. Under such circumstances, the disappearing-phase x-ray method is practically worthless. On the whole, the microscope is superior to x-rays when the disappearing-phase method is used, inasmuch as the sensitivity of the microscope in detecting the presence of a second phase is generally very high and independent of the atomic numbers of the elements involved. However, this sensitivity does depend on the particle size of the second phase, and if this is very small, as it often is at low temperatures, the second phase may not be detectable under the microscope. Hence the method of microscopic examination is not particularly accurate for the determination of solvus curves at low temperatures.

Whichever technique is used to detect the second phase, the accuracy of the disappearing-phase method increases as the width of the two-phase region decreases. If the $(\alpha + \beta)$ region is only a few percent wide, then the relative amounts of α and β will vary rapidly with slight changes in the total composition of the alloy, and this rapid variation of W_α/W_β will enable the phase boundary to be fixed quite precisely. This is true, for the x-ray method, even if the atomic numbers of A and B are widely different, because, if the $(\alpha + \beta)$ region is narrow, the compositions of α and β do not differ very much and neither do their x-ray scattering powers.

12–5 Determination of solvus curves (parametric method).

As we have just seen, the disappearing-phase method of locating the boundary of the α field is based on a determination of the composition at which the β phase just disappears from a series of $(\alpha + \beta)$ alloys. The parametric method, on the other hand, is based on observations of the α solid solution itself. This method depends on the fact, previously mentioned, that the lattice parameter of a solid solution generally changes with composition up to the saturation limit, and then remains constant beyond that point.

Suppose the exact location of the solvus curve shown in Fig. 12–8(a) is to be determined. A series of alloys, 1 to 7, is brought to equilibrium at temperature T_1, where the α field is thought to have almost its maximum width, and quenched to room temperature. The lattice parameter of α is measured for each alloy and plotted against alloy composition, resulting in a curve such as that shown in Fig. 12–8(b). This curve has two branches: an inclined branch bc, which shows how the parameter of α varies with the composition of α, and a horizontal branch de, which shows that the α phase in alloys 6 and 7 is saturated, because its lattice parameter does not change with change in alloy composition. In fact, alloys 6 and 7 are in a two-phase region at temperature T_1, and the only difference between them is in the amounts of saturated α they contain. The limit of the α field at temperature T_1 is therefore given by the intersection of the two branches of

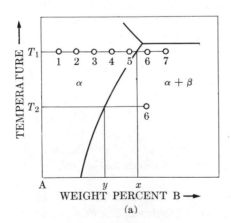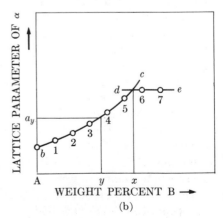

Fig. 12–8. Parametric method for determining a solvus curve.

the parameter curve. In this way, we have located one point on the solvus curve, namely x percent B at T_1.

Other points could be found in a similar manner. For example, if the same series of alloys were equilibrated at temperature T_2, a parameter curve similar to Fig. 12–8(b) would be obtained, but its inclined branch would be shorter and its horizontal branch lower. But heat treatments and parameter measurements on all these alloys are unnecessary, once the parameter-composition curve of the solid solution has been established. Only one two-phase alloy is needed to determine the rest of the solvus. Thus, if alloy 6 is equilibrated at T_2 and then quenched, it will contain α saturated at that temperature. Suppose the measured parameter of α in this alloy is a_y. Then, from the parameter-composition curve, we find that α of parameter a_y contains y percent B. This fixes a point on the solvus at temperature T_2. Points on the solvus at other temperatures may be found by equilibrating the same alloy, alloy 6, at various temperatures, quenching, and measuring the lattice parameter of the contained α.

The parameter-composition curve, branch bc of Fig. 12–8(b), thus serves as a sort of master curve for the determination of the whole solvus. For a given accuracy of lattice parameter measurement, the accuracy with which the solvus can be located depends markedly on the slope of the parameter-composition curve. If this curve is nearly flat, i.e., if changes in the composition of the solid solution produce very small changes in parameter, then the composition, as determined from the parameter, will be subject to considerable error and so will the location of the solvus. However, if the curve is steep, just the opposite is true, and relatively crude parameter measurements may suffice to fix the location of the solvus quite accurately. In either case, relative parameter measurements are just as good as absolute parameter measurements of the same accuracy.

Figure 12–9 illustrates the use of the parametric method in determining the solid solubility of antimony in copper as a function of temperature. The sloping curve in (a) was found from parameter measurements made on a series of alloys, containing from 0 to about 12 weight percent Sb, equilibrated at 630°C. The horizontal lines represent the parameters of two-phase alloys, containing about 12 weight percent Sb, equilibrated at the temperatures indicated. The solvus curve constructed from these data is given in (b), together with adjoining portions of the phase diagram.

In most cases, the parametric method is more accurate than the disappearing-phase method, whether based on x-ray measurements or microscopic examination, in the determination of solvus curves at low temperatures. As mentioned earlier, both x-ray diffraction and microscopic examination may fail to disclose the presence of small amounts of a second phase, although for different reasons. When this occurs, the disappearing-phase method always results in a measured extent of solubility *higher* than

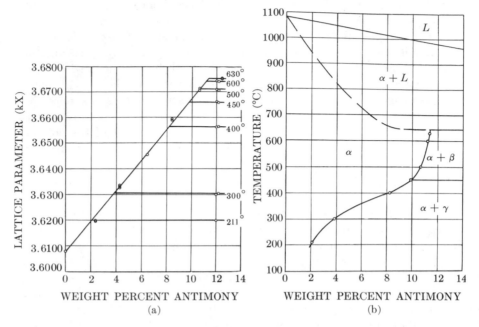

FIG. 12-9. Solvus curve determination in the copper-antimony system by the parametric method: (a) parameter *vs.* composition curve; (b) solubility *vs.* temperature curve. (J. C. Mertz and C. H. Mathewson, *Trans. A.I.M.E.* **124**, 59, 1937.)

the actual extent. But the parametric method, since it is based on measurements made on the phase whose range of solubility is being determined (the α phase), is not influenced by any property of the second phase (the β phase). The β phase may have an x-ray scattering power much higher or lower than that of the α phase, and the β phase may precipitate in the form of large particles or small ones, without affecting the parameter measurements made on the α phase.

Note that the parametric method is not confined to determining the extent of primary solid solutions, as in the examples given above. It may also be used to determine the solvus curves which bound an intermediate solid solution on the phase diagram. Note also that the parametric method may be employed even when the crystal structure of the α phase is so complex that its diffraction lines cannot be indexed. In this case, the plane spacing d corresponding to some high-angle line, or, even more directly, the 2θ value of the line, is plotted against composition and the resulting curve used in exactly the same way as a parameter-composition curve. In fact, the "parametric" method could be based on the measurement of any property of the solid solution which changes with the composition of the solid solution, e.g., its electric resistivity.

12-6 Ternary systems. The determination of a ternary phase diagram is naturally more complicated than that of a binary diagram, because of the extra composition variable involved, but the same general principles can be applied. The x-ray methods described above, based on either the disappearing-phase or the parametric technique, can be used with very little modification and have proved to be very helpful in the study of ternary systems.

Phase equilibria in a ternary system can only be represented completely in three dimensions, since there are three independent variables (two compositions and the temperature). The composition is plotted in an equilateral triangle whose corners represent the three pure components, A, B, and C, and the temperature is plotted at right angles to the plane of the composition triangle. Any isothermal section of the three-dimensional model is thus an equilateral triangle on which the phase equilibria at that temperature can be depicted in two dimensions. For this reason we usually prefer to study ternary systems by determining the phase equilibria at a number of selected temperatures.

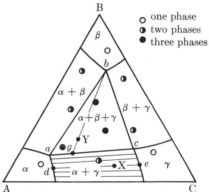

FIG. 12-10. Isothermal section of hypothetical ternary diagram.

The study of a ternary system of components A, B, and C begins with a determination of the three binary phase diagrams AB, BC, and CA, if these are not already known. We then make up a number of ternary alloys, choosing their compositions almost at random but with some regard for what the binary diagrams may suggest the ternary equilibria to be. The diffraction patterns of these exploratory alloys will disclose the number and kind of phases at equilibrium in each alloy at the temperature selected. These preliminary data will roughly delineate the various phase fields on the isothermal section, and will suggest what other alloys need be prepared in order to fix the phase boundaries more exactly.

Suppose these preliminary results suggest an isothermal section of the kind shown in Fig. 12-10, where the phase boundaries have been drawn to conform to the diffraction results represented by the small circles. This section shows three terminal ternary solid solutions, α, β, and γ, joined in pairs by three two-phase regions, ($\alpha + \beta$), ($\beta + \gamma$), and ($\alpha + \gamma$), and in the center a single region where the three phases, α, β, and γ, are in equilibrium.

In a single-phase region the composition of the phase involved, say α, is continuously variable. In a two-phase region tie lines exist, just as in

binary diagrams, along which the relative amounts of the two phases change
but not their compositions. Thus in the $(\alpha + \gamma)$ field of Fig. 12–10, tie
lines have been drawn to connect the single-phase compositions which are
in equilibrium in the two-phase field. Along the line de, for example, α of
composition d is in equilibrium with γ of composition e, and the relative
amounts of these two phases can be found by the lever law. Thus the constitution of alloy X is given by the relation

$$W_\alpha(Xd) = W_\gamma(Xe).$$

Both the relative amounts and the compositions of the two phases will vary
along any line which is not a tie line.

In a three-phase field, the compositions of the phases are fixed and are
given by the corners of the three-phase triangle. Thus the compositions
of α, β, and γ which are at equilibrium in any alloy within the three-phase
field of Fig. 12–10 are given by a, b, and c, respectively. To determine the

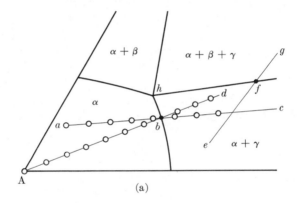

(a)

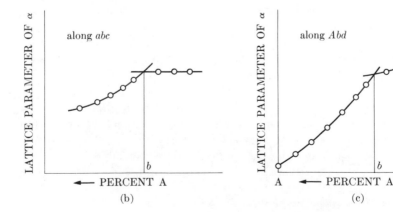

FIG. 12–11. Parametric method of locating phase boundaries in ternary diagrams.

relative amounts of these phases, say in alloy Y, we draw a line through Y to any corner of the triangle, say b, and apply the lever law:

$$W_\beta(bY) = W_{\alpha+\gamma}(Yg)$$

and

$$W_\alpha(ag) = W_\gamma(gc).$$

These relations form the basis of the disappearing-phase method of locating the sides and corners of the three-phase triangle.

Parametric methods are very useful in locating phase boundaries on all portions of the isothermal section. Suppose, for example, that we wish to determine the $\alpha/(\alpha + \gamma)$ boundary of the phase diagram in Fig. 12–11(a). Then we might prepare a series of alloys along the line abc, where bc is a tie line in the $(\alpha + \gamma)$ field, and measure the parameter of α in each one. The resulting parameter-composition curve would then look like Fig. 12–11(b), since the composition and parameter of α in alloys along bc is constant. However, we do not generally know the direction of the line bc at this stage, because tie lines cannot be located by any geometrical construction but must be determined by experiment. But suppose we measure the parameter of α along some arbitrary line, say the line Abd. Then we can expect the parameter-composition curve to resemble Fig. 12–11(c). The parameter of α along the line bd is not constant, since bd is not a tie line, but in general it will change at a different rate than along the line Ab in the one-phase field. This allows us to locate the point b on the phase boundary by the point of inflection on the parameter curve.

The point f on the $(\alpha + \gamma)/(\alpha + \beta + \gamma)$ boundary can be located in similar fashion, along a line such as efg chosen at random. Along ef the parameter of α will change continuously, because ef crosses over a series of tie lines, but along fg in the three-phase field the parameter of α will be constant and equal to the parameter of saturated α of composition h. The parameter-composition curve will therefore have the form of Fig. 12–11(b).

PROBLEMS

12–1. Metals A and B form a terminal solid solution α, cubic in structure. The variation of the lattice parameter of α with composition, determined by quenching single-phase alloys from an elevated temperature, is found to be linear, the parameter varying from 3.6060A for pure A to 3.6140A in α containing 4.0 weight percent B. The solvus curve is to be determined by quenching a two-phase alloy containing 5.0 weight percent B from a series of temperatures and measuring the parameter of the contained α. How accurately must the parameter be measured if the solvus curve is to be located within ± 0.1 weight percent B at any temperature?

12–2. The two-phase alloy mentioned in Prob. 12–1, after being quenched from a series of temperatures, contains α having the following measured parameters:

Temperature	Parameter
100°C	3.6082A
200	3.6086
300	3.6091
400	3.6098
500	3.6106
600	3.6118

Plot the solvus curve over this temperature range. What is the solubility of B in A at 440°C?

CHAPTER 13

ORDER-DISORDER TRANSFORMATIONS

13–1 Introduction. In most substitutional solid solutions, the two kinds of atoms A and B are arranged more or less at random on the atomic sites of the lattice. In solutions of this kind the only major effect of a change in temperature is to increase or decrease the amplitude of thermal vibration. But, as noted in Sec. 2–7, there are some solutions which have this random structure only at elevated temperatures. When these solutions are cooled below a certain critical temperature T_c, the A atoms arrange themselves in an orderly, periodic manner on one set of atomic sites, and the B atoms do likewise on another set. The solution is then said to be *ordered* or to possess a *superlattice*. When this periodic arrangement of A and B atoms persists over very large distances in the crystal, it is known as *long-range order*. If the ordered solution is heated above T_c, the atomic arrangement becomes random again and the solution is said to be *disordered*.

The change in atom arrangement which occurs on ordering produces changes in a large number of physical and chemical properties, and the existence of ordering may be inferred from some of these changes. However, the only conclusive evidence for a disorder-order transformation is a particular kind of change in the x-ray diffraction pattern of the substance. Evidence of this kind was first obtained by the American metallurgist Bain in 1923, for a gold-copper solid solution having the composition $AuCu_3$. Since that time, the same phenomenon has been discovered in many other alloy systems.

13–2 Long-range order in $AuCu_3$. The gold and copper atoms of $AuCu_3$, above a critical temperature of about 395°C, are arranged more or less at random on the atomic sites of a face-centered cubic lattice, as illustrated in Fig. 13–1(a). If the disorder is complete, the probability that a particular site is occupied by a gold atom is simply $\frac{1}{4}$, the atomic fraction of gold in the alloy, and the probability that it is occupied by a copper atom is $\frac{3}{4}$, the atomic fraction of copper. These probabilities are the same for every site and, considering the structure as a whole, we can regard each site as being occupied by a statistically "average" gold-copper atom. Below the critical temperature, the gold atoms in a perfectly ordered alloy occupy only the corner positions of the unit cube and the copper atoms the face-centered positions, as illustrated in Fig. 13–1(b). Both structures are cubic and have practically the same lattice parameters. Figure 13–2 shows

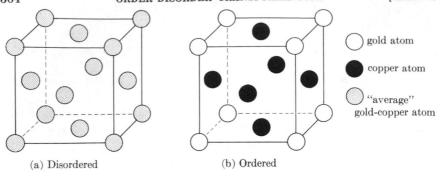

FIG. 13-1.   Unit cells of the disordered and ordered forms of AuCu₃.

how the two atomic arrangements differ on a particular lattice plane. The same kind of ordering has been observed in PtCu₃, FeNi₃, MnNi₃, and (MnFe)Ni₃.

What differences will exist between the diffraction patterns of ordered and disordered AuCu₃? Since there is only a very slight change in the size of the unit cell on ordering, and none in its shape, there will be practically no change in the positions of the diffraction lines. But the change in the positions of the atoms must necessarily cause a change in line intensities. We can determine the nature of these changes by calculating the structure factor F for each atom arrangement:

(a) *Complete disorder.* The atomic scattering factor of the "average" gold-copper atom is given by

$$f_{av} = (\text{atomic fraction Au}) f_{Au} + (\text{atomic fraction Cu}) f_{Cu},$$

$$f_{av} = \tfrac{1}{4}f_{Au} + \tfrac{3}{4}f_{Cu}.$$

There are four "average" atoms per unit cell, at $0\,0\,0$, $\tfrac{1}{2}\,\tfrac{1}{2}\,0$, $\tfrac{1}{2}\,0\,\tfrac{1}{2}$, and $0\,\tfrac{1}{2}\,\tfrac{1}{2}$. Therefore the structure factor is given by

$$F = \Sigma f\, e^{2\pi i(hu+kv+lw)},$$

$$F = f_{av}[1 + e^{\pi i(h+k)} + e^{\pi i(h+l)} + e^{\pi i(k+l)}].$$

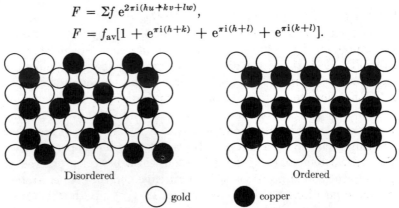

FIG. 13-2.   Atom arrangements on a {100} plane, disordered and ordered AuCu₃.

By example (d) of Sec. 4–6, this becomes

$$F = 4f_{av} = (f_{Au} + 3f_{Cu}), \text{ for } hkl \text{ unmixed,}$$

$$F = 0, \quad\quad\quad\quad\quad \text{for } hkl \text{ mixed.}$$

We therefore find, as might be expected, that the disordered alloy produces a diffraction pattern similar to that of any face-centered cubic metal, say pure gold or pure copper. No reflections of mixed indices are present.

(b) *Complete order.* Each unit cell now contains one gold atom, at 0 0 0, and three copper atoms, at $\frac{1}{2} \frac{1}{2} 0$, $\frac{1}{2} 0 \frac{1}{2}$, and $0 \frac{1}{2} \frac{1}{2}$.

$$F = f_{Au} + f_{Cu}[e^{\pi i(h+k)} + e^{\pi i(h+l)} + e^{\pi i(k+l)}];$$

$$F = (f_{Au} + 3f_{Cu}), \text{ for } hkl \text{ unmixed,}$$

$$F = (f_{Au} - f_{Cu}), \text{ for } hkl \text{ mixed.}$$

(13-1)

The ordered alloy thus produces diffraction lines for all values of hkl, and its diffraction pattern therefore resembles that of a simple cubic substance. In other words, there has been a change of Bravais lattice on ordering; the Bravais lattice of the disordered alloy is face-centered cubic and that of the ordered alloy simple cubic.

The diffraction lines from planes of unmixed indices are called *fundamental lines*, since they occur at the same positions and with the same intensities in the patterns of both ordered and disordered alloys. The extra lines which appear in the pattern of an ordered alloy, arising from planes of mixed indices, are called *superlattice lines*, and their presence is direct evidence that ordering has taken place. The physical reason for the formation of superlattice lines may be deduced from an examination of Fig. 13–1. Consider reflection from the (100) planes of the disordered structure, and let an incident beam of wavelength λ make such an angle of incidence θ that the path difference between rays scattered by adjacent (100) planes is one whole wavelength. But there is another plane halfway between these two, containing, on the average, exactly the same distribution of gold and copper atoms. This plane scatters a wave which is therefore λ/2 out of phase with the wave scattered by either adjacent (100) plane and of exactly the same amplitude. Complete cancellation results and there is no 100 reflection. In the ordered alloy, on the other hand, adjacent (100) planes contain both gold and copper atoms, but the plane halfway between contains only copper atoms. The rays scattered by the (100) planes and those scattered by the midplanes are still exactly out of phase, but they now differ in amplitude because of the difference in scattering power of the gold and copper atoms. The ordered structure therefore produces a weak 100 reflection. And as Eqs. (13–1) show, all the superlattice lines are much weaker than the fundamental lines, since their structure factors involve

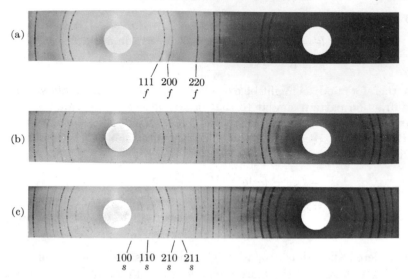

FIG. 13-3. Powder patterns of AuCu₃ (very coarse-grained) made with filtered copper radiation: (a) quenched from 440°C (disordered); (b) held 30 min at 360°C and quenched (partially ordered); (c) slowly cooled from 360°C to room temperature (completely ordered).

the difference, rather than the sum, of the atomic scattering factors of each atom. This effect is shown quite clearly in Fig. 13-3, where f and s are used to designate the fundamental and superlattice lines, respectively.

At low temperatures, the long-range order in AuCu₃ is virtually perfect but, as T_c is approached, some randomness sets in. This departure from perfect order can be described by means of the long-range order parameter S, defined as follows:

$$S = \frac{r_A - F_A}{1 - F_A},\qquad(13\text{-}2)$$

where r_A = fraction of A sites occupied by the "right" atoms, i.e., A atoms, and F_A = fraction of A atoms in the alloy. When the long-range order is perfect, $r_A = 1$ by definition, and therefore $S = 1$. When the atomic arrangement is completely random, $r_A = F_A$ and $S = 0$. For example, consider 100 atoms of AuCu₃, i.e., 25 gold atoms and 75 copper atoms. Suppose the ordering is not perfect and only 22 of these gold atoms are on "gold sites," i.e., cube corner positions, the other 3 being on "copper sites." Then, considering the gold atom as the A atom in Eq. (13-2), we find that $r_A = \frac{22}{25} = 0.88$ and $F_A = \frac{25}{100} = 0.25$. Therefore,

$$S = \frac{0.88 - 0.25}{1.00 - 0.25} = 0.84$$

describes the degree of long-range order present. The same result is obtained if we consider the distribution of copper atoms.

Any departure from perfect long-range order in a superlattice causes the superlattice lines to become weaker. It may be shown that the structure factors of partially ordered AuCu₃ are given by

$$F = (f_{Au} + 3f_{Cu}), \text{ for } hkl \text{ unmixed},$$
$$F = S(f_{Au} - f_{Cu}), \text{ for } hkl \text{ mixed}.$$

(13-3)

Comparing these equations with Eqs. (13-1), we note that only the superlattice lines are affected. But the effect is a strong one, because the intensity of a superlattice line is proportional to $|F|^2$ and therefore to S^2. For example, a decrease in order from $S = 1.00$ to $S = 0.84$ decreases the intensity of a superlattice line by about 30 percent. The weakening of superlattice lines by partial disorder is illustrated in Fig. 13-3. By comparing the integrated intensity ratio of a superlattice and fundamental line, we can determine S experimentally.

Values of S obtained in this way are shown in Fig. 13-4 as a function of the absolute temperature T, expressed as a fraction of the critical temperature T_c. For AuCu₃ the value of S decreases gradually, with increasing temperature, to about 0.8 at T_c and then drops abruptly to zero. Above T_c the atomic distribution is random and there are no superlattice lines. Recalling the approximate law of conservation of diffracted energy, already alluded to in Sec. 4–12, we might expect that the energy lost from the superlattice lines should appear in some form in the pattern of a completely disordered alloy. As a matter of fact it does, in the form of a weak diffuse background extending over the whole

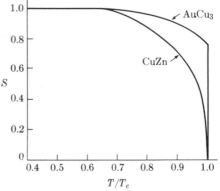

FIG. 13-4. Variation of the long-range order parameter S with temperature, for AuCu₃ and CuZn. (AuCu₃ data from D. T. Keating and B. E. Warren, *J. Appl. Phys.* **22**, 286, 1951; CuZn data from D. Chipman and B. E. Warren, *J. Appl. Phys.* **21**, 696, 1950.)

range of 2θ. This diffuse scattering is due to randomness, and is another illustration of the general law that any departure from perfect periodicity of atom arrangement results in some diffuse scattering at non-Bragg angles.

Von Laue showed that if two kinds of atoms A and B are distributed completely at random in a solid solution, then the intensity of the diffuse scattering produced is given by

$$I_D = k(f_A - f_B)^2,$$

(13-4)

where k is a constant for any one composition, and f_A and f_B are atomic scattering factors. Both f_A and f_B decrease as $(\sin \theta)/\lambda$ increases, and so

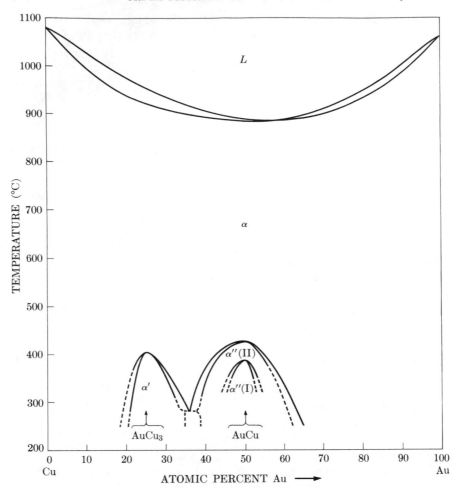

FIG. 13–5. Phase diagram of the gold-copper system. Two-phase fields not labeled for lack of room. (Compiled from *Metals Handbook*, American Society for Metals, 1948; J. B. Newkirk, *Trans. A.I.M.E.* **197**, 823, 1953; F. N. Rhines, W. E. Bond, and R. A. Rummel, *Trans. A.S.M.* **47**, 1955; R. A. Oriani, *Acta Metallurgica* **2**, 608, 1954; and G. C. Kuczynski, unpublished results.)

does their difference; therefore I_D is a maximum at $2\theta = 0$ and decreases as 2θ increases. This diffuse scattering is very difficult to measure experimentally. It is weak to begin with and is superimposed on other forms of diffuse scattering that may also be present, namely, Compton modified scattering, temperature-diffuse scattering, etc. It is worth noting, however, that Eq. (13–4) is quite general and applies to any random solid solution, whether or not it is capable of undergoing ordering at low temperatures. We will return to this point in Sec. 13–5.

Another aspect of long-range order that requires some mention is the effect of change in composition. Since the ratio of corner sites to face-centered sites in the $AuCu_3$ lattice is $1:3$, it follows that perfect order can only be attained when the ratio of gold to copper atoms is also exactly $1:3$. But ordering can also take place in alloys containing somewhat more, or somewhat less, than 25 atomic percent gold, as shown by the phase diagram of Fig. 13–5. (Here the ordered phase is designated α' to distinguish it from the disordered phase α stable at high temperatures.) In an ordered alloy containing somewhat more than 25 atomic percent gold, all the corner sites are occupied by gold atoms, and the remainder of the gold atoms occupy some of the face-centered sites normally occupied by copper atoms. Just the reverse is true for an alloy containing less than 25 atomic percent gold. But, as the phase diagram shows, there are limits to the variation in composition which the ordered lattice will accept without becoming unstable. In fact, if the gold content is increased to about 50 atomic percent, an entirely different ordered alloy, AuCu, can be formed.

13–3 Other examples of long-range order. Before considering the ordering transformation in AuCu, which is rather complex, we might examine the behaviour of β-brass. This alloy is stable at room temperature over a composition range of about 46 to almost 50 atomic percent zinc, and so may be represented fairly closely by the formula CuZn. At high temperatures its structure is, statistically, body-centered cubic, with the copper and zinc atoms distributed at random. Below a critical temperature of about 465°C, ordering occurs; the cell corners are then occupied only by copper atoms and the cell centers only by zinc atoms, as indicated in Fig. 13–6. The ordered alloy therefore has the CsCl structure and its Bravais lattice is simple cubic. Other alloys which have the same ordered structure are CuBe, CuPd, AgZn, FeCo, NiAl,* etc. Not all these alloys, however,

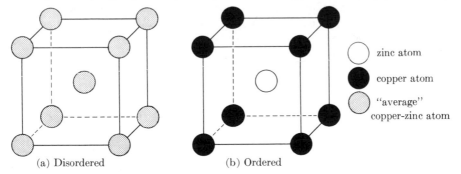

(a) Disordered   (b) Ordered

○ zinc atom

● copper atom

◉ "average" copper-zinc atom

FIG. 13–6.   Unit cells of the disordered and ordered forms of CuZn.

* NiAl is the β phase referred to in Sec. 12–3 as having a defect lattice at certain compositions.

undergo an order-disorder transformation, since some of them remain ordered right up to their melting points.

By calculations similar to those made in the previous section, the structure factors of β-brass, for the ideal composition CuZn, can be shown to be

$$F = (f_{Cu} + f_{Zn}), \text{ for } (h + k + l) \text{ even,}$$
$$F = S(f_{Cu} - f_{Zn}), \text{ for } (h + k + l) \text{ odd.}$$
$$(13\text{--}5)$$

In other words, there are fundamental lines, those for which $(h + k + l)$ is even, which are unchanged in intensity whether the alloy is ordered or not. And there are superlattice lines, those for which $(h + k + l)$ is odd, which are present only in the pattern of an alloy exhibiting some degree of order, and then with an intensity which depends on the degree of order present.

Figure 13–4 indicates how the degree of long-range order in CuZn varies with the temperature. The order parameter for CuZn decreases continuously to zero as T approaches T_c, whereas for AuCu₃ it remains fairly high right up to T_c and then drops abruptly to zero. There is also a notable difference in the velocity of the disorder-order transformation in these two alloys. The transformation in AuCu₃ is relatively so sluggish that the structure of this alloy at any temperature can be retained by quenching to room temperature, as evidenced by the diffraction patterns in Fig. 13–3. In CuZn, on the other hand, ordering is so rapid that disorder existing at an elevated temperature cannot be retained at room temperature, no matter how rapid the quench. Therefore, any specimen of CuZn at room temperature can be presumed to be completely ordered. (The S vs. T/T_c curve for CuZn, shown in Fig. 13–4, was necessarily based on measurements made *at* temperature with a high-temperature diffractometer.)

Not all order-disorder transformations are as simple, crystallographically speaking, as those occurring in AuCu₃ and CuZn. Complexities are encountered, for example, in gold-copper alloys at or near the composition AuCu; these alloys become ordered below a critical temperature of about 420°C or lower, depending on the composition (see Fig. 13–5). Whereas the ratio of gold to copper atoms in AuCu₃ is 1:3, this ratio is 1:1 for AuCu, and the structure of ordered AuCu must therefore be such that the ratio of gold sites to copper sites is also 1:1. Two ordered forms are produced, depending on the ordering temperature, and these have different crystal structures:

(a) Tetragonal AuCu, designated $\alpha''(\text{I})$, formed by slow cooling from high temperatures or by isothermal ordering below about 380°C. The unit cell is shown in Fig. 13–7(a). It is almost cubic in shape, since c/a equals about 0.93, and the gold and copper atoms occupy alternate (002) planes.

(b) Orthorhombic AuCu, designated $\alpha''(\text{II})$, formed by isothermal ordering between about 420° and 380°C. Its very unusual unit cell, shown

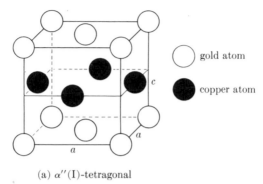

(a) α''(I)-tetragonal

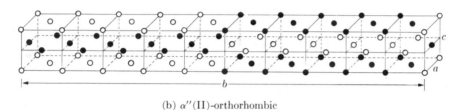

(b) α''(II)-orthorhombic

FIG. 13–7.   Unit cells of the two ordered forms of AuCu.

in Fig. 13–7(b), is formed by placing ten tetragonal cells like that of α''(I) side by side and then translating five of them by the vectors $c/2$ and $a/2$ with respect to the other five. (Some distortion occurs, with the result that each of the ten component cells, which together make up the true unit cell, is not tetragonal but orthorhombic; i.e., b is not exactly ten times a, but equal to about $10.02a$. The c/a ratio is about 0.92.) The result is a structure in which the atoms in any one (002) plane are wholly gold for a distance of $b/2$, then wholly copper for a distance of $b/2$, and so on.

From a crystallographic viewpoint, there is a fundamental difference between the kind of ordering which occurs in AuCu$_3$ or CuZn, on the one hand, and that which occurs in AuCu, on the other. In AuCu$_3$ there is a change in Bravais lattice, but no change in crystal system, accompanying the disorder-order transformation: both the disordered and ordered forms are cubic. In AuCu, the ordering process changes both the Bravais lattice and the crystal system, the latter from cubic to tetragonal, AuCu(I), or orthorhombic, AuCu(II). These changes are due to changes in the symmetry of atom arrangement, because the crystal system to which a given structure belongs depends ultimately on the symmetry of that structure (see Sec. 2–4). In the gold-copper system, the disordered phase α is cubic, because the arrangement of gold and copper atoms on a face-centered lattice has cubic symmetry, in a statistical sense, at any composition. In AuCu$_3$, the ordering process puts the gold and copper atoms in definite positions in each cell (Fig. 13–1), but this arrangement still has cubic symmetry so the cell remains cubic. In ordered AuCu, on the other hand, to consider only the tetragonal modification, the atom arrangement is such that there is no longer three-fold rotational symmetry about directions of the form ⟨111⟩. Inasmuch as this is the minimum symmetry requirement for the cubic system, this cell [Fig. 13–7(a)] is not cubic. There is, however, four-fold rotational symmetry about [001], but not about [010] or [100]. The ordered form is accordingly tetragonal. The segregation of gold and copper atoms on alternate (002) planes causes c to differ from a, in this case in the direction of a small contraction of c relative to a, because of the difference in size between the gold and copper atoms. But even if c were equal to a, the cell shown in Fig. 13–7(a) would still be classified as tetragonal on the basis of its symmetry.

13–4 Detection of superlattice lines. We have already seen that the intensity of a superlattice line from an ordered solid solution is much lower than that of a fundamental line. Will it ever be so low that the line cannot be detected? We can make an approximate estimate by ignoring the variation in multiplicity factor and Lorentz-polarization factor from line to line, and assuming that the relative integrated intensities of a superlattice and fundamental line are given by their relative $|F|^2$ values. For fully ordered AuCu$_3$, for example, we find from Eqs. (13–1) that

$$\frac{\text{Intensity (superlattice line)}}{\text{Intensity (fundamental line)}} \approx \frac{|F|_s^2}{|F|_f^2} = \frac{(f_{\text{Au}} - f_{\text{Cu}})^2}{(f_{\text{Au}} + 3f_{\text{Cu}})^2}. \qquad (13\text{–}6)$$

At $(\sin\theta)/\lambda = 0$ we can put $f = Z$ and, since the atomic numbers of gold and copper are 79 and 29, respectively, Eq. (13–6) becomes, for small scattering angles,

$$\frac{I_s}{I_f} \approx \frac{(79 - 29)^2}{[79 + 3(29)]^2} \approx 0.09.$$

Superlattice lines are therefore only about one-tenth as strong as fundamental lines, but they can still be detected without any difficulty, as shown by Fig. 13–3.

But in CuZn, even when fully ordered, the situation is much worse. The atomic numbers of copper and zinc are 29 and 30, respectively, and, making the same assumptions as before, we find that

$$\frac{I_s}{I_f} \approx \frac{(f_{\text{Cu}} - f_{\text{Zn}})^2}{(f_{\text{Cu}} + f_{\text{Zn}})^2} \approx \frac{(29 - 30)^2}{(29 + 30)^2} \approx 0.0003.$$

This ratio is so low that the superlattice lines of ordered CuZn can be detected by x-ray diffraction only under very special circumstances. The same is true of any superlattice of elements A and B which differ in atomic

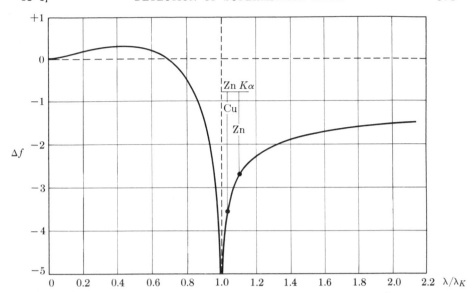

FIG. 13–8.   Variation of Δf with λ/λ_K. (Data from R. W. James, *The Optical Principles of the Diffraction of X-Rays*, G. Bell and Sons, Ltd., London, 1948, p. 608.)

number by only one or two units, because the superlattice-line intensity is generally proportional to $(f_A - f_B)^2$.

There is one way, however, of increasing the intensity of a superlattice line relative to that of a fundamental line, when the two atoms involved have almost the same atomic numbers, and that is by the proper choice of the incident wavelength. In the discussion of atomic scattering factors given in Sec. 4–3 it was tacitly assumed that the atomic scattering factor was independent of the incident wavelength, as long as the quantity $(\sin \theta)/\lambda$ was constant. This is not quite true. When the incident wavelength λ is nearly equal to the wavelength λ_K of the K absorption edge of the scattering element, then the atomic scattering factor of that element may be several units lower than it is when λ is very much shorter than λ_K. If we put f = atomic scattering factor for $\lambda \ll \lambda_K$ (this is the usual value as tabulated, for example, in Appendix 8) and Δf = change in f when λ is near λ_K, then the quantity $f' = f + \Delta f$ gives the value of the atomic scattering factor when λ is near λ_K. Figure 13–8 shows approximately how Δf varies with λ/λ_K, and this curve may be used to estimate the correction Δf which must be applied for any particular combination of wavelength and scattering element.*

---

* Strictly speaking, Δf depends also on the atomic number of the scattering element, which means that a different correction curve is required for every element. But the variation of Δf with Z is not very large, and Fig. 13–8, which is computed for an element of medium atomic number (about 50), can be used with fairly good accuracy as a master correction curve for any element.

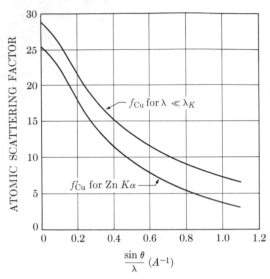

FIG. 13–9. Atomic scattering factors of copper for two different wavelengths.

When λ/λ_K is less than about 0.8, the correction is practically negligible. When λ/λ_K exceeds about 1.6, the correction is practically constant and independent of small variations in λ_K. But when λ is near λ_K, the slope of the correction curve is quite steep, which means that the Δf correction can be quite different for two elements of nearly the same atomic number. By taking advantage of this fact, we can often increase the intensity of a superlattice line above its normal value.

For example, if ordered CuZn is examined with Mo $K\alpha$ radiation, λ/λ_K is 0.52 for the copper atom and 0.55 for the zinc atom. The value of Δf is then about $+0.3$ for either atom, and the intensity of a superlattice line would be proportional to $[(29 + 0.3) - (30 + 0.3)]^2 = 1$ at low values of 2θ. Under these circumstances the line would be invisible in the presence of the usual background. But if Zn $K\alpha$ radiation is used, λ/λ_K becomes 1.04 and 1.11 for the copper and zinc atoms, respectively, and Fig. 13–8 shows that the corrections are -3.6 and -2.7, respectively. The super-lattice-line intensity is now proportional to $[(29 - 3.6) - (30 - 2.7)]^2 = 3.6$, which is large enough to permit detection of the line. Cu $K\alpha$ radia-tion also offers some advantage over Mo $K\alpha$, but not so large an advantage as Zn $K\alpha$, and order in CuZn can be detected with Cu $K\alpha$ only if crystal-monochromated radiation is used.

To a very good approximation, the change in atomic scattering factor Δf is independent of scattering angle and therefore a constant for all lines on the diffraction pattern. Hence, we can construct a corrected f' curve by adding, algebraically, the same value Δf to all the ordinates of the usual f vs. $(\sin \theta)/\lambda$ curve, as in Fig. 13–9.

By thus taking advantage of this anomalous change in scattering factor near an absorption edge, we are really pushing the x-ray method about as far as it will go. A better tool for the detection of order in alloys of metals of nearly the same atomic number is neutron diffraction (Appendix 14). Two elements may differ in atomic number by only one unit and yet their neutron scattering powers may be entirely different, a situation conducive to high superlattice-line intensity.

13–5 Short-range order and clustering. Above the critical temperature T_c long-range order disappears and the atomic distribution becomes more or less random. This is indicated by the absence of superlattice lines from the powder pattern. But careful analysis of the diffuse scattering which forms the background of the pattern shows that perfect randomness is not attained. Instead, there is a greater than average tendency for *unlike* atoms to be nearest neighbors. This condition is known as *short-range order*.

For example, when perfect long-range order exists in $AuCu_3$, a gold atom located at 0 0 0 is surrounded by 12 copper atoms at $\frac{1}{2}$ $\frac{1}{2}$ 0 and equivalent positions (see Fig. 13–1), and any given copper atom is surrounded by 8 copper and 4 gold atoms. This kind of grouping is a direct result of the existing long-range order, which also requires that gold atoms be on corner sites and copper atoms on face-centered sites. Above T_c this order breaks down and, if the atomic distribution became truly random, a given gold atom might be found on either a corner or face-centered site. It would then have only $\frac{3}{4}(12) = 9$ copper atoms as nearest neighbors, since on the average 3 out of 4 atoms in the solution are copper. Actually, it is observed that some short-range order exists above T_c: at 460°C, for example, which is 65°C above T_c, there are on the average about 10.3 copper atoms around any given gold atom.

This is a quite general effect. Any solid solution which exhibits long-range order below a certain temperature exhibits some short-range order above that temperature. Above T_c the degree of short-range order decreases as the temperature is raised; i.e., increasing thermal agitation tends to make the atomic distribution more and more random. One interesting fact about short-range order is that it has also been found to exist in solid solutions which do *not* undergo long-range ordering at low temperatures, such as gold-silver and gold-nickel solutions.

We can imagine another kind of departure from randomness in a solid solution, namely, a tendency of *like* atoms to be close neighbors. This effect is known as *clustering*, and it has been observed in aluminum-silver and aluminum-zinc solutions. In fact, there is probably no such thing as a perfectly random solid solution. All real solutions probably exhibit either short-range ordering or clustering to a greater or lesser degree, simply be-

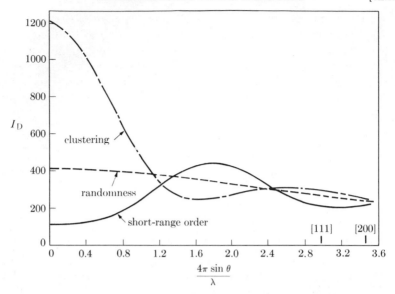

Fig. 13–10.   Calculated intensity I_D of diffuse scattering in powder patterns of solid solutions (here, the face-centered cubic alloy Ni$_4$Au) which exhibit complete randomness, short-range order, and clustering.   The short-range order curve is calculated on the basis of one additional unlike neighbor over the random configuration, and the clustering curve on the basis of one less unlike neighbor. (B. E. Warren and B. L. Averbach, *Modern Research Techniques in Physical Metallurgy*, American Society for Metals, Cleveland, 1953, p. 95.)

cause they are composed of unlike atoms with particular forces of attraction or repulsion operating between them.

The degree of short-range order or clustering may be defined in terms of a suitable parameter, just as long-range order is, and the value of this parameter may be related to the diffraction effects produced.   The general nature of these effects is illustrated in Fig. 13–10, where the intensity of the diffuse scattering is plotted, not against 2θ, but against a function of $\sin\theta$. (The fundamental lines are not included in Fig. 13–10 because their intensity is too high compared with the diffuse scattering shown, but the positions of two of them, 111 and 200, are indicated on the abscissa.)   If the atomic distribution is perfectly random, the scattered intensity decreases gradually as 2θ or $\sin\theta$ increases from zero, in accordance with Eq. (13–4).   If short-range order exists, the scattering at small angles becomes less intense and low broad maxima occur in the scattering curve; these maxima are usually located at the same angular positions as the sharp superlattice lines formed by long-range ordering.   Clustering causes strong scattering at low angles.

These effects, however, are all very weak and are masked by the other forms of diffuse scattering which are always present.   As a result, the details shown in Fig. 13–10 are never observed in an ordinary powder pattern made with filtered radiation. To disclose these details and so learn something about the structure of the solid solution, it is necessary to use strictly monochromatic radiation and to make allowances for the other forms of diffuse scattering, chiefly temperature-diffuse and Compton modified, which are always present.

PROBLEMS

13–1. A Debye-Scherrer pattern is made with Cu $K\alpha$ radiation of $AuCu_3$ quenched from a temperature T_1. The ratio of the integrated intensity of the 420 line to that of the 421 line is found to be 4.38. Calculate the value of the long-range order parameter S at temperature T_1. (Take the lattice parameter of $AuCu_3$ as 3.75A. Ignore the small difference between the Lorentz-polarization factors for these two lines and the corrections to the atomic scattering factors mentioned in Sec. 13–4.)

13–2. Calculate the ratio of the integrated intensity of the 100 superlattice line to that of the 110 fundamental line for fully ordered β-brass, if Cu $K\alpha$ radiation is used. Estimate the corrections to the atomic scattering factors from Fig. 13–8. The lattice parameter of β-brass (CuZn) is 2.95A.

13–3. (a) What is the Bravais lattice of AuCu(I), the ordered tetragonal modification?

(b) Calculate the structure factors for the disordered and ordered (tetragonal) forms of AuCu.

(c) On the basis of the calculations made in (b) and a consideration of the change in the c/a ratio, describe the differences between the powder patterns of the ordered (tetragonal) and disordered forms of AuCu.

CHAPTER 14

CHEMICAL ANALYSIS BY DIFFRACTION

14–1 Introduction. A given substance always produces a characteristic diffraction pattern, whether that substance is present in the pure state or as one constituent of a mixture of substances. This fact is the basis for the diffraction method of chemical analysis. *Qualitative analysis* for a particular substance is accomplished by identification of the pattern of that substance. *Quantitative analysis* is also possible, because the intensities of the diffraction lines due to one constituent of a mixture depend on the proportion of that constituent in the specimen.

The particular advantage of diffraction analysis is that it discloses the presence of a substance *as that substance actually exists in the sample,* and not in terms of its constituent chemical elements. For example, if a sample contains the compound A_xB_y, the diffraction method will disclose the presence of A_xB_y as such, whereas ordinary chemical analysis would show only the presence of elements A and B. Furthermore, if the sample contained both A_xB_y and A_xB_{2y}, both of these compounds would be disclosed by the diffraction method, but chemical analysis would again indicate only the presence of A and B.* To consider another example, chemical analysis of a plain carbon steel reveals only the amounts of iron, carbon, manganese, etc., which the steel contains, but gives no information regarding the phases present. Is the steel in question wholly martensitic, does it contain both martensite and austenite, or is it composed only of ferrite and cementite? Questions such as these can be answered by the diffraction method. Another rather obvious application of diffraction analysis is in distinguishing between different allotropic modifications of the same substance: solid silica, for example, exists in one amorphous and six crystalline modifications, and the diffraction patterns of these seven forms are all different.

Diffraction analysis is therefore useful whenever it is necessary to know the state of chemical combination of the elements involved or the particular phases in which they are present. As a result, the diffraction method

---

* Of course, if the sample contains only A and B, and if it can be safely assumed that each of these elements is wholly in a combined form, then the presence of A_xB_y and A_xB_{2y} can be demonstrated by calculations based on the amounts of A and B in the sample. But this method is not generally applicable, and it usually involves a prior assumption as to the constitution of the sample. For example, a determination of the total amounts of A and B present in a sample composed of A, A_xB_y, and B cannot, in itself, disclose the presence of A_xB_y, either qualitatively or quantitatively.

378

has been widely applied for the analysis of such materials as ores, clays, refractories, alloys, corrosion products, wear products, industrial dusts, etc. Compared with ordinary chemical analysis, the diffraction method has the additional advantages that it is usually much faster, requires only a very small sample, and is nondestructive.

QUALITATIVE ANALYSIS

14–2 Basic principles. The powder pattern of a substance is characteristic of that substance and forms a sort of fingerprint by which the substance may be identified. If we had on hand a collection of diffraction patterns for a great many substances, we could identify an unknown by preparing its diffraction pattern and then locating in our file of known patterns one which matched the pattern of the unknown exactly. The collection of known patterns has to be fairly large, if it is to be at all useful, and then pattern-by-pattern comparison in order to find a matching one becomes out of the question.

What is needed is a system of classifying the known patterns so that the one which matches the unknown can be located quickly. Such a system was devised by Hanawalt in 1936. Any one powder pattern is characterized by a set of *line positions 2θ* and a set of relative *line intensities I*. But the angular positions of the lines depend on the wavelength used, and a more fundamental quantity is the spacing d of the lattice planes forming each line. Hanawalt therefore decided to describe each pattern by listing the d and I values of its diffraction lines, and to arrange the known patterns in decreasing values of d for the strongest line in the pattern. This arrangement made possible a search procedure which would quickly locate the desired pattern. In addition, the problem of solving the pattern was avoided and the method could be used even when the crystal structure of the substance concerned was unknown.

14–3 The Hanawalt method. The task of building up a collection of known patterns was initiated by Hanawalt and his associates, who obtained and classified diffraction data on some 1000 different substances. This work was later extended by the American Society for Testing Materials with the assistance, on an international scale, of a number of other scientific societies. The ASTM first published a collection of diffraction data in 1941 in the form of a set of 3 × 5″ cards which contained data on some 1300 substances. Various supplementary sets have appeared from time to time, the most recent in 1955, and all the sets taken together now cover some 5900 substances. Most of these are elements and inorganic compounds, although some organic compounds and minerals are also included.

The original set (1941) and the first supplementary set (1944) have been out of print since 1947. Both of these sets were revised and reissued in 1949. The following sets are currently available:

Name of set	Section	Year issued	Approx. number of substances
Revised original	1	1949	1300
Revised first supplementary	2	1949	1300
Second supplementary	3	1949	1300
Fourth	4	1952	700
Fifth	5	1954	700
Sixth	6	1955	600

Each card contains a five-digit code number: x-xxxx. The digit before the hyphen is the section number and the digits after the hyphen form the number of that card in the section. Thus, card 3-0167 is the 167th card in Section 3 (the second supplementary set).

Since more than one substance can have the same, or nearly the same, d value for its strongest line and even its second strongest line, Hanawalt decided to characterize each substance by the d values of its *three* strongest lines, namely d_1, d_2, and d_3 for the strongest, second-strongest, and third-strongest line, respectively. The values of d_1, d_2, and d_3, together with relative intensities, are usually sufficient to characterize the pattern of an unknown and enable the corresponding pattern in the file to be located. In each section of the ASTM file, the cards are arranged in groups characterized by a certain range of d_1 spacings. Within each group, e.g., the group covering d_1 values from 2.29 to 2.25A, the cards are arranged in decreasing order of d_2 values, rather than d_1 values. When several substances in the same group have identical d_2 values, the order of decreasing d_3 values is followed. The groups themselves are arranged in decreasing order of their d_1 ranges.

A typical card from the ASTM file is reproduced in Fig. 14–1. At the upper left appear the d values for the three strongest lines (2.28, 1.50, 1.35A) and, in addition, the largest d value (2.60A) for this structure. Listed below these d values are the relative intensities I/I_1, expressed as percentages of the strongest line in the pattern. Immediately below the symbol I/I_1 is the serial number of the card, in this case 1-1188. Below the intensity data are given details of the method used for obtaining the pattern (radiation, camera diameter, method of measuring intensity, etc.), and a reference to the original experimental work. The rest of the left-hand portion of the card contains room for various crystallographic, optical, and chemical data which are fully described on introductory cards of the set. The lower right-hand portion of the card lists the values of d and I/I_1 for all the observed diffraction lines.

| 3276 d 1-1194 | 2.28 | 1.50 | 1.35 | 2.60 | Mo_2C |
| I/I₁ 1-1188 | 100 | 35 | 35 | 29 | MOLYBDENUM CARBIDE |

Rad.	λ 0.709		Filter ZrO₂
Dia. 16 INCHES	Cut off		Coll.
I/I₁ CALIBRATED STRIPS			d corr. abs.? No
Ref. H			

Sys. HEXAGONAL		S.G.	
a_0 2.994	b_0	c_0 4.722 A	C 1.576
α	β	γ Z 2	
Ref. WYS			

δ a	n ω β	ε γ	Sign
2V	D	mp	Color
Ref.			

d Å	I/I₁	hkl	d Å	I/I₁	hkl
2.60	29		0.93	9	
2.36	24		.91	5	
2.28	100		.89	5	
1.75	24		.87	4	
1.50	35		.84	8	
1.35	35		.82	5	
1.30	3				
1.27	35				
1.26	35				
1.18	4				
1.14	6				
1.08	4				
1.01	7				
0.98	3				
.97	19				

FIG. 14–1. Standard $3 \times 5''$ ASTM diffraction data card for molybdenum carbide. (Courtesy of American Society for Testing Materials.)

Although a particular pattern can be located by a direct search of the card file, a great saving in time can usually be effected by use of the index books which accompany the file. Each book contains two indexes:

(1) An *alphabetical index* of each substance by name. After the name are given the chemical formula, the d values and relative intensities of the three strongest lines, and the serial number of the card in the file for the substance involved. All entries are fully cross-indexed; i.e., both "sodium chloride" and "chloride, sodium" are listed. This index is to be used if the investigator has any knowledge of one or more chemical elements in the sample.

(2) A *numerical index*, which gives the spacings and intensities of the three strongest lines, the chemical formula, name, and card serial number. Each substance is listed three times, once with the three strongest lines listed in the usual order $d_1d_2d_3$, again in the order $d_2d_1d_3$, and finally in the order $d_3d_1d_2$. All entries are divided into groups according to the first spacing listed; the arrangement within each group is in decreasing order of the second spacing listed. The purpose of these additional listings (second-strongest line first and third-strongest line first) is to enable the user to match an unknown with an entry in the index even when complicating factors have altered the relative intensities of the three strongest lines of the unknown.* These complicating factors are usually due to the

---

* In the original set of cards (1941) and the first supplementary set (1944), this threefold method of listing extended to the cards themselves, i.e., there were three cards in the file for each substance. Because the resulting card file was too bulky, this method was abandoned in all sets issued in 1949 and thereafter.

presence of more than one phase in the specimen. This leads to additional lines and even superimposed lines. Use of the numerical index requires no knowledge of the chemical composition of the sample.

Qualitative analysis by the Hanawalt method begins with the preparation of the pattern of the unknown. This may be done with a Debye-Scherrer camera or a diffractometer, and any convenient characteristic radiation as long as it is so chosen that fluorescence is minimized and an adequate number of lines appear on the pattern. (Most of the data in the ASTM file were obtained with a Debye-Scherrer camera and Mo $K\alpha$ radiation. Since a change in wavelength alters the relative intensities of the diffraction lines, this means that a pattern made with Cu $K\alpha$ radiation, for example, may not be directly comparable with one in the file. Factors for converting intensities from a Cu $K\alpha$ to a Mo $K\alpha$ basis are given on an introductory card in the ASTM file.) Specimen preparation should be such as to minimize preferred orientation, as the latter can cause relative line intensities to differ markedly from their normal values. If the specimen has a large absorption coefficient and is examined in a Debye-Scherrer camera, the low-angle lines may appear doubled, and both their positions and relative intensities may be seriously in error. This effect may be avoided by dilution of the unknown, as described in Sec. 6–3.

After the pattern of the unknown is prepared, the plane spacing d corresponding to each line on the pattern is calculated, or obtained from tables which give d as a function of 2θ for various characteristic wavelengths. Alternately, a scale may be constructed which gives d directly as a function of line position when laid on the film or diffractometer chart; the accuracy obtainable by such a scale, although not very high, is generally sufficient for identification purposes. If the diffraction pattern has been obtained on film, relative line intensities are estimated by eye. The ASTM suggests that these estimates be assigned the following numerical values:

$$
\begin{array}{ll}
\text{Very, very strong} & \\
\quad \text{(strongest line)} = 100 & \text{Weak} \quad = \begin{cases} 40 \\ 30 \end{cases} \\
\text{Very strong} \qquad = \ \ 90 & \text{Faint} \quad = \ \ 20 \\
\text{Strong} \qquad\qquad = \begin{cases} 80 \\ 70 \end{cases} & \text{Very faint} = \ \ 10 \\
\text{Medium} \qquad\quad = \begin{cases} 60 \\ 50 \end{cases} &
\end{array}
$$

In many cases very rough estimates are all that are needed. If greater accuracy is required, relative line intensities may be obtained by comparison with a graded intensity scale, made by exposing various portions of a strip of film to a constant intensity x-ray beam for known lengths of time. (Many of the intensity data in the ASTM file, including the values shown for molybdenum carbide in Fig. 14–1, were obtained in this way.)

If a diffractometer is used to obtain the pattern, automatic recording will provide sufficient accuracy, and it is customary to take the maximum intensity above the background rather than the integrated intensity as a measure of the "intensity" of each line, even though the integrated intensity is the more fundamental quantity.

After the experimental values of d and I/I_1 are tabulated, the unknown can be identified by the following procedure:

(1) Locate the proper d_1 group in the numerical index.

(2) Read down the second column of d values to find the closest match to d_2. (In comparing experimental and tabulated d values, always allow for the possibility that either set of values may be in error by ± 0.01A.)

(3) After the closest match has been found for d_1, d_2, and d_3, compare their relative intensities with the tabulated values.

(4) When good agreement has been found for the three strongest lines listed in the index, locate the proper data card in the file, and compare the d and I/I_1 values of all the observed lines with those tabulated. When full agreement is obtained, identification is complete.

14–4 Examples of qualitative analysis. When the unknown is a **single phase,** the identification procedure is relatively straightforward. Consider, for example, the pattern described by Table 14–1. It was obtained with Mo $K\alpha$ radiation and a Debye-Scherrer camera; line intensities were estimated. The experimental values of d_1, d_2, and d_3 are 2.27, 1.50, and 1.34A, respectively. By examination of the ASTM numerical index we find that the strongest line falls within the 2.29 to 2.25A group of d_1 values. Inspection of the listed d_2 values discloses four substances having d_2 values close to 1.50A. The data on these substances are shown in Table 14–2, in the form given in the index. Of these four, only molybdenum carbide has a d_3 value close to that of our unknown, and we also note that the relative intensities listed for the three strongest lines of this substance agree well

TABLE 14–1

PATTERN OF UNKNOWN

d(A)	I/I_1	d(A)	I/I_1
2.59	30	1.14	10
2.35	30	1.07	5
2.27	100	1.01	10
1.75	20	0.97	20
1.50	40	0.93	10
1.34	40	0.91	10
1.27	40	0.89	10
1.25	40	0.84	10
1.19	10		

TABLE 14–2

PORTION OF ASTM NUMERICAL INDEX

d(A)			I/I₁			Substance	Serial number
2.28	1.50	1.78	100	100	70	$Cs_3 Bi(NO_2)_6$ Cesium Bismuth Nitrite	2-1129
2.28	1.50	1.35	100	35	35	Mo_2C Molybdenum Carbide	1-1188
2.28	1.49	1.10	100	100	100	$Cs_3 Ir(NO_2)_6$ Cesium Iridium Nitrite	2-1130
2.27	1.49	1.07	100	60	60	α-W_2C Alpha Tungsten Carbide 2:1	2-1134

with the observed intensities. We then refer to the data card bearing serial number 1-1188, reproduced in Fig. 14–1, and compare the complete pattern tabulated there with the observed one. Since the agreement is satisfactory for all the observed lines, the unknown is identified as molybdenum carbide, Mo_2C.

When the unknown is composed of a **mixture of phases,** the analysis naturally becomes more complex, but not impossible. Consider the pattern described in Table 14–3, for which $d_1 = 2.09A$, $d_2 = 2.47A$, and $d_3 = 1.80A$. Examination of the numerical index in the d_1 group 2.09 to 2.05A reveals several substances having d_2 values near 2.47A, but in no case do the three strongest lines, taken together, agree with those of the unknown. This impasse suggests that the unknown is actually a mixture of phases, and that we are incorrect in assuming that the three strongest lines in the pattern of the unknown are all due to the same substance. Suppose we assume that the strongest line ($d = 2.09A$) and the second-strongest line ($d = 2.47A$) are formed by two different phases, and that the third-strongest line ($d = 1.80A$) is due to, say, the first phase. In other words, we will assume that $d_1 = 2.09A$ and $d_2 = 1.80A$ for one phase. A search of the same group of d_1 values, but now in the vicinity of $d_2 = 1.80A$, discloses agreement between the three strongest lines of the pattern of copper, serial number 4-0836, and three lines in the pattern of our unknown. Turning to card 4-0836, we find good agreement between all lines of the copper pattern, described in Table 14–4, with the starred lines in Table 14–3, the pattern of the unknown.

One phase of the mixture is thus shown to be copper, providing we can account for the remainder of the lines as due to some other substance. These remaining lines are listed in Table 14–5. By multiplying all the observed intensities by a normalizing factor of 1.43, we increase the intensity of the strongest line to 100. We then search the index and card file

TABLE 14-3

PATTERN OF UNKNOWN

$d(A)$	I/I_1	$d(A)$	I/I_1
3.01	5	1.28*	20
2.47	70	1.08*	20
2.13	30	1.04*	5
2.09*	100	0.98	5
1.80*	50	0.91*	5
1.50	20	0.83*	10
1.29	10	0.81*	10
1.22	5		

TABLE 14-4

PATTERN OF COPPER

$d(A)$	I/I_1
2.088	100
1.808	46
1.278	20
1.0900	17
1.0436	5
0.9038	3
0.8293	9
0.8083	8

in the usual way and find that these remaining lines agree with the pattern of cuprous oxide, Cu_2O, which is given at the right of Table 14-5. The unknown is thus shown to be a mixture of copper and cuprous oxide.

The analysis of mixtures becomes still more difficult when a line from one phase is superimposed on a line from another, and when this composite line is one of the three strongest lines in the pattern of the unknown. The usual procedure then leads only to a very tentative identification of one phase, in the sense that agreement is obtained for some d values but not for all the corresponding intensities. This in itself is evidence of line super-position. Such patterns can be untangled by separating out lines which agree in d value with those of phase X, the observed intensity of any super-imposed lines being divided into two parts. One part is assigned to phase X, and the balance, together with the remaining unidentified lines, is treated as in the previous example.

Some large laboratories find it advantageous to use diffraction data cards containing a punched code. These are of two kinds, both obtainable from the ASTM: Keysort cards, which can be sorted semimechanically, and

TABLE 14-5

	Remainder of pattern of unknown		Pattern of Cu_2O	
$d(A)$	I/I_1		$d(A)$	I/I_1
	Observed	Normalized		
3.01	5	7	3.020	9
2.47	70	100	2.465	100
2.13	30	43	2.135	37
			1.743	1
1.50	20	29	1.510	27
1.29	10	14	1.287	17
1.22	5	7	1.233	4
			1.0674	2
0.98	5	7	0.9795	4
			0.9548	3
			0.8715	3
			0.8216	3

standard IBM cards, which can be machine-sorted. A card file of either type can be searched on the basis of observed d values, and, in addition, particular categories of cards can be removed from the file more rapidly than by hand. For example, suppose a complex mixture is to be identified and it is known that one particular element, say copper, is present. Then the punch coding will permit rapid removal of the cards of all compounds containing copper, and the diffraction data on these cards can then be compared with the pattern of the unknown.

14–5 Practical difficulties. In theory, the Hanawalt method should lead to the positive identification of any substance whose diffraction pattern is included in the card file. In practice, various difficulties arise, and these are usually due either to errors in the diffraction pattern of the unknown or to errors in the card file.

Errors of the first kind, those affecting the observed positions and intensities of the diffraction lines, have been discussed in various parts of this book and need not be reexamined here. There is, however, one point that deserves some emphasis and that concerns the diffractometer. It must be remembered that the absorption factor for this instrument is independent of the angle 2θ, whereas, in a Debye-Scherrer camera, absorption decreases line intensity more at small than at large angles; the result is that the low-angle lines of most substances appear stronger, relative to medium- or high-angle lines, on a diffractometer chart than on a Debye-Scherrer photograph. This fact should be kept in mind whenever a diffractometer pattern is compared with one of the standard patterns in the ASTM file, because practically all of the latter were obtained with a Debye-Scherrer camera. On the other hand, it should not be concluded that successful use of the Hanawalt method requires relative intensity measurements of extremely high accuracy. It is enough, in most cases, to be able to list the lines in the correct *order* of decreasing intensity.

Errors in the card file itself are generally more serious, since they may go undetected by the investigator and lead to mistaken identifications. Even a casual examination of the ASTM alphabetical index will disclose numerous examples of substances represented in the file by two or more cards, often with major differences in the three strongest lines listed. This ambiguity can make identification of the unknown quite difficult, because the user must decide which pattern in the file is the most reliable. Work is now in progress at the National Bureau of Standards to resolve such ambiguities, correct other kinds of errors, and obtain new standard patterns. The results of this work, which is all done with the diffractometer, are published from time to time in NBS Circular 539, "Standard X-Ray Diffraction Powder Patterns,"* and incorporated in card form in the most

---

* Four sections of this circular have been issued to date: Vols. I and II in 1953, Vol. III in 1954, and Vol. IV in 1955.

recently issued sections of the ASTM file.

Whenever any doubt exists in the investigator's mind as to the validity of a particular identification, he should prepare his own standard pattern. Thus, if the unknown has been tentatively identified as substance X, the pattern of pure X should be prepared under exactly the same experimental conditions used for the pattern of the unknown. Comparison of the two patterns will furnish positive proof, or disproof, of identity.

The Hanawalt method fails completely, of course, when the unknown is a substance not listed in the card file, or when the unknown is a mixture and the component to be identified is not present in sufficient quantity to yield a good diffraction pattern. The latter effect can be quite troublesome, and, as mentioned in Sec. 12–4, mixtures may be encountered which contain more than 50 percent of a particular component without the pattern of that component being visible in the pattern of the mixture.

14–6 Identification of surface deposits. Metal surfaces frequently become contaminated, either by reaction of some substance with the base metal to produce a scale of oxide, sulfide, etc., or by simple adherence of some foreign material. Detection and identification of such deposits is usually an easy matter if the metal object is examined directly by some reflection method of diffraction, without making any attempt to remove the surface deposit for separate examination.

A reflection method is particularly suitable because of the very shallow penetration of x-rays into most metals and alloys, as discussed at length in Sec. 9–5. The result is that most of the recorded diffraction pattern is produced by an extremely thin surface layer, a circumstance favorable to the detection of small amounts of surface deposits. The diffractometer is an ideal instrument for this purpose, particularly for the direct examination of sheet material. Its sensitivity for work of this kind is often surprisingly high, as evidenced by strong diffraction patterns produced by surface deposits which are barely visible.

An example of this kind of surface analysis occurred in the operations of a steel plant making mild steel sheet for "tin" cans. The tin coating was applied by hot-dipping, and the process was entirely satisfactory except for certain batches of sheet encountered from time to time which were not uniformly wetted by the molten tin. The only visible difference between the satisfactory and unsatisfactory steel sheet was that the surface of the latter appeared somewhat duller than that of the former. Examination of a piece of the unsatisfactory sheet in the diffractometer revealed the pattern of iron (ferrite) and a strong pattern of some foreign material. Reference to the ASTM card file showed that the surface deposit was finely divided graphite.

One difficulty that may be encountered in identifying surface deposits from their diffraction patterns is caused by the fact that the individual crystals of such deposits are often preferentially oriented with respect to the surface on which they lie. The result is a marked difference between the observed relative intensities of the diffraction lines and those given on the ASTM cards for specimens composed of randomly oriented crystals. In the example just referred to, the reflection from the basal planes of the hexagonal graphite crystals was abnormally strong, indicating that most of these crystals were oriented with their basal planes parallel to the surface of the steel sheet.

QUANTITATIVE ANALYSIS (SINGLE PHASE)

14–7 Chemical analysis by parameter measurement. The lattice parameter of a binary solid solution of B in A depends only on the percentage of B in the alloy, as long as the solution is unsaturated. This fact can be made the basis for chemical analysis by parameter measurement. All that is needed is a parameter *vs.* composition curve, such as curve *bc* of Fig. 12–8(b), which can be established by measuring the lattice parameter of a series of previously analyzed alloys. This method has been used in diffusion studies to measure the change in concentration of a solution with distance from the original interface. Its accuracy depends entirely on the slope of the parameter-composition curve. In alpha brasses, which can contain from 0 to about 40 percent zinc in copper, an accuracy of ±1 percent zinc can be achieved without difficulty.

This method is applicable only to binary alloys. In ternary solutions, for example, the percentages of two components can be independently varied. The result is that two ternary solutions of quite different compositions can have the same lattice parameter.

QUANTITATIVE ANALYSIS (MULTIPHASE)

14–8 Basic principles. Quantitative analysis by diffraction is based on the fact that the intensity of the diffraction pattern of a particular phase in a mixture of phases depends on the concentration of that phase in the mixture. The relation between intensity and concentration is not generally linear, since the diffracted intensity depends markedly on the absorption coefficient of the mixture and this itself varies with the concentration.

To find the relation between diffracted intensity and concentration, we must go back to the basic equation for the intensity diffracted by a powder specimen. The form of this equation depends on the kind of apparatus used, namely, camera or diffractometer; we shall consider only the diffractometer here. [Although good quantitative work can be done, and has been done, with a Debye-Scherrer camera and microphotometer, the modern trend is toward the use of the diffractometer, because (a) this instrument permits quicker measurement of intensity and (b) its absorption factor is independent of θ.] The exact expression for the intensity diffracted by a single-phase powder specimen in a diffractometer is:

$$I = \left(\frac{I_0 e^4}{m^2 c^4}\right)\left(\frac{\lambda^3 A}{32\pi r}\right)\left(\frac{1}{v^2}\right)\left[|F|^2 p \left(\frac{1+\cos^2 2\theta}{\sin^2 \theta \cos \theta}\right)\right]\left(\frac{e^{-2M}}{2\mu}\right), \quad (14\text{--}1)$$

where I = integrated intensity per unit length of diffraction line, I_0 = intensity of incident beam, e, m = charge and mass of the electron, c = velocity of light, λ = wavelength of incident radiation, r = radius of diffractometer circle, A = cross-sectional area of incident beam, v = volume of unit cell, F = structure factor, p = multiplicity, θ = Bragg angle, e^{-2M} = temperature factor (a function of θ) (previously referred to qualitatively in Sec. 4–11), and μ = linear absorption coefficient (which enters as $1/2\mu$, the absorption factor).

This equation, whose derivation can be found in various advanced texts, applies to a powder specimen in the form of a flat plate of effectively infinite thickness, making equal angles with the incident and diffracted beams. [The fourth term in Eq. (14–1), containing the square of the structure factor, the multiplicity factor, and the Lorentz-polarization factor, will be recognized as the approximate equation for relative integrated intensity used heretofore in this book.]

We can simplify Eq. (14–1) considerably for special cases. As it stands, it applies only to a pure substance. But suppose that we wish to analyze a mixture of two phases, α and β. Then we can concentrate on a particular line of the α phase and rewrite Eq. (14–1) in terms of that phase alone. I now becomes I_α, the intensity of the selected line of the α phase, and the right side of the equation must be multiplied by c_α, the volume fraction of α in the mixture, to allow for the fact that the diffracting volume of α in the mixture is less than it would be if the specimen were pure α. Finally, we must substitute μ_m for μ, where μ_m is the linear absorption coefficient of the mixture. In this new equation, all factors are constant and independent of the concentration of α except c_α and μ_m, and we can write

$$I_\alpha = \frac{K_1 c_\alpha}{\mu_m}, \quad (14\text{--}2)$$

where K_1 is a constant.

To put Eq. (14–2) in a useful form, we must express μ_m in terms of the concentration. From Eq. (1–12) we have

$$\frac{\mu_m}{\rho_m} = w_\alpha\left(\frac{\mu_\alpha}{\rho_\alpha}\right) + w_\beta\left(\frac{\mu_\beta}{\rho_\beta}\right), \quad (14\text{--}3)$$

where w denotes the weight fraction and ρ the density. Consider unit volume of the mixture. Its weight is ρ_m and the weight of contained α is $w_\alpha\rho_m$. Therefore, the volume of α is $w_\alpha\rho_m/\rho_\alpha$, which is equal to c_α, and a similar expression holds for c_β. Equation (14–3) then becomes

$$\mu_m = c_\alpha\mu_\alpha + c_\beta\mu_\beta = c_\alpha\mu_\alpha + (1 - c_\alpha)\mu_\beta$$

$$= c_\alpha(\mu_\alpha - \mu_\beta) + \mu_\beta;$$

$$I_\alpha = \frac{K_1 c_\alpha}{c_\alpha(\mu_\alpha - \mu_\beta) + \mu_\beta}. \qquad (14\text{--}4)$$

This equation relates the intensity of a diffraction line from one phase to the volume fraction of that phase and the linear absorption coefficients of both phases.

We can put Eq. (14–4) on a weight basis by considering unit mass of the mixture. The volume of the contained α is w_α/ρ_α and the volume of β is w_β/ρ_β. Therefore,

$$c_\alpha = \frac{w_\alpha/\rho_\alpha}{w_\alpha/\rho_\alpha + w_\beta/\rho_\beta} \qquad (14\text{--}5)$$

$$= \frac{w_\alpha/\rho_\alpha}{w_\alpha(1/\rho_\alpha - 1/\rho_\beta) + 1/\rho_\beta}. \qquad (14\text{--}6)$$

Combining Eqs. (14–4) and (14–6) and simplifying, we obtain

$$I_\alpha = \frac{K_1 w_\alpha}{\rho_\alpha[w_\alpha(\mu_\alpha/\rho_\alpha - \mu_\beta/\rho_\beta) + \mu_\beta/\rho_\beta]}. \qquad (14\text{--}7)$$

For the pure α phase, either Eq. (14–2) or (14–7) gives

$$I_{\alpha p} = \frac{K_1}{\mu_\alpha}, \qquad (14\text{--}8)$$

where the subscript p denotes diffraction from the pure phase. Division of Eq. (14–7) by Eq. (14–8) eliminates the unknown constant K_1 and gives

$$\frac{I_\alpha}{I_{\alpha p}} = \frac{w_\alpha(\mu_\alpha/\rho_\alpha)}{w_\alpha(\mu_\alpha/\rho_\alpha - \mu_\beta/\rho_\beta) + \mu_\beta/\rho_\beta}. \qquad (14\text{--}9)$$

This equation permits quantitative analysis of a two-phase mixture, provided that the mass absorption coefficients of each phase are known. If they are not known, a calibration curve can be prepared by using mixtures of known composition. In each case, a specimen of pure α must be available as a reference material, and the measurements of I_α and $I_{\alpha p}$ must be made under identical conditions.

In general, the variation of the intensity ratio $I_\alpha/I_{\alpha p}$ with w_α is not linear, as shown by the curves of Fig. 14–2. The experimental points were obtained by measurements on synthetic binary mixtures of powdered quartz, cristobalite, beryllium oxide, and potassium chloride; the curves were calculated by Eq. (14–9). The agreement is excellent. The line obtained for the quartz-cristobalite mixture is straight because these substances are two allotropic forms of silica and hence have identical mass absorption coefficients. When the mass absorption coefficients of the two phases are equal, Eq. (14–9) becomes simply

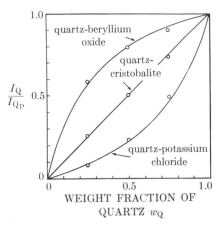

$$\frac{I_\alpha}{I_{\alpha p}} = w_\alpha.$$

Fig. 14–2 illustrates very clearly how the intensity of a particular diffraction line from one phase depends on the absorption coefficient of the other phase. For Cu $K\alpha$ radiation, the mass absorption coefficient of BeO is 8.6, of SiO_2 is 34.9, and of KCl is 124.

Fig. 14–2. Diffractometer measurements made with Cu $K\alpha$ radiation on binary mixtures. I_Q is the intensity of the reflection from the $d = 3.34A$ planes of quartz in a mixture. I_{Qp} is the intensity of the same reflection from pure quartz. (L. E. Alexander and H. P. Klug, *Anal. Chem.* **20,** 886, 1948.)

For various reasons, the analytical procedure just outlined cannot be applied to most specimens of industrial interest. A variety of other methods, however, has been devised to solve particular problems, and the two most important of these, the *direct comparison method* and the *internal standard method*, will be described in succeeding sections. It is worth noting that all these methods of analysis have one essential feature in common: the measurement of the concentration of a particular phase depends on the measurement of the ratio of the intensity of a diffraction line from that phase to the intensity of some standard *reference line*. In the "single line" method described above, the reference line is a line from the pure phase. In the direct comparison method, it is a line from another phase in the mixture. In the internal standard method, it is a line from a foreign material mixed with the specimen.

14–9 Direct comparison method. This method is of greatest metallurgical interest because it can be applied directly to massive, polycrystalline specimens. It has been widely used for measuring the amount of retained austenite in hardened steel and will be described here in terms of that specific problem, although the method itself is quite general.

Many steels, when quenched from the austenite region, do not transform completely to martensite even at the surface. At room temperature, such steels consist of martensite and retained austenite; in addition, undissolved carbides may or may not be present. The retained austenite is unstable and may slowly transform while the steel is in service. Since this transformation is accompanied by an increase in volume of about 4 percent, residual stress is set up in addition to that already present, or actual dimensional changes occur. For these reasons, the presence of even a few percent retained austenite is undesirable in some applications, such as gage blocks, closely fitting machine parts, etc. There is therefore considerable interest in methods of determining the exact amount of austenite present. Quantitative microscopic examination is fairly satisfactory as long as the austenite content is fairly high, but becomes unreliable below about 15 percent austenite in many steels. The x-ray method, on the other hand, is quite accurate in this low-austenite range, often the range of greatest practical interest.

Assume that a hardened steel contains only two phases, martensite and austenite. The problem is to determine the composition of the mixture, when the two phases have the same composition but different crystal structure (martensite is body-centered tetragonal and austenite is face-centered cubic). The "single line" method could be used if a sample of pure austenite or of known austenite content is available as a standard. Ordinarily, however, we proceed as follows. In the basic intensity equation, Eq. (14–1), we put

$$K_2 = \left(\frac{I_0 e^4}{m^2 c^4}\right)\left(\frac{\lambda^3 A}{32\pi r}\right)$$

and

$$R = \left(\frac{1}{v^2}\right)\left[|F|^2 p \left(\frac{1 + \cos^2 2\theta}{\sin^2 \theta \cos \theta}\right)\right]\left(e^{-2M}\right). \qquad (14\text{–}10)$$

The diffracted intensity is therefore given by

$$I = \frac{K_2 R}{2\mu}, \qquad (14\text{–}11)$$

where K_2 is a constant, independent of the kind and amount of the diffracting substance, and R depends on θ, hkl, and the kind of substance. Designating austenite by the subscript γ and martensite by the subscript α, we can write Eq. (14–11) for a particular diffraction line of each phase:

$$I_\gamma = \frac{K_2 R_\gamma c_\gamma}{2\mu_m},$$

$$I_\alpha = \frac{K_2 R_\alpha c_\alpha}{2\mu_m}.$$

Division of these equations yields

$$\frac{I_\gamma}{I_\alpha} = \frac{R_\gamma c_\gamma}{R_\alpha c_\alpha}. \tag{14-12}$$

The value of c_γ/c_α can therefore be obtained from a measurement of I_γ/I_α and a calculation of R_γ and R_α. Once c_γ/c_α is found, the value of c_γ can be obtained from the additional relationship:

$$c_\gamma + c_\alpha = 1.$$

We can thus make an absolute measurement of the austenite content of the steel by direct comparison of the integrated intensity of an austenite line with the integrated intensity of a martensite line.* By comparing several pairs of austenite-martensite lines, we can obtain several independent values of the austenite content; any serious disagreement between these values indicates an error in observation or calculation.

If the steel contains a third phase, namely, iron carbide (cementite), we can determine the cementite concentration either by quantitative microscopic examination or by diffraction. If we measure I_C, the integrated intensity of a particular cementite line, and calculate R_C, then we can set up an equation similar to Eq. (14-12) from which c_γ/c_C can be obtained. The value of c_γ is then found from the relation

$$c_\gamma + c_\alpha + c_C = 1.$$

In choosing diffraction lines to measure, we must be sure to avoid overlapping or closely adjacent lines from different phases. Figure 14-3 shows the calculated patterns of austenite and martensite in a 1.0 percent carbon steel, made with Co $K\alpha$ radiation. Suitable austenite lines are the 200, 220, and 311 lines; these may be compared with the 002-200 and 112-211 martensite doublets. These doublets are not usually resolvable into separate lines because all lines are usually quite broad, both from the martensite and austenite, as shown in Fig. 14-4. (Figure 14-4 also shows how refrigeration, immediately after quenching to room temperature, can decrease the amount of retained austenite and how an interruption in the quench, followed by air cooling, can increase it.) The causes of line broadening are the nonuniform microstrains present in both phases of the quenched steel and, in many cases, the very fine grain size.

---

* Recalling the earlier discussion of the disappearing-phase x-ray method of locating a solvus line (Sec. 12-4), we note from Eq. (14-12) that the intensity ratio I_γ/I_α is not a linear function of the volume fraction c_γ, or, for that matter, of the weight fraction w_γ.

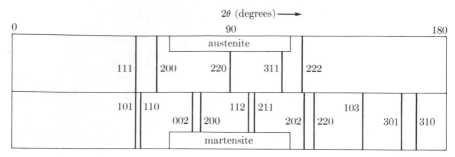

FIG. 14–3. Calculated powder patterns of austenite and martensite, each containing 1.0 percent carbon. Co $K\alpha$ radiation.

In calculating the value of R for a particular diffraction line, various factors should be kept in mind. The unit cell volume v is calculated from the measured lattice parameters, which are a function of carbon and alloy content. When the martensite doublets are unresolved, the structure factor and multiplicity of the martensite are calculated on the basis of a body-

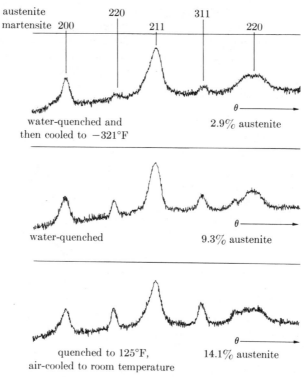

FIG. 14–4. Microphotometer traces of Debye-Scherrer patterns of hardened 1.07 percent carbon steel. Co $K\alpha$ radiation, monochromated by reflection from an NaCl crystal. (B. L. Averbach and M. Cohen, *Trans. A.I.M.E.* **176,** 401, 1948.)

centered *cubic* cell; this procedure, in effect, adds together the integrated intensities of the two lines of the doublet, which is exactly what is done experimentally when the integrated intensity of an unresolved doublet is measured. For greatest accuracy in the calculation of F, the atomic scattering factor f should be corrected for anomalous scattering by an amount Δf (see Fig. 13–8), particularly when Co $K\alpha$ radiation is used. The Lorentz-polarization factor given in Eq. (14–10) applies only to unpolarized incident radiation; if crystal-monochromated radiation is used, this factor will have to be changed to that given in Sec. 6–12. The value of the temperature factor e^{-2M} can be taken from the curve of Fig. 14–5.

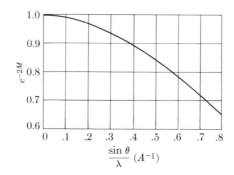

FIG. 14–5. Temperature factor e^{-2M} of iron at 20°C as a function of $(\sin\theta)/\lambda$.

Specimen preparation involves wet grinding to remove the surface layer, which may be decarburized or otherwise nonrepresentative of the bulk of the specimen, followed by standard metallographic polishing and etching. This procedure ensures a flat, reproducible surface for the x-ray examination, and allows a preliminary examination of the specimen to be made with the microscope. In grinding and polishing, care should be taken not to produce excessive heat or plastic deformation, which would cause partial decomposition of both the martensite and austenite.

In the measurement of diffraction line intensity, it is essential that the *integrated intensity*, not the maximum intensity, be measured. Large variations in line shape can occur because of variations in microstrain and grain size. These variations in line shape will not affect the integrated intensity, but they can make the values of maximum intensity absolutely meaningless.

The sensitivity of the x-ray method in determining small amounts of retained austenite is limited chiefly by the intensity of the continuous background present. The lower the background, the easier it is to detect and measure weak austenite lines. Best results are therefore obtained with crystal-monochromated radiation, which permits the detection of as little as 0.1 volume percent austenite. With ordinary filtered radiation, the minimum detectible amount is 5 to 10 volume percent.

TABLE 14-6

COMPARISON OF AUSTENITE DETERMINATION BY X-RAY DIFFRACTION AND
LINEAL ANALYSIS*

Austenitizing temperature (°C)	Volume percent carbides	Volume percent retained austenite	
		x - ray	lineal analysis
955	0.2	20.0 ± 1.0	20.1 ± 1.0
900	2.6	14.0 ± 0.8	13.8 ± 1.0
845	4.0	7.0 ± 0.4	6.0 ± 1.0
790	10.0	3.1 ± 0.3	2.0 ± 1.0

* B. L. Averbach and M. Cohen, *Trans. A.I.M.E.* **176**, 401 (1948).

Table 14-6 gives a comparison between retained austenite determinations made on the same steel (1.0 percent C, 1.5 percent Cr, and 0.2 percent V) by x-ray diffraction and by quantitative microscopic examination (lineal analysis). The steel was austenitized for 30 minutes at the temperatures indicated and quenched in oil. The x-ray results were obtained with a Debye-Scherrer camera, a stationary flat specimen, and crystal-monochromated radiation. The carbide content was determined by lineal analysis. Note that the agreement between the two methods is good when the austenite content is fairly high, and that lineal analysis tends to show lower austenite contents than the x-ray method when the austenite content itself is low (low austenitizing temperatures). This is not unexpected, in that the austenite particles become finer with decreasing austenitizing temperatures and therefore more difficult to measure microscopically. Under such circumstances, the x-ray method is definitely more accurate.

14-10 Internal standard method. In this method a diffraction line from the phase being determined is compared with a line from a standard substance mixed with the sample in known proportions. The internal standard method is therefore restricted to samples in powder form.

Suppose we wish to determine the amount of phase A in a mixture of phases A, B, C, ..., where the relative amounts of the other phases present (B, C, D, ...) may vary from sample to sample. With a known amount of original sample we mix a known amount of a standard substance S to form a new composite sample. Let c_A and c_A' be the volume fractions of phase A in the original and composite samples, respectively, and let c_S be the volume fraction of S in the composite sample. If a diffraction pattern is now prepared from the composite sample, then from Eq. (14-2) the intensity of a particular line from phase A is given by

$$I_A = \frac{K_3 c_A'}{\mu_m},$$

and the intensity of a particular line from the standard S by

$$I_S = \frac{K_4 c_S}{\mu_m}.$$

Division of one expression by the other gives

$$\frac{I_A}{I_S} = \frac{K_3 c_A'}{K_4 c_S}. \qquad (14\text{--}13)$$

(Note that μ_m, the linear absorption coefficient of the mixture and an unknown quantity, drops out. Physically, this means that variations in absorption, due to variations in the relative amounts of B, C, D, $\ldots$, have no effect on the ratio I_A/I_S since they affect I_A and I_S in the same proportion.)

By extending Eq. (14–5) to a number of components, we can write

$$c_A' = \frac{w_A'/\rho_A}{w_A'/\rho_A + w_B'/\rho_B + w_C'/\rho_C + \cdots + w_S/\rho_S}$$

and a similar expression for c_S. Therefore,

$$\frac{c_A'}{c_S} = \frac{w_A'\rho_S}{\rho_A w_S}.$$

Substitution of this relation into Eq. (14–13) gives

$$\frac{I_A}{I_S} = K_5 w_A', \qquad (14\text{--}14)$$

if w_S is kept constant in all the composite samples. The relation between the weight fractions of A in the original and composite samples is:

$$w_A' = w_A(1 - w_S). \qquad (14\text{--}15)$$

Combination of Eqs. (14–14) and (14–15) gives

$$\frac{I_A}{I_S} = K_6 w_A. \qquad (14\text{--}16)$$

The intensity ratio of a line from phase A and a line from the standard S is therefore a linear function of w_A, the weight fraction of A in the original sample. A calibration curve can be prepared from measurements on a set of synthetic samples, containing known concentrations of A and a constant concentration of a suitable standard. Once the calibration curve is established, the concentration of A in an unknown sample is obtained simply by measuring the ratio I_A/I_S for a composite sample containing the unknown and the same proportion of standard as was used in the calibration.

The internal standard method has been widely used for the measurement of the quartz content of industrial dusts. (Knowledge of the quartz content is important in industrial health programs, because inhaled quartz or other siliceous material is the cause of the lung disease known as silicosis.) In this analysis, fluorite (CaF_2) has been found to be a suitable internal standard. Figure 14–6 shows a calibration curve prepared from mixtures of quartz and calcium carbonate, of known composition, each mixed with enough fluorite to make the weight fraction of fluorite in each composite sample equal to 0.20. The curve is linear and through the origin, as predicted by Eq. (14–16).

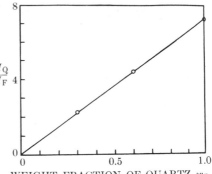

FIG. 14–6. Calibration curve for quartz analysis, with fluorite as internal standard. I_Q is the intensity of the $d = 3.34A$ line of quartz, and I_F is the intensity of the $d = 3.16A$ line of fluorite. (L. E. Alexander and H. P. Klug, *Anal. Chem.* **20**, 886, 1948.)

Strictly speaking, Eq. (14–16) is valid only for integrated intensities, and the same is true of all other intensity equations in this chapter. Yet it has been found possible to determine the quartz content of dusts with satisfactory accuracy by simply measuring maximum intensities. This short cut is permissible here only because the shape of the diffraction lines is found to be essentially constant from sample to sample. There is therefore a constant proportionality between maximum and integrated intensity and, as long as all patterns are made under identical experimental conditions, the measurement of maximum intensities gives satisfactory results. Quite erroneous results would be obtained by this procedure if the particle size of the samples were very small and variable, since then a variable amount of line broadening would occur, and this would cause a variation in maximum intensity independent of sample composition.

14–11 Practical difficulties. There are certain effects which can cause great difficulty in quantitative analysis because they cause observed intensities to depart widely from the theoretical. The most important of these complicating factors are:

(1) **Preferred orientation.** The basic intensity equation, Eq. (14–1), is derived on the premise of random orientation of the constituent crystals in the sample and is not valid if any preferred orientation exists. It follows that, in the preparation of powder samples for the diffractometer, every effort should be made to avoid preferred orientation. If the sample is a solid polycrystalline aggregate, the analyst has no control over the

distribution of orientations in it, but he should at least be aware of the possibility of error due to preferred orientation.

(2) **Microabsorption.** Consider diffraction from a given crystal of α in a mixture of α and β crystals. The incident beam passes through both α and β crystals on its way to a particular diffracting α crystal, and so does the diffracted beam on its way out of the sample. Both beams are decreased in intensity by absorption, and the decrease can be calculated from the total path length and μ_m, the linear absorption coefficient of the mixture. But a small part of the total path lies entirely within the diffracting α crystal, and for this portion μ_α is the applicable absorption coefficient. If μ_α is much larger than μ_β, or if the particle size of α is much larger than that of β, then the total intensity of the beam diffracted by the α crystals will be much less than that calculated, since the effect of microabsorption in each diffracting α crystal is not included in the basic intensity equation. Evidently, the microabsorption effect is negligible when $\mu_\alpha \approx \mu_\beta$ and both phases have the same particle size, or when the particle size of both phases is very small. Powder samples should therefore be finely ground before analysis.

(3) **Extinction.** As mentioned in Sec. 3–7, all real crystals are imperfect, in the sense that they have a mosaic structure, and the degree of imperfection can vary greatly from one crystal to another. Equation (14–1) is derived on the basis of the so-called "ideally imperfect" crystal, one in which the mosaic blocks are quite small (of the order of 10^{-4} to 10^{-5} cm in thickness) and so disoriented that they are all essentially nonparallel. Such a crystal has maximum reflecting power. A crystal made up of large mosaic blocks, some or all of which are accurately parallel to one another, is more nearly perfect and has a lower reflecting power. This *decrease* in the intensity of the diffracted beam as the crystal becomes more nearly perfect is called *extinction*. Extinction is absent for the ideally imperfect crystal, and the presence of extinction invalidates Eq. (14–1). Any treatment which will make a crystal more imperfect will reduce extinction and, for this reason alone, powder specimens should be ground as fine as possible. Grinding not only reduces the crystal size but also tends to decrease the mosaic block size, disorient the blocks, and strain them nonuniformly.

Microabsorption and extinction, if present, can seriously decrease the accuracy of the direct comparison method, because this is an absolute method. Fortunately, both effects are negligible in the case of hardened steel. Inasmuch as both the austenite and martensite have the same composition and only a 4 percent difference in density, their linear absorption coefficients are practically identical. Their average particle sizes are also roughly the same. Therefore, microabsorption does not occur. Extinction is absent because of the very nature of hardened steel. The change in specific volume accompanying the transformation of austenite to martensite sets up nonuniform strains in both phases so severe that both kinds of crystals can be considered highly imperfect. If these fortunate circumstances do not exist, and they do not in most other alloy systems, the direct comparison method should be used with caution and checked by some independent method.

On the other hand, the presence of microabsorption and extinction does not invalidate the internal standard method, provided these effects are constant from sample to sample, including the calibration samples. Microabsorption and extinction affect only the values of the constants K_3 and K_4 in Eq. (14–13), and therefore the constant K_6 in Eq. (14–16), and the latter constant determines only the slope of the calibration curve. Therefore, microabsorption and extinction, if present, will have no effect on the accuracy of the internal standard method as long as the crystals of the phase being determined, and those of the standard substance, do not vary in degree of perfection or particle size from one sample to another.

Problems

The d and I/I_1 values tabulated in Probs. 14–1 to 14–4 represent the diffraction patterns of various unknown substances. Identify the substances involved by reference to an ASTM diffraction file.

14–1.

$d(A)$	I/I_1	$d(A)$	I/I_1	$d(A)$	I/I_1
3.66	50	1.46	10	1.06	10
3.17	100	1.42	50	1.01	10
2.24	80	1.31	30	0.96	10
1.91	40	1.23	10	0.85	10
1.83	30	1.12	10		
1.60	20	1.08	10		

14–2.

$d(A)$	I/I_1	$d(A)$	I/I_1	$d(A)$	I/I_1
5.85	60	2.08	10	1.47	20
3.05	30	1.95	20	1.42	10
2.53	100	1.80	60	1.14	20
2.32	10	1.73	20	1.04	10

14–3.

$d(A)$	I/I_1	$d(A)$	I/I_1	$d(A)$	I/I_1
2.40	50	1.25	20	0.85	10
2.09	50	1.20	10	0.81	20
2.03	100	1.06	20	0.79	20
1.75	40	1.02	10		
1.47	30	0.92	10		
1.26	10				

14–4.

$d(A)$	I/I_1	$d(A)$	I/I_1	$d(A)$	I/I_1
3.02	100	2.11	10	1.46	10
2.79	10	1.90	20	1.17	10
2.52	10	1.65	10		
2.31	30	1.62	10		

14–5. Microscopic examination of a hardened 1.0 percent carbon steel shows no undissolved carbides. X-ray examination of this steel in a diffractometer with filtered cobalt radiation shows that the integrated intensity of the 311 austenite line is 2.325 and the integrated intensity of the unresolved 112–211 martensite doublet is 16.32, both in arbitrary units. Calculate the volume percent austenite in the steel. (Take lattice parameters from Fig. 12–5, Δf corrections from Fig. 13–8, and temperature factors e^{-2M} from Fig. 14–5.)

CHAPTER 15

CHEMICAL ANALYSIS BY FLUORESCENCE

15–1 Introduction. We saw in Chap. 1 that any element, if made the target in an x-ray tube and bombarded with electrons of high enough energy, would emit a characteristic line spectrum. The most intense lines of this spectrum are the $K\alpha$ and $K\beta$ lines. They are always called "characteristic lines" to emphasize the fact that their wavelengths are fixed and characteristic of the emitting element. We also saw that these same lines would be emitted if the element were bombarded with x-rays of high enough energy (fluorescence).

In these phenomena we have the basis for a method of chemical analysis. If the various elements in the sample to be analyzed are made to emit their characteristic lines by electron or x-ray bombardment, then these elements may be identified by analyzing the emitted radiation and showing that these specific wavelengths are present. The analysis is carried out in an x-ray spectrometer by diffracting the radiation from lattice planes of known d spacing in a single crystal. In accordance with the Bragg law, radiation of only a single wavelength is reflected for each angular setting of the crystal and the intensity of this radiation can be measured with a suitable counter. The analysis of the sample may be either *qualitative*, if the various characteristic lines in the emitted spectrum are simply identified, or *quantitative*, if the intensities of these lines are compared with the intensities of lines from a suitable standard.

Two kinds of x-ray spectroscopy are possible, depending on the means used to excite the characteristic lines:

(1) The sample is made the target in an x-ray tube and bombarded with electrons. Historically, this was the first method. It was employed by Moseley in his work on the relation between characteristic wavelength and atomic number. It is not used today, except as an occasional research tool, because it has certain disadvantages for routine work. For example, the specimen must be placed in a demountable x-ray tube, which must then be evacuated before the analysis can begin. The same procedure has to be repeated for each sample. In addition, the heat produced in the sample by electron bombardment may cause some contained elements to vaporize.

(2) The sample is placed outside the x-ray tube and bombarded with x-rays. The primary radiation (Fig. 15–1) causes the sample to emit secondary fluorescent radiation, which is then analyzed in a spectrometer. This method, commonly known as *fluorescent analysis*, has come into wide

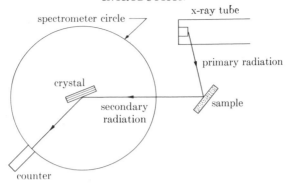

Fig. 15–1.   Fluorescent x-ray spectroscopy.

use in recent years.   The phenomenon of fluorescence, which is just a nuisance in diffraction experiments, is here made to serve a useful purpose.

It may be helpful to compare some features of x-ray fluorescent analysis with those of optical spectroscopy, i.e., spectroscopy in the visible region of the spectrum, since the latter method has been used for years as a routine analytical tool and its essential features at least are well known.   The main differences between the two methods are the following:

	Optical spectroscopy	Fluorescent analysis
Exciting agent	arc or spark	x-rays
Emitted radiation	visible light	x-rays
Analyzer	prism or grating	crystal
Detector	photographic film or phototube	photographic film or counter
Nature of spectra	complex	simple

Both these methods give information about the chemical *elements* present in the sample, irrespective of their state of chemical combination or the phases in which they exist.   X-ray diffraction, on the other hand, as we saw in the previous chapter, discloses the various compounds and phases present in the sample.   Fluorescent analysis and diffraction analysis therefore complement one another in the kind of information they provide.

Fluorescent analysis is nondestructive and much more rapid than the ordinary wet methods of chemical analysis.   It is best suited to determining elements present in amounts ranging from a few percent up to 100 percent, and in this range it is superior to optical spectroscopy.   In general, fluorescent analysis is inferior to optical spectroscopy in the concentration range below 1 percent, but it can be used to advantage in this range in special cases.   Fluorescent analysis is used today in the analysis of alloys (particularly high-alloy steels and high-temperature alloys), ores, oils, gasoline, etc.

Chemical analysis by x-ray spectroscopy dates back to the pioneer work of von Hevesy and Coster in Germany about 1923. They used photographic film to record the spectra. The x-ray method never became popular, however, until recent years, when the development of various kinds of counters allowed direct measurement of x-ray intensity and thus decreased the time required for analysis. The methods of fluorescent analysis are still undergoing rapid development, and a wider range of application, together with greater speed and accuracy, can be expected in the near future.

15–2 General principles. Most fluorescent spectrometers, of which there are many forms, have the analyzing crystal and counter mechanically coupled, as in a diffractometer. Thus, when the crystal is set at a particular Bragg angle θ, the counter is automatically set at the corresponding angle 2θ. The counter is connected to a scaler, or to a ratemeter and automatic recorder. The intensity of individual spectral lines emitted by the sample may be measured with the counter-scaler combination, or the whole spectrum may be continuously scanned and recorded automatically.

Figure 15–2 shows an example of a fluorescent spectrum automatically recorded with a commercial spectrometer. The wavelength of each spectral line is calculable from the corresponding Bragg angle and the interplanar spacing of the analyzing crystal used. The primary radiation was supplied by a tungsten-target tube operated at 50 kv, and the sample was stainless steel containing 18 percent chromium and 8 percent nickel. The K lines of all the major constituents (Fe, Cr, and Ni) and of some of the minor constituents (Mn and Co) are apparent. (In addition, tungsten L lines can be seen; these will always be present when a tungsten tube is used, since they are excited in the tube and scattered by the sample into the beam of secondary radiation. The copper K lines are due to copper existing as an impurity in the tungsten target.)

In fluorescent spectrometry, the fluorescent radiation emitted by the sample and diffracted by the crystal should be as intense as possible, so that it will be accurately measurable in a short counting time. The intensity of this emitted radiation depends on both the wavelength and the intensity of the incident primary radiation from the x-ray tube. Suppose that monochromatic radiation of constant intensity and of wavelength λ is incident on an element which has a K absorption edge at λ_K, and that we can continuously vary λ. As we decrease λ from a value larger than λ_K, no K fluorescence occurs until λ is just shorter than λ_K. The fluorescent intensity is then a maximum. Further decrease in λ causes the fluorescent intensity to decrease, in much the same manner as the absorption coefficient. This is natural since, as mentioned in Sec. 1–5, fluorescence and true absorption are but two aspects of the same phenomenon. At any

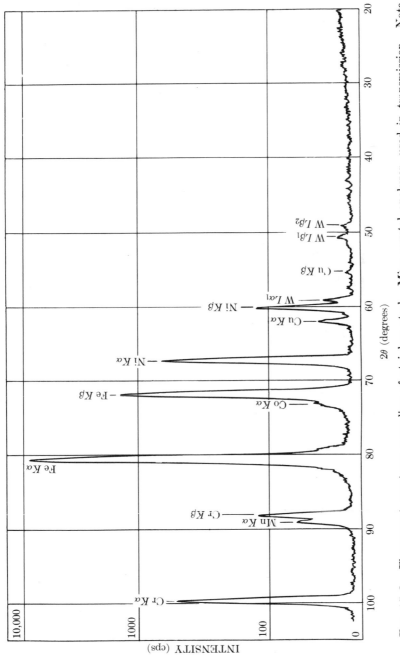

FIG. 15–2. Fluorescent spectrum recording of stainless steel. Mica crystal analyzer, used in transmission. Note logarithmic intensity scale. (Courtesy of General Electric Co., X-Ray Department.)

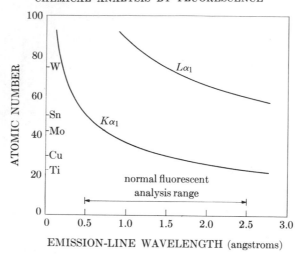

FIG. 15–3. Variation with atomic number of the wavelength of the strongest lines of the K and L series.

one value of λ, the fluorescent intensity is directly proportional to the incident intensity.

The best exciting agent would therefore be a strong characteristic line of wavelength just shorter than λ_K. It is clearly impossible to satisfy this requirement for more than one fluorescing element at a time, and in practice we use a tungsten-target tube with as high a power rating as possible. The exciting radiation is then that part of the continuous spectrum and such L lines of tungsten as have shorter wavelengths than the absorption edge of the fluorescing element. Molybdenum-target tubes are also used.

The beam of secondary radiation issuing from the sample consists largely of fluorescent radiation, but there are some other weak components present as well. These are coherent scattered radiation, coherent diffracted radiation, and incoherent (Compton modified) radiation. These components are partially scattered and diffracted by the analyzing crystal into the counter, and appear as a background on which the spectral lines are superimposed. This background is normally low (see Fig. 15–2), but it may become rather high if the sample contains a large proportion of elements of low atomic number, because the sample will then emit a large amount of Compton modified radiation.

The useful range of fluorescent wavelengths extends from about 0.5 to about 2.5A. The lower limit is imposed by the maximum voltage which can be applied to the x-ray tube, which is 50 kv in commercial instruments. At this voltage the short-wavelength limit of the continuous spectrum from the tube is $12{,}400/50{,}000 = 0.25A$. The maximum intensity occurs at about 1.5 times this value, or 0.38A. Incident radiation of this wavelength would cause K fluorescence in tellurium (atomic number 52), and the emitted $K\alpha$ radiation would have a wavelength of 0.45A. At a tube voltage of 50 kv, little or no K fluorescence is produced in elements with atomic numbers greater than about 55, and for such elements the L lines have to be used. Figure 15–3 shows how the wavelength of the strongest line in each of these series varies with atomic number.

The upper limit of about 2.5A is imposed by the very large absorption of radiation of this wavelength by air and the counter window. This factor limits the elements detectable by fluorescence to those with atomic numbers greater than about 22 (titanium). Ti $K\alpha$ radiation ($\lambda = 2.75$A) is decreased to one-half its original intensity by passage through only 10 cm of air. If a path filled with helium is provided for the x-rays traversing the spectrometer, absorption is decreased to such an extent that the lower limit of atomic number is decreased to about 13 (aluminum). Boron (atomic number 5) should be detectable in a vacuum spectrometer.

Another important factor which limits the detection of light elements is absorption in the sample itself. Fluorescent radiation is produced not only at the surface of the sample but also in its interior, to a depth depending on the depth of effective penetration by the primary beam, which in turn depends on the over-all absorption coefficient of the sample. The fluorescent radiation produced within the sample then undergoes absorption on its way out. Since long-wavelength fluorescent radiation will be highly absorbed by the sample, the fluorescent radiation outside the sample comes only from a thin surface skin and its intensity is accordingly low. It follows that detection of small amounts of a light element in a heavy-element matrix is practically impossible. On the other hand, even a few parts per million of a heavy element in a light-element matrix can be detected.

15–3 Spectrometers. There are various types of fluorescent spectrometers, differentiated by the kind of analyzing crystal used: flat, curved transmitting, or curved reflecting.

The **flat crystal** type, illustrated in Fig. 15–4, is the simplest in design. The x-ray tube is placed as close as possible to the sample, so that the primary radiation on it, and the fluorescent radiation it emits, will be as intense as possible. For the operator's protection against scattered radiation, the sample is enclosed in a thick metal box, which contains a single opening through which the fluorescent beam leaves. The sample area irradiated is of the order of $\frac{3}{4}$ in. square. Fluorescent radiation is emitted in all directions by this area, which acts as a source of radiation for the spectrometer proper. Because of the large size of this source, the beam of fluorescent radiation issuing from the protective box contains a large proportion of widely divergent and convergent radiation. Collimation of this beam before it strikes the analyzing crystal is therefore absolutely necessary, if any

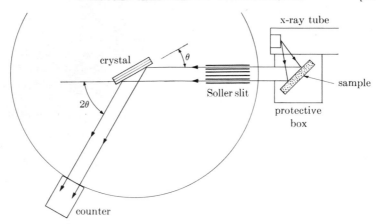

FIG. 15-4.   Essential parts of a fluorescent x-ray spectrometer, flat-crystal type (schematic).

resolution at all is to be obtained.   This collimation is achieved by passing the beam through a Soller slit whose plates are at right angles to the plane of the spectrometer circle, because it is the divergence (and convergence) in this plane that we want to eliminate.

Essentially parallel radiation from the collimator is then incident on the flat crystal, and a portion of it is diffracted into the counter by lattice planes parallel to the crystal face.   Since no focusing occurs, the beam diffracted by the crystal is fairly wide and the counter receiving slit must also be wide. The analyzing crystal is usually NaCl or LiF, with its face cut parallel to the (200) planes.

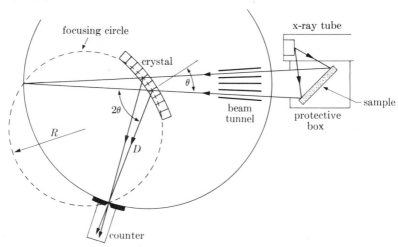

FIG. 15-5.   Fluorescent x-ray spectrometer, curved-transmitting-crystal type (schematic).

Both the commercial diffractometers mentioned in Sec. 7–2 can be readily converted into fluorescent spectrometers of this kind. The conversion involves the substitution of a high-powered (50-kv, 50-ma) tungsten- or molybdenum-target tube for the usual tube used in diffraction experiments, and the addition of an analyzing crystal, a shielded sample box, and a different Soller slit.

The main features of a spectrometer employing a **curved transmitting crystal** are shown in Fig. 15–5. The crystal is usually mica, which is easily obtainable in the form of thin flexible sheets. The beam of secondary radiation from the sample passes through a baffled tunnel, which removes most of the nonconverging radiation. The convergent beam is then reflected by the transverse $(33\bar{1})$ planes of the bent mica crystal, and focused on the receiving slit of the counter. (The focusing action of such a crystal is described in Sec. 6–12.) The beam tunnel is not an essential part of the instrument; for a given setting of the crystal, only incident convergent radiation of a single wavelength will be diffracted into the counter slit. The only purpose of the tunnel is to protect the operator by limiting the beam.

A set of two or three mica crystals of different thicknesses is needed to obtain the highest diffraction efficiency over the whole range of wavelengths, inasmuch as thin crystals must be used in analyzing easily absorbed long-wavelength radiation and thicker crystals for harder radiation. The thickness range is about 0.0006 to 0.004 in.

Besides the usual two-to-one coupling between the counter and crystal, this spectrometer must also have a mechanism for changing the radius of curvature of the crystal with every change in θ, in order that the diffracted rays be always focused at the counter slit. The necessary relation between the radius of curvature $2R$ (R is the radius of the focusing circle) and the crystal-to-focus distance D is given by Eq. (6–15), which we can write in the form

$$2R = \frac{D}{\cos\theta}$$

to emphasize the fact that D is fixed and equal to the radius of the spectrometer circle. The change in $2R$ with change in θ is accomplished automatically in commercial instruments of this type. The General Electric diffractometer shown in Fig. 7–2 may be converted into either this kind of spectrometer or the flat crystal type.

The **curved reflecting crystal** spectrometer is illustrated in Fig. 15–6. Radiation from the sample passes through the narrow slit S and diverges to the crystal (usually NaCl or LiF), which has its reflecting planes bent to a radius of $2R$ and its surface ground to a radius R. Diffracted radiation of a single wavelength is brought to a focus at the counter receiving slit, located on the focusing circle passing through S and the face of the crystal,

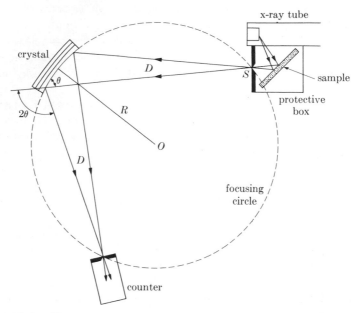

FIG. 15–6.   Fluorescent x-ray spectrometer, curved-reflecting-crystal type.

as described in Sec. 6–12.   But now the radius R of the focusing circle is fixed, for a crystal of given curvature, and the slit-to-crystal and crystal-to-focus distances must both be varied as θ is varied.   The focusing relation, found from Eq. (6–13), is

$$D = 2R \sin \theta,$$

where D stands for both the slit-to-crystal and crystal-to-focus distances, which must be kept equal to one another.   This is accomplished by rotation of both the crystal and the counter about the center O of the focusing circle, in such a manner that rotation of the crystal through an angle x (about O) is accompanied by rotation of the counter through an angle $2x$.   At the same time the counter is rotated about a vertical axis through its slit, by means of another coupling, so that it always points at the crystal.

D increases as θ increases and may become inconveniently large, for a crystal of given radius of curvature R_1, at large θ values.   In order to keep D within reasonable limits, it is necessary to change to another crystal, of smaller radius R_2, for this high-θ (long-wavelength) range.

Spectrometers employing curved reflecting crystals are manufactured by Applied Research Laboratories.

15–4 Intensity and resolution.   We must now consider the two main problems in fluorescent analysis, namely the attainment of adequate *intensity* and adequate *resolution*.   The intensity of the fluorescent radiation emitted by the sample is very much less than that of the primary radiation incident on it, and can become very low indeed when the fluorescing element is only a minor constituent of the sample. This fluorescent radiation is then diffracted by the analyzing crystal, and another large loss of intensity occurs, because diffraction is such an inefficient process. The diffracted beam entering the counter may therefore be very weak, and a long counting time will be necessary to measure its intensity with acceptable accuracy. Spectrometer design must therefore ensure maximum intensity of the radiation entering the counter. At the same time, the spectrometer must be capable of high resolution, if the sample contains elements which have characteristic lines of very nearly the same wavelength and which must be separately identified. Both these factors, intensity and resolution, are affected by the kind of analyzing crystal used and by other details of spectrometer design.

If we define resolution, or resolving power, as the ability to separate spectral lines of nearly the same wavelength, then we see from Fig. 15–7 that resolution depends both on $\Delta 2\theta$, the dispersion, or separation, of line centers, and on B, the line breadth at half-maximum intensity. The resolution will be adequate if $\Delta 2\theta$ is equal to or greater than $2B$. By differentiating the Bragg law, we obtain

$$\frac{\lambda}{\Delta\lambda} = \frac{2\tan\theta}{\Delta 2\theta}. \qquad (15\text{–}1)$$

When the minimum value of $\Delta 2\theta$, namely $2B$, is inserted, this becomes

$$\frac{\lambda}{\Delta\lambda} = \frac{\tan\theta}{B}. \qquad (15\text{–}2)$$

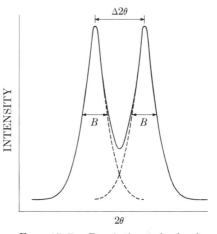

Fig. 15–7. Resolution of closely spaced spectral lines. The lines shown have $\Delta 2\theta = 2B$. Any smaller separation might make the two lines appear as one.

The left-hand side of this equation gives the resolution required to separate two lines of mean wavelength λ and wavelength difference $\Delta\lambda$. The right-hand side gives the resolving power available, and this involves both the mean Bragg angle of the lines and their breadth. Note that the available resolving power increases rapidly with θ, for a given line breadth. This means that, of two crystals producing the same line breadth, the one with the smaller plane spacing d will have the greater resolving power, because it will reflect to higher 2θ angles. The crystals normally used in spectrometers have the following d values: mica, ($33\bar{1}$) planes, 1.5A; LiF, (200) planes, 2.01A; NaCl, (200) planes, 2.82A. For a given crystal, second-order reflections provide greater resolving power than first-order reflections, because they occur at larger angles, but their intensity is less than a fifth of that of first-order reflections.

The factors affecting the line width B can be discussed only with reference to particular spectrometers. In the flat crystal type (Fig. 15–4), the value of B depends partly on the collimation of the beam striking the crystal and partly on the perfection of the crystal itself. The beam reflected by the crystal into the counter is fairly wide, in a linear sense, but almost parallel; its *angular* width is measured by its divergence, and this is equal, if the crystal is perfect, to the divergence of the beam striking the crystal. The latter divergence is controlled by the Soller slit. If l is the length of the slit and s the spacing between plates, then the maximum divergence allowed is

$$\alpha = \frac{2s}{l} \text{ radian.}$$

For a typical slit with $l = 4$ in. and $s = 0.010$ in., $\alpha = 0.3°$. But further divergence is produced by the mosaic structure of the analyzing crystal: this divergence is related to the extent of disorientation of the mosaic blocks, and has a value of about 0.2° for the crystals normally used. The line width B is the sum of these two effects and is therefore of the order of 0.5°. The line width can be decreased by increasing the degree of collimation, but the intensity will also be decreased. Conversely, if the problem at hand does not require fine resolution, a more "open" collimator is used in order to increase intensity. Normally, the collimation is designed to produce a line width of about 0.5°, which will provide adequate resolution for most work.

In the curved transmitting crystal spectrometer (Fig. 15–5), the line width B depends almost entirely on the degree of focusing of the reflected beam at the counter slit. The focusing action of the bent mica crystal, although never perfect, can be made good enough to produce extremely fine lines if a very narrow slit is used; however, the intensity would then be low, so the width of the counter slit is usually made equal to 0.3° to achieve a reasonable balance between line width and intensity. Even so, the intensity is still less than that produced by a flat crystal of NaCl or LiF.

When a curved reflecting crystal (Fig. 15–6) is used, the line width depends mainly on the width of the source slit S and the precision with which the crystal is ground and bent. The line width is normally about the same as that obtained with a flat crystal, namely, about 0.5°.

When intensities are considered, we find that a curved reflecting crystal provides the greatest intensity and a curved transmitting crystal the least, with a flat crystal in an intermediate position.

Returning to the question of resolution, we can now calculate the resolving powers available with typical spectrometers, and compare these values with the maximum resolution required to separate closely spaced spectral lines. The smallest wavelength difference in the K series occurs between the $K\beta$ line of an element of atomic number Z and the $K\alpha$ line of an element of atomic number $(Z + 1)$. This difference itself varies with atomic number and is least for the $K\beta$ line of vanadium ($Z = 23$) and the $K\alpha$ line of chromium ($Z = 24$); these two wavelengths are 2.284 and 2.291A, respectively, and their difference is only 0.007A. A more common problem is the separation of the $K\beta$ line of chromium ($Z = 24$) from the $K\alpha$ line of manganese ($Z = 25$), since both of these elements occur in all stainless steels. The wavelength difference here is 0.018A and the mean wavelength 2.094A. The required resolution $\lambda/\Delta\lambda$ is therefore 2.094/0.018 or 116. The available resolving powers are given by $(\tan \theta)/B$, and are equal to 182 for curved mica in transmission, 70 for flat or curved LiF in reflection, and 46 for flat or curved NaCl in reflection, for assumed line widths of 0.3, 0.5, and 0.5°, respectively, and first-order reflections. Mica would therefore provide adequate resolution, but LiF and NaCl would not.* Figure 15–2 shows the Cr $K\beta$ and Mn $K\alpha$ lines resolved with a mica crystal in the spectrum of a stainless steel.

To sum up, flat or curved crystals of either LiF or NaCl produce much higher reflected intensities but have lower resolution than curved mica crystals. High intensity is desirable in fluorescent analysis in order that the counting time required to obtain good accuracy be reasonably short; if the element to be detected is present only in small concentrations and a crystal of low reflecting power is used, the required counting times will be prohibitively long. In the determination of major elements, any of the three types of crystals will give adequate intensity. High resolution is desirable whenever the analysis requires use of a spectral line having very nearly the same wavelength as another line from the sample or the x-ray tube target.

There is another point that deserves some consideration, namely, the angle 2θ at which a particular wavelength is reflected by the analyzing crystal. This angle depends only on the d spacing of the crystal. The Bragg law shows that the longest wavelength that can be reflected is equal to $2d$. But wavelengths approaching $2d$ in magnitude are reflected almost backward, and their reflected intensity is low at these large angles. We are consequently limited in practice to wavelengths not much longer than d. This means that a crystal like gypsum ($d = 7.6$A) must be used to detect a light element like aluminum whose $K\alpha$ wavelength is 8.3A. Some of the

---

* An alternative, but equivalent, way of arriving at the same result is to calculate the dispersion $\Delta 2\theta$ produced by a given crystal and compare it with the dispersion required, namely, $2B$. The value of $\Delta 2\theta$ is given by $2 \tan \theta(\Delta\lambda/\lambda)$, from Eq. (15–1), and is equal to 1.0° for mica, 0.6° for LiF, and 0.4° for NaCl, for first-order reflections. The corresponding assumed values of $2B$ are 0.6, 1.0, and 1.0°.

other crystals that have been used for light-element detection are oxalic acid ($d = 6.1A$) and mica in reflection ($d = 10.1A$).

15–5 Counters. The reader is advised to review at this point the general discussion of counters given in Chap. 7. Here we are concerned mainly with the variation in counter behavior with variation in x-ray wavelength. This variation is of no great importance in diffractometer measurements, since all diffracted beams have the same wavelength. In spectrometry, however, each spectral line has a different wavelength, and variations in counter behavior with wavelength must be considered.

The pulse size is inversely proportional to x-ray wavelength in proportional and scintillation counters, but independent of wavelength in Geiger counters. Of more importance, however, is the variation of counter efficiency with wavelength. The efficiency of a gas-filled counter (proportional or Geiger) depends on the gas used; in this respect, krypton is superior to argon for fluorescent analysis, in that krypton detects all radiation having wavelengths greater than 0.5A fairly efficiently while argon does not (see Fig. 7–17). Below 0.5A, both gases have low efficiency. The scintillation counter, on the other hand, is almost 100 percent efficient for all wavelengths. The use of scintillation counters in conjunction with x-ray tubes operable at higher voltages than those now available would permit the detection of heavy elements by their fluorescent K lines having wavelengths below 0.5A.

Counter speed is another important factor in quantitative analysis, because a counter which can operate at high counting rates without losses can be used to measure both strong lines and weak lines without corrections or the use of absorbing foils. In this respect, proportional and scintillation counters are definitely superior to Geiger counters.

15–6 Qualitative analysis. In qualitative work sufficient accuracy can be obtained by automatic scanning of the spectrum, with the counter output fed to a chart recorder. Interpretation of the recorded spectrum will be facilitated if the analyst has on hand (a) a table of corresponding values of λ and 2θ for the particular analyzing crystal used, and (b) a single table of the principal K and L lines of all the elements arranged in numerical order of wavelength.

Since it is important to know whether an observed line is due to an element in the sample or to an element in the x-ray tube target, a preliminary investigation should be made of the spectrum emitted by the target alone. For this purpose a substance like carbon or plexiglass is placed in the sample holder and irradiated in the usual way; such a substance merely scatters part of the primary radiation into the spectrometer, and does not contribute any observable fluorescent radiation of its own. The spectrum so obtained will disclose the L lines of tungsten, if a tungsten-target tube is used, as well as the characteristic lines of whatever impurities happen to be present in the target.

15–7 Quantitative analysis. In determining the amount of element A in a sample, the single-line method is normally used: the intensity I_u of a particular characteristic line of A from the unknown is compared with the intensity I_s of the same line from a standard, normally pure A. The way in which the ratio I_u/I_s varies with the concentration of A in the sample depends markedly on the other elements present and cannot in general be predicted by calculation. It is therefore necessary to establish the variation by means of measurements made on samples of known composition. Figure 15–8 illustrates typical curves of this kind for three binary mixtures containing iron.

These curves show that the intensity of a fluorescent line from element A is not in general proportional to the concentration of A. This nonlinear behavior is due mainly to two effects:

(1) *Matrix absorption.* As the composition of the alloy changes, so does its absorption coefficient. As a result there are changes both in the absorption of the primary radiation traveling into the sample and in the absorption of the fluorescent radiation traveling out. The absorption of the primary radiation is difficult to calculate, because the part of that radiation effective in causing K fluorescence, for example, in A has wavelengths ex-

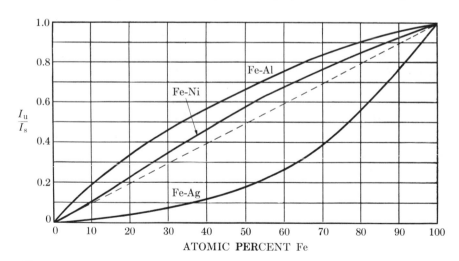

FIG. 15–8. Effect of iron concentration on the intensity of Fe $K\alpha$ radiation fluoresced by various mixtures. I_u and I_s are the Fe $K\alpha$ intensities from the mixture and from pure iron, respectively. (H. Friedman and L. S. Birks, *Rev. Sci. Inst.* **19**, 323, 1948.)

tending from λ_{SWL}, the short-wavelength limit of the continuous spectrum, to λ_{KA}, the K absorption edge of A. To each of these incident wavelengths corresponds a different incident intensity and a different matrix absorption coefficient. The absorption of the fluorescent radiation, of wavelength λ_{fA}, depends only on the absorption coefficient of the specimen for that particular wavelength. (Absorption effects are particularly noticeable in the Fe-Al and Fe-Ag curves of Fig. 15–8. The absorption coefficient of an Fe-Al alloy is less than that of an Fe-Ag alloy of the same iron content, with the result that the depth of effective penetration of the incident beam is greater for the Fe-Al alloy. A larger number of iron atoms can therefore contribute to the fluorescent beam, and this beam itself will undergo less absorption than in the Fe-Ag alloy. The over-all result is that the intensity of the fluorescent Fe $K\alpha$ radiation outside the specimen is greater for the Fe-Al alloy.)

(2) *Multiple excitation.* If the primary radiation causes element B in the specimen to emit its characteristic radiation, of wavelength λ_{fB}, and if λ_{fB} is less than λ_{KA}, then fluorescent K radiation from A will be excited not only by the incident beam but also by fluorescent radiation from B. (This effect is evident in the Fe-Ni curve of Fig. 15–8. Ni $K\alpha$ radiation can excite Fe $K\alpha$ radiation, and the result is that the observed intensity of the Fe $K\alpha$ radiation from an Fe-Ni alloy is closer to that for an Fe-Al alloy of the same iron content than one would expect from a simple comparison of the absorption coefficients of the two alloys. In the case of an Fe-Ag alloy, the observed Fe $K\alpha$ intensity is much lower, even though Ag $K\alpha$ can excite Fe $K\alpha$, because of the very large absorption in the specimen.)

Because of the complications these effects introduce into any calculation of fluorescent intensities, quantitative analysis is always performed on an empirical basis, i.e., by the use of standard samples of known composition. The greatest use of fluorescent analysis is in control work, where a great many samples of approximately the same composition have to be analyzed to see if their composition falls within specified limits. For such work, the calibration curves need not be prepared over a 0–100 percent range, as in Fig. 15–8, but only over quite limited composition ranges. The usual reference material for such analyses is one of the standard samples used in the calibration, rather than a pure metal.

Sample preparation for fluorescent analysis is not particularly difficult. Solid samples are ground to produce a flat surface but need not be polished; however, a standardized method of sample preparation should be adhered to for best results. Powder specimens, finely ground and well mixed, can be pressed into special holders; adequate mixing is essential, since only a thin surface layer is actually analyzed and this must be representative of the whole sample. Liquid samples can be contained in various kinds of cells.

Line intensities should be measured with a scaler rather than taken from a recorded chart. For a given line intensity, the accuracy of the analysis depends on the time spent in counting, since the relative probable error in a measurement of N counts is proportional to $1/\sqrt{N}$. If a line is weak, a correction must be made for the background of scattered and diffracted radiation. Because of this background, the number of counts required to obtain a given accuracy in the measurement of a weak line is larger than that required for a strong line (see Eq. 7–7).

Since the intensity of a particular line from the sample is usually compared with the intensity of the same line from a standard, the output of the x-ray tube must be stabilized or the tube must be monitored.

The resolution of the spectrometer should be no greater than that required by the particular analytical problem involved. The analyzing crystal and collimator or counter slit should be chosen to produce this minimum amount of resolution and as much intensity as possible, since the greater the intensity, the less time required for analysis.

15–8 Automatic spectrometers. Automatic direct-reading optical spectrometers have been in use for several years and have proved to be of great value in industrial process control. A sample is inserted and the concentrations of a number of selected elements are rapidly and directly indicated on a chart or set of dials. Because such spectrometers must be preset and precalibrated for each particular element determined, they are suitable only for control laboratories where large numbers of samples must be analyzed for the same set of elements, each of which is variable only over a limited range of concentration.

Recently, x-ray counterparts of these direct-reading optical spectrometers have become available. There are two types:

(1) *Single-channel type.* An instrument of this kind is manufactured by North American Philips Co. and called the Autrometer. It uses a flat analyzing crystal in reflection and a scintillation counter as a detector. Corresponding to the elements A, B, C, ... to be detected are the wavelengths λ_{fA}, λ_{fB}, λ_{fC}, ... of their characteristic spectral lines, and to these correspond certain diffraction angles $2\theta_A$, $2\theta_B$, $2\theta_C$, ... at which these wavelengths will be diffracted by the crystal. The counter is designed to move stepwise from one predetermined angular position to another rather than to scan a certain angular range. The various elements are determined in sequence: the counter moves to position $2\theta_A$, remains there long enough to accurately measure the intensity of the spectral line from element A, moves rapidly to position $2\theta_B$, measures the intensity of the line from B, and so on. At each step the intensity of the line from the sample is automatically compared with the intensity of the same line from the standard and the ratio of these two intensities is printed on a paper tape. The instrument may also be

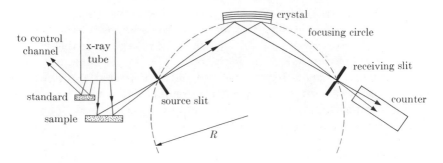

Fig. 15–9. Relative arrangement of x-ray tube, sample, and one analyzing channel of the X-Ray Quantometer (schematic). (The tube is of the "end-on" type: the face of the target is inclined to the tube axis and the x-rays produced escape through a window in the end of the tube.)

adjusted so that the actual concentration of the element involved is printed on the tape. As many as twelve elements per sample may be determined. The curved reflecting crystal spectrometer manufactured by Applied Research Laboratories (see Sec. 15–3) may also be arranged for this kind of automatic, sequential line measurement.

(2) *Multichannel type*, manufactured by Applied Research Laboratories and called the X-Ray Quantometer. The analyzing crystal is a bent and cut LiF or NaCl crystal, used in reflection. Near the sample is a slit which acts as a virtual source of divergent radiation for the focusing crystal (Fig. 15–9). Eight assemblies like the one shown, each consisting of slits, analyzing crystal, and counter, are arranged in a circle about the centrally located x-ray tube; seven of these receive the same fluorescent radiation from the sample, while the eighth receives fluorescent radiation from a standard. Each of these seven assemblies forms a separate "channel" for the determination of one particular element in the sample. In channel A, for example, which is used to detect element A, the positions of the crystal and counter are preset so that only radiation of wavelength λ_{fA} can be reflected into the counter. The components of the other analyzing channels are positioned in similar fashion, so that a separate spectral line is measured in each channel. The eighth, or control, channel monitors the output of the x-ray tube.

In this instrument each counter delivers its pulses, not to a scaler or ratemeter, but to an integrating capacitor in which the total charge delivered by the counter in a given length of time is collected. When a sample is being analyzed, all counters are started simultaneously. When the control counter has delivered to its capacitor a predetermined charge, i.e., a predetermined total number of counts, all counters are automatically stopped. Then the integrating capacitor in each analyzing channel discharges in turn into a measuring circuit and recorder, and the total charge collected in each channel is recorded in sequence on a chart. The quantity indicated on the chart for each element is the ratio of the intensity of a given spectral line from the sample to that of a line from the standard, and the instrument can be calibrated so that the concentration of each element in the sample can be read directly from the chart recording. Because the total fluorescent energy received in each analyzing counter is related to a fixed amount of energy entering the control counter, variations in the x-ray tube output do not affect the accuracy of the results.

15–9 Nondispersive analysis. Up to this point we have considered only methods of *dispersive analysis*, i.e., methods in which x-ray beams of different wavelengths are physically separated, or dispersed, in space by an analyzing crystal so that the intensity of each may be separately measured. But the separate measurement of the intensities of beams of different wavelengths can often be accomplished without the spatial separation of these beams. Methods for doing this are called *nondispersive*. No analyzing crystal is used and the experimental arrangement takes on the simple form illustrated in Fig. 15–10. The counter receives fluorescent radiation directly from the sample, and the filter shown may or may not be present.* Three methods of nondispersive analysis have been used: selective excitation, selective filtration, and selective counting.

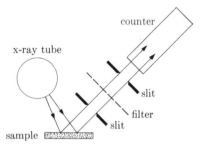

FIG. 15–10. Apparatus for nondispersive analysis.

Selective excitation of a particular spectral line is accomplished simply by control of the x-ray tube voltage. Suppose, for example, that a Cu-Sn alloy is to be analyzed. If the tube is operated at 28 kv, then Cu $K\alpha$ will be excited (excitation voltage = 9 kv) but not Sn $K\alpha$ (excitation voltage = 29 kv). The L lines of Sn will be excited at 28 kv but their wavelengths are so long (about 3A) that this radiation will be almost completely absorbed in air. The radiation entering the counter therefore consists almost entirely of Cu $K\alpha$ together with a small amount of white radiation scattered from the primary beam by the sample; the counter output can therefore be calibrated in terms of the copper concentration of the sample. Evi-

---

* The x-ray tube and counter should be as close as possible to the sample but, if necessary, a fluorescent spectrometer may be used, with the analyzing crystal removed and the counter set at $2\theta = 0$. Or a diffractometer may be used, with the sample in the usual position and the counter set almost anywhere *except* at the position of a diffracted beam. In either case, since no focusing of the fluorescent beam occurs, the counter receiving slit should be removed in order to gain intensity.

dently, the selective excitation method works best where the elements involved differ fairly widely in atomic number.

When the K radiations of both elements are excited in the sample, **selective filtration** can be used to ensure that only one of them enters the counter. Consider the analysis of a Cu-Zn alloy. The K excitation voltage of copper is 9.0 kv and that of zinc 9.7 kv. Even if the operating voltage could be accurately set between these values, the intensity of the fluorescent Cu $K\alpha$ radiation would be very low. It is better to operate at a voltage higher than either of these, say 12–15 kv, and use a nickel filter between the sample and the counter. This filter will absorb most of the Zn $K\alpha$ and pass most of the Cu $K\alpha$ radiation. Selective filtration of this kind is most effective when the two elements have either nearly the same atomic numbers or widely different atomic numbers, because, in either case, a filter material can be chosen which will have quite different absorption coefficients for the two radiations. (Of course, the air between the sample and counter itself acts as a very effective selective filter in many applications. Consider the determination of copper in a Cu-Al alloy. The K lines of both elements will be excited at any voltage above 9 kv but Al $K\alpha$, of wavelength 8.3A, is so strongly absorbed by air that practically none of it reaches the counter.) Balanced filters do not appear to have been used in nondispersive analysis, but there is no reason why they should not be just as effective in this field as in diffractometry.

Finally, the method of **selective counting** may be used. As mentioned in Sec. 7–5, it is possible to measure the intensity of radiation of one wavelength in the presence of radiations of other wavelengths by means of a proportional counter and a single-channel pulse-height analyzer. Thus the counter-analyzer combination can receive two or more characteristic radiations from the sample and be responsive to only one of them. No filtration is needed and the measured intensities are very high. This method works best when the elements involved differ in atomic number by at least three. If the difference is less, their characteristic radiations will not differ sufficiently in wavelength for efficient discrimination by the analyzer.

There is, of course, no reason why any one of these methods cannot be combined with any other, or all three may be used together. Thus a particular analytical problem may require the use of selective excitation and selective filtration, one technique aiding the other. Such combinations will usually be necessary when the sample contains more than two elements. In general, nondispersive analysis is most effective when applied to binary alloys, since the difficulties involved in distinguishing between one characteristic radiation and another, or in exciting one and not another, increase with the number of elements in the sample. These difficulties can be alleviated by a multichannel arrangement, and the X-Ray Quantometer described in the previous section can be used for nondispersive analysis in that manner, simply by removing the analyzing crystals and changing the counter positions. Each channel contains a different filter material, chosen in accordance with the particular element being determined in that channel.

The main advantage of nondispersive methods of analysis is the very large gain in intensity over dispersive methods. The high loss of intensity involved in diffraction from an analyzing crystal is completely avoided. As a result, the beam entering the counter of a nondispersive system is relatively intense, even after passing through the rather thick filters which are used to prevent interference from other wavelengths. The greater the intensity, the shorter the counting time required to obtain a given accuracy, or the higher the accuracy for a given counting time.

15–10 Measurement of coating thickness. Fluorescent radiation can be utilized not only as a means of chemical analysis but also as a method for measuring the thickness of surface layers. The following methods, both based on **fluorescence,** have been used to measure the thickness of a surface coating of A on B:

(1) A dispersive system is used and the counter is positioned to receive the A $K\alpha$ line from the sample. The intensity of the A $K\alpha$ line increases with the thickness of the A layer up to the point at which this layer becomes effectively of infinite thickness, and then becomes constant. (Effectively infinite thickness, which is about 0.001 in. for a metal like nickel, corresponds to the effective depth of penetration of the primary beam striking the sample, and this method is in fact a way of determining this depth.) The relation between A $K\alpha$ intensity and the thickness of A must be obtained by calibration. The operation of this method is independent of the composition of the base material B, which may be either a metal or a nonmetal. This method may also be used with a nondispersive system, provided that B is a nonmetal, or, if B is a metal, provided that the atomic numbers of A and B are such that nondispersive separation of A $K\alpha$ and B $K\alpha$ is practical (see the previous section).

(2) A dispersive system is used and the intensity of B $K\alpha$ radiation is measured. This intensity decreases as the thickness of A increases, and becomes effectively zero at a certain limiting thickness which depends on the properties of both A and B. Calibration is again necessary. A nondispersive system may also be used if conditions are favorable, as they are, for example, in the measurement of the thickness of tin plate on sheet steel. In this case, selective excitation of Fe $K\alpha$ is the simplest procedure inasmuch as the operating conditions are exactly similar to those involved in the analysis of Cu-Sn alloys described in the previous section. This method is used industrially: tinned sheet steel passes continuously beneath a nondispersive analyzer, and the thickness of the tin coating is continuously recorded on a chart.

Although they have nothing to do with fluorescence, it is convenient to mention here the corresponding **diffraction** methods for measuring the thickness of a coating of A on B:

(1) The specimen is placed in a diffractometer and the intensity of a strong diffraction line from A is measured. The intensity of this line, relative to the intensity of the same line from an infinitely thick sample of A, is a measure of the thickness of A. The thickness may be directly calculated from this intensity ratio by means of Eq. (9–4) and the form of the line intensity *vs.* thickness curve will resemble that of Fig. 9–6. The coating A must be crystalline, but B can be any material.

(2) The intensity of a strong diffraction line from B is measured in a diffractometer. The observed intensity I depends on the thickness t of the A layer in an easily calculable manner. Since the total path length of the incident and diffracted beams in the A layer is $2t/\sin\theta$, the intensity of a diffraction line from B is given by

$$I = I_0 e^{-2\mu t/\sin\theta},$$

where I_0 = intensity of the same diffraction line from uncoated B, and μ = linear absorption coefficient of A. In this case B must be crystalline, but A can be anything.

Any one of these methods, whether based on fluorescence or diffraction, may be used for measuring the thickness of thin foils, simply by mounting the foil on a suitable backing material.

PROBLEMS

15–1. Assume that the line breadth B in a fluorescent x-ray spectrometer is 0.3° for a mica analyzing crystal used in transmission and 0.5° for either a LiF or NaCl crystal in reflection. Which of these crystals will provide adequate resolution of the following pairs of lines?

(a) Co $K\beta$ and Ni $K\alpha$ (b) Sn $K\beta$ and Sb $K\alpha$

Calculate $\Delta 2\theta$ values for each crystal.

15–2. What operating conditions would you recommend for the nondispersive fluorescent analysis of the following alloys with a scintillation counter?

(a) Cu-Ni   (b) Cu-Ag

15–3. Diffraction method (2) of Sec. 15–10 is used to measure the thickness of a nickel electroplate on copper with Cu $K\alpha$ incident radiation. What is the maximum measurable thickness of nickel if the minimum measurable line intensity is 1 percent of that from uncoated copper?

CHAPTER 16

CHEMICAL ANALYSIS BY ABSORPTION

16–1 Introduction. Just as the wavelength of a characteristic line is characteristic of an emitting element, so is the wavelength of an absorption edge characteristic of an absorbing element. Therefore, if a sample containing a number of elements is used as an absorber and if the absorption it produces is measured as a function of wavelength, absorption edges will be disclosed, and the wavelengths of these edges will serve to identify the various elements in the sample. The method may also be made quantitative, if the change in absorption occurring at each edge is measured.

Such measurements require monochromatic radiation of controlled wavelength, and this is usually obtained by reflection from a single crystal in a diffractometer. The sample whose absorption is to be measured is placed in the diffracted beam, as indicated in Fig. 16–1(a), and x-rays of any desired wavelength are picked out of the white radiation issuing from the tube simply by setting the analyzing crystal at the appropriate angle θ. Alternately, the sample may be placed in the beam incident on the crystal.

Another source of monochromatic radiation of controlled wavelength is an element fluorescing its characteristic radiation. The arrangement shown in Fig. 16–1(b) is used, with the crystal set to reflect the characteristic radiation of whatever element is used as radiator. By having on hand a set of elements of atomic number Z, $(Z + 1)$, $(Z + 2)$, $\ldots$, we have available a discontinuous range of characteristic wavelengths, and

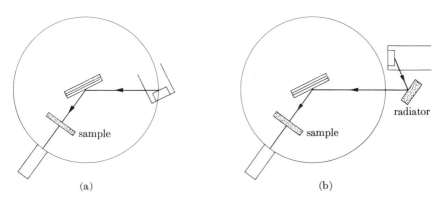

Fig. 16–1. Experimental arrangement for absorption measurements: (a) with diffractometer, (b) with fluorescent spectrometer.

423

the intensity of this radiation at the sample will be considerably larger than that of the white radiation components used in the diffractometer method. Even though the wavelengths furnished by fluorescence do not form a continuum, they are spaced closely enough to be useful in measuring the variation in absorption of the sample with wavelength. In the wavelength range from 0.5 to 1.5A, for example, the average difference between the $K\alpha$ wavelengths of an element of atomic number Z and one of $(Z + 1)$ is only 0.06A. If a particular element is not available in the pure form, its oxide, or some other compound or alloy containing a substantial amount of the element, can be used as a radiator of fluorescent radiation.

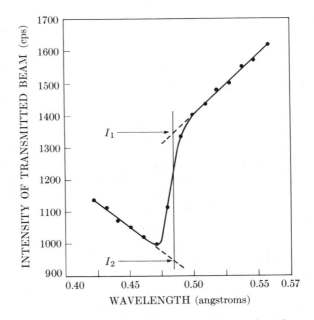

Fig. 16–2. Variation of transmitted intensity with wavelength near an absorption edge. (For this particular curve, three thicknesses of photographic film were used as an absorber and the absorption edge shown is the K edge of the silver in the emulsion.)

16–2 Absorption-edge method. Suppose we wish to determine the concentration of element A in a sample containing a number of other elements. The sample, prepared in the form of a flat plate or sheet of uniform thickness, is placed in a beam of controllable wavelength, and the intensity I of the transmitted radiation is measured for a series of wavelengths on either side of an absorption edge of element A. The resulting curve of I vs. λ will have the form of Fig. 16–2, since the transmitted intensity will increase abruptly on the long wavelength side of the edge. (The exact form of the curve depends on the kind of radiation available. The data in Fig. 16–2 were obtained with radiation reflected from the continuous spectrum in a diffractometer; the upward slope of the curve at wavelengths longer than the edge is due to the fact that the intensity of the incident beam increases with wavelength in this region of the continuous spectrum and this effect more than compensates for the increase in the absorption coefficient of the sample with wavelength.) By the extrapolations shown we obtain the values of I_1 and I_2, the transmitted intensities for wavelengths just longer and just shorter, respectively, than the wavelength of the edge.

The mass absorption coefficient of the sample is given by

$$\left(\frac{\mu}{\rho}\right)_m = w_A \left(\frac{\mu}{\rho}\right)_A + w_r \left(\frac{\mu}{\rho}\right)_r,$$

where w denotes weight fraction, and the subscripts m, A, and r denote the mixture of elements in the sample, element A, and the remaining elements in the sample, respectively. At a wavelength not equal to that of an absorption edge the transmitted intensity is given by

$$I = I_0 e^{-(\mu/\rho)_m \rho_m t},$$

where I_0 is the intensity of the incident beam, ρ_m is the density of the sample, and t is the thickness of the sample. At wavelengths just longer and just shorter than that of the absorption edge of A, let the mass absorption coefficients of A be $(\mu/\rho)_{A1}$ and $(\mu/\rho)_{A2}$, respectively. Then the transmitted intensities for these two wavelengths will be

$$I_1 = I_0 e^{-[w_A(\mu/\rho)_{A1} + w_r(\mu/\rho)_r]\rho_m t}$$

$$I_2 = I_0 e^{-[w_A(\mu/\rho)_{A2} + w_r(\mu/\rho)_r]\rho_m t},$$

since $(\mu/\rho)_r$ is the same for both. Division of one equation by the other gives

$$\frac{I_1}{I_2} = e^{w_A[(\mu/\rho)_{A2} - (\mu/\rho)_{A1}]\rho_m t}. \tag{16–1}$$

If we put $[(\mu/\rho)_{A2} - (\mu/\rho)_{A1}] = k_A$ and $\rho_m t = M_m$, then Eq. (16–1) becomes

$$\ln \frac{I_1}{I_2} = w_A k_A M_m. \tag{16–2}$$

This equation can be used to determine w_A from measured and tabulated quantities. The constant k_A, which measures the change in the mass absorption coefficient of A at the absorption edge, is a property of the element involved and decreases as the atomic number increases. M_m is the mass of sample per unit area and is given by the mass of the sample divided by the area of one face.

Since M_m varies with w_A for samples of constant thickness, and may in fact vary independently of w_A, it is convenient to lump the two together and put $w_A M_m = M_A$ = mass of A per unit area of sample. A plot of $\ln (I_1/I_2)$ vs. M_A will then be a straight line through the origin with a slope of k_A. If there is any doubt about the accuracy of the tabulated absorption coefficients from which k_A is derived, this curve can be established by measurements on samples of known A content. It is important to note that the slope of this curve depends only on the element A being determined and is independent, not only of the other elements present, but also of any variations in the concentrations of these elements with respect to one another. The other elements present affect only M_m, which must be measured for each sample. The value of w_A is then given by M_A/M_m.

The fact that the curve of $\ln (I_1/I_2)$ vs. M_A forms a master plot for the determination of A whatever the other constituents of the sample represents a distinct advantage of the absorption-edge method over fluorescent analysis. For example, if element A is being determined by fluorescence in samples containing A, B, and C, a calibration curve for the determination of A is valid only for samples containing a fixed concentration of B or C.

The main disadvantage of the absorption-edge method, when applied to the analysis of alloys, is the very thin sample required to obtain measurable

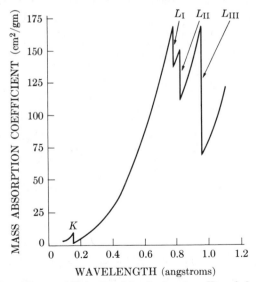

FIG. 16–3. Absorption coefficients of lead, showing K and L absorption edges. (Plotted from data in *Handbook of Chemistry and Physics*, 23rd ed., Chemical Rubber Publishing Co., Cleveland, 1939.)

transmitted intensity. Many alloy samples have to be ground down to a thickness of one or two thousandths of an inch, and this is a tedious and time-consuming operation. The method is best suited to the determination of a fairly heavy element in a light-element matrix. It is difficult to determine light elements, even though they have large values of k, because their absorption edges occur at such long wavelengths that the incident radiation is almost completely absorbed even by very thin samples. (However, the difficulties involved in preparing thin samples of solid materials may be avoided by dissolving the sample, in a known concentration, in a suitable liquid. The resulting solution is contained in a flat-sided cell of some highly transparent material, and the total sample thickness may be several millimeters.)

When the atomic number of the element being determined exceeds about 50, the L_{III} rather than the K absorption edge should be used. Not only is k much larger for the L_{III} edge of such elements, but their K absorption edges occur at wavelengths shorter than those available from an x-ray tube operated at 50 kv. Figure 16–3 shows the relative size and location of the K and L absorption edges of lead.

16–3 Direct-absorption method (monochromatic beam). Absorption methods not involving measurements at an absorption edge have also been used. The mass absorption coefficient of a mixture of two elements A and B, for a wavelength not equal to that of an absorption edge of either, is given by

$$\left(\frac{\mu}{\rho}\right)_m = w_A \left(\frac{\mu}{\rho}\right)_A + (1 - w_A) \left(\frac{\mu}{\rho}\right)_B .$$

The relation between the incident intensity I_0 and the transmitted intensity I is therefore

$$\ln \frac{I_0}{I} = \left[w_A \left(\frac{\mu}{\rho}\right)_A + (1 - w_A) \left(\frac{\mu}{\rho}\right)_B \right] \rho_m t. \qquad (16\text{–}3)$$

This relation can be used for the determination of the amount of A present, provided that ρ_m, the density of the sample, is known as a function of composition. A strong characteristic line is normally used for such measurements: for greatest sensitivity its wavelength should lie between the absorption edges of A and B.

Naturally, if ρ_m is known as a function of composition, density measurements alone can disclose the composition of an unknown without any necessity for absorption measurements. But there are circumstances in which an absorption measurement is more convenient than a density measurement. Such circumstances arise in diffusion studies. Metals A and B are joined together to form a diffusion couple [Fig. 16–4(a)], held

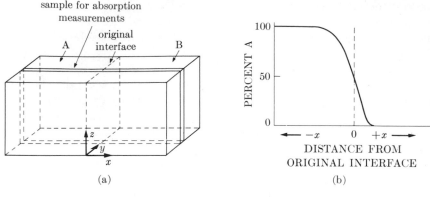

FIG. 16–4.   Application of the direct-absorption method to diffusion measurements.

at a constant elevated temperature for a given period of time, and then cooled to room temperature. The problem is to determine the penetration of one metal into another, i.e., to arrive at a curve like Fig. 16–4(b), showing the change in composition of the alloy along a line normal to the original interface. This is usually done by cutting the couple into a number of thin slices, parallel to the yz-plane of the original interface, and determining the composition of each slice. In the absorption method, a single slice is taken parallel to the xz-plane, normal to the original interface. This slice is then placed between the diffractometer counter and a narrow fixed slit which defines the x coordinate of the area irradiated. If the sample is then moved stepwise relative to the slit in the x direction, a series of measurements can be made from which the composition $vs.$ distance curve can be plotted.

Another way in which the direct absorption method can be made useful involves making measurements at two wavelengths, λ_1 and λ_2, since no knowledge of the density or thickness of the sample is then required. Designating measurements made at each of these wavelengths by subscripts 1 and 2, we find from Eq. (16–3) that

$$\frac{\ln (I_{01}/I_1)}{\ln (I_{02}/I_2)} = \frac{w_A[(\mu/\rho)_{A1} - (\mu/\rho)_{B1}] + (\mu/\rho)_{B1}}{w_A[(\mu/\rho)_{A2} - (\mu/\rho)_{B2}] + (\mu/\rho)_{B2}}. \tag{16–4}$$

The wavelengths λ_1 and λ_2 should be chosen to lie near, and on either side of, an absorption edge of A. One way of applying this method to routine analyses is to use a multichannel nondispersive fluorescent analyzer. Three channels are required: channel 1 contains an element which fluoresces characteristic radiation of wavelength λ_1, channel 2 contains another element producing radiation of wavelength λ_2, and channel 3 is used for control. The absorption produced by the sample is measured first in channel 1 and then in channel 2, and the ratio of the intensities I_1 and I_2

transmitted in these two channels is taken as a measure of the A content of the sample. The control channel is used to ensure that all samples receive the same total energy of incident radiation. No use is made of Eq. (16–4). Instead, a calibration curve showing the relation between w_A and $\ln (I_1/I_2)$ is prepared from samples of known composition.

The methods outlined in this section are normally used only for the analysis of two-component samples. If more than two components are present and equations of the form of (16–3) and (16–4) are used, then all but two components in the sample must have known concentrations. If the concentration of a particular element is obtained from a calibration curve rather than from these equations, the calibration curve applies only to samples containing fixed concentrations of all but two components.

16–4 Direct-absorption method (polychromatic beam). The absorption of a polychromatic beam, made up of the sum total of continuous and characteristic radiation issuing from an x-ray tube, may also be made the basis for chemical analysis. The experimental arrangement is very simple: the sample is merely placed in the direct beam from the x-ray tube, and a counter behind the sample measures the transmitted intensity. Because of the multiplicity of wavelengths present, no exact calculation of transmitted intensity as a function of sample composition can be made. However, a calibration curve can be set up on the basis of measurements made on samples of known composition, and this curve will be valid for the determination of a particular element in a series of samples, provided all samples have the same thickness and the concentrations of all but two components are fixed.

The chief advantage of this method is the very large gain in intensity over methods involving monochromatic beams. A monochromatic beam, whether produced by diffraction or fluorescence, is quite feeble in comparison to the direct beam from an x-ray tube. The higher the incident intensity, the thicker the sample that can be used; or, for the same sample thickness, the higher the intensity, the shorter the analysis time for a given accuracy of counting.

16–5 Applications. Absorption methods of analysis are limited to samples whose total absorption is low enough to produce a transmitted beam of accurately measurable intensity. This means that samples of most metallic alloys have to be made extremely thin, at least for methods involving low-intensity monochromatic beams, or they have to be dissolved in a liquid.

In industry today, absorption methods are almost entirely confined to the analysis of organic liquids and similar materials of low absorption coefficient. A typical example of such analyses is the determination of tetraethyl lead in gasoline.

PROBLEMS

16-1. The values of I_1 and I_2, taken from Fig. 16-2, for the absorption produced by three thicknesses of unprocessed x-ray film are 1337 and 945 cps, respectively. The upper and lower values of the mass absorption coefficient of silver at its K absorption edge are 62.5 and 9.8 cm²/gm, respectively. Calculate the silver content (in mg/cm²) of a single piece of this film.

16-2. If the minimum detectable increase in transmitted intensity at an absorption edge is 5 percent, what is the minimum detectable amount of copper (in weight percent) in an Al-Cu alloy if the absorption-edge method is used on a sample 1 mm thick? Assume that the density of the sample is the same as that of pure aluminum. The upper and lower values of the mass absorption coefficient of copper at its K absorption edge are 307 and 37 cm²/gm, respectively.

16-3. The composition of an Fe-Ni alloy, known to contain about 50 weight percent iron, is to be determined by the direct absorption method with Cu $K\alpha$ radiation. Its density is 8.3 gm/cm³. The maximum available incident intensity is 10,000 cps. The minimum transmitted intensity accurately measurable in a reasonable length of time in the presence of the background is 30 cps. What is the maximum specimen thickness?

CHAPTER 17

STRESS MEASUREMENT

17–1 Introduction. When a polycrystalline piece of metal is deformed elastically in such a manner that the strain is uniform over relatively large distances, the lattice plane spacings in the constituent grains change from their stress-free value to some new value corresponding to the magnitude of the applied stress, this new spacing being essentially constant from one grain to another for any particular set of planes. This uniform macro-strain, as we saw in Sec. 9–4, causes a *shift* of the diffraction lines to new 2θ positions. On the other hand, if the metal is deformed plastically, the lattice planes usually become distorted in such a way that the spacing of any particular (hkl) set varies from one grain to another or from one part of a grain to another. This nonuniform microstrain causes a *broadening* of the corresponding diffraction line. Actually, both kinds of strain are usually superimposed in plastically deformed metals, and diffraction lines are both shifted and broadened, because not only do the plane spacings vary from grain to grain but their mean value differs from that of the undeformed metal.

In this chapter we will be concerned with the line shift due to uniform strain. From this shift the strain may be calculated and, knowing the strain, we can determine the stress present, either by a calculation involving the mechanically measured elastic constants of the material, or by a calibration procedure involving measurement of the strains produced by known stresses. X-ray diffraction can therefore be used as a method of "stress" measurement. Note, however, that stress is not measured directly by the x-ray method or, for that matter, by any other method of "stress" measurement. It is always strain that is measured; the stress is deter-mined indirectly, by calculation or calibration.

The various methods of "stress" measurement differ only in the kind of strain gauge used. In the common electric-resistance method, the gauge is a short length of fine wire cemented to the surface of the metal being tested; any strain in the metal is shared by the wire, and any extension or contraction of the wire is accompanied by a change in its resistance, which can therefore be used as a measure of strain. In the x-ray method, the strain gauge is the spacing of lattice planes.

17–2 Applied stress and residual stress. Before the x-ray method is examined in any detail, it is advisable to consider first a more general subject, namely, the difference between applied stress and residual stress, and to gain a clear idea of what these terms mean. Consider a metal bar deformed elastically, for example in uniform tension. The *applied stress* is given simply by the applied force per unit area of cross section. If the external force is removed, the stress disappears, and the bar regains its initial stress-free dimensions. On the other hand, there are certain operations which can be performed on a metal part, which will leave it in a stressed condition even after all external forces have been removed. This stress, which persists in the absence of external force, is called *residual stress*.

For example, consider the assembly shown in Fig. 17–1(a). It consists of a hollow section through which is passed a loosely fitting bolt with threaded ends. If nuts are screwed on these ends and tightened, the sides of the assembly are compressed and the bolt is placed in tension. The stresses present are residual, inasmuch as there are no external forces acting on the assembly as a whole. Notice also that the tensile stresses in one part of the assembly are balanced by compressive stresses in other parts. This balance of opposing stresses, required by the fact that the assembly as a whole is in equilibrium, is characteristic of all states of residual stress.

An exactly equivalent condition of residual stress can be produced by welding a cross bar into an open section, as shown in Fig. 17–1(b). We can reasonably assume that, at the instant the second weld is completed, a substantial portion of the central bar is hot but that the two side members are far enough from the heated zone to be at room temperature. On cooling, the central bar tries to contract thermally but is restrained by the side members. It does contract partially, but not as much as it would if it were free, and the end result is that the side members are placed in compression and the central rod in tension when the whole assembly is at

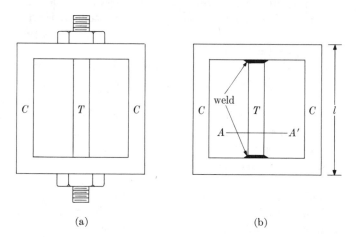

(a)   (b)

Fig. 17–1. Examples of residual stress. T = tension, C = compression.

room temperature. Residual stress is quite commonly found in welded structures.

Plastic flow can also set up residual stresses. The beam shown in Fig. 17–2(a) is supported at two points and loaded by two equal forces F applied near each end. At any point between the two supports the stress in the outside fibers is constant, tensile on the top of the beam and compressive on the bottom. These stresses are a maximum on the outside surfaces and decrease to zero at the neutral axis, as indicated by the stress diagram at the right of (a). This diagram shows how the longitudinal stress varies across the section AA', when all parts of the beam are below the elastic limit. Suppose the load on the beam is now increased to the point where the elastic limit is exceeded, not only in the outer fibers but to a considerable depth. Then plastic flow will take place in the outer portions of the beam, indicated by shading in (b), but there will be an inner region still only elastically strained, because the stress there is still below the elastic limit. The stresses above the neutral axis are still entirely tensile, both in the elastically and plastically strained portions, and those below entirely compressive. If the load is now removed, these stresses try to relieve themselves by straightening the beam. Under the action of these internal forces, the beam does partially straighten itself, and to such an extent that

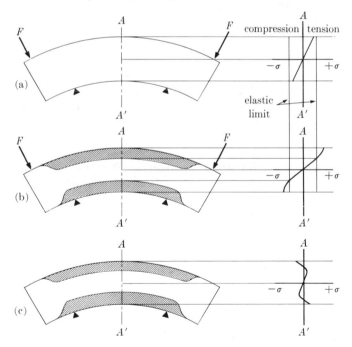

Fig. 17–2. Residual stress induced by plastic flow in bending: (a) loaded below elastic limit; (b) loaded beyond elastic limit; (c) unloaded. Shaded regions have been plastically strained.

the stress in the outer regions is not only reduced to zero but is actually changed in sign, as indicated in (c). The end result is that the unloaded beam contains residual compressive stress in its top outside portion and residual tensile stress in its lower outside portion. It is quite common to find residual stress in metal parts which have been plastically deformed, not only by bending but by drawing, swaging, extrusion, etc.

17–3 Uniaxial stress. With these basic ideas in mind, we can now go on to a consideration of the x-ray method of stress measurement. The simplest way to approach this method is through the case of pure tension, where the stress acts only in a single direction. Consider a cylindrical rod of cross-sectional area A stressed elastically in tension by a force F (Fig. 17–3). There is a stress $\sigma_y = F/A$ in the y-direction but none in the x- or z-directions. (This stress is the only *normal stress* acting; there are also *shear stresses* present, but these are not measurable by x-ray diffraction.) The stress σ_y produces a strain ϵ_y in the y-direction given by

$$\epsilon_y = \frac{\Delta L}{L} = \frac{L_f - L_0}{L_0},$$

where L_0 and L_f are the original and final lengths of the bar. This strain is related to the stress by the fundamental elastic equation

$$\sigma_y = E\epsilon_y, \tag{17–1}$$

where E is Young's modulus. The elongation of the bar is accompanied by a decrease in its diameter D. The strains in the x- and z-directions are therefore given by

$$\epsilon_x = \epsilon_z = \frac{D_f - D_0}{D_0},$$

where D_0 and D_f are the original and final diameters of the bar. If the material of the bar is isotropic, these strains are related by the equation

$$\epsilon_x = \epsilon_z = -\nu\epsilon_y, \tag{17–2}$$

where ν is Poisson's ratio for the material of the bar. The value of ν ranges from about 0.25 to about 0.45 for most metals and alloys.

To measure ϵ_y by x-rays would require diffraction from planes perpendicular to the axis of the bar. Since this is usually physically impossible, we utilize instead reflecting planes which are parallel, or nearly parallel, to the axis of the bar by taking a back-reflection photograph at *normal* incidence, as shown in Fig. 17–3. (It is essential that a back-reflection technique be used, in order to gain sufficient precision in the measurement of plane spacing. Even quite large stresses cause only a very small change

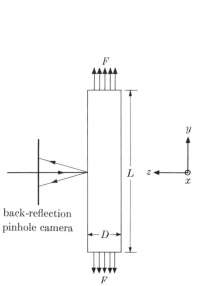

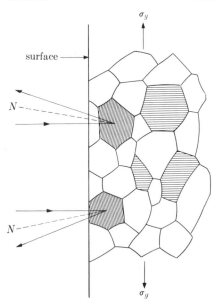

FIG. 17–3.   Pure tension.

FIG. 17–4.   Diffraction from strained aggregate, tension axis vertical. Lattice planes shown belong to the same (hkl) set. N = reflecting-plane normal.

in d.)   In this way we obtain a measurement of the strain in the z direction since this is given by

$$\epsilon_z = \frac{d_n - d_0}{d_0},\qquad (17\text{–}3)$$

where d_n is the spacing of the planes reflecting at normal incidence under stress, and d_0 is the spacing of the same planes in the absence of stress. Combining Eqs. (17–1), (17–2), and (17–3), we obtain the relation

$$\sigma_y = -\frac{E}{\nu}\left(\frac{d_n - d_0}{d_0}\right),\qquad (17\text{–}4)$$

which gives the required stress in terms of known and observed quantities.

It should be noted that only a particular set of grains contributes to a particular hkl reflection. These are grains whose (hkl) planes are almost parallel to the surface of the bar, as indicated in Fig. 17–4, and which are compressed by the applied stress, that is, d_n is less than d_0. Grains whose (hkl) planes are normal to the surface have these planes extended, as shown in an exaggerated fashion in the drawing. The spacing d_{hkl} therefore varies with crystal orientation, and there is thus no possibility of using any of the extrapolation procedures described in Chap. 11 to measure

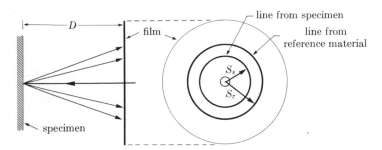

FIG. 17–5.   Back-reflection method at normal incidence.

d_{hkl} accurately.   Instead we must determine this spacing from the position of a single diffraction line on the film.

A direct comparison method is usually used.   A powder of some reference material of known lattice parameter is smeared on the surface of the specimen, and the result is a photograph like that illustrated in Fig. 17–5, where the $K\alpha$ lines are shown unresolved for greater clarity.   Since the line from the reference material calibrates the film, it is unnecessary to know the specimen-to-film distance D.   The plane spacings of the specimen are determined simply by measuring the diameters of the Debye rings from the specimen ($2S_s$) and from the reference material ($2S_r$).

Equation (17–4) shows that a measurement of d_0 on the unstressed material must be made.   If the specimen contains only applied stress, then d_0 is obtained from a measurement on the unloaded specimen.   But if residual stress is present, d_0 must be measured on a small stress-free portion cut out of the specimen.

17–4 Biaxial stress.   In a bar subject to pure tension the normal stress acts only in a single direction.   But in general there will be stress components in two or three directions at right angles to one another, forming so-called biaxial or triaxial stress systems.   However, the stress at right angles to a free surface is always zero, so that at the surface of a body, which is the only place where we can measure stress, we never have to deal with more than two stress components and these lie in the plane of the surface.   Only in the interior of a body can the stresses be triaxial.

Consider a portion of the surface of a stressed body, shown in Fig. 17–6. We set up a rectangular coordinate system xyz, with x and y lying in the plane of the surface in any convenient orientation.   Whatever the stress system, three mutually perpendicular directions (1, 2, and 3) can be found which are perpendicular to planes on which no shear stress acts.   These are called the *principal directions*, and the stresses acting in these directions, σ_1, σ_2, and σ_3, are called the *principal stresses*.   At the free surface shown, σ_3, like σ_z, is equal to zero.   However, ϵ_3, the strain normal to the

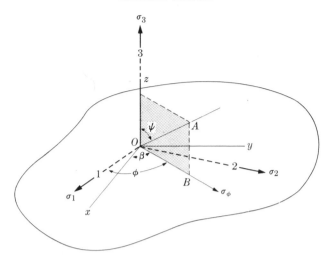

FIG. 17–6. Angular relations between stress to be measured (σ_ϕ), principal stresses (σ_1, σ_2, and σ_3), and arbitrary axes (x, y, z).

surface, is not zero. It is given by

$$\epsilon_3 = \epsilon_z = -\frac{\nu}{E}(\sigma_1 + \sigma_2). \tag{17–5}$$

The value of ϵ_3 can be measured by means of a diffraction pattern made at normal incidence and is given by Eq. (17–3). Substituting this value into (17–5), we obtain

$$\frac{d_n - d_0}{d_0} = -\frac{\nu}{E}(\sigma_1 + \sigma_2). \tag{17–6}$$

Therefore, in the general case, only the sum of the principal stresses can be obtained from a pattern at normal incidence. [If only a single stress is acting, say a tensile stress in direction 1, then $\sigma_2 = 0$ and Eq. (17–6) reduces to Eq. (17–4).]

Normally, however, we want to measure the stress σ_ϕ acting in some specified direction, say the direction OB of Fig. 17–6, where OB makes an angle ϕ with principal direction 1 and an angle β with the x-axis. This is done by making two photographs, one with the incident beam normal to the surface and one with it inclined along OA at some angle ψ to the surface normal. OA lies in a vertical plane through the direction OB in which it is desired to measure the stress, and ψ is usually made equal to 45°. The normal-incidence pattern measures the strain approximately normal to the surface, and the inclined-incidence pattern measures the strain approximately parallel to OA. These measured strains are therefore approximately equal to ϵ_3 and ϵ_ψ, respectively, where ϵ_ψ is the strain in a direction at an angle ψ to the surface normal. Elasticity theory gives the following relation for the difference between these two strains:

$$\epsilon_\psi - \epsilon_3 = \frac{\sigma_\phi}{E}(1 + \nu)\sin^2\psi. \tag{17-7}$$

But

$$\epsilon_\psi = \frac{d_i - d_0}{d_0}, \tag{17-8}$$

where d_i is the spacing of the inclined reflecting planes, approximately normal to OA, under stress, and d_0 is their stress-free spacing. Combining Eqs. (17–3), (17–7), and (17–8), we obtain

$$\frac{d_i - d_0}{d_0} - \frac{d_n - d_0}{d_0} = \frac{d_i - d_n}{d_0} = \frac{\sigma_\phi}{E}(1 + \nu)\sin^2\psi. \tag{17-9}$$

Since d_0, occurring in the denominator above, can be replaced by d_n with very little error, Eq. (17–9) can be written in the form

$$\sigma_\phi = \frac{E}{(1 + \nu)\sin^2\psi}\left(\frac{d_i - d_n}{d_n}\right). \tag{17-10}$$

This equation allows us to calculate the stress in any chosen direction from plane spacings determined from two photographs, one made at normal incidence and the other with the incident beam inclined at an angle ψ to the surface normal. Notice that the angle ϕ does not appear in this equation and fortunately so, since we do not generally know the directions of the principal stresses *a priori*. Nor is it necessary to know the unstressed plane spacing d_0; the measurement is therefore nondestructive, because there is no necessity for cutting out part of the specimen to obtain a stress-free sample.

The direct comparison method is again used to obtain an accurate measurement of the spacings, and Fig. 17–7 illustrates the appearance of the film in the inclined-incidence exposure. The Debye ring from the specimen is no longer perfectly circular. The reason lies in the fact that the strain along the normal to reflecting planes varies with the angle ψ between these plane normals and the surface normal, as shown by Eq. (17–7). There will therefore be slightly different diffraction angles 2θ for planes reflecting to the "low" side of the film (point 1) and those reflecting to the "high" side (point 2). These planes therefore form two sets of slightly different orientation, sets 1 and 2, having normals N_1 and N_2 at angles of α_1 and α_2 to the incident beam. (α_1 and α_2 are nearly equal to one another and to $90° - \theta$.) Measurements of the specimen Debye-ring radii S_1 and S_2 therefore give information about strains in directions at angles of $(\psi + \alpha_1)$ and $(\psi - \alpha_2)$ to the surface normal. The usual practice is to

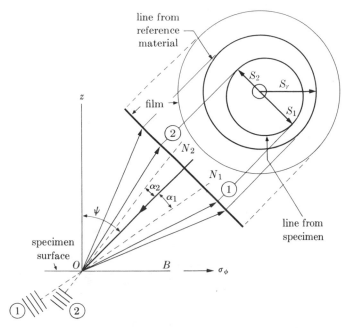

FIG. 17–7.   Back-reflection method at inclined incidence.

measure only S_1, since the position of this side of the ring is more sensitive to strain.*

To save time in calculation, we can put Eq. (17–10) in more usable form.   By differentiating the Bragg law, we obtain

$$\frac{\Delta d}{d} = -\cot \theta \, \Delta\theta. \qquad (17\text{–}11)$$

The Debye-ring radius S, in back reflection, is related to the specimen-to-film distance D by

$$S = D \tan(180° - 2\theta) = -D \tan 2\theta,$$

$$\Delta S = -2D \sec^2 2\theta \, \Delta\theta. \qquad (17\text{–}12)$$

Combining Eqs. (17–11) and (17–12), we obtain

$$\Delta S = 2D \sec^2 2\theta \tan \theta \, \frac{\Delta d}{d}.$$

* S_1 and S_2 cannot be measured directly because of the hole in the center of the film, but they can be found indirectly.   If the measured diameter of the Debye ring from the reference material is $2S_r$, then the point where the incident beam passed through the film is located at a distance S_r from any point on the reference ring.   If x_1 and x_2 are the measured distances between the specimen and reference rings on the "low" side and "high" side, respectively, of the film [see Fig. 17–8(c)], then $S_1 = S_r - x_1$ and $S_2 = S_r - x_2$.

Put
$$\frac{\Delta d}{d} = \frac{d_i - d_n}{d_n}$$
and
$$\Delta S = S_i - S_n,$$

where S_i is the Debye-ring radius in the inclined-incidence photograph, usually taken as the radius S_1 in Fig. 17–7, and S_n is the ring radius in the normal incidence photograph. Combining the last three equations with Eq. (17–10), we find

$$\sigma_\phi = \frac{E(S_i - S_n)}{2D(1 + \nu)\sec^2 2\theta \tan \theta \sin^2 \psi}.$$

Put

$$K_1 = \frac{E}{2D(1 + \nu)\sec^2 2\theta \tan \theta \sin^2 \psi}. \qquad (17\text{–}13)$$

Then

$$\sigma_\phi = K_1(S_i - S_n). \qquad (17\text{–}14)$$

This forms a convenient working equation. K_1 is known as the stress factor, and it can be calculated once and for all for a given specimen, radiation, and specimen-to-film distance. To ensure that the specimen-to-film distance D is effectively equal for both the inclined- and normal-incidence exposures, it is enough to adjust this distance to within ± 1 mm of its nominal value with a distance gauge and make the final correction by means of the measured diameter $2S_r$ of the Debye ring from the reference material. For example, with tungsten powder as a reference material, Co $K\alpha$ radiation, and a specimen-to-film distance of 57.8 mm, $2S_r$ is 50 mm for the 222 line from tungsten. Then for each film a multiplying factor is found which will make the tungsten-ring diameter equal to exactly 50.00 mm; this same factor is then applied to the measured radii S_i and S_n of the specimen rings before inserting them in Eq. (17–14). All measurements are best made on the α_1 component of the $K\alpha$ doublet.

What sort of accuracy can be expected in the measurement of stress by x-rays? For a steel specimen examined with Co $K\alpha$ radiation, the highest-angle reflection is the 310 line, which occurs at about 160° 2θ. Then $E = 30 \times 10^6$ psi, $\nu = 0.28$, $D = 57.8$ mm, $\theta = 80°$, and $\psi = 45° + (90° - \theta) = 55°$, if the incident beam is inclined at an angle of 45° to the surface normal and we measure the radius S_1, rather than S_2, in the inclined-incidence photograph. Putting these values into Eq. (17–13), we find the stress factor K_1 to be 47,000 psi/mm. If the quantity $(S_i - S_n)$ is measured to an accuracy of 0.1 mm, which requires an accuracy of 0.05 mm in the measurement of the separate quantities S_i and S_n, then the stress can be determined with an accuracy of 4700 psi. Accuracies somewhat better than this can sometimes be obtained in practice, but a probable error of ± 4000 to 5000 psi is probably typical of most measurements made on steel specimens. Higher accuracies are attainable on materials having substantially lower elastic moduli, such as aluminum-base alloys, since the stress factor is directly proportional to the modulus.

The stress σ_ϕ acting in any specified direction may also be measured by a *single* inclined exposure like that shown in Fig. 17–7, the normal-incidence exposure being omitted. Both Debye-ring radii, S_1 and S_2, are measured, the former being used to calculate the strain at an angle $(\psi + \alpha_1)$ to the surface normal and the latter the strain at an angle $(\psi - \alpha_2)$. Equation (17–9) is then applied separately to each measurement:

$$\sigma_\phi = \frac{E}{(1 + \nu) \sin^2 (\psi + \alpha_1)} \left(\frac{d_{i1} - d_n}{d_0} \right),$$

$$\sigma_\phi = \frac{E}{(1 + \nu) \sin^2 (\psi - \alpha_2)} \left(\frac{d_{i2} - d_n}{d_0} \right),$$

where d_{i1} and d_{i2} are the plane spacings calculated from S_1 and S_2, respectively. Putting $\alpha_1 = \alpha_2 = \alpha = (90° - \theta)$, and eliminating d_n from the two equations above, we find

$$\sigma_\phi = \left(\frac{E}{1 + \nu} \right) \left(\frac{d_{i1} - d_{i2}}{d_0} \right) \left(\frac{1}{\sin 2\psi \sin 2\alpha} \right).$$

In this equation d_0 need not be known accurately. Since only one exposure is required, this method is twice as fast as the usual two-exposure method, but it entails a probable error two or three times as large.

17–5 Experimental technique (pinhole camera). In this and the next section we shall consider the techniques used in applying the two-exposure method to the measurement of stress.

Pinhole cameras of special design are used for stress measurement. The design is dictated by two requirements not ordinarily encountered:

(1) Since the specimens to be examined are frequently large and unwieldy, it is necessary to bring the camera to the specimen rather than the specimen to the camera.

(2) Since the highest accuracy is required in the measurement of diffraction-line positions, the lines must be smooth and continuous, not spotty. This is achieved by rotating or oscillating the film about the incident-beam axis. (Complete rotation of the film is permissible in the normal-incidence exposure but not in the one made at inclined incidence. In the latter case the Debye ring is noncircular to begin with, and complete rotation of the film would make the line very broad and diffuse. Instead, the film is oscillated through an angle of about 10°. If the specimen grain size is extremely coarse, the specimen itself should be oscillated, if possible, through an angle of 2° or 3° about an axis normal to the incident beam.)

These two requirements are satisfied by the camera design illustrated in Fig. 17–8(a). The camera is rigidly attached to a portable x-ray tube (a shockproof tube energized through a flexible shockproof cable), which is held in an adjustable support, permitting the camera to be oriented in any desired way relative to the specimen. The film is held in a circular cassette which can be oscillated or rotated by means of a gear-and-worm arrangement. Both the normal-incidence and inclined-incidence photographs may be registered on one film by using the opaque metal film cover shown in (b). It has two openings diametrically opposite; after one exposure is made, the film holder is rotated 90° in its own plane with respect to the cover, and the other exposure made. The resulting film has the appearance of (c). Figure 17–9 shows a typical camera used for stress measurements.

Some investigators like to use a well-collimated incident beam, like the one indicated in Fig. 17–8(a). Others prefer to use a divergent beam and utilize the focusing principle shown in Fig. 17–10. A fine pinhole is located behind the film at the point A and a larger one, to limit the divergence, at point B. Then a circle passing through A and tangent to the specimen

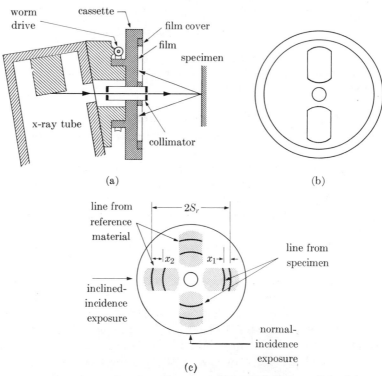

Fig. 17–8. Pinhole camera for stress measurement (schematic): (a) section through incident beam; (b) front view of cassette; (c) appearance of exposed film.

Fig. 17–9.   Stress camera in position for the measurement of stress in a welded steel plate.   A combined distance gauge and beam indicator has been temporarily attached to the collimator to aid in adjusting the specimen-film distance and the angle between the incident beam and the specimen surface.   The latter adjustment may be quickly made with the protractor shown.   (H. J. Isenburger, *Machinery*, July 1947, p. 167.)

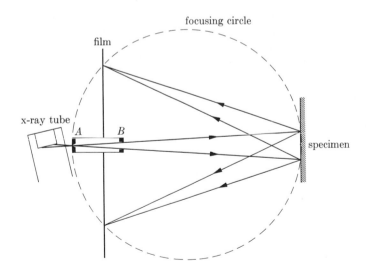

Fig. 17–10.   Back-reflection pinhole camera used under semifocusing conditions.

will intersect the film at the point where a reflected beam will focus. The result is a sharper line and reduced exposure time. Note, however, that the focusing condition can only be satisfied for one line on the pattern.

But line sharpness and exposure time are not the only criteria to be considered in deciding between the collimated and divergent beam techniques. One of the real advantages of the x-ray method over all other methods of stress measurement is the ability to measure the stress almost at a point on the specimen. This can be done with a collimated beam, which can be made very narrow, but not with a divergent beam, which covers a fairly wide area of the specimen. The collimated-beam technique is therefore to be preferred when the stress in the specimen varies rapidly from point to point on the surface, and when it is important that the existing stress gradient be evaluated.

When the stress gradient *normal* to the surface is large, errors of interpretation may arise unless it is realized that the effective depth of x-ray penetration varies with the angle of incidence of the x-rays. Suppose, for example, that $\theta = 80°$ and $\psi = 45°$. Then it may be shown, by means of Eq. (9–3), that the effective penetration depth is 83 percent greater in the normal-incidence exposure than it is in the inclined one.

Correct specimen preparation is extremely important. If dirt and scale are present, they may be ground off, but the grinding must be followed by deep etching to remove the surface layer left in compression by the grinding. The surface is then lightly polished with fine emery paper, to remove the roughness caused by deep etching, and lightly re-etched. Surface roughness must be strictly avoided, because the high points in a rough surface are not stressed in the same way as the bulk of the material and yet they contribute most to the diffraction pattern, especially the one made at inclined incidence, as indicated in Fig. 17–11. Of course, the surface should not be touched at all prior to the stress measurement, if the object is to measure residual surface stresses caused by some treatment such as machining, grinding, shot peening, etc. Such treatments produce steep stress gradients normal to the surface, and the removal of any material by polishing or etching would defeat the purpose of the measurement.

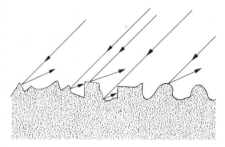

FIG. 17–11. Diffraction from a rough surface when the incident beam is inclined.

17–6 Experimental technique (diffractometer). The diffractometer may also be used for stress measurement, and many details of the diffractometer technique, e.g., specimen preparation, are identical to those mentioned in the preceding section.   The only instrumental changes necessary are the addition of a specimen holder which will allow independent rotation of the specimen about the diffractometer axis, and a change in the position of the receiving slit.

Figure 17–12 illustrates the angular relationships involved.   In (a), the specimen is equally inclined to the incident and diffracted beams; ψ is zero and the specimen normal N_s coincides with the reflecting plane normal N_p.   Radiation divergent from the source S is diffracted to a focus at F on the diffractometer circle.   Even though the primary beam is incident on the surface at an angle θ rather than at 90°, a diffraction measurement made with the sample in this position corresponds to a normal-incidence photograph made with a camera, except that the reflecting planes are now exactly parallel to the surface and the strain is measured exactly normal to the surface.   In (b) the specimen has been turned through an angle ψ for the inclined measurement.   Since the focusing circle is always tangent to the specimen surface, rotation of the specimen alters the focusing circle both in position and radius, and the diffracted rays now come to a focus at F', located a distance r from F.   If R is the radius of the diffractometer circle, then it may be shown that

$$\frac{r}{R} = 1 - \frac{\cos\,[\psi + (90° - \theta)]}{\cos\,[\psi - (90° - \theta)]}.$$

If $\psi = 45°$, then r/R is 0.30 for $\theta = 80°$ and 0.53 for $\theta = 70°$

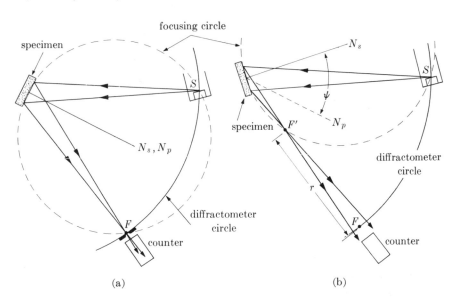

FIG. 17–12.   Use of a diffractometer for stress measurement: (a) $\psi = 0$; (b) $\psi = \psi$.

When ψ is not zero, the focal point of the diffracted beam therefore lies between F, the usual position of the counter receiving slit, and the specimen. If the receiving slit is kept at F, the intensity of the beam entering the counter will be very low. On the other hand, if a wide slit is used at F, resolution will suffer. The proper thing to do is to put a narrow slit at F' and a wide slit at F, or put a narrow slit at F' and move the counter to a position just behind it. In theory, different slit arrangements are therefore necessary for the measurement made at $\psi = 0$ and the one made at $\psi = 45°$. In practice, a change in slit position between each of these measurements is avoided by making a compromise between intensity and resolution, and placing a narrow slit at some point between F and F' where experiment indicates that satisfactory results are obtained. The slit is then left in this position for both measurements.

Since the angular position 2θ of the diffracted beam is measured directly with a diffractometer, it is convenient to write the stress equation in terms of 2θ rather than plane spacings. Differentiating the Bragg law, we obtain

$$\frac{\Delta d}{d} = -\frac{\cot \theta \, \Delta 2\theta}{2}.$$

Combining this relation with Eq. (17–10) gives

$$\sigma_\phi = \frac{E \cot \theta (2\theta_n - 2\theta_i)}{2(1 + \nu) \sin^2 \psi}.$$

Put

$$K_2 = \frac{E \cot \theta}{2(1 + \nu) \sin^2 \psi}.$$

Then

$$\sigma_\phi = K_2(2\theta_n - 2\theta_i), \tag{17–15}$$

where $2\theta_n$ is the observed value of the diffraction angle in the "normal" measurement ($\psi = 0$) and $2\theta_i$ its value in the inclined measurement ($\psi = \psi$). For measurements made on the 310 line of steel with Co $K\alpha$ radiation, putting $E = 30 \times 10^6$ psi, $\nu = 0.28$, $\theta = 80°$, and $\psi = 45°$, we obtain for the stress factor K_2 a value of 720 psi/0.01° 2θ. If $2\theta_n$ and $2\theta_i$ are both measured to an accuracy of 0.02°, then the probable error in the stress measured is ± 2880 psi.

Essentially, the quantity measured in the diffractometer method is $\Delta 2\theta = (2\theta_n - 2\theta_i)$, the shift in the diffraction line due to stress as the angle ψ is changed. But certain geometrical effects, particularly the compromise position of the receiving slit, introduce small errors which cause a change in 2θ even for a stress-free specimen, when ψ is changed from 0° to 45°. It is therefore necessary to determine this change experimentally and apply it as a correction $(\Delta 2\theta)_0$ to all $\Delta 2\theta$ values measured on stressed specimens. The correction is best determined by measurements on a sample of fine powder, which is necessarily free of macrostrain, at $\psi = 0°$ and $\psi = 45°$. The powder should have the same composition as the material in which stress is to be measured in order that its diffraction line occur at the same position 2θ, since the correction itself, $(\Delta 2\theta)_0$, depends on 2θ.

17–7 Superimposed macrostress and microstress. As mentioned in the introduction, a specimen may contain both a uniform macrostress and a nonuniform microstress. The result is a diffraction line which is both shifted and broadened. This effect occurs quite commonly in hardened steel parts: nonuniform microstress is set up by the austenite-to-martensite transformation and on this is superimposed a uniform residual macrostress, due to any one of a number of causes, such as quenching, prior plastic deformation, or grinding.

Stress measurement by x-rays requires the measurement of diffraction-line shift. If the lines are sharp, it is relatively easy to measure this shift visually with a device such as shown in Fig. 6–18. But if the lines are broad (and a breadth at half-maximum intensity of 5 to 10° 2θ is not uncommon in the case of hardened steel), an accurate visual measurement becomes impossible. It is then necessary to determine the profile of the line, either from a microphotometer record of the film if a camera was used, or by directly measuring the intensity at various angles 2θ with the diffractometer.

After the line profile is obtained, the problem still remains of locating the "center" of the line. Since the line may be, and frequently is, unsymmetrical, "center" has no precise meaning but is usually taken as the peak of the line, i.e., the point of maximum intensity. But the top of a broad line is often almost flat so that direct determination of the exact point of maximum intensity is extremely difficult.

Two methods have been used to fix the positions of broadened lines. The first is illustrated in Fig. 17–13(a) and may be used whenever the lines

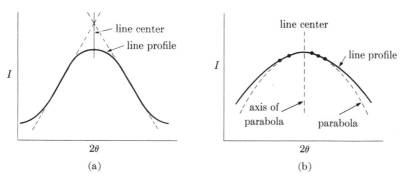

FIG. 17–13. Methods of locating the centers of broad diffraction lines.

involved have straight sides. The linear portions are simply extrapolated and their point of intersection taken as the "center" of the line. If the line is unsymmetrical, the point so found will not have the same 2θ value as the point of maximum intensity. But this is of no consequence in the measurement of stress, as long as this "center" is reproducible, since all that is required is the difference between two values of 2θ and not the absolute magnitude of either.

The other method depends on the fact that the profile of a broad line near its peak has the shape of a parabola with a vertical axis, as shown in Fig. 17–13(b), even when the over-all shape of the line is unsymmetrical. Now the equation

$$y = ax^2 + bx + c \tag{17-16}$$

is the general equation of a parabola whose axis is parallel to the y axis. The maximum on this curve occurs when

$$\frac{dy}{dx} = 2ax + b = 0,$$

$$x = -\frac{b}{2a}. \tag{17-17}$$

If we put $x = 2\theta$ and $y = I$, then Eq. (17–16) represents the shape of the diffraction line near its peak. We then substitute several pairs of observed 2θ, I values into this equation and solve for the best values of the constants a and b by the method of least squares. Equation (17–17) then gives the exact value of x ($= 2\theta$) at which the maximum occurs. Only two or three points on either side of the peak near its maximum are sufficient to locate the parabola with surprising accuracy. The positions of diffraction lines as broad as $8°$ 2θ at half-maximum intensity have been reproducibly determined to within $0.02°$ by this method.

Choice of the proper radiation is an important matter when the positions of broad diffraction lines have to be accurately measured. Every effort should be made to reduce the background, since the accurate measurement of a broad, diffuse diffraction line superimposed on a high-intensity background is very difficult. Thus, cobalt radiation filtered through iron oxide is satisfactory for annealed steel, because the diffraction lines are sharp. However, the background is high, since the short wavelength components of the continuous spectrum cause fluorescence of iron K radiation by the specimen. For this reason cobalt radiation is completely unsuitable for stress measurements on hardened steel, where very broad lines have to be measured. For such specimens chromium radiation should be used, in conjunction with a vanadium filter between the specimen and the photographic film or diffractometer counter. The vanadium filter suppresses not only the Cr $K\beta$ component of the incident radiation but also the fluorescent iron K radiation from the specimen, since the K edge of vanadium lies between the wavelengths of Fe $K\alpha$ and Cr $K\alpha$. The tube voltage should also be kept rather low, at about 30 to 35 kv, to minimize the intensity of the fluorescent radiation. The large gain in the line-to-background intensity ratio obtained by using chromium instead of cobalt radiation more than compensates for the fact that the diffraction lines occur at smaller 2θ values with the former.

17–8 Calibration.   For the measurement of stress by x-rays we have developed two working equations, Eqs. (17–14) and (17–15), one for the pinhole camera and one for the diffractometer. Each of them contains an appropriate stress factor K, by which diffraction line shift is converted to stress. Furthermore each was derived on the assumption that the material under stress was an isotropic body obeying the usual laws of elasticity. This assumption has to be examined rather carefully if a calculated value of K is to be used for stress measurement.

The stress factor K contains the quantity $E/(1 + \nu)$, and we have tacitly assumed that the values of E and ν measured in the ordinary way during a tensile test are to be used in calculating the value of K. But these mechanically measured values are not necessarily the correct ones to apply to a diffraction measurement. In the latter, strains are measured in particular crystallographic directions, namely, the directions normal to the (hkl) reflecting planes, and we know that both E and ν vary with crystallographic direction. This anisotropy of elastic properties varies from one metal to another: for example, measurements on single crystals of α-iron show that E has a value of 41.2×10^6 psi in the direction [111] and 19.2×10^6 psi in [100], whereas the values of E for aluminum show very little variation, being 10.9×10^6 psi in [111] and 9.1×10^6 psi in [100]. The mechanically measured values are 30×10^6 and 10×10^6 psi for polycrystalline iron and aluminum, respectively. These latter values are evidently average values for aggregates of contiguous grains having random orientation. In the x-ray method, however, only grains having a particular orientation relative to the incident beam, and therefore a particular orientation with respect to the measured stress, are able to reflect. There is therefore no good reason why the mechanically measured values of E and ν should be applied to these particular grains. Stated alternately, an aggregate of randomly oriented grains may behave isotropically but individual grains of particular orientations in that aggregate may not.

These considerations are amply supported by experiment. By making x-ray measurements on materials subjected to known stresses, we can determine the stress factor K experimentally. The values of K so obtained differ by as much as 40 percent from the values calculated from the mechanically measured elastic constants. Moreover, for the same material, the

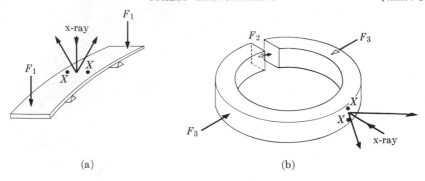

Fig. 17–14.   Specimens used for calibrating x-ray method.

measured values of K vary with the wavelength of the radiation used and the Miller indices of the reflecting planes. With steel, for example, the calculated value of K happens to be in good agreement with the measured value if Co $K\alpha$ radiation is reflected from the (310) planes but not if some other combination of λ and (hkl) is employed.

Methods have been proposed for calculating the proper values of E and ν to use with x-ray measurements from the values measured in various directions in single crystals, but such calculations are not very accurate. The safest procedure is to measure K on specimens subjected to known stresses. We will consider this calibration in terms of the diffractometer method, but the same procedure may also be used for calibrating the camera method.

The usual practice is to set up known stresses in a body by bending. Both flat beams and heavy split rings have been used, as illustrated in Fig. 17–14. The beam shown in (a) is supported at two points and loaded by the two forces F_1; tensile stress is therefore produced in the top surface on which the x-ray measurements are made. The split ring shown in (b) may be either expanded by the forces F_2, producing compressive stress at the point of x-ray measurement, or compressed by the forces F_3, producing tensile stress at the same point. If the applied forces and the dimensions and over-all elastic properties of the stressed member are known, then the stress at the point of x-ray measurement may be computed from elasticity theory. If not, the stress must be measured by an independent method, usually by means of electric-resistance strain gauges placed at the points marked X. At no time during the calibration should the elastic limit of the material be exceeded.

A typical calibration curve might have the appearance of Fig. 17–15, where the known stress σ_ϕ is plotted against the observed value of $\Delta 2\theta = (2\theta_n - 2\theta_i)$, in this case for an applied positive (tensile) stress. The slope of this line is the stress factor K_2. However, the experimental curve must be corrected by an amount $(\Delta 2\theta)_0$, measured on a stress-free sample in the manner previously described. The corrected working curve is therefore a line of the same slope as the experimental curve but shifted by an amount $(\Delta 2\theta)_0$. The working curve may or may not pass through zero, depending on whether or not the calibrating member contains residual stress. In the example shown here, a small residual tensile stress was present.

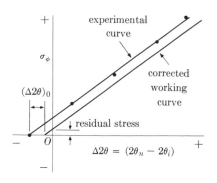

FIG. 17–15. Calibration curve for stress measurement.

17–9 Applications. The proper field of application of the x-ray method will become evident if we compare its features with those of other methods of stress, or rather strain, measurement. If a camera with a pinhole collimator is used, the incident x-ray beam can be made quite small in diameter, say $\frac{1}{16}$ in., and the strain in the specimen may therefore be measured almost at a point. On the other hand, strain gauges of the electrical or mechanical type have a length of an inch or more, and they therefore measure only the average strain over this distance. Consequently, the x-ray method is preferable whenever we wish to measure highly localized stresses which vary rapidly from point to point, in a macroscopic sense.

There is a still more fundamental difference between the x-ray method and methods involving electrical or mechanical gauges. The latter measure the total strain, elastic plus plastic, which has occurred, whereas x-rays measure only the elastic portion. The reason for this is the fact that the spacing of lattice planes is not altered by plastic flow, in itself, but only by changes in the elastic stress to which the grains are subjected. The x-ray "strain gauge" can therefore measure residual stress, but an electric-resistance gauge can not. Suppose, for example, that an electric-resistance gauge is fixed to the surface of a metal specimen which is then deformed plastically in an inhomogeneous manner. The strain indicated by the gauge after the deforming forces are removed is not the residual elastic strain from which the residual stress can be computed, since the indicated strain includes an unknown plastic component which is not recovered when the deforming force is removed. The x-ray method, on the other hand, reveals the residual elastic stress actually present at the time the measurement is made.

However, the x-ray method is not the only way of measuring residual stress. There is another widely used method (called mechanical relaxation), which involves (a) removing part of the metal by cutting, grinding,

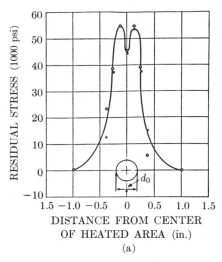

(a)

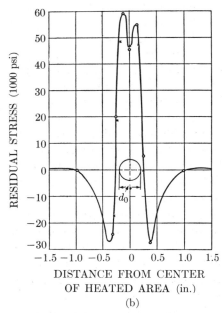

DISTANCE FROM CENTER
OF HEATED AREA (in.)

(b)

FIG. 17–16. Residual stress pattern set up by localized heating: (a) transverse stress; (b) longitudinal stress. d_0 is diameter of heated area. (J. T. Norton and D. Rosenthal, *Proc. Soc. Exp. Stress Analysis* **1** (2), 77, 1943.)

etching, etc., and (b) measuring the change in shape or dimensions produced as a result of this removal. For example, the residual stress in the weldment discussed earlier [Fig. 17–1(b)] could be measured by cutting through the central rod along the line AA' and measuring the length l before and after cutting. When the rod is cut through, the tensile stress in it is relieved and the two side members, originally in compression, are free to elongate. The final length l_f is therefore greater than the original length l_0 and the strain present before the cut was made must have been $(l_f - l_0)/l_f$. This strain, multiplied by the elastic modulus, gives the residual compressive stress present in the side members before the central rod was cut. Similarly, the residual stress at various depths of the bent beam shown in Fig. 17–2(c) may be measured by successive removal of layers parallel to the neutral plane, and a measurement of the change in curvature of the beam produced by each removal.

There are many variations of this method and they are all destructive, inasmuch as they depend on the partial or total relaxation of residual stress by the removal of a part of the stressed metal. The x-ray method, on the other hand, is completely nondestructive: all the necessary measurements may be made on the stressed metal, which need not be damaged in any way.

We can conclude that the x-ray method is most usefully employed for the nondestructive measurement of residual stress, particularly when the stress varies rapidly over the surface of the specimen. This latter condition is frequently found in welded structures, and the measurement of residual stress in and near welds is one of the major applications of the x-ray method. For the measurement of *applied* stress, methods involving electrical or mechanical gauges are definitely superior: they are much more accurate, faster, and require less expensive apparatus. In fact, they are commonly used to calibrate the x-ray method.

Figure 17–16 shows an example of residual stress measurement by x-rays. The specimen was a thin steel bar, 3 in. wide and 10 in. long. A small circular area, whose size is indicated on the graph, was heated locally to above 1100°F for a few seconds by clamping the bar at this point between the two electrodes of a butt-welding machine. The central area rapidly expanded but was constrained by the relatively cold metal around it. As a result, plastic flow took place in and near the central region on heating and probably also on cooling as the central region tried to contract. Residual stresses were therefore set up, and the curves show how these stresses, both longitudinal and transverse, vary along a line across the specimen through the heated area. In and near this area there is a state of biaxial tension amounting to about 55,000 psi, which is very close to the yield point of this particular steel, namely, 60,500 psi. There is also a very steep stress gradient just outside the heated area: the transverse stress drops from 55,000 psi tension to zero in a distance of one inch, and the longitudinal stress drops from 55,000 psi tension to 25,000 psi compression in less than half an inch. Residual stresses of similar magnitude and gradient can be expected in many welded structures.

PROBLEMS

17–1. Calculate the probable error in measuring stress in aluminum by the two-exposure pinhole-camera method. Take $E = 10 \times 10^6$ psi and $\nu = 0.33$. The highest-angle line observed with Cu $K\alpha$ radiation is used. For the inclined-incidence photograph, the incident beam makes an angle of 45° with the specimen surface, and the radius S_1 (see Fig. 17–7) of the Debye ring from the specimen is measured. Assume an accuracy of 0.05 mm in the measurement of line position and a specimen-to-film distance of 57.8 mm. Compare your result with that given in Sec. 17–4 for steel.

17–2. A certain aluminum part is examined in the diffractometer, and the 2θ value of the 511,333 line is observed to be 163.75° when $\psi = 0$, and 164.00° for $\psi = 45°$. The same values for a specimen of aluminum powder are 163.81° and 163.88°, respectively. What is the stress in the aluminum part, if it is assumed that the stress factor calculable from the elastic constants given in Prob. 17–1 is correct?

17–3. Verify the statement made in Sec. 17–5 that the effective depth of x-ray penetration is 83 percent greater in normal incidence than at an incidence of 45°, when $\theta = 80°$.

CHAPTER 18

SUGGESTIONS FOR FURTHER STUDY

18–1 Introduction. In the previous chapters an attempt has been made to supply a broad and basic coverage of the theory and practice of x-ray diffraction and its applications to metallurgical problems. But in a book of this scope much fundamental theory and many details of technique have had to be omitted. The reader who wishes to go on to advanced work in this field will therefore have to turn to other sources for further information. The purpose of the following sections is to point out these sources and indicate the sort of material each contains, particularly material which is mentioned only briefly or not at all in this book.

One thing is absolutely necessary in advanced work on diffraction and that is familiarity with the concept of the reciprocal lattice. This concept provides a means of describing diffraction phenomena quite independently of the Bragg law and in a much more powerful and general manner. In particular, it supplies a way of visualizing diffuse scattering effects which are difficult, if not impossible, to understand in terms of the Bragg law. Such effects are due to crystal imperfections of one kind and another, and they provide a valuable means of studying such imperfections. These faults in the crystal lattice, though seemingly minor in character, can have a profound effect on the physical and mechanical properties of metals and alloys; for this reason, there is no doubt that much of the metallurgical research of the future will be concerned with crystal imperfections, and in this research the study of diffuse x-ray scattering will play a large role. The utility of the reciprocal lattice in dealing with diffuse scattering effects is pointed out in Appendix 15, where the interested reader will find the basic principles and more important applications of the reciprocal lattice briefly described.

18–2 Textbooks. The following is a partial list of books in English which deal with the theory and practice of x-ray diffraction and crystallography.

(1) *Structure of Metals*, 2nd ed., by Charles S. Barrett. (McGraw-Hill Book Company, Inc., New York, 1952.) Deservedly the standard work in the field, it has long served as a text and reference book in the crystallographic aspects of physical metallurgy. Really two books in one, the first part dealing with the theory and methods of x-ray diffraction, and the second part with the structure of metals in the wider sense of the word.

Includes a very lucid account of the stereographic projection. Contains an up-to-date treatment of transformations, plastic deformation, structure of cold-worked metal, and preferred orientations. Gives a wealth of references to original papers.

(2) *X-Ray Crystallographic Technology*, by André Guinier. (Hilger and Watts Ltd., London, 1952. Translation by T. L. Tippel, edited by Kathleen Lonsdale, of Guinier's *Radiocristallographie*, Dunod, Paris, 1945.) Written with true French clarity, this book gives an excellent treatment of the theory and practice of x-ray diffraction. A considerable body of theory is presented, although this is not suggested by the title of the English translation, and experimental techniques are given in detail. The theory and applications of the reciprocal lattice are very well described. Unusual features include a full description of the use of focusing monochromators and chapters on small-angle scattering and diffraction by amorphous substances. Crystal-structure determination is not included.

(3) *X-Ray Diffraction Procedures*, by Harold P. Klug and Leroy E. Alexander. (John Wiley & Sons, Inc., New York, 1954.) As its title indicates, this book stresses experimental methods. The theory and operation of powder cameras and diffractometers are described in considerable and useful detail. (Single-crystal methods, Laue and rotating crystal, are not included.) Particularly valuable for its discussion of quantitative analysis by diffraction, a subject to which these authors have made important contributions. Also includes chapters on particle-size measurement from line broadening, diffraction by amorphous substances, and small-angle scattering.

(4) *X-Ray Diffraction by Polycrystalline Materials*, edited by H. S. Peiser, H. P. Rooksby, and A. J. C. Wilson. (The Institute of Physics, London, 1955.) This book contains some thirty chapters, contributed by some thirty different authors, on the theory and practice of the powder method in its many variations. These chapters are grouped into three major sections: experimental technique, interpretation of data, and applications in specific fields of science and industry. A great deal of useful information is presented in this book, which will be of more value to the research worker than to the beginning student, in that most of the contributors assume some knowledge of the subject on the part of the reader.

(5) *Applied X-Rays*, 4th ed., by George L. Clark. (McGraw-Hill Book Company, Inc., New York, 1955.) A very comprehensive book, devoted to the applications of x-rays in many branches of science and industry. Besides diffraction, both medical and industrial radiography (and microradiography) are included, as well as sections on the chemical and biological effects of x-rays. The crystal structures of a wide variety of substances, ranging from organic compounds to alloys, are fully described.

(6) *X-Rays in Practice*, by Wayne T. Sproull. (McGraw-Hill Book Company, Inc., New York, 1946.) X-ray diffraction and radiography, with emphasis on their industrial applications.

(7) *An Introduction to X-Ray Metallography*, by A. Taylor. (John Wiley & Sons, Inc., New York, 1945.) Contains extensive material on the crystallographic structure of metals and alloys and on methods of determining alloy equilibrium diagrams by x-ray diffraction. Sections on radiography and microradiography also included.

(8) *X-Rays in Theory and Experiment*, by Arthur H. Compton and Samuel K. Allison. (D. Van Nostrand Company, Inc., New York, 1935.) A standard treatise on the physics of x-rays and x-ray diffraction, with emphasis on the former.

(9) *The Crystalline State. Vol. I: A General Survey*, by W. L. Bragg. (The Macmillan Company, New York, 1934.) This book and the two listed immediately below form a continuing series, edited by W. L. Bragg, to which this book forms an introduction. It is a very readable survey of the field by the father of structure analysis. Contains very clear accounts in broad and general terms of crystallography (including space-group theory), diffraction, and structure analysis. An historical account of the development of x-ray crystallography is also included.

(10) *The Crystalline State. Vol. II: The Optical Principles of the Diffraction of X-Rays*, by R. W. James. (George Bell & Sons, Ltd., London, 1948.) Probably the best book available in English on advanced theory of x-ray diffraction. Includes thorough treatments of diffuse scattering (due to thermal agitation, small particle size, crystal imperfections, etc.), the use of Fourier series in structure analysis, and scattering by gases, liquids, and amorphous solids.

(11) *The Crystalline State. Vol. III: The Determination of Crystal Structures*, by H. Lipson and W. Cochran. (George Bell & Sons, Ltd., London, 1953.) Advanced structure analysis by means of space-group theory and Fourier series. Experimental methods are not included; i.e., the problem of structure analysis is covered from the point at which $|F|^2$ values have been determined by experiment to the final solution. Contains many illustrative examples.

(12) *The Interpretation of X-Ray Diffraction Photographs*, by N. F. M. Henry, H. Lipson, and W. A. Wooster. (The Macmillan Company, London, 1951.) Rotating and oscillating crystal methods, as well as powder methods, are described. Good section on analytical methods of indexing powder photographs.

(13) *X-Ray Crystallography*, by M. J. Buerger. (John Wiley & Sons, Inc., New York, 1942.) Theory and practice of rotating and oscillating crystal methods. Space-group theory.

(14) *Small-Angle Scattering of X-Rays*, by André Guinier and Gerard Fournet. Translated by Christopher B. Walker, and followed by a bibli-

ography by Kenneth L. Yudowitch. (John Wiley & Sons, Inc., New York, 1955.) A full description of small-angle scattering phenomena, including theory, experimental technique, interpretation of results, and applications.

18–3 Reference books. Physical and mathematical data and information on specific crystal structures may be found in the following books:

(1) *Internationale Tabellen zur Bestimmung von Kristallstrukturen* [International Tables for the Determination of Crystal Structures]. (Gebrüder Borntraeger, Berlin, 1935. Also available from Edwards Brothers, Ann Arbor, Mich., 1944.)

Vol. 1. Space-group tables.

Vol. 2. Mathematical and physical tables (e.g., values of $\sin^2 \theta$, atomic scattering factors, absorption coefficients, etc.).

(2) *International Tables for X-ray Crystallography.* (Kynoch Press, Birmingham, England.) These tables are published by the International Union of Crystallography and are designed to replace the *Internationale Tabellen* (1935), much of which was in need of revision.

Vol. I. Symmetry groups (tables of point groups and space groups) (1952). The reader should not overlook the interesting Historical Introduction written by M. von Laue.

Vol. II. Mathematical tables (in preparation).

Vol. III. Physical and chemical tables (in preparation).

(3) Absorption coefficients and the wavelengths of emission lines and absorption edges, not included in the *Internationale Tabellen* (1935), can generally be found in the book by Compton and Allison (item 8 of the previous section) or in the *Handbook of Chemistry and Physics* (Chemical Rubber Publishing Co., Cleveland). Wavelengths are given in kX units.

(4) *Longueurs d'Onde des Emissions X et des Discontinuités d'Absorption X* [Wavelengths of X-Ray Emission Lines and Absorption Edges], by Y. Caüchois and H. Hulubei. (Hermann & Cie, Paris, 1947.) Wavelengths of emission lines and absorption edges in X units, listed both in numerical order of wavelength (useful in fluorescent analysis) and in order of atomic number.

(5) *Strukturbericht.* (Akademische Verlagsgesellschaft, Leipzig, 1931–1943. Also available from Edwards Brothers, Ann Arbor, Mich., 1943.) A series of seven volumes describing crystal structures whose solutions were published in the years 1913 to 1939, inclusive.

(6) *Structure Reports.* (Oosthoek, Utrecht, 1951 to date.) A continuation, sponsored by the International Union of Crystallography, of *Strukturbericht.* The volume numbers take up where *Strukturbericht* left off:

Vol. 8. (In preparation.)

Vol. 9. (1956) Structure results published from 1942 to 1944.

Vol. 10. (1953) Structure results published in 1945 and 1946.

Vol. 11. (1952) Structure results published in 1947 and 1948.

Vol. 12.   (1951)   Structure results published in 1949.

Vol. 13.   (1954)   Structure results published in 1950.

The results of structure determinations are usually given in sufficient detail that the reader has no need to consult the original paper.

(7) *The Structure of Crystals*, 2nd ed., by Ralph W. G. Wyckoff. (Chemical Catalog Company, New York, 1931. Supplement for 1930–34, Reinhold Publishing Corporation, New York, 1935.) Crystallography (including space-group theory) and x-ray diffraction. In addition, full descriptions are given of a large number of known crystal structures.

(8) *Crystal Structures*, by Ralph W. G. Wyckoff. (Interscience Publishers, Inc., New York.) A continuation of Wyckoff's work (see previous item) of classification and presentation of crystal structure data. Three volumes have been issued to date (Vol. I, 1948; Vol. II, 1951; Vol. III, 1953) and more are planned for the future. Each volume is in loose-leaf form so that later information on a particular structure can be inserted in the appropriate place.

(9) Lists of known structures and lattices parameters can also be found in the *Handbook of Chemistry and Physics* (organic and inorganic compounds) and in the book by Taylor, item 7 of the previous section (intermetallic "compounds").

18–4 Periodicals. Broadly speaking, technical papers involving x-ray crystallography are of two kinds:

(a) Those in which crystallography or some aspect of x-ray diffraction form the central issue, e.g., papers describing crystal structures, crystallographic transformations, diffraction theory, diffraction methods, etc. Such papers were published in the international journal *Zeitschrift für Kristallographie*, in which each paper appeared in the language of the author (English, French, or German). Publication of this journal ceased in 1945 and a new international journal, *Acta Crystallographica*, a publication of the International Union of Crystallography, was established to take its place, publication beginning in 1948. (Publication of *Zeitschrift für Kristallographie* was resumed in 1954.) Although the bulk of the papers appearing in *Acta Crystallographica* are confined to structure results on complex organic and inorganic compounds, occasional papers of metallurical interest appear. Papers on diffraction theory and methods are also found in journals of physics, applied physics, and instrumentation.

(b) Those in which x-ray diffraction appears in the role of an experimental tool in the investigation of some other phenomenon. Much can be learned from such papers about the applications of x-ray diffraction. Many papers of this sort are to be found in various metallurgical journals.

APPENDIX 1

LATTICE GEOMETRY

A1–1 Plane spacings. The value of d, the distance between adjacent planes in the set (hkl), may be found from the following equations.

Cubic:
$$\frac{1}{d^2} = \frac{h^2 + k^2 + l^2}{a^2}$$

Tetragonal:
$$\frac{1}{d^2} = \frac{h^2 + k^2}{a^2} + \frac{l^2}{c^2}$$

Hexagonal:
$$\frac{1}{d^2} = \frac{4}{3}\left(\frac{h^2 + hk + k^2}{a^2}\right) + \frac{l^2}{c^2}$$

Rhombohedral:

$$\frac{1}{d^2} = \frac{(h^2 + k^2 + l^2)\sin^2\alpha + 2(hk + kl + hl)(\cos^2\alpha - \cos\alpha)}{a^2(1 - 3\cos^2\alpha + 2\cos^3\alpha)}$$

Orthorhombic:
$$\frac{1}{d^2} = \frac{h^2}{a^2} + \frac{k^2}{b^2} + \frac{l^2}{c^2}$$

Monoclinic:
$$\frac{1}{d^2} = \frac{1}{\sin^2\beta}\left(\frac{h^2}{a^2} + \frac{k^2\sin^2\beta}{b^2} + \frac{l^2}{c^2} - \frac{2hl\cos\beta}{ac}\right)$$

Triclinic:
$$\frac{1}{d^2} = \frac{1}{V^2}(S_{11}h^2 + S_{22}k^2 + S_{33}l^2 + 2S_{12}hk + 2S_{23}kl + 2S_{13}hl)$$

In the equation for triclinic crystals

$$V = \text{volume of unit cell (see below)},$$
$$S_{11} = b^2c^2\sin^2\alpha,$$
$$S_{22} = a^2c^2\sin^2\beta,$$
$$S_{33} = a^2b^2\sin^2\gamma,$$
$$S_{12} = abc^2(\cos\alpha\cos\beta - \cos\gamma),$$
$$S_{23} = a^2bc(\cos\beta\cos\gamma - \cos\alpha),$$
$$S_{13} = ab^2c(\cos\gamma\cos\alpha - \cos\beta).$$

A1–2 Cell volumes. The following equations give the volume V of the unit cell.

Cubic: $$V = a^3$$

Tetragonal: $$V = a^2 c$$

Hexagonal: $$V = \frac{\sqrt{3}\, a^2 c}{2} = 0.866 a^2 c$$

Rhombohedral: $$V = a^3 \sqrt{1 - 3\cos^2 \alpha + 2\cos^3 \alpha}$$

Orthorhombic: $$V = abc$$

Monoclinic: $$V = abc \sin \beta$$

Triclinic: $$V = abc \sqrt{1 - \cos^2 \alpha - \cos^2 \beta - \cos^2 \gamma + 2\cos \alpha \cos \beta \cos \gamma}$$

A1–3 Interplanar angles. The angle ϕ between the plane $(h_1 k_1 l_1)$, of spacing d_1, and the plane $(h_2 k_2 l_2)$, of spacing d_2, may be found from the following equations. (V is the volume of the unit cell.)

Cubic: $$\cos \phi = \frac{h_1 h_2 + k_1 k_2 + l_1 l_2}{\sqrt{(h_1{}^2 + k_1{}^2 + l_1{}^2)(h_2{}^2 + k_2{}^2 + l_2{}^2)}}$$

Tetragonal: $$\cos \phi = \frac{\dfrac{h_1 h_2 + k_1 k_2}{a^2} + \dfrac{l_1 l_2}{c^2}}{\sqrt{\left(\dfrac{h_1{}^2 + k_1{}^2}{a^2} + \dfrac{l_1{}^2}{c^2}\right)\left(\dfrac{h_2{}^2 + k_2{}^2}{a^2} + \dfrac{l_2{}^2}{c^2}\right)}}$$

Hexagonal:

$$\cos \phi = \frac{h_1 h_2 + k_1 k_2 + \dfrac{1}{2}(h_1 k_2 + h_2 k_1) + \dfrac{3a^2}{4c^2} l_1 l_2}{\sqrt{\left(h_1{}^2 + k_1{}^2 + h_1 k_1 + \dfrac{3a^2}{4c^2} l_1{}^2\right)\left(h_2{}^2 + k_2{}^2 + h_2 k_2 + \dfrac{3a^2}{4c^2} l_2{}^2\right)}}$$

Rhombohedral:

$$\cos \phi = \frac{a^4 d_1 d_2}{V^2} [\sin^2 \alpha (h_1 h_2 + k_1 k_2 + l_1 l_2)$$

$$+ (\cos^2 \alpha - \cos \alpha)(k_1 l_2 + k_2 l_1 + l_1 h_2 + l_2 h_1 + h_1 k_2 + h_2 k_1)]$$

Orthorhombic: $\cos \phi = \dfrac{\dfrac{h_1h_2}{a^2} + \dfrac{k_1k_2}{b^2} + \dfrac{l_1l_2}{c^2}}{\sqrt{\left(\dfrac{h_1{}^2}{a^2} + \dfrac{k_1{}^2}{b^2} + \dfrac{l_1{}^2}{c^2}\right)\left(\dfrac{h_2{}^2}{a^2} + \dfrac{k_2{}^2}{b^2} + \dfrac{l_2{}^2}{c^2}\right)}}$

Monoclinic:

$$\cos \phi = \frac{d_1d_2}{\sin^2 \beta}\left[\frac{h_1h_2}{a^2} + \frac{k_1k_2\sin^2 \beta}{b^2} + \frac{l_1l_2}{c^2} - \frac{(l_1h_2 + l_2h_1)\cos \beta}{ac}\right]$$

Triclinic:

$$\cos \phi = \frac{d_1d_2}{V^2}[S_{11}h_1h_2 + S_{22}k_1k_2 + S_{33}l_1l_2$$

$$+ S_{23}(k_1l_2 + k_2l_1) + S_{13}(l_1h_2 + l_2h_1) + S_{12}(h_1k_2 + h_2k_1)]$$

THE RHOMBOHEDRAL-HEXAGONAL TRANSFORMATION

The lattice of points shown in Fig. A2–1 is rhombohedral, that is, it possesses the symmetry elements characteristic of the rhombohedral system. The primitive rhombohedral cell has axes $\mathbf{a}_1(\mathbf{R})$, $\mathbf{a}_2(\mathbf{R})$, and $\mathbf{a}_3(\mathbf{R})$. The same lattice of points, however, may be referred to a hexagonal cell having axes $\mathbf{a}_1(\mathbf{H})$, $\mathbf{a}_2(\mathbf{H})$, and $\mathbf{c}(\mathbf{H})$. The hexagonal cell is no longer primitive, since it contains three lattice points per unit cell (at $0\,0\,0$, $\frac{2}{3}\,\frac{1}{3}\,\frac{1}{3}$, and $\frac{1}{3}\,\frac{2}{3}\,\frac{2}{3}$), and it has three times the volume of the rhombohedral cell.

If one wishes to know the indices $(HK \cdot L)$, referred to hexagonal axes, of a plane whose indices (hkl), referred to rhombohedral axes, are known, the following equations may be used:

$$H = h - k,$$
$$K = k - l,$$
$$L = h + k + l.$$

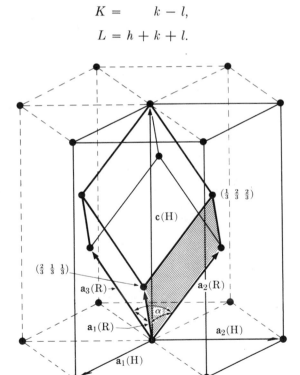

FIG. A2–1. Rhombohedral and hexagonal unit cells in a rhombohedral lattice.

Thus, the (001) face of the rhombohedral cell (shown shaded in the figure) has indices $(0\bar{1}\cdot1)$ when referred to hexagonal axes.

Since a rhombohedral lattice may be referred to hexagonal axes, it follows that the powder pattern of a rhombohedral substance can be indexed on a hexagonal Hull-Davey or Bunn chart. How then can we recognize the true nature of the lattice? From the equations given above, it follows that

$$-H + K + L = 3k.$$

If the lattice is really rhombohedral, then k is an integer and the only lines appearing in the pattern will have hexagonal indices $(HK\cdot L)$ such that the sum $(-H + K + L)$ is always an integral multiple of 3. If this condition is not satisfied, the lattice is hexagonal.

When the pattern of a rhombohedral substance has been so indexed, i.e., with reference to hexagonal axes, and the true nature of the lattice determined, we usually want to know the indices (hkl) of the reflecting planes when referred to rhombohedral axes. The transformation equations are

$$h = \tfrac{1}{3}(2H + K + L),$$

$$k = \tfrac{1}{3}(-H + K + L),$$

$$l = \tfrac{1}{3}(-H - 2K + L).$$

There is then the problem of determining the lattice parameters a_R and α of the rhombohedral unit cell. But the dimensions of the rhombohedral cell can be determined from the dimensions of the hexagonal cell, and this is an easier process than solving the rather complicated plane-spacing equation for the rhombohedral system. The first step is to index the pattern on the basis of hexagonal axes. Then the parameters a_H and c of the hexagonal cell are calculated in the usual way. Finally, the parameters of the rhombohedral cell are determined from the following equations:

$$a_R = \tfrac{1}{3}\sqrt{3a_H{}^2 + c^2},$$

$$\sin\frac{\alpha}{2} = \frac{3}{2\sqrt{3 + (c/a_H)^2}}.$$

Finally, it should be noted that if the c/a ratio of the hexagonal cell in Fig. A2–1 takes on the special value of 2.45, then the angle α of the rhombohedral cell will equal 60° and the lattice of points will be face-centered cubic. Compare Fig. A2–1 with Figs. 2–7 and 2–16.

Further information on the rhombohedral-hexagonal relationship and on unit cell transformations in general may be obtained from the *International Tables for X-Ray Crystallography* (1952), Vol. 1, pp. 15–21.

WAVELENGTHS (IN ANGSTROMS) OF SOME CHARACTERISTIC EMISSION LINES AND ABSORPTION EDGES

Element	Z	$K\alpha$ (weighted average)*	$K\alpha_2$ strong	$K\alpha_1$ very strong	$K\beta_1$ weak	K edge	$L\alpha_1$ very strong	L_{III} edge
Na	11		11.909	11.909	11.617			
Mg	12		9.8889	9.8889	9.558	9.5117		
Al	13		8.33916	8.33669	7.981	7.9511		
Si	14		7.12773	7.12528	6.7681	6.7446		
P	15		6.1549	6.1549	5.8038	5.7866		
S	16		5.37471	5.37196	5.03169	5.0182		
Cl	17		4.73050	4.72760	4.4031	4.3969		
A	18		4.19456	4.19162	. . . .	3.8707		
K	19		3.74462	3.74122	3.4538	3.43645		
Ca	20		3.36159	3.35825	3.0896	3.07016		
Sc	21		3.03452	3.03114	2.7795	2.7573		
Ti	22		2.75207	2.74841	2.51381	2.49730		
V	23		2.50729	2.50348	2.28434	2.26902		
Cr	24	2.29092	2.29351	2.28962	2.08480	2.07012		
Mn	25		2.10568	2.10175	1.91015	1.89636		
Fe	26	1.93728	1.93991	1.93597	1.75653	1.74334		
Co	27	1.79021	1.79278	1.78892	1.62075	1.60811		
Ni	28		1.66169	1.65784	1.50010	1.48802		
Cu	29	1.54178	1.54433	1.54051	1.39217	1.38043	13.357	13.2887
Zn	30		1.43894	1.43511	1.29522	1.28329	12.282	12.1309
Ga	31		1.34394	1.34003	1.20784	1.19567	11.313	
Ge	32		1.25797	1.25401	1.12889	1.11652	10.456	
As	33		1.17981	1.17581	1.05726	1.04497	9.671	9.3671
Se	34		1.10875	1.10471	0.99212	0.97977	8.990	8.6456
Br	35		1.04376	1.03969	0.93273	0.91994	8.375	
Kr	36		0.9841	0.9801	0.87845	0.86546		
Rb	37		0.92963	0.92551	0.82863	0.81549	7.3181	6.8633
Sr	38		0.87938	0.875214	0.78288	0.76969	6.8625	6.3868
Y	39		0.83300	0.82879	0.74068	0.72762	6.4485	5.9618
Zr	40		0.79010	0.78588	0.701695	0.68877	6.0702	5.5829
Nb	41		0.75040	0.74615	0.66572	0.65291	5.7240	5.2226
Mo	42	0.71069	0.713543	0.70926	0.632253	0.61977	5.40625	4.9125
Tc	43		0.676	0.673	0.602			
Ru	44		0.64736	0.64304	0.57246	0.56047	4.84552	4.3689
Rh	45		0.617610	0.613245	0.54559	0.53378	4.59727	4.1296
Pd	46		0.589801	0.585415	0.52052	0.50915	4.36760	3.9081
Ag	47		0.563775	0.559363	0.49701	0.48582	4.15412	3.6983
Cd	48		0.53941	0.53498	0.475078	0.46409	3.95628	3.5038
In	49		0.51652	0.51209	0.454514	0.44387	3.77191	3.3244
Sn	50		0.49502	0.49056	0.435216	0.42468	3.59987	3.1559
Sb	51		0.47479	0.470322	0.417060	0.40663	3.43915	2.9999
Te	52		0.455751	0.451263	0.399972	0.38972	3.28909	2.8554
I	53		0.437805	0.433293	0.383884	0.37379	3.14849	2.7194
Xe	54		0.42043	0.41596	0.36846	0.35849	. . . .	2.5924
Cs	55		0.404812	0.400268	0.354347	0.34473	2.8920	2.4739

(cont.)

* In averaging, $K\alpha_1$ is given twice the weight of $K\alpha_2$.

Element	Z	Kα (weighted average)	$K\alpha_2$ strong	$K\alpha_1$ very strong	$K\beta_1$ weak	K edge	$L\alpha_1$ very strong	L_{III} edge
Ba	56		0.389646	0.385089	0.340789	0.33137	2.7752	2.3628
La	57		0.375279	0.370709	0.327959	0.31842	2.6651	2.2583
Ce	58		0.361665	0.357075	0.315792	0.30647	2.5612	2.1639
Pr	59		0.348728	0.344122	0.304238	0.29516	2.4627	2.0770
Nd	60		0.356487	0.331822	0.293274	0.28451	2.3701	1.9947
Il	61		0.3249	0.3207	0.28209	. . . .	2.2827	
Sm	62		0.31365	0.30895	0.27305	0.26462	2.1994	1.8445
Eu	63		0.30326	0.29850	0.26360	0.25551	2.1206	1.7753
Gd	64		0.29320	0.28840	0.25445	0.24680	2.0460	1.7094
Tb	65		0.28343	0.27876	0.24601	0.23840	1.9755	1.6486
Dy	66		0.27430	0.26957	0.23758	0.23046	1.90875	1.579
Ho	67		0.26552	0.26083	. . . .	0.22290	1.8447	1.5353
Er	68		0.25716	0.25248	0.22260	0.21565	1.78428	1.48218
Tm	69		0.24911	0.24436	0.21530	0.2089	1.7263	1.4328
Yb	70		0.24147	0.23676	0.20876	0.20223	1.6719	1.38608
Lu	71		0.23405	0.22928	0.20212	0.19583	1.61943	1.34135
Hf	72		0.22699	0.22218	0.19554	0.18981	1.56955	1.29712
Ta	73		0.220290	0.215484	0.190076	0.18393	1.52187	1.25511
W	74		0.213813	0.208992	0.184363	0.17837	1.47635	1.21546
Re	75		0.207598	0.202778	0.178870	0.17311	1.43286	1.17700
Os	76		0.201626	0.196783	0.173607	0.16780	1.39113	1.14043
Ir	77		0.195889	0.191033	0.168533	0.16286	1.35130	1.10565
Pt	78		0.190372	0.185504	0.163664	0.15816	1.31298	1.07239
Au	79		0.185064	0.180185	0.158971	0.15344	1.27639	1.03994
Hg	80		. . . .	. . . .	. . . .	0.14923	1.24114	1.00898
Tl	81		0.175028	0.170131	0.150133	0.14470	1.20735	0.97930
Pb	82		0.170285	0.165364	0.145980	0.14077	1.17504	0.95029
Bi	83		0.165704	0.160777	0.141941	0.13706	1.14385	0.92336
Th	90		0.137820	0.132806	0.117389	0.11293	0.95598	0.76062
U	92		0.130962	0.125940	0.111386	0.1068	0.91053	0.72216

CHARACTERISTIC L LINES OF TUNGSTEN

Line	Relative intensity	Wavelength (A)
$L\alpha_1$	Very strong	1.47635
$L\alpha_2$	Weak	1.48742
$L\beta_1$	Strong	1.28176
$L\beta_2$	Medium	1.24458
$L\beta_3$	Weak	1.26285
$L\gamma_1$	Weak	1.09852

The above wavelengths are based on those in *Longueurs d'Onde des Emissions X et des Discontinuités d'Absorption X* by Y. Cauchois and H. Hulubei (Hermann, Paris, 1947). The Cauchois-Hulubei values have been multiplied by 1.00202×10^{-3} to convert them from X units to angstroms. Values, in angstroms, for the K lines and K absorption edge were kindly furnished by G. D. Rieck prior to publication in Vol. III of the *International Tables for X-Ray Crystallography*, and are published here with the permission of the Editorial Commission of the International Tables.

MASS ABSORPTION COEFFICIENTS (μ/ρ, cm²/gm) AND DENSITIES (ρ)

Atomic number	Element	Density (gm/cm³)	Mo Kα λ = 0.711 Å	Zn Kα λ = 1.436 Å	Cu Kα λ = 1.542 Å	Ni Kα λ = 1.659 Å	Co Kα λ = 1.790 Å	Fe Kα λ = 1.937 Å	Mn Kα λ = 2.103 Å	Cr Kα λ = 2.291 Å
2	He	0.1664×10^{-3}	0.18	0.31	0.37	0.43	0.52	0.64	0.74	0.86
3	Li	0.53	0.22	0.54	0.68	0.87	1.13	1.48	1.76	2.11
4	Be	1.82	0.30	1.02	1.35	1.80	2.42	3.24	3.90	4.74
5	B	2.3	0.45	2.51	3.06	3.79	4.67	5.80	7.36	9.37
6	C	2.22 (graphite)	0.70	4.43	5.50	6.76	8.50	10.7	13.8	17.9
7	N	1.1649×10^{-3}	1.10	6.85	8.51	10.7	13.6	17.3	21.8	27.7
8	O	1.3318×10^{-3}	1.50	11.4	12.7	16.2	20.2	25.2	32.2	40.1
9	F	1.696×10^{-3}	1.93	14.4	17.5	21.5	26.6	33.0	41.1	51.6
10	Ne	0.8387×10^{-3}	2.67	20.2	24.6	30.2	37.2	46.0	57.6	72.7
11	Na	0.97	3.36	25.6	30.9	37.9	46.2	56.9	72.3	92.5
12	Mg	1.74	4.38	33.0	40.6	47.9	60.0	75.7	95.2	120
13	Al	2.70	5.30	40.0	48.7	58.4	73.4	92.8	117	149
14	Si	2.33	6.70	49.5	60.3	75.8	94.1	116	146	192
15	P	1.82 (yellow)	7.98	59.4	73.0	90.5	113	141	177	223
16	S	2.07 (yellow)	10.0	75.0	91.3	112	139	175	217	273
17	Cl	3.214×10^{-3}	11.6	85.0	103	126	158	199	245	308
18	A	1.6626×10^{-3}	12.6	93.0	113	141	174	217	270	341
19	K	0.86	16.7	119	143	179	218	269	330	425
20	Ca	1.55	19.8	142	172	210	257	317	400	508
21	Sc	2.5	21.1	153	185	222	273	338	428	545
22	Ti	4.54	23.7	167	204	247	304	377	475	603
23	V	6.0	26.5	186	227	275	339	422	530	77.3
24	Cr	7.19	30.4	213	259	316	392	490	70.5	89.9
25	Mn	7.43	33.5	234	284	348	431	63.6	79.6	99.4
26	Fe	7.87	38.3	270	324	397	59.5	72.8	90.9	115
27	Co	8.9	41.6	292	354	54.4	65.9	80.6	102	126
28	Ni	8.90	47.4	325	49.3	61.0	75.1	93.1	116	145
29	Cu	8.96	49.7	42.0	52.7	65.0	79.8	98.8	123	154
30	Zn	7.13	54.8	49.3	59.0	72.1	88.5	109	135	169

(cont.)

Atomic number	Element	Density (gm/cm³)	Mo Kα λ = 0.711 A	Zn Kα λ = 1.436 A	Cu Kα λ = 1.542 A	Ni Kα λ = 1.659 A	Co Kα λ = 1.790 A	Fe Kα λ = 1.937 A	Mn Kα λ = 2.103 A	Cr Kα λ = 2.291 A
31	Ga	5.91	57.3	52.4	63.3	76.9	94.3	116	144	179
32	Ge	5.36	63.4	57.6	69.4	84.2	104	128	158	196
33	As	5.73	69.5	63.5	76.5	93.8	115	142	175	218
34	Se	4.81	74.0	69.4	82.8	101	125	152	188	235
35	Br	3.12 (liquid)	82.2	77.0	92.6	112	137	169	206	264
36	Kr	3.488 X 10⁻³	88.1	83.0	100	122	148	182	226	285
37	Rb	1.53	94.4	91.5	109	133	161	197	246	309
38	Sr	2.6	101.2	100	119	145	176	214	266	334
39	Y	5.51	108.9	107	129	158	192	235	289	360
40	Zr	6.5	17.2	118	143	173	211	260	317	391
41	Nb	8.57	18.7	126	153	183	225	279	338	415
42	Mo	10.2	20.2	136	164	197	242	299	360	439
44	Ru	12.2	23.4	153	185	221	272	337	404	488
45	Rh	12.44	25.3	165	198	240	293	361	432	522
46	Pd	12.0	26.7	173	207	254	308	376	450	545
47	Ag	10.49	28.6	192	223	276	332	402	483	585
48	Cd	8.65	29.9	202	234	289	352	417	500	608
49	In	7.31	31.8	214	252	307	366	440	531	648
50	Sn	7.30	33.3	230	265	322	382	457	555	681
51	Sb	6.62	35.3	245	284	342	404	482	589	727
52	Te	6.24	36.1	248	289	347	410	488	598	742
53	I	4.93	39.2	269	314	375	442	527	650	808
54	Xe	5.495 X 10⁻³	41.3	283	330	392	463	552	680	852
55	Cs	1.9	43.3	298	347	410	486	579	715	844
56	Ba	3.5	45.2	307	359	423	501	599	677	819
58	Ce	6.9	52.0	358	407	476	549	636	670	235
73	Ta	16.6	101	136	164	200	246	305	364	440
74	W	19.3	105	143	171	209	258	320	380	456

(cont.)

Atomic number	Element	Density (gm/cm^3)	Mo Kα λ = 0.711 A	Zn Kα λ = 1.436 A	Cu Kα λ = 1.542 A	Ni Kα λ = 1.659 A	Co Kα λ = 1.790 A	Fe Kα λ = 1.937 A	Mn Kα λ = 2.103 A	Cr Kα λ = 2.291 A
76	Os	22.5	113	152	186	226	278	346	406	480
77	Ir	22.5	118	160	194	237	292	362	422	498
78	Pt	21.4	123	172	205	248	304	376	436	518
79	Au	19.32	128	179	214	260	317	390	456	537
80	Hg	13.55	132	186	223	272	330	404	471	552
81	Tl	11.85	136	194	231	282	341	416	484	568
82	Pb	11.34	141	202	241	294	354	429	499	585
83	Bi	9.80	145	214	253	310	372	448	522	612
88	Ra	5.0	172	258	304	371	433	509	598	708
90	Th	11.5	143	286	327	399	460	536	633	755
92	U	18.7	153	310	352	423	488	566	672	805

Mass absorption coefficients from *X-Ray Diffraction by Polycrystalline Materials*, edited by H. S. Peiser, H. P. Rooksby, and A. J. C. Wilson (The Institute of Physics, London, 1955). Densities from *Metals Handbook*, 1948 edition (The American Society for Metals, Cleveland).

APPENDIX 5

VALUES OF $\sin^2 \theta$

$\theta°$	.0	.1	.2	.3	.4	.5	.6	.7	.8	.9	.01	.02	.03	.04	.05
00	.0000	0000	0000	0000	0000	0001	0001	0001	0002	0002					
1	.0003	0004	0004	0005	0006	0007	0008	0009	0010	0011					
2	.0012	0013	0015	0016	0018	0019	0021	0022	0024	0026					
3	.0027	0029	0031	0033	0035	0037	0039	0042	0044	0046					
4	.0049	0051	0054	0056	0059	0062	0064	0067	0070	0073			Interpolate		
5	.0076	0079	0082	0085	0089	0092	0095	0099	0102	0106					
6	.0109	0113	0117	0120	0124	0128	0132	0136	0140	0144					
7	.0149	0153	0157	0161	0166	0170	0175	0180	0184	0189					
8	.0194	0199	0203	0208	0213	0218	0224	0229	0234	0239					
9	.0245	0250	0256	0261	0267	0272	0278	0284	0290	0296					
10	.0302	0308	0314	0320	0326	0332	0338	0345	0351	0358	1	1	2	2	3
1	.0364	0371	0377	0384	0391	0397	0404	0411	0418	0425	1	1	2	3	3
2	.0432	0439	0447	0454	0461	0468	0476	0483	0491	0498	1	1	2	3	4
3	.0506	0514	0521	0529	0537	0545	0553	0561	0569	0577	1	2	2	3	4
4	.0585	0593	0602	0610	0618	0627	0635	0644	0653	0661	1	2	3	3	4
15	.0670	0679	0687	0696	0705	0714	0723	0732	0741	0751	1	2	3	4	4
6	.0760	0769	0778	0788	0797	0807	0816	0826	0835	0845	1	2	3	4	5
7	.0855	0865	0874	0884	0894	0904	0914	0924	0934	0945	1	2	3	4	5
8	.0955	0965	0976	0986	0996	1007	1017	1028	1039	1049	1	2	3	4	5
9	.1060	1071	1082	1092	1103	1114	1125	1136	1147	1159	1	2	3	4	6
20	.1170	1181	1192	1204	1215	1226	1238	1249	1261	1273	1	2	3	5	6
1	.1284	1296	1308	1320	1331	1343	1355	1367	1379	1391	1	2	4	5	6
2	.1403	1415	1428	1440	1452	1464	1477	1489	1502	1514	1	2	4	5	6
3	.1527	1539	1552	1565	1577	1590	1603	1616	1628	1641	1	3	4	5	6
4	.1654	1667	1680	1693	1707	1720	1733	1746	1759	1773	1	3	4	5	7
25	.1786	1799	1813	1826	1840	1853	1867	1881	1894	1908	1	3	4	5	7
6	.1922	1935	1949	1963	1977	1991	2005	2019	2033	2047	1	3	4	6	7
7	.2061	2075	2089	2104	2118	2132	2146	2161	2175	2190	1	3	4	6	7
8	.2204	2219	2233	2248	2262	2277	2291	2306	2321	2336	1	3	4	6	7
9	.2350	2365	2380	2395	2410	2425	2440	2455	2470	2485	2	3	5	6	8
30	.2500	2515	2530	2545	2561	2576	2591	2607	2622	2637	2	3	5	6	8
1	.2653	2668	2684	2699	2715	2730	2746	2761	2777	2792	2	3	5	6	8
2	.2808	2824	2840	2855	2871	2887	2903	2919	2934	2950	2	3	5	6	8
3	.2966	2982	2998	3014	3030	3046	3062	3079	3095	3111	2	3	5	6	8
4	.3127	3143	3159	3176	3192	3208	3224	3241	3257	3274	2	3	5	7	8
35	.3290	3306	3323	3339	3356	3372	3389	3405	3422	3438	2	3	5	7	8
6	.3455	3472	3488	3505	3521	3538	3555	3572	3588	3605	2	3	5	7	8
7	.3622	3639	3655	3672	3689	3706	3723	3740	3757	3773	2	3	5	7	8
8	.3790	3807	3824	3841	3858	3875	3892	3909	3926	3943	2	3	5	7	8
9	.3960	3978	3995	4012	4029	4046	4063	4080	4097	4115	2	3	5	7	9
40	.4132	4149	4166	4183	4201	4218	4235	4252	4270	4287	2	3	5	7	9
1	.4304	4321	4339	4356	4373	4391	4408	4425	4443	4460	2	3	5	7	9
2	.4477	4495	4512	4529	4547	4564	4582	4599	4616	4634	2	3	5	7	9
3	.4651	4669	4686	4703	4721	4738	4756	4773	4791	4808	2	3	5	7	9
4	.4826	4843	4860	4878	4895	4913	4930	4948	4965	4983	2	3	5	7	9

(cont.)

469

$\theta°$	.0	.1	.2	.3	.4	.5	.6	.7	.8	.9	.01	.02	.03	.04	.05
													Differences		
45	.5000	5017	5035	5052	5070	5087	5105	5122	5140	5157	2	3	5	7	9
6	.5174	5192	5209	5227	5244	5262	5279	5297	5314	5331	2	3	5	7	9
7	.5349	5366	5384	5401	5418	5436	5453	5471	5488	5505	2	3	5	7	9
8	.5523	5540	5557	5575	5592	5609	5627	5644	5661	5679	2	3	5	7	9
9	.5696	5713	5730	5748	5765	5782	5799	5817	5834	5851	2	3	5	7	9
50	.5868	5885	5903	5920	5937	5954	5971	5988	6005	6022	2	3	5	7	9
1	.6040	6057	6074	6091	6108	6125	6142	6159	6176	6193	2	3	5	7	9
2	.6210	6227	6243	6260	6277	6294	6311	6328	6345	6361	2	3	5	7	8
3	.6378	6395	6412	6428	6445	6462	6479	6495	6512	6528	2	3	5	7	8
4	.6545	6562	6578	6595	6611	6628	6644	6661	6677	6694	2	3	5	7	8
55	.6710	6726	6743	6759	6776	6792	6808	6824	6841	6857	2	3	5	7	8
6	.6873	6889	6905	6921	6938	6954	6970	6986	7002	7018	2	3	5	7	8
7	.7034	7050	7066	7081	7097	7113	7129	7145	7160	7176	2	3	5	6	8
8	.7192	7208	7223	7239	7254	7270	7285	7301	7316	7332	2	3	5	6	8
9	.7347	7363	7378	7393	7409	7424	7439	7455	7470	7485	2	3	5	6	8
60	.7500	7515	7530	7545	7560	7575	7590	7605	7620	7635	2	3	5	6	8
1	.7650	7664	7679	7694	7709	7723	7738	7752	7767	7781	2	3	5	6	8
2	.7796	7810	7825	7839	7854	7868	7882	7896	7911	7925	1	3	4	6	7
3	.7939	7953	7967	7981	7995	8009	8023	8037	8051	8065	1	3	4	6	7
4	.8078	8092	8106	8119	8133	8147	8160	8174	8187	8201	1	3	4	6	7
65	.8214	8227	8241	8254	8267	8280	8293	8307	8320	8333	1	3	4	5	7
6	.8346	8359	8372	8384	8397	8410	8423	8435	8448	8461	1	3	4	5	7
7	.8473	8486	8498	8511	8523	8536	8548	8560	8572	8585	1	3	4	5	6
8	.8597	8609	8621	8633	8645	8657	8669	8680	8692	8704	1	2	4	5	6
9	.8716	8727	8739	8751	8762	8774	8785	8796	8808	8819	1	2	4	5	6
70	.8830	8841	8853	8864	8875	8886	8897	8908	8918	8929	1	2	3	5	6
1	.8940	8951	8961	8972	8983	8993	9004	9014	9024	9035	1	2	3	4	6
2	.9045	9055	9066	9076	9086	9096	9106	9116	9126	9135	1	2	3	4	5
3	.9145	9155	9165	9174	9184	9193	9203	9212	9222	9231	1	2	3	4	5
4	.9240	9249	9259	9268	9277	9286	9295	9304	9313	9321	1	2	3	4	5
75	.9330	9339	9347	9356	9365	9373	9382	9390	9398	9407	1	2	3	4	4
6	.9415	9423	9431	9439	9447	9455	9463	9471	9479	9486	1	2	3	3	4
7	.9494	9502	9509	9517	9524	9532	9539	9546	9553	9561	1	2	2	3	4
8	.9568	9575	9582	9589	9596	9603	9609	9616	9623	9629	1	1	2	3	4
9	.9636	9642	9649	9655	9662	9668	9674	9680	9686	9692	1	1	2	3	3
80	.9698	9704	9710	9716	9722	9728	9733	9739	9744	9750.	1	1	2	2	3
1	.9755	9761	9766	9771	9776	9782	9787	9792	9797	9801					
2	.9806	9811	9816	9820	9825	9830	9834	9839	9843	9847					
3	.9851	9856	9860	9864	9868	9872	9876	9880	9883	9887					
4	.9891	9894	9898	9901	9905	9908	9911	9915	9918	9921					
85	.9924	9927	9930	9933	9936	9938	9941	9944	9946	9949			Interpolate		
6	.9951	9954	9956	9958	9961	9963	9965	9967	9969	9971					
7	.9973	9974	9976	9978	9979	9981	9982	9984	9985	9987					
8	.9988	9989	9990	9991	9992	9993	9994	9995	9996	9996					
9	.9997	9998	9998	9999	9999	9999	1.00	1.00	1.00	1.00					

From *The Interpretation of X-Ray Diffraction Photographs,* by N. F. M. Henry, H. Lipson, and W. A. Wooster (Macmillan, London, 1951).

QUADRATIC FORMS OF MILLER INDICES

	Cubic				Hexagonal	
	hkl					
$h^2 + k^2 + l^2$	Simple	Face-centered	Body-centered	Diamond	$h^2 + hk + k^2$	hk
1	100				1	10
2	110	. . .	110		2	
3	111	111	. . .	111	3	11
4	200	200	200		4	20
5	210				5	
6	211	. . .	211		6	
7					7	21
8	220	220	220	220	8	
9	300, 221				9	30
10	310	. . .	310		10	
11	311	311	. . .	311	11	
12	222	222	222		12	22
13	320				13	31
14	321	. . .	321		14	
15					15	
16	400	400	400	400	16	40
17	410, 322				17	
18	411, 330	. . .	411, 330		18	
19	331	331	. . .	331	19	32
20	420	420	420		20	
21	421				21	41
22	332	. . .	332		22	
23					23	
24	422	422	422	422	24	
25	500, 430				25	50
26	510, 431	. . .	510, 431		26	
27	511, 333	511, 333	. . .	511, 333	27	33
28					28	42
29	520, 432				29	
30	521	. . .	521		30	
31					31	51
32	440	440	440	440	32	
33	522, 441				33	
34	530, 433	. . .	530, 433		34	
35	531	531	. . .	531	35	
36	600, 442	600, 442	600, 442		36	60
37	610				37	43
38	611, 532	. . .	611, 532		38	
39					39	52
40	620	620	620	620	40	
41	621, 540, 443				41	
42	541	. . .	541		42	
43	533	533	. . .	533	43	61
44	622	622	622		44	
45	630, 542				45	
46	631	. . .	631		46	
47					47	
48	444	444	444	444	48	44
49	700, 632				49	70, 53

(cont.)

$h^2 + k^2 + l^2$	Cubic				Hexagonal	
	hkl				$h^2 + hk + k^2$	hk
	Simple	Face-centered	Body-centered	Diamond		
50	710, 550, 543	. . .	710, 550, 543		50	
51	711, 551	711, 551	. . .	711, 551	51	
52	640	640	640		52	62
53	720, 641				53	
54	721, 633, 552	. . .	721, 633, 552		54	
55					55	
56	642	642	642	642	56	
57	722, 544				57	71
58	730	. . .	730		58	
59	731, 553	731, 553	. . .	731, 553	59	

APPENDIX 7

VALUES OF $(\sin \theta)/\lambda$ (A^{-1})

θ	Radiation				
	Mo $K\alpha$ (0.711 A)	Cu $K\alpha$ (1.542 A)	Co $K\alpha$ (1.790 A)	Fe $K\alpha$ (1.937 A)	Cr $K\alpha$ (2.291 A)
0°	0.00	0.00	0.00	0.00	0.00
1	0.02	0.01	0.01	0.01	0.01
2	0.05	0.02	0.02	0.02	0.02
3	0.07	0.03	0.03	0.03	0.02
4	0.10	0.05	0.04	0.04	0.03
5	0.12	0.06	0.05	0.04	0.04
6	0.15	0.07	0.06	0.05	0.05
7	0.17	0.08	0.07	0.06	0.05
8	0.20	0.09	0.08	0.07	0.06
9	0.22	0.10	0.09	0.08	0.07
10	0.24	0.11	0.10	0.09	0.08
11	0.27	0.12	0.11	0.10	0.08
12	0.29	0.13	0.12	0.11	0.09
13	0.32	0.15	0.13	0.12	0.10
14	0.34	0.16	0.14	0.12	0.11
15	0.36	0.17	0.14	0.13	0.11
16	0.39	0.18	0.15	0.14	0.12
17	0.41	0.19	0.16	0.15	0.13
18	0.43	0.20	0.17	0.16	0.13
19	0.46	0.21	0.18	0.17	0.14
20	0.48	0.22	0.19	0.18	0.15
21	0.51	0.23	0.20	0.18	0.15
22	0.53	0.24	0.21	0.19	0.16
23	0.55	0.25	0.22	0.20	0.17
24	0.57	0.26	0.23	0.21	0.18
25	0.60	0.27	0.24	0.22	0.18
26	0.62	0.28	0.24	0.23	0.19
27	0.64	0.29	0.25	0.23	0.20
28	0.66	0.30	0.26	0.24	0.20
29	0.68	0.31	0.27	0.25	0.21

(cont.)

θ	Radiation				
	Mo $K\alpha$ (0.711 A)	Cu $K\alpha$ (1.542 A)	Co $K\alpha$ (1.790 A)	Fe $K\alpha$ (1.937 A)	Cr $K\alpha$ (2.291 A)
30	0.70	0.32	0.28	0.26	0.22
31	0.72	0.33	0.29	0.27	0.22
32	0.75	0.34	0.30	0.27	0.23
33	0.77	0.35	0.30	0.28	0.24
34	0.79	0.36	0.31	0.29	0.24
35	0.81	0.37	0.32	0.29	0.25
36	0.83	0.38	0.33	0.30	0.26
37	0.85	0.39	0.34	0.31	0.26
38	0.87	0.40	0.34	0.32	0.27
39	0.89	0.41	0.35	0.32	0.27
40	0.91	0.42	0.36	0.33	0.28
41	0.93	0.43	0.37	0.34	0.29
42	0.94	0.43	0.37	0.35	0.29
43	0.96	0.44	0.38	0.35	0.30
44	0.98	0.45	0.39	0.36	0.30
45	0.99	0.46	0.40	0.36	0.31
46	1.01	0.47	0.40	0.37	0.31
47	1.03	0.47	0.41	0.38	0.32
48	1.05	0.48	0.42	0.38	0.32
49	1.06	0.49	0.42	0.39	0.33
50	1.08	0.50	0.43	0.39	0.33
52	1.11	0.51	0.44	0.41	0.34
54	1.14	0.52	0.45	0.42	0.35
56	1.17	0.54	0.46	0.43	0.36
58	1.20	0.55	0.47	0.44	0.37
60	1.22	0.56	0.48	0.45	0.38
62	1.24	0.57	0.49	0.46	0.39
64	1.26	0.58	0.50	0.46	0.39
66	1.28	0.59	0.51	0.47	0.40
68	1.30	0.60	0.52	0.48	0.40
70	1.32	0.61	0.53	0.48	0.41
72	1.34	0.62	0.53	0.49	0.41
74	1.35	0.62	0.54	0.50	0.42
76	1.37	0.63	0.54	0.50	0.42
78	1.38	0.63	0.55	0.50	0.43
80	1.39	0.64	0.55	0.51	0.43
82	1.39	0.64	0.55	0.51	0.43
84	1.40	0.64	0.56	0.51	0.43
86	1.40	0.65	0.56	0.51	0.43
88	1.41	0.65	0.56	0.52	0.43
90	1.41	0.65	0.56	0.52	0.43

ATOMIC SCATTERING FACTORS

$\frac{\sin \theta}{\lambda} (A^{-1})$		0.0	0.1	0.2	0.3	0.4	0.5	0.6	0.7	0.8	0.9	1.0	1.1	1.2
H	1	0.81	0.48	0.25	0.13	0.07	0.04	0.03	0.02	0.01	0.00	0.00	
He	2	1.88	1.46	1.05	0.75	0.52	0.35	0.24	0.18	0.14	0.11	0.09	
Li$^+$	2	1.96	1.8	1.5	1.3	1.0	0.8	0.6	0.5	0.4	0.3	0.3	
Li	3	2.2	1.8	1.5	1.3	1.0	0.8	0.6	0.5	0.4	0.3	0.3	
Be^{+2}	2	2.0	1.9	1.7	1.6	1.4	1.2	1.0	0.9	0.7	0.6	0.5	
Be	4	2.9	1.9	1.7	1.6	1.4	1.2	1.0	0.9	0.7	0.6	0.5	
B^{+3}	2	1.99	1.9	1.8	1.7	1.6	1.4	1.3	1.2	1.0	0.9	0.7	
B	5	3.5	2.4	1.9	1.7	1.5	1.4	1.2	1.2	1.0	0.9	0.7	
C	6	4.6	3.0	2.2	1.9	1.7	1.6	1.4	1.3	1.16	1.0	0.9	
N^{+5}	2	2.0	2.0	1.9	1.9	1.8	1.7	1.6	1.5	1.4	1.3	1.16	
N^{+3}	4	3.7	3.0	2.4	2.0	1.8	1.66	1.56	1.49	1.39	1.28	1.17	
N	7	5.8	4.2	3.0	2.3	1.9	1.65	1.54	1.49	1.39	1.29	1.17	
O	8	7.1	5.3	3.9	2.9	2.2	1.8	1.6	1.5	1.4	1.35	1.26	
O^{-2}	10	8.0	5.5	3.8	2.7	2.1	1.8	1.5	1.5	1.4	1.35	1.26	
F	9	7.8	6.2	4.45	3.35	2.65	2.15	1.9	1.7	1.6	1.5	1.35	
F$^-$	10	8.7	6.7	4.8	3.5	2.8	2.2	1.9	1.7	1.55	1.5	1.35	
Ne	10	9.3	7.5	5.8	4.4	3.4	2.65	2.2	1.9	1.65	1.55	1.5	
Na$^+$	10	9.5	8.2	6.7	5.25	4.05	3.2	2.65	2.25	1.95	1.75	1.6	
Na	11	9.65	8.2	6.7	5.25	4.05	3.2	2.65	2.25	1.95	1.75	1.6	
Mg^{+2}	10	9.75	8.6	7.25	5.95	4.8	3.85	3.15	2.55	2.2	2.0	1.8	
Mg	12	10.5	8.6	7.25	5.95	4.8	3.85	3.15	2.55	2.2	2.0	1.8	
Al^{+3}	10	9.7	8.9	7.8	6.65	5.5	4.45	3.65	3.1	2.65	2.3	2.0	
Al	13	11.0	8.95	7.75	6.6	5.5	4.5	3.7	3.1	2.65	2.3	2.0	
Si^{+4}	10	9.75	9.15	8.25	7.15	6.05	5.05	4.2	3.4	2.95	2.6	2.3	
Si	14	11.35	9.4	8.2	7.15	6.1	5.1	4.2	3.4	2.95	2.6	2.3	
P^{+5}	10	9.8	9.25	8.45	7.5	6.55	5.65	4.8	4.05	3.4	3.0	2.6	
P	15	12.4	10.0	8.45	7.45	6.5	5.65	4.8	4.05	3.4	3.0	2.6	
P^{-3}	18	12.7	9.8	8.4	7.45	6.5	5.65	4.85	4.05	3.4	3.0	2.6	
S^{+6}	10	9.85	9.4	8.7	7.85	6.85	6.05	5.25	4.5	3.9	3.35	2.9	
S	16	13.6	10.7	8.95	7.85	6.85	6.0	5.25	4.5	3.9	3.35	2.9	
S^{-2}	18	14.3	10.7	8.9	7.85	6.85	6.0	5.25	4.5	3.9	3.35	2.9	
Cl	17	14.6	11.3	9.25	8.05	7.25	6.5	5.75	5.05	4.4	3.85	3.35	
Cl$^-$	18	15.2	11.5	9.3	8.05	7.25	6.5	5.75	5.05	4.4	3.85	3.35	
A	18	15.9	12.6	10.4	8.7	7.8	7.0	6.2	5.4	4.7	4.1	3.6	
K$^+$	18	16.5	13.3	10.8	8.85	7.75	7.05	6.44	5.9	5.3	4.8	4.2	
K	19	16.5	13.3	10.8	9.2	7.9	6.7	5.9	5.2	4.6	4.2	3.7	3.3
Ca^{+2}	18	16.8	14.0	11.5	9.3	8.1	7.35	6.7	6.2	5.7	5.1	4.6	
Ca	20	17.5	14.1	11.4	9.7	8.4	7.3	6.3	5.6	4.9	4.5	4.0	3.6
Sc^{+3}	18	16.7	14.0	11.4	9.4	8.3	7.6	6.9	6.4	5.8	5.35	4.85	
Sc	21	18.4	14.9	12.1	10.3	8.9	7.7	6.7	5.9	5.3	4.7	4.3	3.9
Ti^{+4}	18	17.0	14.4	11.9	9.9	8.5	7.85	7.3	6.7	6.15	5.65	5.05	
Ti	22	19.3	15.7	12.8	10.9	9.5	8.2	7.2	6.3	5.6	5.0	4.6	4.2
V	23	20.2	16.6	13.5	11.5	10.1	8.7	7.6	6.7	5.9	5.3	4.9	4.4
Cr	24	21.1	17.4	14.2	12.1	10.6	9.2	8.0	7.1	6.3	5.7	5.1	4.6
Mn	25	22.1	18.2	14.9	12.7	11.1	9.7	8.4	7.5	6.6	6.0	5.4	4.9

(cont.)

$\frac{\sin \theta}{\lambda}$ (A^{-1})		0.0	0.1	0.2	0.3	0.4	0.5	0.6	0.7	0.8	0.9	1.0	1.1	1.2
Fe	26	23.1	18.9	15.6	13.3	11.6	10.2	8.9	7.9	7.0	6.3	5.7	5.2
Co	27	24.1	19.8	16.4	14.0	12.1	10.7	9.3	8.3	7.3	6.7	6.0	5.5
Ni	28	25.0	20.7	17.2	14.6	12.7	11.2	9.8	8.7	7.7	7.0	6.3	5.8
Cu	29	25.9	21.6	17.9	15.2	13.3	11.7	10.2	9.1	8.1	7.3	6.6	6.0
Zn	30	26.8	22.4	18.6	15.8	13.9	12.2	10.7	9.6	8.5	7.6	6.9	6.3
Ga	31	27.8	23.3	19.3	16.5	14.5	12.7	11.2	10.0	8.9	7.9	7.3	6.7
Ge	32	28.8	24.1	20.0	17.1	15.0	13.2	11.6	10.4	9.3	8.3	7.6	7.0
As	33	29.7	25.0	20.8	17.7	15.6	13.8	12.1	10.8	9.7	8.7	7.9	7.3
Se	34	30.6	25.8	21.5	18.3	16.1	14.3	12.6	11.2	10.0	9.0	8.2	7.5
Br	35	31.6	26.6	22.3	18.9	16.7	14.8	13.1	11.7	10.4	9.4	8.6	7.8
Kr	36	32.5	27.4	23.0	19.5	17.3	15.3	13.6	12.1	10.8	9.8	8.9	8.1
Rb^{+}	36	33.6	28.7	24.6	21.4	18.9	16.7	14.6	12.8	11.2	9.9	8.9	
Rb	37	33.5	28.2	23.8	20.2	17.9	15.9	14.1	12.5	11.2	10.2	9.2	8.4
Sr	38	34.4	29.0	24.5	20.8	18.4	16.4	14.6	12.9	11.6	10.5	9.5	8.7
Y	39	35.4	29.9	25.3	21.5	19.0	17.0	15.1	13.4	12.0	10.9	9.9	9.0
Zr	40	36.3	30.8	26.0	22.1	19.7	17.5	15.6	13.8	12.4	11.2	10.2	9.3
Nb	41	37.3	31.7	26.8	22.8	20.2	18.1	16.0	14.3	12.8	11.6	10.6	9.7
Mo	42	38.2	32.6	27.6	23.5	20.8	18.6	16.5	14.8	13.2	12.0	10.9	10.0
Tc	43	39.1	33.4	28.3	24.1	21.3	19.1	17.0	15.2	13.6	12.3	11.3	10.3
Ru	44	40.0	34.3	29.1	24.7	21.9	19.6	17.5	15.6	14.1	12.7	11.6	10.6
Rh	45	41.0	35.1	29.9	25.4	22.5	20.2	18.0	16.1	14.5	13.1	12.0	11.0
Pd	46	41.9	36.0	30.7	26.2	23.1	20.8	18.5	16.6	14.9	13.6	12.3	11.3
Ag	47	42.8	36.9	31.5	26.9	23.8	21.3	19.0	17.1	15.3	14.0	12.7	11.7
Cd	48	43.7	37.7	32.2	27.5	24.4	21.8	19.6	17.6	15.7	14.3	13.0	12.0
In	49	44.7	38.6	33.0	28.1	25.0	22.4	20.1	18.0	16.2	14.7	13.4	12.3
Sn	50	45.7	39.5	33.8	28.7	25.6	22.9	20.6	18.5	16.6	15.1	13.7	12.7
Sb	51	46.7	40.4	34.6	29.5	26.3	23.5	21.1	19.0	17.0	15.5	14.1	13.0
Te	52	47.7	41.3	35.4	30.3	26.9	24.0	21.7	19.5	17.5	16.0	14.5	13.3
I	53	48.6	42.1	36.1	31.0	27.5	24.6	22.2	20.0	17.9	16.4	14.8	13.6
Xe	54	49.6	43.0	36.8	31.6	28.0	25.2	22.7	20.4	18.4	16.7	15.2	13.9
Cs	55	50.7	43.8	37.6	32.4	28.7	25.8	23.2	20.8	18.8	17.0	15.6	14.5
Ba	56	51.7	44.7	38.4	33.1	29.3	26.4	23.7	21.3	19.2	17.4	16.0	14.7
La	57	52.6	45.6	39.3	33.8	29.8	26.9	24.3	21.9	19.7	17.9	16.4	15.0
Ce	58	53.6	46.5	40.1	34.5	30.4	27.4	24.8	22.4	20.2	18.4	16.6	15.3
Pr	59	54.5	47.4	40.9	35.2	31.1	28.0	25.4	22.9	20.6	18.8	17.1	15.7
Nd	60	55.4	48.3	41.6	35.9	31.8	28.6	25.9	23.4	21.1	19.2	17.5	16.1
Pm	61	56.4	49.1	42.4	36.6	32.4	29.2	26.4	23.9	21.5	19.6	17.9	16.4
Sm	62	57.3	50.0	43.2	37.3	32.9	29.8	26.9	24.4	22.0	20.0	18.3	16.8
Eu	63	58.3	50.9	44.0	38.1	33.5	30.4	27.5	24.9	22.4	20.4	18.7	17.1
Gd	64	59.3	51.7	44.8	38.8	34.1	31.0	28.1	25.4	22.9	20.8	19.1	17.5
Tb	65	60.2	52.6	45.7	39.6	34.7	31.6	28.6	25.9	23.4	21.2	19.5	17.9
Dy	66	61.1	53.6	46.5	40.4	35.4	32.2	29.2	26.3	23.9	21.6	19.9	18.3
Ho	67	62.1	54.5	47.3	41.1	36.1	32.7	29.7	26.8	24.3	22.0	20.3	18.6
Er	68	63.0	55.3	48.1	41.7	36.7	33.3	30.2	27.3	24.7	22.4	20.7	18.9
Tm	69	64.0	56.2	48.9	42.4	37.4	33.9	30.8	27.9	25.2	22.9	21.0	19.3

(cont.)

$\dfrac{\sin\theta}{\lambda}\ (A^{-1})$	0.0	0.1	0.2	0.3	0.4	0.5	0.6	0.7	0.8	0.9	1.0	1.1	1.2
Yb	70	64.9	57.0	49.7	43.2	38.0	34.4	31.3	28.4	25.7	23.3	21.4	19.7
Lu	71	65.9	57.8	50.4	43.9	38.7	35.0	31.8	28.9	26.2	23.8	21.8	20.0
Hf	72	66.8	58.6	51.2	44.5	39.3	35.6	32.3	29.3	26.7	24.2	22.3	20.4
Ta	73	67.8	59.5	52.0	45.3	39.9	36.2	32.9	29.8	27.1	24.7	22.6	20.9
W	74	68.8	60.4	52.8	46.1	40.5	36.8	33.5	30.4	27.6	25.2	23.0	21.3
Re	75	69.8	61.3	53.6	46.8	41.1	37.4	34.0	30.9	28.1	25.6	23.4	21.6
Os	76	70.8	62.2	54.4	47.5	41.7	38.0	34.6	31.4	28.6	26.0	23.9	22.0
Ir	77	71.7	63.1	55.3	48.2	42.4	38.6	35.1	32.0	29.0	26.5	24.3	22.3
Pt	78	72.6	64.0	56.2	48.9	43.1	39.2	35.6	32.5	29.5	27.0	24.7	22.7
Au	79	73.6	65.0	57.0	49.7	43.8	39.8	36.2	33.1	30.0	27.4	25.1	23.1
Hg	80	74.6	65.9	57.9	50.5	44.4	40.5	36.8	33.6	30.6	27.8	25.6	23.6
Tl	81	75.5	66.7	58.7	51.2	45.0	41.1	37.4	34.1	31.1	28.3	26.0	24.1
Pb	82	76.5	67.5	59.5	51.9	45.7	41.6	37.9	34.6	31.5	28.8	26.4	24.5
Bi	83	77.5	68.4	60.4	52.7	46.4	42.2	38.5	35.1	32.0	29.2	26.8	24.8
Po	84	78.4	69.4	61.3	53.5	47.1	42.8	39.1	35.6	32.6	29.7	27.2	25.2
At	85	79.4	70.3	62.1	54.2	47.7	43.4	39.6	36.2	33.1	30.1	27.6	25.6
Rn	86	80.3	71.3	63.0	55.1	48.4	44.0	40.2	36.8	33.5	30.5	28.0	26.0
Fr	87	81.3	72.2	63.8	55.8	49.1	44.5	40.7	37.3	34.0	31.0	28.4	26.4
Ra	88	82.2	73.2	64.6	56.5	49.8	45.1	41.3	37.8	34.6	31.5	28.8	26.7
Ac	89	83.2	74.1	65.5	57.3	50.4	45.8	41.8	38.3	35.1	32.0	29.2	27.1
Th	90	84.1	75.1	66.3	58.1	51.1	46.5	42.4	38.8	35.5	32.4	29.6	27.5
Pa	91	85.1	76.0	67.1	58.8	51.7	47.1	43.0	39.3	36.0	32.8	30.1	27.9
U	92	86.0	76.9	67.9	59.6	52.4	47.7	43.5	39.8	36.5	33.3	30.6	28.3
Np	93	87	78	69	60	53	48	44	40	37	34	31	29
Pu	94	88	79	69	61	54	49	44	41	38	34	31	29
Am	95	89	79	70	62	55	50	45	42	38	35	32	30
Cm	96	90	80	71	62	55	50	46	42	39	35	32	30
Bk	97	91	81	72	63	56	51	46	43	39	36	33	30
Cf	98	92	82	73	64	57	52	47	43	40	36	33	31
	99	93	83	74	65	57	52	48	44	40	37	34	31
	100	94	84	75	66	58	53	48	44	41	37	34	31

From *X-Ray Diffraction by Polycrystalline Materials,* edited by H. S. Peiser, H. P. Rooksby, and A. J. C. Wilson (The Institute of Physics, London, 1955).

APPENDIX 9

MULTIPLICITY FACTORS FOR POWDER PHOTOGRAPHS

Cubic:	hkl	hhl	$0kl$	$0kk$	hhh	$00l$	
	48*	24	24*	12	8	6	

Hexagonal and Rhombohedral:	$hk \cdot l$	$hh \cdot l$	$0k \cdot l$	$hk \cdot 0$	$hh \cdot 0$	$0k \cdot 0$	$00 \cdot l$
	24*	12*	12*	12*	6	6	2

Tetragonal:	hkl	hhl	$0kl$	$hk0$	$hh0$	$0k0$	$00l$
	16*	8	8	8*	4	4	2

Orthorhombic:	hkl	$0kl$	$h0l$	$hk0$	$h00$	$0k0$	$00l$
	8	4	4	4	2	2	2

Monoclinic:	hkl	$h0l$	$0k0$
	4	2	2

Triclinic:	hkl
	2

---

* These are the usual multiplicity factors. In some crystals, planes having these indices comprise two forms with the same spacing but different structure factor, and the multiplicity factor for each form is half the value given above. In the cubic system, for example, there are some crystals in which permutations of the indices (hkl) produce planes which are not structurally equivalent; in such crystals (AuBe, discussed in Sec. 2–7, is an example), the plane (123), for example, belongs to one form and has a certain structure factor, while the plane (321) belongs to another form and has a different structure factor. There are $\frac{48}{2} = 24$ planes in the first form and 24 planes in the second. This question is discussed more fully by Henry, Lipson, and Wooster: *The Interpretation of X-Ray Diffraction Photographs* (MacMillan).

LORENTZ-POLARIZATION FACTOR $\left(\dfrac{1 + \cos^2 2\theta}{\sin^2 \theta \cos \theta}\right)$

$\theta°$	.0	.1	.2	.3	.4	.5	.6	.7	.8	.9
2	1639	1486	1354	1239	1138	1048	968.9	898.3	835.1	778.4
3	727.2	680.9	638.8	600.5	565.6	533.6	504.3	477.3	452.3	429.3
4	408.0	388.2	369.9	352.7	336.8	321.9	308.0	294.9	282.6	271.1
5	260.3	250.1	240.5	231.4	222.9	214.7	207.1	199.8	192.9	186.3
6	180.1	174.2	168.5	163.1	158.0	153.1	148.4	144.0	139.7	135.6
7	131.7	128.0	124.4	120.9	117.6	114.4	111.4	108.5	105.6	102.9
8	100.3	97.80	95.37	93.03	90.78	88.60	86.51	84.48	82.52	80.63
9	78.79	77.02	75.31	73.66	72.05	70.49	68.99	67.53	66.12	64.74
10	63.41	62.12	60.87	59.65	58.46	57.32	56.20	55.11	54.06	53.03
11	52.04	51.06	50.12	49.19	48.30	47.43	46.58	45.75	44.94	44.16
12	43.39	42.64	41.91	41.20	40.50	39.82	39.16	38.51	37.88	37.27
13	36.67	36.08	35.50	34.94	34.39	33.85	33.33	32.81	32.31	31.82
14	31.34	30.87	30.41	29.96	29.51	29.08	28.66	28.24	27.83	27.44
15	27.05	26.66	26.29	25.92	25.56	25.21	24.86	24.52	24.19	23.86
16	23.54	23.23	22.92	22.61	22.32	22.02	21.74	21.46	21.18	20.91
17	20.64	20.38	20.12	19.87	19.62	19.38	19.14	18.90	18.67	18.44
18	18.22	18.00	17.78	17.57	17.36	17.15	16.95	16.75	16.56	16.36
19	16.17	15.99	15.80	15.62	15.45	15.27	15.10	14.93	14.76	14.60
20	14.44	14.28	14.12	13.97	13.81	13.66	13.52	13.37	13.23	13.09
21	12.95	12.81	12.68	12.54	12.41	12.28	12.15	12.03	11.91	11.78
22	11.66	11.54	11.43	11.31	11.20	11.09	10.98	10.87	10.76	10.65
23	10.55	10.45	10.35	10.24	10.15	10.05	9.951	9.857	9.763	9.671
24	9.579	9.489	9.400	9.313	9.226	9.141	9.057	8.973	8.891	8.810
25	8.730	8.651	8.573	8.496	8.420	8.345	8.271	8.198	8.126	8.054
26	7.984	7.915	7.846	7.778	7.711	7.645	7.580	7.515	7.452	7.389
27	7.327	7.266	7.205	7.145	7.086	7.027	6.969	6.912	6.856	6.800
28	6.745	6.692	6.637	6.584	6.532	6.480	6.429	6.379	6.329	6.279
29	6.230	6.183	6.135	6.088	6.042	5.995	5.950	5.905	5.861	5.817
30	5.774	5.731	5.688	5.647	5.605	5.564	5.524	5.484	5.445	5.406
31	5.367	5.329	5.292	5.254	5.218	5.181	5.145	5.110	5.075	5.040
32	5.006	4.972	4.939	4.906	4.873	4.841	4.809	4.777	4.746	4.715
33	4.685	4.655	4.625	4.595	4.566	4.538	4.509	4.481	4.453	4.426
34	4.399	4.372	4.346	4.320	4.294	4.268	4.243	4.218	4.193	4.169
35	4.145	4.121	4.097	4.074	4.052	4.029	4.006	3.984	3.962	3.941
36	3.919	3.898	3.877	3.857	3.836	3.816	3.797	3.777	3.758	3.739
37	3.720	3.701	3.683	3.665	3.647	3.629	3.612	3.594	3.577	3.561
38	3.544	3.527	3.513	3.497	3.481	3.465	3.449	3.434	3.419	3.404
39	3.389	3.375	3.361	3.347	3.333	3.320	3.306	3.293	3.280	3.268
40	3.255	3.242	3.230	3.218	3.206	3.194	3.183	3.171	3.160	3.149
41	3.138	3.127	3.117	3.106	3.096	3.086	3.076	3.067	3.057	3.048
42	3.038	3.029	3.020	3.012	3.003	2.994	2.986	2.978	2.970	2.962
43	2.954	2.946	2.939	2.932	2.925	2.918	2.911	2.904	2.897	2.891
44	2.884	2.878	2.872	2.866	2.860	2.855	2.849	2.844	2.838	2.833

(cont.)

$\theta°$	.0	.1	.2	.3	.4	.5	.6	.7	.8	.9
45	2.828	2.824	2.819	2.814	2.810	2.805	2.801	2.797	2.793	2.789
46	2.785	2.782	2.778	2.775	2.772	2.769	2.766	2.763	2.760	2.757
47	2.755	2.752	2.750	2.748	2.746	2.744	2.742	2.740	2.738	2.737
48	2.736	2.735	2.733	2.732	2.731	2.730	2.730	2.729	2.729	2.728
49	2.728	2.728	2.728	2.728	2.728	2.728	2.729	2.729	2.730	2.730
50	2.731	2.732	2.733	2.734	2.735	2.737	2.738	2.740	2.741	2.743
51	2.745	2.747	2.749	2.751	2.753	2.755	2.758	2.760	2.763	2.766
52	2.769	2.772	2.775	2.778	2.782	2.785	2.788	2.792	2.795	2.799
53	2.803	2.807	2.811	2.815	2.820	2.824	2.828	2.833	2.838	2.843
54	2.848	2.853	2.858	2.863	2.868	2.874	2.879	2.885	2.890	2.896
55	2.902	2.908	2.914	2.921	2.927	2.933	2.940	2.946	2.953	2.960
56	2.967	2.974	2.981	2.988	2.996	3.004	3.011	3.019	3.026	3.034
57	3.042	3.050	3.059	3.067	3.075	3.084	3.092	3.101	3.110	3.119
58	3.128	3.137	3.147	3.156	3.166	3.175	3.185	3.195	3.205	3.215
59	3.225	3.235	3.246	3.256	3.267	3.278	3.289	3.300	3.311	3.322
60	3.333	3.345	3.356	3.368	3.380	3.392	3.404	3.416	3.429	3.441
61	3.454	3.466	3.479	3.492	3.505	3.518	3.532	3.545	3.559	3.573
62	3.587	3.601	3.615	3.629	3.643	3.658	3.673	3.688	3.703	3.718
63	3.733	3.749	3.764	3.780	3.796	3.812	3.828	3.844	3.861	3.878
64	3.894	3.911	3.928	3.946	3.963	3.980	3.998	4.016	4.034	4.052
65	4.071	4.090	4.108	4.127	4.147	4.166	4.185	4.205	4.225	4.245
66	4.265	4.285	4.306	4.327	4.348	4.369	4.390	4.412	4.434	4.456
67	4.478	4.500	4.523	4.546	4.569	4.592	4.616	4.640	4.664	4.688
68	4.712	4.737	4.762	4.787	4.812	4.838	4.864	4.890	4.916	4.943
69	4.970	4.997	5.024	5.052	5.080	5.109	5.137	5.166	5.195	5.224
70	5.254	5.284	5.315	5.345	5.376	5.408	5.440	5.471	5.504	5.536
71	5.569	5.602	5.636	5.670	5.705	5.740	5.775	5.810	5.846	5.883
72	5.919	5.956	5.994	6.032	6.071	6.109	6.149	6.189	6.229	6.270
73	6.311	6.352	6.394	6.437	6.480	6.524	6.568	6.613	6.658	6.703
74	6.750	6.797	6.844	6.892	6.941	6.991	7.041	7.091	7.142	7.194
75	7.247	7.300	7.354	7.409	7.465	7.521	7.578	7.636	7.694	7.753
76	7.813	7.874	7.936	7.999	8.063	8.128	8.193	8.259	8.327	8.395
77	8.465	8.536	8.607	8.680	8.754	8.829	8.905	8.982	9.061	9.142
78	9.223	9.305	9.389	9.474	9.561	9.649	9.739	9.831	9.924	10.02
79	10.12	10.21	10.31	10.41	10.52	10.62	10.73	10.84	10.95	11.06
80	11.18	11.30	11.42	11.54	11.67	11.80	11.93	12.06	12.20	12.34
81	12.48	12.63	12.78	12.93	13.08	13.24	13.40	13.57	13.74	13.92
82	14.10	14.28	14.47	14.66	14.86	15.07	15.28	15.49	15.71	15.94
83	16.17	16.41	16.66	16.91	17.17	17.44	17.72	18.01	18.31	18.61
84	18.93	19.25	19.59	19.94	20.30	20.68	21.07	21.47	21.89	22.32
85	22.77	23.24	23.73	24.24	24.78	25.34	25.92	26.52	27.16	27.83
86	28.53	29.27	30.04	30.86	31.73	32.64	33.60	34.63	35.72	36.88
87	38.11	39.43	40.84	42.36	44.00	45.76	47.68	49.76	52.02	54.50

From *The Interpretation of X-Ray Diffraction Photographs*, by N. F. M. Henry, H. Lipson, and W. A. Wooster (Macmillan, London, 1951).

APPENDIX 11

PHYSICAL CONSTANTS

Charge on the electron (e) = 4.80×10^{-10} esu

Mass of electron (m) = 9.11×10^{-28} gm

Mass of neutron = 1.67×10^{-24} gm

Velocity of light (c) = 3.00×10^{10} cm/sec

Planck's constant (h) = 6.62×10^{-27} erg·sec

Boltzmann's constant (k) = 1.38×10^{-16} erg/°A

Avogadro's number (N) = 6.02×10^{23} per mol

Gas constant (R) = 1.99 cal/°A/mol

1 electron volt = 1.602×10^{-12} erg

1 cal = 4.182×10^{7} ergs

1 kX = 1.00202A

APPENDIX 12

INTERNATIONAL ATOMIC WEIGHTS, 1953

	Symbol	Atomic number	Atomic weight*		Symbol	Atomic number	Atomic weight*
Actinium	Ac	89	227	Molybdenum	Mo	42	95.95
Aluminum	Al	13	26.98	Neodymium	Nd	60	144.27
Americium	Am	95	[243]	Neptunium	Np	93	[237]
Antimony	Sb	51	121.76	Neon	Ne	10	20.183
Argon	A	18	39.944	Nickel	Ni	28	58.69
Arsenic	As	33	74.91	Niobium	Nb	41	92.91
Astatine	At	85	[210]	Nitrogen	N	7	14.008
Barium	Ba	56	137.36	Osmium	Os	76	190.2
Berkelium	Bk	97	[245]	Oxygen	O	8	16
Beryllium	Be	4	9.013	Palladium	Pd	46	106.7
Bismuth	Bi	83	209.00	Phosphorus	P	15	30.975
Boron	B	5	10.82	Platinum	Pt	78	195.23
Bromine	Br	35	79.916	Plutonium	Pu	94	[242]
Cadmium	Cd	48	112.41	Polonium	Po	84	210
Calcium	Ca	20	40.08	Potassium	K	19	39.100
Californium	Cf	98	[246]	Praseodymium	Pr	59	140.92
Carbon	C	6	12.011	Promethium	Pm	61	[145]
Cerium	Ce	58	140.13	Protactinium	Pa	91	231
Caesium	Cs	55	132.91	Radium	Ra	88	226.05
Chlorine	Cl	17	35.457	Radon	Rn	86	222
Chromium	Cr	24	52.01	Rhenium	Re	75	186.31
Cobalt	Co	27	58.94	Rhodium	Rh	45	102.91
Copper	Cu	29	63.54	Rubidium	Rb	37	85.48
Curium	Cm	96	[243]	Ruthenium	Ru	44	101.1
Dysprosium	Dy	66	162.46	Samarium	Sm	62	150.43
Erbium	Er	68	167.2	Scandium	Sc	21	44.96
Europium	Eu	63	152.0	Selenium	Se	34	78.96
Fluorine	F	9	19.00	Silicon	Si	14	28.09
Francium	Fr	87	[223]	Silver	Ag	47	107.880
Gadolinium	Gd	64	156.9	Sodium	Na	11	22.991
Gallium	Ga	31	69.72	Strontium	Sr	38	87.63
Germanium	Ge	32	72.60	Sulfur	S	16	32.066†
Gold	Au	79	197.0	Tantalum	Ta	73	180.95
Hafnium	Hf	72	178.6	Technetium	Tc	43	[99]
Helium	He	2	4.003	Tellurium	Te	52	127.61
Holmium	Ho	67	164.94	Terbium	Tb	65	158.93
Hydrogen	H	1	1.0080	Thallium	Tl	81	204.39
Indium	In	49	114.76	Thorium	Th	90	232.05
Iodine	I	53	126.91	Thulium	Tm	69	168.94
Iridium	Ir	77	192.2	Tin	Sn	50	118.70
Iron	Fe	26	55.85	Titanium	Ti	22	47.90
Krypton	Kr	36	83.80	Tungsten	W	74	183.92
Lanthanum	La	57	138.92	Uranium	U	92	238.07
Lead	Pb	82	207.21	Vanadium	V	23	50.95
Lithium	Li	3	6.940	Xenon	Xe	54	131.3
Lutetium	Lu	71	174.99	Ytterbium	Yb	70	173.04
Magnesium	Mg	12	24.32	Yttrium	Y	39	88.92
Manganese	Mn	25	54.94	Zinc	Zn	30	65.38
Mercury	Hg	80	200.61	Zirconium	Zr	40	91.22

* A bracketed value is the mass number of the isotope of longest known half-life.
† Because of natural variations in the relative abundance of its isotopes, the atomic weight of sulfur has a range of ± 0.003.

APPENDIX 13

CRYSTAL STRUCTURE DATA

(N.B. The symbols A1, B1, etc., in this Appendix are those used in *Strukturbericht* to designate certain common structural types.)

TABLE A13–1 THE ELEMENTS

Element and modification	Type of structure	Lattice parameters (A) a	Lattice parameters (A) b	c or axial angle	Temperature for which constants apply	Distance of closest approach (A)
Actinium						
Alabamine	See Francium					
Aluminum	FCC, A1	4.0490	. . .	. . . .	20°C	2.862
Americium						
Antimony	Rhombohedral, A7	4.5064	. . .	57°6.5'	20°C	2.903
Argon	FCC, A1	5.43	. . .	. . . .	−233°C	3.84
Arsenic	Rhombohedral, A7	4.159	. . .	53°49'	20°C	2.51
Astatine						
Barium	BCC, A2	5.025	. . .	. . . .	20°C	4.35
Beryllium, α*	HCP, A3	2.2854	. . .	3.5841	20°C	2.225
β (doubtful)	Hexagonal	7.1	. . .	10.8	Room	
Bismuth	Rhombohedral, A7	4.7356	. . .	57°14.2'	20°C	3.111
Boron	Rhombohedral	9.45	. . .	23.8	Room	
Bromine	Orthorhombic	4.49	6.68	8.74	−150°C	2.27
Cadmium	HCP, A3	2.9787	. . .	5.617	20°C	2.979
Calcium, α	FCC, A1	5.57	. . .	. . . .	20°C	3.94
β (300–450°C)						
γ (> 450°C)	HCP, A3	3.99	. . .	6.53	460°C	3.95
Carbon, diamond*	Diamond cubic, A4	3.568	. . .	. . . .	18°C	1.544
Graphite, α*	Hexagonal, A9	2.4614	. . .	6.7014	20°C	1.42
Graphite, β	Rhombohedral, D^5_{3d}	2.461	. . .	10.064		
Cerium*	FCC, A1	5.140	. . .	. . . .	Room	3.64
	FCC, A1	4.82	. . .	. . . .	−180°C	3.40
At 15,000 atm	FCC, A1	4.84	. . .	. . . .	Room	3.42
Cesium	BCC, A2	6.06	. . .	. . . .	−173°C	5.25
Chlorine, α	Tetragonal	8.58	. . .	6.13	−110°C	1.88
Chromium	BCC, A2	2.8845	. . .	. . . .	20°C	2.498
(Transit. at 37°C)	BCC, A2	2.8851	. . .	. . . .	38°C	
Cobalt, α*	HCP, A3	2.507	. . .	4.069	20°C	2.506
β	FCC, A1	3.552	. . .	. . . .	Room	2.511
Columbium	See Niobium					
Copper	FCC, A1	3.6153	. . .	. . . .	20°C	2.556
Dysprosium	HCP, A3	3.585	. . .	5.659	20°C	3.506
Erbium	HCP, A3	3.539	. . .	5.601	20°C	3.466
Europium	BCC, A2	4.582	. . .	. . . .	20°C	2.968
Francium	(Formerly Alabamine)					
Gadolinium	HCP, A3	3.629	. . .	5.759	20°C	3.561
Gallium	One FC orthorhombic, A11	3.526	4.520	7.660	20°C	2.442
Germanium	Diamond cubic, A4	5.658	. . .	. . . .	20°C	2.450
Gold	FCC, A1	4.0783	. . .	. . . .	20°C	2.884
Hafnium	HCP, A3	3.206	. . .	5.087	20°C	3.15
Helium	HCP, A3 (?)	3.58	. . .	5.84	−271.5°C	3.58
Holmium	HCP, A3	3.564	. . .	5.631	20°C	3.487

(*cont.*)

* Ordinary form of an element that exists (or is thought to exist) in more than one form.

Element and modification	Type of structure	Lattice parameters (A)		c or axial angle	Temperature for which constants apply	Distance of closest approach (A)
		a	b			
Hydrogen, para	Hexagonal	3.76	. . .	6.13	− 271°C	
Illinium	See Promethium					
Indium	FC tetragonal, A6	4.594	. . .	4.951	20°C	3.25
Iodine	Orthorhombic	4.787	7.266	9.793	20°C	2.71
Iridium	FCC, A1	3.8389	. . .	. . . .	20°C	2.714
Iron, α*	BCC, A2	2.8664	. . .	. . . .	20°C	2.481
γ (extrapolated)	FCC, A1	3.571	. . .	. . . .	20°C	2.525
γ (908 – 1403°C)	. . . .	3.656	. . .	. . . .	950°C	2.585
δ (> 1403°C)	BCC, A2	2.94	. . .	. . . .	1425°C	2.54
Krypton	FCC, A1	5.69	. . .	. . . .	− 191°C	4.03
Lanthanum, α*	HCP, A3	3.762	. . .	6.075	20°C	3.74
β	FCC, A1	5.307	. . .	. . . .	Room	3.762
Lead	FCC, A1	4.9495	. . .	. . . .	20°C	3.499
Lithium	BCC, A2	3.5089	. . .	. . . .	20°C	3.039
(cold worked)	FCC, A1	4.40	. . .	. . . .	− 195°C	3.11
	HCP, A3 (?)	3.08	. . .	4.82	− 195°C	3.08
Lutecium	HCP, A3	3.516	. . .	5.570	20°C	3.446
Magnesium	HCP, A3	3.2092	. . .	5.2103	20°C	3.196
Manganese, α*	Cubic, A12	8.912	. . .	. . . .	20°C	2.24
β (727 – 1095°C)	Cubic, A13	6.313	. . .	. . . .	Room	2.373
γ (1095 – 1133°C)	FC tetragonal, A6	3.782	. . .	3.533	Room	2.587
δ (> 1133°C)						
Masurium	(Technetium)					
Mercury	Rhombohedral, A11	2.006	. . .	70°31.7'	− 46°C	3.006
Molybdenum	BCC, A2	3.1466	. . .	. . . .	20°C	2.725
Neodymium, α*	HCP, A3 (?)	3.657	. . .	. . . .	20°C	5.902
Neon	FCC, A1	4.51	. . .	. . . .	− 268°C	3.21
Neptunium						
Nickel*	FCC, A1	3.5238	. . .	. . . .	20°C	2.491
(unstable, with H_2 or N_3?)	HCP, A3	2.66	. . .	4.32	Room	
(unstable) (?)	Tetragonal, D^{17}_{4h}	4.00	. . .	3.77	Room	
Niobium	BCC, A2	3.3007	. . .	. . . .	. . . . .	2.859
Nitrogen, α	Cubic	5.67	. . .	. . . .	− 252°C	1.06
β	Hexagonal	4.04	. . .	6.60	− 234°C	
Osmium	HCP, A3	2.7333	. . .	4.3191	. . . . .	2.675
Oxygen, α	Orthorhombic	5.51	3.83	3.45	− 252°C	
β	Rhombohedral	6.20	. . .	99.1°	− 238°C	
γ	Cubic	6.84	. . .	. . . .	− 225°C	
Palladium	FCC, A1	3.8902	. . .	. . . .	20°C	2.750
Phosphorus, white	Cubic	7.18	. . .	. . . .	− 35°C	
Black*	Orthorhombic, A16	3.32	4.39	10.52	Room	2.17
Platinum	FCC, A1	3.9237	. . .	. . . .	20°C	2.775
Plutonium						
Polonium, α	Simple cubic	3.345	. . .	. . . . .	. . . . .	3.35
β (above 75°C)	Simple rhombohedral	3.359	. . .	98°13'	. . . . .	4.40
Potassium	BCC, A2	5.344	. . .	. . . .	20°C	4.627
Praseodymium, α*	HCP, A3 (?)	3.669	. . .	5.920	20°C	3.640
β	FCC, A1	5.161	. . .	. . . .	Room	3.649
Promethium						
Protactinium						
Radium						
Radon						

(cont.)

*Ordinary form of an element that exists (or is thought to exist) in more than one form.

Element and modification	Type of structure	Lattice parameters (A)		c or axial angle	Temperature for which constants apply	Distance of closest approach (A)
		a	b			
Rhenium	HCP, A3	2.7609	. . .	4.4583	20°C	2.740
Rhodium, β*	FCC, A1	3.8034	. . .	. . . .	20°C	2.689
α (electrolytic)	Cubic	9.230	. . .	. . . .	Room	
Rubidium	BCC, A2	5.63	. . .	. . . .	− 173°C	4.88
Ruthenium, α*	HCP, A3	2.7038	. . .	4.2816	20°C	2.649
Samarium	FC tetragonal (?)					
Scandium, α*	FCC, A1	4.541	. . .	. . . . .	20°C	3.2110
β	HCP, A3	3.31	. . .	5.24	Room	3.24
Selenium* (gray, stable, metallic)	Hexagonal, A8	4.3640	. . .	4.9594	20°C	2.32
α (red, metastable)	Monoclinic, P2$_{1/n}$	9.05	9.07	$\begin{cases}β = 90°46'\\ 11.61\end{cases}$	Room	2.34
β (red, metastable)	Monoclinic, C$^5_{2h}$ or C$^4_{2h}$ or C$^2_5$	12.76	8.06	$\begin{cases}β = 93°4'\\ 9.27\end{cases}$	Room	
Silicon	Diamond cubic, A4	5.4282	. . .	. . . . .	20°C	2.351
Silver	FCC, A1	4.0856	. . .	. . . . .	20°C	2.888
Sodium	BCC, A2	4.2906	. . .	. . . . .	20°C	3.715
Strontium	FCC, A1	6.087	. . .	. . . . .	20°C	4.31
Sulfur, α, yellow*	Orthorhombic, A17	10.50	12.94	24.60	20°C	2.12
β	Monoclinic	10.92	11.04	$\begin{cases}β = 83°16'\\ 10.98\end{cases}$	103°C	
Tantalum	BCC, A2	3.3026	. . .	. . . . .	20°C	2.860
Tellurium	Hexagonal, A8	4.4559	. . .	5.9268	20°C	2.87
Terbium	HCP, A3	3.592	. . .	5.675	20°C	3.515
Thallium, α*	HCP, A3	3.4564	. . .	5.531	Room	3.407
β	BCC, A2	3.882	. . .	. . . . .	262°C	3.362
Thorium	FCC, A1	5.088	. . .	. . . . .	20°C	3.60
Thulium	HCP	3.530	. . .	5.575	20°C	3.453
Tin, α, gray	Diamond cubic, A4	6.47	. . .	. . . . . .	18°C	2.81
β, white*	Tetragonal, A5	5.8311	. . .	3.1817	20°C	3.022
Titanium, α*	HCP, A3	2.9504	. . .	4.6833	25°C	2.89
β	BCC, A2	3.33	. . .	. . . . .	900°C	2.89
Tungsten (wolfram), α*	BCC, A2	3.1648	. . .	. . . . .	20°C	2.739
β (unstable)	Cubic, A15	5.049	. . .	. . . . .	20°C	2.524
Uranium, α* (< 665°C)	Orthorhombic, A20	2.858	5.877	4.955	20°C	2.77
β (665–775°C)	Low symmetry					
γ (775–1130°C)	BCC, A2	3.49	. . .	. . . . .	800°C	3.02
Vanadium	BCC, A2	3.039	. . .	. . . . .	20°C	2.632
Virginium	See Astatine					
Wolfram	See Tungsten					
Xenon	FCC, A1	6.25	. . .	. . . . .	− 185°C	4.42
Ytterbium	FCC, A1	5.488	. . .	. . . . .	. . . . .	3.874
Yttrium	HCP, A3	3.670	. . .	5.826	. . . . .	3.60
Zinc	HCP, A3	2.664	. . .	4.945	. . . . .	2.664
Zirconium, α*	HCP, A3	3.230	. . .	5.133	. . . . .	3.17
β	BCC	3.62	. . .	. . . . .	867°C	3.13

* Ordinary form of an element that exists (or is thought to exist) in more than one form.

From *Structure of Metals*, 2nd edition, by Charles S. Barrett (McGraw-Hill Book Company, Inc., New York, 1952).

TABLE A13-2. SOME COMPOUNDS AND SOLID SOLUTIONS

Substance	Type of structure	Lattice parameters (A)	Spacing of cleavage planes (A)
NaCl KCl AgBr	FCC, B1 FCC, B1 FCC, B1	$a = 5.639$ $a = 6.290$ $a = 5.77$	2.820
CaF_2(fluorite)	FCC, C1	$a = 5.46$	
$CaCO_3$(calcite)	Rhombohedral, G1	$a = 6.37$ $\alpha = 46.1°$	3.036
SiO_2(α-quartz)	Hexagonal, C8	$a = 4.90$ $c = 5.39$	
$H_2KAl_2(SiO_4)_3$ (mica, muscovite)	Monoclinic	$a = 5.18$ $b = 8.96$ $c = 20.15$ $\beta = 98.6°$	10.08
Fe_3C (cementite)	Orthorhombic	$a = 4.525$ $b = 5.088$ $c = 6.740$	
Austenite	FCC, A1	$a = 3.555 + 0.044x$ (x = weight percent carbon)	
Martensite	BC Tetragonal	$a = 2.867 - 0.013x$ $c = 2.867 + 0.116x$ (x = weight percent carbon)	

APPENDIX 14

ELECTRON AND NEUTRON DIFFRACTION

A14–1 Introduction. Just as a beam of x-rays has a dual wave-particle character so, inversely, does a stream of particles have certain properties peculiar to wave motion. In particular, such a stream of particles can be diffracted by a periodic arrangement of scattering centers. This was first predicted theoretically by de Broglie in 1924 and demonstrated experimentally by Davisson and Germer in 1927 (for electrons) and by Von Halban and Preiswerk in 1936 (for neutrons).

If a stream of particles can behave like wave motion, it must have a wavelength associated with it. The theory of wave mechanics indicates that this wavelength is given by the ratio of Planck's constant h to the momentum of the particle, or

$$\lambda = \frac{h}{mv}, \tag{1}$$

where m is the mass and v the velocity of the particle. If a stream of particles is directed at a crystal under the proper conditions, diffraction will occur in accordance with the Bragg law just as for x-rays, and the directions of diffraction can be predicted by the use of that law and the wavelength calculated from Eq. (1). Both electrons and neutrons have proved to be useful particles for the study of crystalline structure by diffraction and numerous applications of these techniques have been found in metallurgy. The differences between x-ray, electron, and neutron diffraction by crystals are such that these three techniques supplement one another to a remarkable degree, each giving a particular kind of information which the others are incapable of supplying.

A14–2 Electron diffraction. A stream of fast electrons is obtained in a tube operating on much the same principles as an x-ray tube. The wavelength associated with the electrons depends on the applied voltage, since the kinetic energy of the electrons is given by

$$\tfrac{1}{2}mv^2 = e\mathcal{V}, \tag{2}$$

where e is the charge on the electron and $\mathcal{V}$ the applied voltage (in esu). Combination of Eqs. (1) and (2) shows the inverse relation between wavelength and voltage:

$$\lambda = \sqrt{\frac{150}{V}},$$

where λ is in angstroms and the applied voltage V is in volts. This equation requires small relativistic corrections at high voltages, due to the variation of electron mass with velocity. At an operating voltage of 50,000 volts, the electron wavelength is about 0.05A, or considerably shorter than the wavelength of x-rays used in diffraction.

The important fact to note about electrons is that they are much less penetrating than x-rays. They are easily absorbed by air, which means that the specimen and the photographic plate on which the diffraction pattern is recorded must both be enclosed within the evacuated tube in which the electron beam is produced. An electron-diffraction "camera" therefore contains source, specimen, and detector all in one apparatus. Another result is that transmission patterns can be made only of specimens so thin as to be classified as foils or films, and reflection patterns will be representative only of a thin surface layer of the specimen, since diffraction occurs over a depth of only a few hundred angstroms or less. But even these thin layers of material will give good electron-diffraction patterns, since electrons are scattered much more intensely than x-rays.

These characteristics of electron diffraction give it a particular advantage over x-ray diffraction when it is a question of investigating the structure of thin films, foils, and the like. Electron diffraction has been successfully used to study the structures of metal foils, electrodeposits, oxide films on metal, surface layers due to polishing, and metal films deposited by evaporation.

A14–3 Neutron diffraction. By making a small opening in the wall of a chain-reacting pile, a beam of neutrons can be obtained. The neutrons in such a beam have kinetic energies extending over a considerable range, but a "monochromatic" beam, i.e., a beam composed of neutrons with a single energy, can be obtained by diffraction from a single crystal and this diffracted beam can be used in diffraction experiments. If E is the kinetic energy of the neutrons, then

$$E = \tfrac{1}{2}mv^2, \tag{3}$$

where m is the mass of the neutron (1.67×10^{-24} gm) and v is its velocity. Combination of Eqs. (1) and (3) gives the wavelength of the neutron beam:

$$\lambda = \frac{h}{\sqrt{2mE}}. \tag{4}$$

The neutrons issuing from a pile have their kinetic energies distributed in much the same way as those of gas molecules in thermal equilibrium; i.e., they follow the Maxwell distribution law. The largest fraction of these so-called "thermal neutrons" therefore has kinetic energy equal to kT, where k is Boltzmann's constant and T the absolute temperature. If this fraction is selected by the monochromating crystal, then we can insert $E = kT$ in Eq. (4) and find

$$\lambda = \frac{h}{\sqrt{2mkT}}. \tag{5}$$

T is of the order of 300° to 400°A, which means that λ is about 1 or 2A, i.e., of the same order of magnitude as x-ray wavelengths. Diffraction experiments are performed with a neutron diffractometer, in which the intensity of the beam diffracted by the specimen is measured with a proportional counter filled with BF_3 gas.

The main difference between neutron diffraction on the one hand and x-ray and electron diffraction on the other lies in the variation of atomic scattering power* with atomic number Z and with scattering angle 2θ. The scattering power of an atom increases as Z increases and decreases as 2θ increases, both for x-rays and for electrons, although not in exactly the same manner. Neutrons, however, are scattered with the same intensity at all scattering angles and with a fine disregard for atomic number; in other words, there is no regular variation between scattering power for neutrons and the atomic number of the scatterer. Elements with almost the same values of Z may have quite different neutron-scattering powers and elements with widely separated values of Z may scatter neutrons equally well. Furthermore, some light elements scatter neutrons more intensely than some heavy elements. The following values† illustrate how irregularly the scattering power for neutrons varies with atomic number:

Element	Atomic Number	Neutron-scattering Power
H	1	2.0
C	6	5.2
Al	13	1.5
Fe	26	11.4
Co	27	1.0
Ni	28	13.4
Cu	29	7.3
W	74	3.3
U	92	9.0

It follows that structure analyses can be carried out with neutron diffraction that are impossible, or possible only with great difficulty, with x-ray

---

* This term is here used as a loose designation for the effectiveness of an atom in coherently scattering incident radiation or particles. The "atomic scattering power" for x-rays is evidently proportional to f^2, the square of the atomic scattering factor.

† Largely from *Experimental Nuclear Physics*, Vol. 2. Edited by E. Segré. (John Wiley & Sons, Inc., New York, 1953.)

or electron diffraction. In a compound of hydrogen or carbon, for example, with a heavy metal, x-rays will not "see" the light hydrogen or carbon atom because of its relatively low scattering power, whereas its position in the lattice can be determined with ease by neutron diffraction. Neutrons can also distinguish in many cases between elements differing by only one atomic number, elements which scatter x-rays with almost equal intensity; neutron diffraction, for example, shows strong superlattice lines from ordered FeCo, whereas with x-rays they are practically invisible. Neutron diffraction therefore complements x-ray diffraction in a very useful way, and the only obstacle to its more widespread application would seem to be the very small number of high-intensity neutron sources available for general use.

APPENDIX 15

THE RECIPROCAL LATTICE

A15–1 Introduction. All the diffraction phenomena described in this book have been discussed in terms of the Bragg law. This simple law, admirable for its very simplicity, is in fact applicable to a very wide range of phenomena and is all that is needed for an understanding of a great many applications of x-ray diffraction. Yet there are diffraction effects which the Bragg law is totally unable to explain, notably those involving diffuse scattering at non-Bragg angles, and these effects demand a more general theory of diffraction for their explanation. The reciprocal lattice provides the framework for such a theory. This powerful concept was introduced into the field of diffraction by the German physicist Ewald in 1921 and has since become an indispensable tool in the solution of many problems.

Although the reciprocal lattice may at first appear rather abstract or artificial, the time spent in grasping its essential features is time well spent, because the reciprocal-lattice theory of diffraction, being general, is applicable to all diffraction phenomena from the simplest to the most intricate. Familiarity with the reciprocal lattice will therefore not only provide the student with the necessary key to complex diffraction effects but will deepen his understanding of even the simplest.

A15–2 Vector multiplication. Since the reciprocal lattice is best formulated in terms of vectors, we shall first review a few theorems of vector algebra, namely, those involving the multiplication of vector quantities.

The *scalar product* (or dot product) of two vectors* $\mathbf{a}$ and $\mathbf{b}$, written $\mathbf{a} \cdot \mathbf{b}$, is a scalar quantity equal in magnitude to the product of the absolute values of the two vectors and the cosine of the angle α between them, or

$$\mathbf{a} \cdot \mathbf{b} = ab \cos \alpha.$$

Geometrically, Fig. A15–1 shows that the scalar product of two vectors may be regarded as the product of the length of one vector and the projection of the other upon the first. If one of the vectors, say $\mathbf{a}$, is a unit vector (a vector of unit length), then $\mathbf{a} \cdot \mathbf{b}$ gives immediately the length of the projection of $\mathbf{b}$ on $\mathbf{a}$. The scalar product of sums or differences of vectors is formed simply by term-by-term multiplication:

$$(\mathbf{a} + \mathbf{b}) \cdot (\mathbf{c} - \mathbf{d}) = (\mathbf{a} \cdot \mathbf{c}) - (\mathbf{a} \cdot \mathbf{d}) + (\mathbf{b} \cdot \mathbf{c}) - (\mathbf{b} \cdot \mathbf{d}).$$

---

* Bold-face symbols stand for vectors. The same symbol in italic stands for the absolute value of the vector.

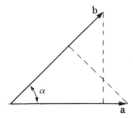

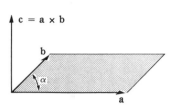

FIG. A15–1. Scalar product of two vectors.

FIG. A15–2. Vector product of two vectors.

The order of multiplication is of no importance; i.e.,

$$\mathbf{a} \cdot \mathbf{b} = \mathbf{b} \cdot \mathbf{a}.$$

The *vector product* (or cross product) of two vectors $\mathbf{a}$ and $\mathbf{b}$, written $\mathbf{a} \times \mathbf{b}$, is *a vector* $\mathbf{c}$ at right angles to the plane of $\mathbf{a}$ and $\mathbf{b}$, and equal in magnitude to the product of the absolute values of the two vectors and the sine of the angle α between them, or

$$\mathbf{c} = \mathbf{a} \times \mathbf{b},$$

$$c = ab \sin \alpha.$$

The magnitude of $\mathbf{c}$ is simply the area of the parallelogram constructed on $\mathbf{a}$ and $\mathbf{b}$, as suggested by Fig. A15–2. The direction of $\mathbf{c}$ is that in which a right-hand screw would move if rotated in such a way as to bring $\mathbf{a}$ into $\mathbf{b}$. It follows from this that the direction of the vector product $\mathbf{c}$ is reversed if the order of multiplication is reversed, or that

$$\mathbf{a} \times \mathbf{b} = -(\mathbf{b} \times \mathbf{a}).$$

A15–3 The reciprocal lattice. Corresponding to any crystal lattice, we can construct a *reciprocal lattice*, so called because many of its properties are reciprocal to those of the crystal lattice. Let the crystal lattice have a unit cell defined by the vectors $\mathbf{a}_1$, $\mathbf{a}_2$, and $\mathbf{a}_3$. Then the corresponding reciprocal lattice has a unit cell defined by the vectors $\mathbf{b}_1$, $\mathbf{b}_2$, and $\mathbf{b}_3$, where

$$\mathbf{b}_1 = \frac{1}{V} (\mathbf{a}_2 \times \mathbf{a}_3), \tag{1}$$

$$\mathbf{b}_2 = \frac{1}{V} (\mathbf{a}_3 \times \mathbf{a}_1), \tag{2}$$

$$\mathbf{b}_3 = \frac{1}{V} (\mathbf{a}_1 \times \mathbf{a}_2), \tag{3}$$

and V is the volume of the crystal unit cell. This way of defining the vectors $\mathbf{b}_1$, $\mathbf{b}_2$, $\mathbf{b}_3$ in terms of the vectors $\mathbf{a}_1$, $\mathbf{a}_2$, $\mathbf{a}_3$ gives the reciprocal lattice certain useful properties which we will now investigate.

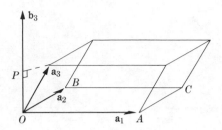

FIG. A15–3.   Location of the reciprocal-lattice axis $\mathbf{b}_3$.

Consider the general triclinic unit cell shown in Fig. A15–3.   The reciprocal-lattice axis $\mathbf{b}_3$ is, according to Eq. (3), normal to the plane of $\mathbf{a}_1$ and $\mathbf{a}_2$, as shown.   Its length is given by

$$b_3 = \frac{|\mathbf{a}_1 \times \mathbf{a}_2|}{V}$$

$$= \frac{\text{(area of parallelogram } OACB)}{\text{(area of parallelogram } OACB)(\text{height of cell})}$$

$$= \frac{1}{OP} = \frac{1}{d_{001}},$$

since OP, the projection of $\mathbf{a}_3$ on $\mathbf{b}_3$, is equal to the height of the cell, which in turn is simply the spacing d of the (001) planes of the crystal lattice. Similarly, we find that the reciprocal lattice axes $\mathbf{b}_1$ and $\mathbf{b}_2$ are normal to the (100) and (010) planes, respectively, of the crystal lattice, and are equal in length to the reciprocals of the spacings of these planes.

By extension, similar relations are found for all the planes of the crystal lattice.   The whole reciprocal lattice is built up by repeated translations of the unit cell by the vectors $\mathbf{b}_1$, $\mathbf{b}_2$, $\mathbf{b}_3$.   This produces an array of points each of which is labeled with its coordinates in terms of the basic vectors. Thus, the point at the end of the $\mathbf{b}_1$ vector is labeled 100, that at the end of the $\mathbf{b}_2$ vector 010, etc.   This extended reciprocal lattice has the following properties:

(1) A vector $\mathbf{H}_{hkl}$ drawn from the origin of the reciprocal lattice to any point in it having coordinates hkl is perpendicular to the plane in the crystal lattice whose Miller indices are hkl.   This vector is given in terms of its coordinates by the expression

$$\mathbf{H}_{hkl} = h\mathbf{b}_1 + k\mathbf{b}_2 + l\mathbf{b}_3.$$

(2) The length of the vector $\mathbf{H}_{hkl}$ is equal to the reciprocal of the spacing d of the (hkl) planes, or

$$H_{hkl} = \frac{1}{d_{hkl}}.$$

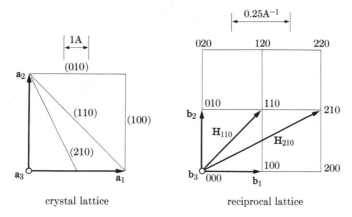

FIG. A15–4.   The reciprocal lattice of a cubic crystal which has $a_1 = 4A$.   The axes $\mathbf{a}_3$ and $\mathbf{b}_3$ are normal to the drawing.

The important thing to note about these relations is that the reciprocal-lattice array of points completely describes the crystal, in the sense that each reciprocal-lattice point is related to a set of planes in the crystal and represents the orientation and spacing of that set of planes.

Before proving these general relations, we might consider particular examples of the reciprocal lattice as shown in Figs. A15–4 and A15–5 for cubic and hexagonal crystals.   In each case, the reciprocal lattice is drawn from any convenient origin, not necessarily that of the crystal lattice, and to any convenient scale of reciprocal angstroms.   Note that Eqs. (1) through (3) take on a very simple form for any crystal whose unit cell is

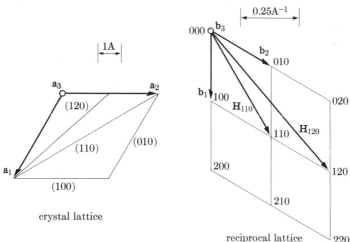

FIG. A15–5.   The reciprocal lattice of a hexagonal crystal which has $a_1 = 4A$. (Here the three-symbol system of plane indexing is used and $\mathbf{a}_3$ is the axis usually designated $\mathbf{c}$.)   The axes $\mathbf{a}_3$ and $\mathbf{b}_3$ are normal to the drawing.

based on mutually perpendicular vectors, i.e., cubic, tetragonal, or ortho-rhombic. For such crystals, $\mathbf{b}_1$, $\mathbf{b}_2$, and $\mathbf{b}_3$ are parallel, respectively, to $\mathbf{a}_1$, $\mathbf{a}_2$, and $\mathbf{a}_3$, while b_1, b_2, and b_3 are simply the reciprocals of a_1, a_2, and a_3. In Figs. A15–4 and A15–5, four cells of the reciprocal lattice are shown, together with two $\mathbf{H}$ vectors in each case. By means of the scales shown, it may be verified that each $\mathbf{H}$ vector is equal in length to the reciprocal of the spacing of the corresponding planes and normal to them. Note that reciprocal lattice points such as nh, nk, nl, where n is an integer, correspond to planes parallel to (hkl) and having $1/n$ their spacing. Thus, $\mathbf{H}_{220}$ is perpendicular to (220) planes and therefore parallel to $\mathbf{H}_{110}$, since (110) and (220) are parallel, but $\mathbf{H}_{220}$ is twice as long as $\mathbf{H}_{110}$ since the (220) planes have half the spacing of the (110) planes.

Other useful relations between the crystal and reciprocal vectors follow from Eqs. (1) through (3). Since $\mathbf{b}_3$, for example, is normal to both $\mathbf{a}_1$ and $\mathbf{a}_2$, its dot product with either one of these vectors is zero, or

$$\mathbf{b}_3 \cdot \mathbf{a}_1 = \mathbf{b}_3 \cdot \mathbf{a}_2 = 0.$$

The dot product of $\mathbf{b}_3$ and $\mathbf{a}_3$, however, is unity, since (see Fig. A15–3)

$$\mathbf{b}_3 \cdot \mathbf{a}_3 = (b_3)\,(\text{projection of } \mathbf{a}_3 \text{ on } \mathbf{b}_3)$$

$$= \left(\frac{1}{OP}\right)(OP)$$

$$= 1.$$

In general,

$$\mathbf{a}_m \cdot \mathbf{b}_n = 1, \quad \text{if } m = n, \tag{4}$$

$$= 0, \quad \text{if } m \neq n. \tag{5}$$

The fact that $\mathbf{H}_{hkl}$ is normal to (hkl) and H_{hkl} is the reciprocal of d_{hkl} may be proved as follows. Let ABC of Fig. A15–6 be part of the plane nearest the origin in the set (hkl). Then, from the definition of Miller indices, the vectors from the origin to the points A, B, and C are $\mathbf{a}_1/h$, $\mathbf{a}_2/k$, and $\mathbf{a}_3/l$, respectively. Consider the vector $\mathbf{AB}$, that is, a vector drawn from A to B, lying in the plane (hkl). Since

$$\frac{\mathbf{a}_1}{h} + \mathbf{AB} = \frac{\mathbf{a}_2}{k},$$

then

$$\mathbf{AB} = \frac{\mathbf{a}_2}{k} - \frac{\mathbf{a}_1}{h}.$$

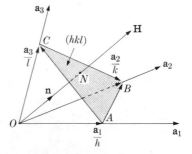

FIG. A15–6. Relation between reciprocal-lattice vector $\mathbf{H}$ and crystal plane (hkl).

Forming the dot product of $\mathbf{H}$ and $\mathbf{AB}$, we have

$$\mathbf{H} \cdot \mathbf{AB} = (h\mathbf{b}_1 + k\mathbf{b}_2 + l\mathbf{b}_3) \cdot \left(\frac{\mathbf{a}_2}{k} - \frac{\mathbf{a}_1}{h} \right).$$

Evaluating this with the aid of Eqs. (4) and (5), we find

$$\mathbf{H} \cdot \mathbf{AB} = 1 - 1 = 0.$$

Since this product is zero, $\mathbf{H}$ must be normal to $\mathbf{AB}$. Similarly, it may be shown that $\mathbf{H}$ is normal to $\mathbf{AC}$. Since $\mathbf{H}$ is normal to two vectors in the plane (hkl), it is normal to the plane itself.

To prove the reciprocal relation between H and d, let $\mathbf{n}$ be a unit vector in the direction of $\mathbf{H}$, i.e., normal to (hkl). Then

$$d = ON = \frac{\mathbf{a}_1}{h} \cdot \mathbf{n}.$$

But

$$\mathbf{n} = \frac{\mathbf{H}}{H}.$$

Therefore

$$d = \frac{\mathbf{a}_1}{h} \cdot \frac{\mathbf{H}}{H}$$

$$= \frac{\mathbf{a}_1}{h} \cdot \frac{(h\mathbf{b}_1 + k\mathbf{b}_2 + l\mathbf{b}_3)}{H}$$

$$= \frac{1}{H}.$$

Used purely as a geometrical tool, the reciprocal lattice is of considerable help in the solution of many problems in crystal geometry. Consider, for example, the relation between the planes of a zone and the axis of that zone. Since the planes of a zone are all parallel to one line, the zone axis, their normals must be coplanar. This means that planes of a zone are represented, in the reciprocal lattice, by a set of points lying on a plane passing through the origin of the reciprocal lattice. If the plane (hkl) belongs to the zone whose axis is $[uvw]$, then the normal to (hkl), namely, $\mathbf{H}$, must be perpendicular to $[uvw]$. Express the zone axis as a vector in the crystal lattice and $\mathbf{H}$ as a vector in the reciprocal lattice:

$$\text{Zone axis} = u\mathbf{a}_1 + v\mathbf{a}_2 + w\mathbf{a}_3,$$

$$\mathbf{H} = h\mathbf{b}_1 + k\mathbf{b}_2 + l\mathbf{b}_3.$$

If these two vectors are perpendicular, their dot product must be zero:

$$(u\mathbf{a}_1 + v\mathbf{a}_2 + w\mathbf{a}_3) \cdot (h\mathbf{b}_1 + k\mathbf{b}_2 + l\mathbf{b}_3) = 0,$$

$$hu + kv + lw = 0.$$

This is the relation given without proof in Sec. 2–6. By similar use of reciprocal-lattice vectors, other problems of crystal geometry, such as the derivation of the plane-spacing equations given in Appendix 1, may be greatly simplified.

A15–4 Diffraction and the reciprocal lattice. The great utility of the reciprocal lattice, however, lies in its connection with diffraction problems. We shall consider how x-rays scattered by the atom O at the origin of the crystal lattice (Fig. A15–7) are affected by those scattered by any other atom A whose coordinates with respect to the origin are $p\mathbf{a}_1$, $q\mathbf{a}_2$ and $r\mathbf{a}_3$, where p, q, and r are integers. Thus,

$$\mathbf{OA} = p\mathbf{a}_1 + q\mathbf{a}_2 + r\mathbf{a}_3.$$

Let the incident x-rays have a wavelength λ, and let the incident and diffracted beams be represented by the unit vectors $\mathbf{S}_0$ and $\mathbf{S}$, respectively. $\mathbf{S}_0$, $\mathbf{S}$, and $\mathbf{OA}$ are, in general, not coplanar.

   To determine the conditions under which diffraction will occur, we must determine the phase difference between the rays scattered by the atoms O and A. The lines Ou and Ov in Fig. A15–7 are wave fronts perpendicular to the incident beam $\mathbf{S}_0$ and the diffracted beam $\mathbf{S}$, respectively. Let δ be the path difference for rays scattered by O and A. Then

$$\delta = uA + Av$$

$$= Om + On$$

$$= \mathbf{S}_0 \cdot \mathbf{OA} + (-\mathbf{S}) \cdot \mathbf{OA}$$

$$= -\mathbf{OA} \cdot (\mathbf{S} - \mathbf{S}_0).$$

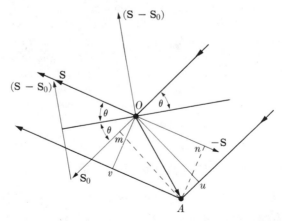

FIG. A15–7.   X-ray scattering by atoms at O and A.   (After Guinier, *X-Ray Crystallographic Technology*, Hilger & Watts, Ltd., London, 1952.)

The corresponding phase difference is given by

$$\phi = \frac{2\pi\delta}{\lambda}$$

$$= -2\pi \left(\frac{\mathbf{S} - \mathbf{S}_0}{\lambda}\right) \cdot \mathbf{OA}. \tag{6}$$

Diffraction is now related to the reciprocal lattice by expressing the vector $(\mathbf{S} - \mathbf{S}_0)/\lambda$ as a vector in that lattice. Let

$$\frac{\mathbf{S} - \mathbf{S}_0}{\lambda} = h\mathbf{b}_1 + k\mathbf{b}_2 + l\mathbf{b}_3.$$

This is now in the form of a vector in reciprocal space but, at this point, no particular significance is attached to the parameters h, k, and l. They are continuously variable and may assume any values, integral or nonintegral. Equation (6) now becomes

$$\phi = -2\pi(h\mathbf{b}_1 + k\mathbf{b}_2 + l\mathbf{b}_3) \cdot (p\mathbf{a}_1 + q\mathbf{a}_2 + r\mathbf{a}_3) = -2\pi(hp + kq + lr).$$

A diffracted beam will be formed only if reinforcement occurs, and this requires that ϕ be an integral multiple of 2π. This can happen only if h, k, and l are integers. Therefore the condition for diffraction is that the vector $(\mathbf{S} - \mathbf{S}_0)/\lambda$ end on a *point* in the reciprocal lattice, or that

$$\boxed{\frac{\mathbf{S} - \mathbf{S}_0}{\lambda} = \mathbf{H} = h\mathbf{b}_1 + k\mathbf{b}_2 + l\mathbf{b}_3}, \tag{7}$$

where h, k, and l are now restricted to integral values.

Both the Laue equations and the Bragg law can be derived from Eq. (7). The former are obtained by forming the dot product of each side of the equation and the three crystal-lattice vectors $\mathbf{a}_1$, $\mathbf{a}_2$, $\mathbf{a}_3$ successively. For example,

$$\mathbf{a}_1 \cdot \left(\frac{\mathbf{S} - \mathbf{S}_0}{\lambda}\right) = \mathbf{a}_1 \cdot (h\mathbf{b}_1 + k\mathbf{b}_2 + l\mathbf{b}_3)$$

$$= h,$$

or

$$\mathbf{a}_1 \cdot (\mathbf{S} - \mathbf{S}_0) = h\lambda. \tag{8}$$

Similarly,

$$\mathbf{a}_2 \cdot (\mathbf{S} - \mathbf{S}_0) = k\lambda, \tag{9}$$

$$\mathbf{a}_3 \cdot (\mathbf{S} - \mathbf{S}_0) = l\lambda. \tag{10}$$

Equations (8) through (10) are the vector form of the equations derived by von Laue in 1912 to express the necessary conditions for diffraction. They must be satisfied simultaneously for diffraction to occur.

As shown in Fig. A15–7, the vector $(\mathbf{S} - \mathbf{S}_0)$ bisects the angle between the incident beam $\mathbf{S}_0$ and the diffracted beam $\mathbf{S}$. The diffracted beam $\mathbf{S}$ can therefore be considered as being reflected from a set of planes perpendicular to $(\mathbf{S} - \mathbf{S}_0)$. In fact, Eq. (7) states that $(\mathbf{S} - \mathbf{S}_0)$ is parallel to $\mathbf{H}$, which is in turn perpendicular to the planes (hkl). Let θ be the angle between $\mathbf{S}$ (or $\mathbf{S}_0$) and these planes. Then, since $\mathbf{S}$ and $\mathbf{S}_0$ are unit vectors,

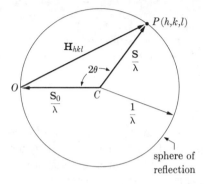

$$(S - S_0) = 2 \sin \theta.$$

Therefore

$$\frac{2 \sin \theta}{\lambda} = \frac{S - S_0}{\lambda} = H = \frac{1}{d},$$

or

$$\lambda = 2d \sin \theta.$$

Fig. A15–8. The Ewald construction. Section through the sphere of reflection containing the incident and diffracted beam vectors.

The conditions for diffraction expressed by Eq. (7) may be represented graphically by the "Ewald construction" shown in Fig. A15–8. The vector $\mathbf{S}_0/\lambda$ is drawn parallel to the incident beam and $1/\lambda$ in length. The terminal point O of this vector is taken as the origin of the reciprocal lattice, drawn to the same scale as the vector $\mathbf{S}_0/\lambda$. A sphere of radius $1/\lambda$ is drawn about C, the initial point of the incident-beam vector. Then the condition for diffraction from the (hkl) planes is that the point hkl in the reciprocal lattice (point P in Fig. A15–8) touch the surface of the sphere, and the direction of the diffracted-beam vector $\mathbf{S}/\lambda$ is found by joining C to P. When this condition is fulfilled, the vector $\mathbf{OP}$ equals both $\mathbf{H}_{hkl}$ and $(\mathbf{S} - \mathbf{S}_0)/\lambda$, thus satisfying Eq. (7). Since diffraction depends on a reciprocal-lattice point's touching the surface of the sphere drawn about C, this sphere is known as the "sphere of reflection."

Our initial assumption that p, q, and r are integers apparently excludes all crystals except those having only one atom per cell, located at the cell corners. For if the unit cell contains more than one atom, then the vector $\mathbf{OA}$ from the origin to "any atom" in the crystal may have nonintegral coordinates. However, the presence of these additional atoms in the unit cell affects only the intensities of the diffracted beams, not their directions, and it is only the diffraction directions which are predicted by the Ewald construction. Stated in another way, the reciprocal lattice depends only on the shape and size of the unit cell of the crystal lattice and not at all on the arrangement of atoms within that cell. If we wish to take atom arrangement into consideration, we may weight each reciprocal-lattice point hkl with the appropriate value of the scattering power $(= |F|^2,$ where F is the structure factor) of the particular (hkl) planes involved. Some planes may then have zero scattering power, thus eliminating some reciprocal-lattice points from consideration, e.g., all reciprocal-lattice points having odd values of $(h + k + l)$ for body-centered crystals.

The common methods of x-ray diffraction are differentiated by the methods used for bringing reciprocal-lattice points into contact with the surface of the sphere of reflection. The radius of the sphere may be varied by varying the incident wavelength (Laue method), or the position of the reciprocal lattice may be varied by changes in the orientation of the crystal (rotating-crystal and powder methods).

A15–5 The rotating-crystal method. As stated in Sec. 3–6, when monochromatic radiation is incident on a single crystal rotated about one of its axes, the reflected beams lie on the surface of imaginary cones coaxial with the rotation axis. The way in which this reflection occurs may be shown very nicely by the Ewald construction. Suppose a simple cubic crystal is rotated about the axis [001]. This is equivalent to rotation of the reciprocal lattice about the b_3 axis. Figure A15–9 shows a portion of the reciprocal lattice oriented in this manner, together with the adjacent sphere of reflection.

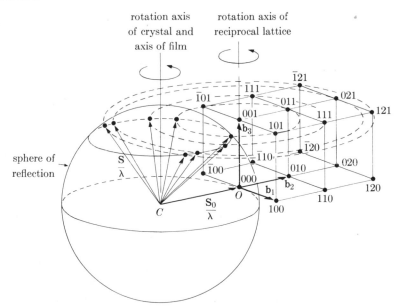

FIG. A15–9. Reciprocal-lattice treatment of rotating-crystal method.

All crystal planes having indices ($hk1$) are represented by points lying on a plane (called the "$l = 1$ layer") in the reciprocal lattice, normal to $\mathbf{b_3}$. When the reciprocal lattice rotates, this plane cuts the reflection sphere in the small circle shown, and any points on the $l = 1$ layer which touch the sphere surface must touch it on this circle. Therefore all diffracted-beam vectors $\mathbf{S}/\lambda$ must end on this circle, which is equivalent to saying that the diffracted beams must lie on the surface of a cone. In this particular case, all the $hk1$ points shown intersect the surface of the sphere sometime during their rotation about the $\mathbf{b_3}$ axis, producing the diffracted beams shown in Fig. A15–9. In addition many $hk0$ and $hk\bar{1}$ reflections would be produced, but these have been omitted from the drawing for the sake of clarity.

This simple example may suggest how the rotation photograph of a crystal of unknown structure, and therefore having an unknown reciprocal lattice, can yield clues as to the distribution in space of reciprocal-lattice points. By taking a number of photographs with the crystal rotated successively about various axes, the crystallographer gradually discovers the complete distribution of reflecting points. Once the reciprocal lattice is known, the crystal lattice is easily derived, because it is a corollary of Eqs. (1) through (3) that the reciprocal of the reciprocal lattice is the crystal lattice.

A15–6 The powder method. The random orientations of the individual crystals in a powder specimen are equivalent to the rotation of a single crystal about all possible axes during the x-ray exposure. The reciprocal lattice therefore takes on all possible orientations relative to the incident beam, but its origin remains fixed at the end of the $\mathbf{S_0}/\lambda$ vector.

Consider any point hkl in the reciprocal lattice, initially at P_1 (Fig. A15–10). This point can be brought into a reflecting position on the surface of the reflection sphere by a rotation of the lattice about an axis through O and normal to OC, for example. Such a rotation would move P_1 to P_2. But the point hkl can still remain on the surface of the sphere [i.e., reflection will still occur from the same set of planes (hkl)] if the reciprocal lattice is then rotated about the axis OC, since the point hkl will then move around the small circle P_2P_3. During this motion, the $\mathbf{H}$ vector sweeps out a cone whose apex is at O, and the diffracted beams all lie on the surface of another cone whose apex is at C. The axes of both cones coincide with the incident beam.

The number of different hkl reflections obtained on a powder photograph depends, in part, on the relative magnitudes of the wavelength and the crystal-lattice parameters or, in reciprocal-lattice language, on the relative sizes of the sphere of reflection and the reciprocal-lattice unit cell. To find the number of reflections we may regard the reciprocal lattice as fixed and the incident-beam vector $\mathbf{S_0}/\lambda$ as rotating about its terminal point

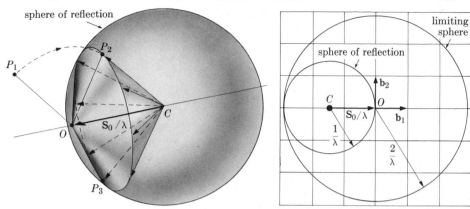

FIG. A15–10. Formation of a cone of diffracted rays in the powder method.

FIG. A15–11. The limiting sphere for the powder method.

through all possible positions. The reflection sphere therefore swings about the origin of the reciprocal lattice and sweeps out a sphere of radius $2/\lambda$, called the "limiting sphere" (Fig. A15–11). All reciprocal-lattice points within the limiting sphere can touch the surface of the reflection sphere and cause reflection to occur.

It is also a corollary of Eqs. (1) through (3) that the volume v of the reciprocal-lattice unit cell is the reciprocal of the volume V of the crystal unit cell. Since there is one reciprocal-lattice point per cell of the reciprocal lattice, the number of reciprocal-lattice points within the limiting sphere is given by

$$ n = \frac{(4\pi/3)(2/\lambda)^3}{v} = \frac{32\pi V}{3\lambda^3}. \tag{11} $$

Not all of these n points will cause a separate reflection: some of them may have a zero structure factor, and some may be at equal distances from the reciprocal-lattice origin, i.e., correspond to planes of the same spacing. (The latter effect is taken care of by the multiplicity factor, since this gives the number of different planes in a form having the same spacing.) However, Eq. (11) may always be used directly to obtain an upper limit to the number of possible reflections. For example, if $V = 50A^3$ and $\lambda = 1.54A$, then $n = 460$. If the specimen belongs to the triclinic system, this number will be reduced by a factor of only 2, the multiplicity factor, and the powder photograph will contain 230 separate diffraction lines! As the symmetry of the crystal increases, so does the multiplicity factor and the fraction of reciprocal-lattice points which have zero structure factor, resulting in a decrease in the number of diffraction lines. For example, the powder pattern of a diamond cubic crystal has only 5 lines, for the same values of V and λ assumed above.

A15–7 The Laue method.   Diffraction occurs in the Laue method because of the continuous range of wavelengths present in the incident beam. Stated alternatively, contact between a fixed reciprocal-lattice point and the sphere of reflection is produced by continuously varying the radius of the sphere.   There is therefore a whole set of reflection spheres, not just one; each has a different center, but all pass through the origin of the reciprocal lattice.   The range of wavelengths present in the incident beam is of course not infinite.   It has a sharp lower limit at λ_{SWL}, the short-wavelength limit of the continuous spectrum; the upper limit is less definite but is often taken as the wavelength of the K absorption edge of the silver in the emulsion (0.48A), because the effective photographic intensity of the continuous spectrum drops abruptly at that wavelength [see Fig. 1–18(c)].

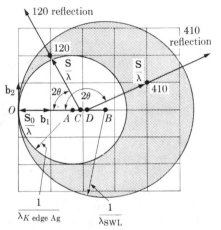

To these two extreme wavelengths correspond two extreme reflection spheres, as shown in Fig. A15–12, which is a section through these spheres and the $l = 0$ layer of a reciprocal lattice.   The incident beam is along the $\mathbf{b}_1$ vector, i.e., perpendicular to the $(h00)$ planes of the crystal. The larger sphere shown is centered at B and has a radius equal to the reciprocal of λ_{SWL}, while the smaller sphere is centered at A and has a radius equal to the reciprocal of the wavelength of the silver K absorption edge.

FIG. A15–12.   Reciprocal-lattice treatment of the Laue method. $(\mathbf{S} - \mathbf{S}_0)/\lambda = \mathbf{H}$.

There is a whole series of spheres lying between these two and centered on the line segment AB.   Therefore any reciprocal-lattice point lying in the shaded region of the diagram is on the surface of one of these spheres and corresponds to a set of crystal planes oriented to reflect one of the incident wavelengths.   In the forward direction, for example, a 120 reflection will be produced.   To find its direction, we locate a point C on AB which is equidistant from the origin O and the reciprocal-lattice point 120; C is therefore the center of the reflection sphere passing through the point 120. Joining C to 120 gives the diffracted-beam vector $\mathbf{S}/\lambda$ for this reflection. The direction of the 410 reflection, one of the many backward-reflected beams, is found in similar fashion; here the reciprocal-lattice point in question is situated on a reflection sphere centered at D.

There is another way of treating the Laue method which is more convenient for many purposes.   The basic diffraction equation, Eq. (7), is rewritten in the form

$$\boxed{\mathbf{S} - \mathbf{S}_0 = \lambda\mathbf{H}}.\tag{12}$$

Both sides of this equation are now dimensionless and the radius of the sphere of reflection is simply unity, since $\mathbf{S}$ and $\mathbf{S}_0$ are unit vectors. But the position of the reciprocal-lattice points is now dependent on the wavelength used, since their distance from the origin of the reciprocal lattice is now given by λH.

In the Laue method, each reciprocal-lattice point (except 0 0 0) is drawn out into a line segment directed to the origin, because of the range of wavelengths present in the incident beam. The result is shown in Fig. A15–13,* which is drawn to correspond to Fig. A15–12. The point nearest the origin on each line segment has a value of λH corresponding to the shortest wavelength present, while the point on the other end has a value of λH corresponding to the longest effective wavelength. Thus the 100 reciprocal-lattice line extends from A to B, where $OA = \lambda_{min}H_{100}$ and $OB = \lambda_{max}H_{100}$. Since the length of any line increases as H increases, for a given range of wavelengths, overlapping occurs for the higher orders, as shown by 200, 300, 400, etc. The reflection sphere is drawn with unit radius, and reflection occurs whenever a reciprocal-lattice line intersects the sphere surface. Graphically, the advantage of this construction over that of Fig. A15–12 is that all diffracted beams are now drawn from the same point C, thus facilitating the comparison of the diffraction angles 2θ for different reflections.

This construction also shows why the diffracted beams from planes of a zone are arranged on a cone in the Laue method. All reciprocal-lattice lines representing the planes of one zone lie on a plane passing through

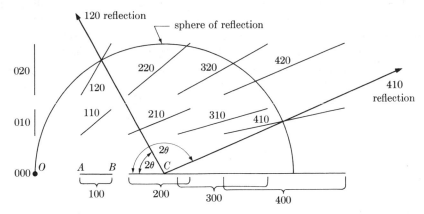

Fig. A15–13. Alternate reciprocal-lattice treatment of the Laue method. $\mathbf{S} - \mathbf{S}_0 = \lambda\mathbf{H}$.

* In this figure, as well as in Figs. A15–11 and A15–12, the size of the reciprocal lattice, relative to the size of the reflection sphere, has been exaggerated for clarity.

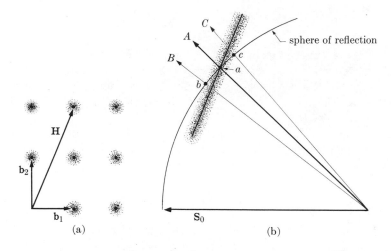

Fɪɢ. A15–14.   The effect of thermal vibration on the reciprocal lattice.

the origin of the reciprocal lattice. This plane cuts the reflection sphere in a circle, and all the diffracted beam vectors **S** must end on this circle, thus producing a conical array of diffracted beams, the axis of the cone coinciding with the zone axis.

Another application of this construction, to the problem of temperature-diffuse scattering, will illustrate the general utility of the reciprocal-lattice method in treating diffuse scattering phenomena. The reciprocal lattice of any crystal may be regarded as a distribution of "scattered intensity" in reciprocal space, in the sense that a scattered beam will be produced whenever the sphere of reflection intersects a point in reciprocal space where the "scattered intensity" is not zero. If the crystal is perfect, the scattered intensity is concentrated at points in reciprocal space, the points of the reciprocal lattice, and is zero everywhere else. But if anything occurs to disturb the regularity of the crystal lattice, then these points become smeared out, and appreciable scattered intensity exists in regions of reciprocal space where h, k, and l are nonintegral. For example, if the atoms of the crystal are undergoing thermal vibration, then each point of the reciprocal lattice spreads out into a region which may be considered, to a first approximation, as roughly spherical in shape, as suggested by Fig. A15–14(a). In other words, the thermally produced elastic waves which run through the crystal lattice so disturb the regularity of the atomic planes that the corresponding **H** vectors end, not on points, but in small spherical regions. The scattered intensity is not distributed uniformly within each region: it remains very high at the central point, where h, k, and l are integral, and is very weak and diffuse in the surrounding volume, as indicated in the drawing.

What then will be the effect of thermal agitation on, for example, a transmission Laue pattern? If we use the construction of Fig. A15–13, i.e., if we make distances in the reciprocal lattice equal to λH, then each spherical volume in the reciprocal lattice will be drawn out into a rod, roughly cylindrical in shape and directed to the origin, as indicated in Fig. A15–14(b), which is a section through the reflection sphere and one such rod. The axis of each rod is a line of high intensity and this is surrounded by a low-intensity region. This line intersects the reflection sphere at a and produces the strong diffracted beam A, the ordinary Laue reflection. But on either side of A there are weak scattered rays, extending from B to C, due to the intersec-

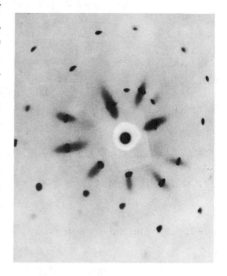

FIG. A15–15. Transmission Laue pattern showing thermal asterism. Aluminum crystal, 280°C, 5 min exposure.

tion, extending from b to c, of the diffuse part of the rod with the sphere of reflection. In a direction normal to the drawing, however, the diffuse rod intersects the sphere in an arc equal only to the rod diameter, which is much shorter than the arc bc. We are thus led to expect, on a film placed in the transmission position, a weak and diffuse streak running *radially* through the usual sharp, intense Laue spot.

Figure A15–15 shows an example of this phenomenon, often called thermal asterism because of the radial direction of the diffuse streaks. This photograph was obtained from aluminum at 280°C in 5 minutes. Actually, thermal agitation is quite pronounced in aluminum even at room temperature, and thermal asterism is usually evident in overexposed room-temperature photographs. Even in Fig. 3–6(a), which was given a normal exposure of about 15 minutes, radial streaks are faintly visible. In this latter photograph, there is a streak near the center which does not pass through any Laue spot: it is due to a reciprocal-lattice rod so nearly tangent to the reflection sphere that the latter intersects only the diffuse part of the rod and not its axis.

ANSWERS TO SELECTED PROBLEMS

CHAPTER 1

1–1. 4.22×10^{18} sec^{-1}, 2.79×10^{-8} erg; 1.95×10^{18} sec^{-1}, 1.29×10^{-8} erg
1–5. 4 cm^2/gm   **1–7.** (a) 30.2 cm^2/gm, 3.88×10^{-2} cm^{-1} **1–9.** 8980 volts
1–11. 1.54A   **1–14.** 0.000483 in., 0.58   **1–16.** 1000 watts, 20 ma   **1–18.**
3.28 to 1

CHAPTER 2

2–7. A section on $(1\bar{2}10)$ will show this   **2–11.** Shear strain $= 0.707$
2–14. (a) 20°S, 30°W; (b) 27°S, 48°E; (c) 39°S, 61°E   **2–19.** 42°N, 26°E;
19°S, 45°W; 42°S, 63°E

CHAPTER 3

3–1. 8.929 gm/cm^3 **3–3.** 63.5°

3–5.

t	B	θ	B
1000A	0.11°	10°	0.31°
750	0.14	45	0.43
500	0.22	80	1.76
250	0.43		

CHAPTER 4

4–3. $F^2 = 0$ for mixed indices; $F^2 = 0$ for $(h + k + l)$ an odd multiple of 2;
$F^2 = 64f_c^2$ for $(h + k + l)$ an even multiple of 2; $F^2 = 32f_c^2$ for $(h + k + l)$ odd.

4–5.

$h + 2k$	l	F^2
$3n$	$2p + 1$ (as 1, 3, 5, 7 ...)	0
$3n$	$8p$ (as 8, 16, 24 ...)	$4(f_{Zn} + f_S)^2$
$3n$	$4(2p + 1)$ (as 4, 12, 20, 28 ...)	$4(f_{Zn} - f_S)^2$
$3n$	$2(2p + 1)$ (as 2, 6, 10, 14 ...)	$4(f_{Zn}^2 + f_S^2)$
$3n \pm 1$	$8p \pm 1$ (as 1, 7, 9, 15, 17 ...)	$3(f_{Zn}^2 + f_S^2 - \sqrt{2}\, f_{Zn}f_S)$
$3n \pm 1$	$4(2p + 1) \pm 1$ (as 3, 5, 11, 13, 19, 21 ...)	$3(f_{Zn}^2 + f_S^2 + \sqrt{2}\, f_{Zn}f_S)$
$3n \pm 1$	$8p$	$(f_{Zn} + f_S)^2$
$3n \pm 1$	$4(2p + 1)$	$(f_{Zn} - f_S)^2$
$3n \pm 1$	$2(2p + 1)$	$(f_{Zn}^2 + f_S^2)$

n and p are any integers, including zero.

4–8.

Line	hkl	Calc. Int.
1	110	10.0
2	200	1.7
3	211	3.3
4	220	1.1

4–10. 111 and 200.   The ratio is 2100 to 1.

CHAPTER 5

5-1. 0.67 cm for (111); 0.77 cm for (200)   **5-3.** (a) 3rd to 18th;
(b) 3rd to 15th.

CHAPTER 6

6-1. 38 minutes

6-3.

θ	ΔS	$\Delta 2\theta$
10°	0.00252 cm	0.0504°
35	0.0100	0.200
60	0.0248	0.496
85	0.1633	3.266

6-5. (a) 144; (b) 67; (c) 12.3 cm   **6-7.** 1.58 to 1

CHAPTER 7

7-1. 0.44°   **7-4.** (a) 1.14 (Co) to 1 (Ni); (b) 10.5

CHAPTER 8

8-1. 8°N, 23°E; 74°S, 90°E; 16°S, 64°W   **8-3.** 26° about beam axis, clockwise, looking from crystal to x-ray source; 3° about EW, clockwise, looking from E to W; 9° about NS, counterclockwise, looking from N to S   **8-5.** Habit plane is {100}.   26°N, 14°W; 14°S, 69°E; 60°S, 46°W.

CHAPTER 9

9-1. 45,000 psi   **9-3.** Diffractometer   **9-5.** (b) 0.11, 0.18, 0.28, and 0.43, listed in the order in which the incident beam traverses the layers

CHAPTER 10

10-1. 111, 200, 220, 311, 222, 400, 331, 420, 422, and 511 (333); $a = 4.05A$
10-4. 100, 002, 101, 102, 110   **10-6.** 111, 220, 311, 400, 331, 422, 511 (333), 440.   Diamond cubic; $a = 5.4A$; silicon.   **10-8.** 100, 002, 101, 102, 110, 103, 200, 112.   Hexagonal close-packed; $a = 3.2A$, $c = 5.2A$; magnesium.

CHAPTER 11

11-1. $\pm 1.7°C$ **11-3.** 4.997A   **11-5.** Near $\theta = 30°$

CHAPTER 12

12-1. $\pm 0.0002A$

CHAPTER 13

13-2. 0.0015

CHAPTER 14

14–1. BaS   **14–3.** Mixture of Ni and NiO   **14–5.** 12.5 volume percent austenite

CHAPTER 15

15–1. (*a*) $\Delta 2\theta$ = 1.75° (mica), 1.20° (LiF), 0.81° (NaCl).   Mica and LiF adequate, NaCl inadequate.   (*b*) $\Delta 2\theta$ = 1.41° (mica), 1.05° (LiF), 0.75° (NaCl). Mica and LiF adequate, NaCl inadequate.   **15–3.** 0.0020 in.

CHAPTER 16

16–1. 2.20 mg/cm² **16–3.** 0.00147 in.

CHAPTER 17

17–1. ±1300 psi

INDEX